Algebra 2

AMSCO

AMSCO SCHOOL PUBLICATIONS, INC.,
a division of Perfection Learning®

Reviewers

John Beyers, PhD
Program Chair and Professor, Mathematics
and Statistics
University of Maryland University College
College Park, MD

Kristina Horan
Mathematics Teacher
St. Bonaventure High School
Archdiocese of Los Angeles
Ventura, CA

Karen Brunner
Mathematics Teacher
Okemos High School
Okemos Public Schools
Okemos, Michigan

Diane M. Mayer
Mathematics Teacher & Physics Teacher
Lopez Island High School
Lopez Island School District
Lopez Island, WA

Robert Costello
Mathematics Chairman
New Design High School
New York City Department of Education
New York, NY

Lisa Wheeler
Mathematics Teacher
Central High School
Omaha Public Schools
Omaha, Nebraska

Andrea Harkey
Mathematics Teacher
Hickory Ridge High School
Cabarrus County Schools
Harrisburg, North Carolina

Lisa Williksen
Secondary Math, CTE and Online
Instructor
Washington Academy of Arts and
Technology
East Valley School District
Spokane, WA

Contents

Key to the icons:

The computer icon indicates Digital Activities that can be found at **www.amscomath.com**.

The globe icon indicates where Real-World Model Problems are found in the text.

Getting Started

About This Book

Algebra 2 is a full-year course, written to give students a strong understanding of the concepts of algebra as well as prepare them for new statewide end-of-course examinations. All instruction, model problems, and practice items were developed to support the new math standards. Each chapter opens with lesson-by-lesson alignment with the standards. The eight Mathematical Practice Standards are imbedded throughout the text in selected Model Problems, extensive practice problem sets, and the comprehensive Chapter and Cumulative Reviews.

In *Algebra 2*, students will explore quadratic, polynomial, rational, exponential, logarithmic, and trigonometric functions and apply their knowledge to contextual problems. *Algebra 2* builds on the themes of *Algebra 1*. Students see structure in expressions, transform functions, and use regressions as a method to analyze and model data. Finally, students will expand their understanding of probability by building on concepts introduced in earlier years. Throughout the text, prior learning is accessed to build a strong foundation for learning new concepts.

Each chapter incorporates multiple performance tasks that measure the ability of students to think critically and apply their knowledge in real-world situations. In addition, students and teachers have access to a companion Web site (**www.amscomath.com**) with activities and simulations linked directly to lessons in *Algebra 2*. Teachers also have the option to include a full range of digital simulations, electronic whiteboard lessons, videos, and interactive problems to stimulate conceptual understanding through the digital teacher edition. Through the online Math^X program, available separately, students and teachers have access to a comprehensive suite of instructional videos, adaptive practice exercises, quizzes, and tests with automated grading and reporting.

Careful and consistent use of this text and the supporting materials will give students a firm grasp of Algebra 2, prepare them for new end-of-course examinations, and give them the tools they need to be college and career ready.

Eight Standards for Mathematical Practice

The mathematical practices are a common thread for students to think about and understand math as they progress from Kindergarten through high school. Students should use the mathematical practices as a method to break down concepts and solve problems, including representing problems logically, justifying conclusions, applying mathematics to practical situations, explaining the mathematics accurately to other students, or deviating from a known procedure to find a shortcut.

MP 1 Make sense of problems and persevere in solving them.

Attack new problems by analyzing what students already know. Students should understand that many different strategies can work. Ask leading questions to direct the discussion. Take time to think.

- explain the meaning of the problem
- analyze given information, constraints, and relationships
- plan a solution route
- try simpler forms of the initial problem
- use concrete objects to help conceptualize
- monitor progress and change course, if needed
- continually ask, "Does this make sense?"

MP 2 Reason abstractly and quantitatively.

Represent problems with symbols and/or pictures.

- make sense of quantities and their relationships
- decontextualize—represent a situation symbolically and contextualize—consider what given symbols represent
- create a clear representation of the problem
- consider the units involved
- attend to the meaning of numbers and variables, not just how to compute them
- use properties of operations and objects

MP 3 Construct viable arguments and critique the reasoning of others.

Ask questions, defend answers, and/or make speculations using correct math vocabulary.

- use assumptions, definitions, and previously established results
- make conjectures and build a valid progression of statements
- use counterexamples
- justify conclusions and communicate them to others
- determine whether the arguments of others seem right

MP 4 Model with mathematics.

Show the relevance of math by solving real-world problems. Look for opportunities to use math for current situations in and outside of school in all subject areas.

- apply mathematics to solve everyday problems
- analyze and chart relationships using diagrams, two-way tables, graphs, flowcharts, and formulas to draw conclusions
- apply knowledge to simplify a complicated situation
- interpret results and consider whether answers make sense

MP 5 Use appropriate tools strategically.

Provide an assortment of tools for students and let them decide which ones to use.

- choose appropriately from existing tools (pencil and paper, concrete models, ruler, protractor, calculator, spreadsheet, dynamic geometry software, etc.) when solving mathematical problems
- detect possible errors by using estimation or other mathematical knowledge
- use technology to explore and compare predictions and deepen understanding of concepts

MP 6 Attend to precision.

Use precise and detailed language in math. Instead of saying "I don't get it," students should be able to elaborate on where they lost the connection. Students should specify units in their answers and correctly label diagrams.

- speak and write precisely using correct mathematical language
- state the meaning of symbols and use them properly
- specify units of measure and label axes appropriately
- calculate precisely and efficiently
- express answers with the proper degree of accuracy

MP 7 Look for and make use of structure.

See patterns and the significance of given information and objects. Use these to solve more complex problems.

- see the big picture
- discern a pattern or structure

- recognize the significance of given aspects
- apply strategies to similar problems
- step back for an overview and shift perspective
- see complicated things as being composed of several objects

MP 8 **Look for and express regularity in repeated reasoning.**
Understand why a process works so students can apply it to new situations.

- notice repeated calculations and look for both general methods and shortcuts
- maintain oversight of the process while paying attention to the details
- evaluate the reasonableness of intermediate results
- create generalizations founded on observations

Test-Taking Strategies

General Strategies

- **Become familiar with the directions and format of the test ahead of time.** There will be both multiple-choice and extended response questions where you must show the steps you used to solve a problem, including formulas, diagrams, graphs, charts, and so on, where appropriate.
- **Pace yourself.** Do not race to answer every question immediately. On the other hand, do not linger over any question too long. Keep in mind that you will need more time to complete the extended response questions than to complete the multiple-choice questions.
- **Speed comes from practice.** The more you practice, the faster you will become and the more comfortable you will be with the material. Practice as often as you can.

Specific Strategies

- **Always scan the answer choices** before beginning to work on a multiple-choice question. This will help you to focus on the kind of answer that is required. Are you looking for fractions, decimals, percents, integers, squares, cubes, and so on? Eliminate choices that clearly do not answer the question asked.
- **Do not assume that your answer is correct just because it appears among the choices.** The wrong choices are usually there because they represent common student errors. After you find an answer, always reread the problem to make sure you have chosen the answer to the question that is asked, not the question you have in your mind.
- **Sub-in.** To sub-in means to substitute. You can sub-in friendly numbers for the variables to find a pattern and determine the solution to the problem.
- **Backfill.** If a problem is simple enough and you want to avoid doing the more complex algebra, or if a problem presents a phrase such as $x = ?$, then just fill in the answer choices that are given in the problem until you find the one that works.
- **Do the math.** This is the ultimate strategy. Don't go wild searching in your mind for tricks, gimmicks, or math magic to solve every problem. Most of the time the best way to get the right answer is to do the math and solve the problem.

Chapter R Review

Chapter Content

Lessons

R.1 Expressions, Equations, and Functions   A-CED.1; A-CED.4;
A-REI.3

    Writing and Evaluating Algebraic Expressions

    Solving Equations

    Literal Equations

R.2 Linear Functions and Rate of Change

    The Slope-Intercept Form of a Line

    Rate of Change

R.3 Functions   A-REI.10; F-IF.1; F-IF.2

    Graphs of Functions

R.4 Solving Systems of Linear Equations and Inequalities   A-CED.3; A-REI.5; A-REI.6;
A-REI.11; A-REI.12

    Solving Systems of Equations by Graphing

    Solving Systems by Elimination or Substitution

    Graphing Linear Inequalities

    Solving Systems of Linear Inequalities by Graphing

R.5 Polynomial Operations   A-SSE.2; A-APR.1

    Power Rules

    Products and Quotients to a Power

    Zero and Negative Exponents

    Multiplying Polynomials

R.6 Parabolas   F-BF.3

    Translating Parabolas in Vertex Form

Vocabulary

axis of symmetry	parabola	rate of change
binomial	polynomial	slope
boundary line	power of a power rule	slope-intercept form
domain	power of a product rule	standard form of a polynomial
function	power of a quotient rule	system of equations
intercept	product rule	system of inequalities
monomial	quotient rule	vertex
order of operations	range	vertex form for a parabola

LESSON R.1

R.1 Expressions, Equations, and Functions

Writing and Evaluating Algebraic Expressions

You have been evaluating algebraic expressions for a while in your studies. In this lesson, we provide some practice with exponents, negative numbers, and a few other complications.

When evaluating expressions, the mathematical operations are done in the following order: **p**arentheses, **e**xponents, **m**ultiplication and **d**ivision from left to right, and **a**ddition and **s**ubtraction from left to right (PEMDAS). This is called the **order of operations**.

 In this activity, practice your skills by writing equations and moving between equations and words.

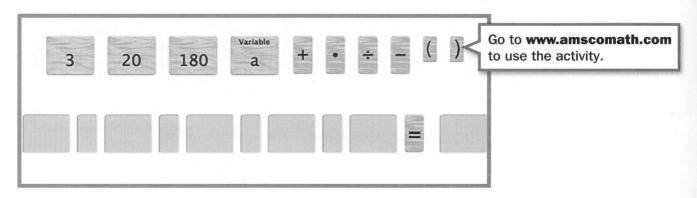

Go to **www.amscomath.com** to use the activity.

MODEL PROBLEMS

1. Evaluate $-4x + 3x^2$ when $x = 2$.

SOLUTION

Substitute	$-4x + 3x^2$ $-4 \cdot (2) + 3 \cdot (2)^2$	Given $x = 2$, substitute 2 for x.
Evaluate exponents	$-4 \cdot 2 + 3 \cdot 4$	Applying order of operations (PEMDAS), since there are no parentheses, first evaluate the exponents.
Multiplication and division	$-8 + 12$	Next, evaluate any multiplication and division from left to right.
Addition and subtraction last	4	Finally, evaluate addition and subtraction from left to right.

> If a variable needs to have a value substituted for it, completing the substitution will start the process of evaluating the equation.

2. Evaluate $4(x - 1)^3 - 2x^2 + 5$ when $x = 3$.

SOLUTION

Substitute	$4(x - 1)^3 - 2x^2 + 5$ $4 \cdot (3 - 1)^3 - 2 \cdot (3)^2 + 5$	Substitute 3 for x.
Parentheses first	$4 \cdot (2)^3 - 2 \cdot (3)^2 + 5$	Applying the order of operations (PEMDAS), first evaluate whatever is in parentheses.
Exponents second	$4 \cdot 8 - 2 \cdot 9 + 5$	Next, evaluate exponents.
Multiplication and division third	$32 - 18 + 5$	Evaluate any multiplication and division from left to right.
Addition and subtraction last	$14 + 5$ 19	Finally, evaluate any addition and subtraction from left to right.

3. Evaluate $-3x^3 - x^2 - x$ when $x = -2$.

SOLUTION

Substitute	$-3x^3 - x^2 - x$ $-3 \cdot (-2)^3 - (-2)^2 - (-2)$	Given $x = -2$, substitute -2 for x into the original equation.
Evaluate terms with exponents	$-3 \cdot (-8) - 4 - (-2)$	Evaluate the terms with exponents first.
Multiply	$24 - 4 - (-2)$	Multiplication and division come next.
Subtract	$24 - 4 - (-2)$ $20 - (-2)$ 22	Finally, add and subtract from left to right.

> This problem supplies some practice with negative numbers and exponents. Note that $-2^2 = -4$. With this expression, the exponent is applied first. In contrast, to square -2, you would use parentheses: $(-2)^2 = 4$ since $(-2) \cdot (-2) = 4$.

Model Problems continue . . .

4. Evaluate $\dfrac{2a-b}{-b+2}$ when $a=5$ and $b=3$.

> In this problem, we evaluate an expression with multiple variables and a fraction bar. The fraction bar is a grouping symbol, as are parentheses—do the operations above and below it before doing the division at the end.

SOLUTION

Substitute numbers for the variables	$\dfrac{2a-b}{-b+2}$ $\dfrac{2\cdot5-3}{-3+2}$	Substitute $a=5$ and $b=3$.
Simplify numerator	$\dfrac{2\cdot5-3}{-3+2}=\dfrac{10-3}{-3+2}=\dfrac{7}{-3+2}$	In fractions, group the numerator as one expression and the denominator as another expression. First, simplify the numerator by multiplying then subtracting. (We also could have simplified the denominator first.)
Simplify denominator	$\dfrac{7}{-3+2}=\dfrac{7}{-1}=-7$	Simplify the denominator. Last, divide.

5. It costs \$500 to rent a movie theater. Tickets cost \$9. Write an expression for the profits.

> Algebraic expressions are the building blocks of algebra. In this problem, write an expression for calculating profits at a movie theater. Profits are the difference between sales and costs.

SOLUTION

State relationship	Profits equal sales minus costs	Start with the relationship between profits, sales, and costs.
Use facts from problem	$9n$	Sales equal the number of tickets sold times their price, \$9. If we let n be the number of tickets sold, then $9n$ is the total sales.
	$9n-500$	The profits equal the sales, $9n$, minus the cost, \$500.

6. Elena is 100 meters away from the finish line and is approaching it at 4 m/s. Write an expression for her distance from the finish line as a function of time.

SOLUTION

State relationships	$100-$ distance she runs distance $=$ speed $\cdot$ time	Her distance from the finish line is 100 meters minus how far she runs. The distance, she runs equals the product of her speed and time.
Use facts from problem	$100-s\cdot t$ $100-4t$	Use s to represent speed and t to represent time. The product of speed and time is distance so subtract that from the 100 meters she has to go to the finish line. She is running at 4 meters per second, so substitute that value into the expression for s.

PRACTICE

1. Paul evaluates the expression $2(x - 3)^3 + 4x^2 - 6$ for $x = -2$. His solution steps are stated below.

   Step 1: $2(-2 - 3)^3 + 4(-2)^2 - 6$
   Step 2: $2(-5)^3 + 4(-4) - 6$
   Step 3: $2(-125) - 16 - 6$
   Step 4: -272

   Which is the first incorrect step?

   A. Step 1   C. Step 3
   B. Step 2   D. Step 4

2. George is three years older than twice his brother's age. If x represents his brother's age, which expression best represents George's age?

   A. $2x + 3$ C. $3x + 2$
   B. $2x - 3$ D. $3x - 2$

3. If the sum of all the positive odd integers less than 1000 is S, what is the sum of all the positive even integers less than 1000?

   A. $S - 500$ C. $2S$
   B. $S + 500$ D. $2S + 500$

4. Evaluate $\frac{1}{8}(x + 2)^2 - \frac{4}{3}$ when $x = 3$.

5. Evaluate $\frac{3}{6}(x + 2)^2 - \frac{4}{3}$ when $x = 3$.

6. Evaluate $5\left(x - \frac{1}{2}\right)^2 + \frac{5}{8}x$ when $x = -1$.

7. Evaluate $4\left(x - \frac{3}{8}\right)^2 + \frac{3}{2}x$ when $x = -3$.

8. Write an expression for the total number of calories in 10 fries when there are x calories per fry.

9. 518 dollars worth of tips were made at a restaurant one night. If there were x number of waiters working that night and each received an equal cut, write an expression for the amount each waiter made.

10. You pay \$9 to join a music-download service, then \$0.45 for each download. Write an algebraic expression for the total amount you spend on x downloads.

11. You pay \$29 to get into an amusement park, then \$3 for each ride. Write an algebraic expression for the total amount you spend on x rides.

12. A soccer team played g games and lost l games. Write an algebraic expression for the fraction of games won in terms of l and g.

13. You have Q quarters, D dimes, and N nickels. You then pay for candy with 4 quarters, 5 dimes, and 6 nickels. Write an expression for how much money you have in cents after the purchase.

14. The number of fans who will attend a soccer match equals 69,000 minus 40 times the square of the price of a ticket. Write an expression for the number of fans who will attend, using P to represent the price of the ticket.

15. Jean can complete a school science project in h hours. Write an algebraic expression for the number of projects she can finish in m minutes.

Exercises 16–19: Simplify.

16. $-10(8x - 3)$

17. $-5(8x - 2)$

18. $-(-3 + x)$

19. $-(-16 + x)$

Solving Equations

You have been solving equations for several years. We provide a bit of practice with slightly more complicated equations.

Algebraic Properties of Equality	
Addition property	If $a = b$, then $a + c = b + c$ and $a - c = b - c$.
Multiplication property	If $a = b$, then $ac = bc$.
Division property	If $a = b$ and $c \neq 0$, then $a \div c = b \div c$.
Substitution property	If $a = b$, then a can be replaced by b in expressions or equations.

Properties of Addition and Multiplication	
Commutative properties	$a + b = b + a$ $ab = ba$
Associative properties	$(x + y) + z = x + (y + z)$ $(a \cdot b) \cdot c = a \cdot (b \cdot c)$

Distributive Property	
Multiplication	$a(b + c) = ab + ac$ $a(b - c) = ab - ac$
Division	If $c \neq 0$, then $(a + b) \div c = \dfrac{a}{c} + \dfrac{b}{c}$

 In this activity, you can write a computer program to solve equations using properties of equality.

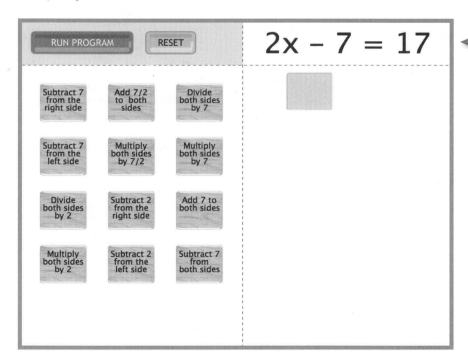

Go to **www.amscomath.com** to use the activity.

MODEL PROBLEMS

1. Solve $-13 + d = 11 - 3d$.

SOLUTION

Combine like terms	$-13 + 4d = 11$	To solve for d, isolate it on one side of the equation. Add $3d$ to both sides so that d will be only on the left side of the equation. Combine the like terms.
Isolate the variable	$4d = 24$	Isolate the variable on the left by adding 13 to both sides.
Divide both sides by the coefficient	$d = 6$	Divide both sides by the coefficient, 4.

2. Solve $-(-7 + x) = 12$.

SOLUTION

Distribute	$-1 \cdot (-7 + x) = 12$ $-1 \cdot (-7) + (-1 \cdot x) = 12$ $7 - x = 12$	Distribute the negative sign by multiplying each term in parentheses by -1.
Isolate the variable	$-x = 5$	To solve the equation, isolate the variable term. To do this, subtract 7 from both sides.
Divide by the coefficient	$\dfrac{-1 \cdot x}{-1} = \dfrac{5}{-1}$	To isolate x, divide by the coefficient of x, which is -1. Since $\dfrac{-1}{-1}$ equals 1, x is by itself.
Divide	$x = -5$	Divide 5 by -1, which gives us the solution, -5.

> As always, you must be careful with negative signs.

3. **MP 2, 4** A regional airline sells first-class tickets for \$125 and economy tickets for \$75. The airline sold 30 more economy tickets than first-class tickets for a total of \$4250.

  a Write an equation that models the total ticket sales in terms of the number of first-class tickets sold, x.

  b Find the number of first-class tickets sold by solving the equation found in part **a**.

SOLUTION

a Make a table

	Price	Quantity	Sales
First class	125	x	$125x$
Economy	75	$x + 30$	$75(x + 30)$
Total			4250

> A table can help you organize the information in a problem.

Label the type of tickets in the left column. Label the ticket price, number of tickets sold, and the total amount of money in the top row.

Filling in the "First class" row, the price of a first-class ticket is \$125. Let x be the number of first-class tickets sold, since we don't know how many have been sold. Sales equal price times the quantity, which is $125x$.

Filling in the "Economy" row, the price of economy tickets is \$75. The number of economy tickets sold is $x + 30$ (which is 30 more than the number of first-class tickets sold, x). Sales of these tickets equal the price times quantity.

The total sales, \$4250, is given.

Use facts to write equation

$$125x + 75(x + 30) = 4250$$

The sales for first class plus the sales for economy equals total sales. These are the expressions in the column on the far right. The first two rows under Sales sum to the third.

Model Problems continue . . .

b Distribute and combine like terms

$$125x + 75x + 2250 = 4250$$
$$200x = 2000$$

Distribute the 75, then combine like terms, both terms with x and constants.

State answer

$$x = 10 \text{ first-class tickets}$$

Divide by the coefficient 200. The variable x represents the number of first-class tickets. The airline sold 10. Check the answer. Thirty more economy tickets were sold than first class, so 40 economy tickets were sold. Multiply 10 by \$125 and 40 by \$75. The sum of the products is \$4250, the amount stated in the problem.

PRACTICE

1. Cole was so confident in his athletic ability that he gave Trang a 5-minute running head start on an 8000-foot race. Trang can run about one mile every ten minutes, while Cole can run about one mile every 8 minutes. Who wins the race, and by how many feet?

   A.   Trang wins by 1100 feet
   B.   Trang wins by 1300 feet
   C.   Cole wins by 1100 feet
   D.   Cole wins by 500 feet

2. A car leaves at 6 A.M. traveling 60 mph. Another car starts at 8 A.M. down the same highway, traveling at 70 mph. At what time will the second car catch up with the other car?

   A.   11 A.M.
   B.   6 P.M.
   C.   8 P.M.
   D.   10 P.M.

3. At an opera theatre you manage, you sell balcony seats for \$150 and first-level seats for \$75. You sell \$13,500 worth of tickets, with 120 more first-level seats than balcony seats. How many balcony seats do you sell?

   A.   10
   B.   15
   C.   20
   D.   30

4. Matt decides to open a doughnut shop. The startup costs will be \$2525. Each doughnut will cost \$0.50 to make. He intends to sell each doughnut for \$1.25. How many doughnuts does he have to sell to make money?

   A.   1443 doughnuts
   B.   2020 doughnuts
   C.   3189 doughnuts
   D.   3367 doughnuts

Exercises 5–20: Solve.

5. $38 = 3d + 8$

6. $69 = 9d + 6$

7. $5 - 8z = -11$

8. $8 - 8z = -40$

9. $6 - 9z = -30$

10. $7 - 6z = -23$

11. $-5(5x - 6) = -45$

12. $-6(6x - 4) = -120$

13. $-45 = 5(-5w + 1)$

14. $-12 = 4(-3w + 6)$

15. $5y + 125 = 5(5y + 5)$

16. $4y + 20 = 2(3y + 5)$

17. $5y - 4 - 2y = 2y - 9$

Practice Problems continue . . .

18. $6y - 5 - 2y = 2y - 17$

19. $169 - (10x - 5) = 9(4x + 4)$

20. $241 - (9x - 2) = 6(6x + 3)$

21. The perimeter of the figure below is 40. If $W = 4x + 3$ and $L = 6x - 3$, what is x?

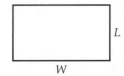

22. The perimeter of the figure below is 31. If $B = 4x - 5$, $L = 6x + 2$, and $H = 7x$, what is x?

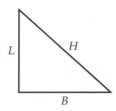

23. The sum of the angles in a triangle is 180°. If $A : B : C = 2 : 3 : 3$, what is $C - A$?

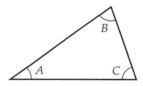

24. A cross-country skier is 19 kilometers closer to the start of a 45-kilometer race than she is from the finish. How many kilometers is she from the finish?

25. A runner is running a total of 55 miles and has m miles to go. If the runner has already run $10m$ miles, how many miles does m represent?

26. Sam and Sue are joggers. Sam is trying to catch up with Sue, who has a head start of 4 miles. Sam jogs at 7 miles per hour and Sue at 4 miles per hour. How many hours will it take Sam to catch up? Round your answer to the nearest tenth.

27. You have 6 times as many dimes as nickels and have a total of $3.90. How many coins do you have?

28. In a video game, a player can score either 4 or 10 points in a level. After 10 levels, Tamara has 88 points. How many 10-point levels did she have?

29. You get 60 points for just taking the test. You get 8 points for correct answers and lose 2 points for wrong answers. You answered 10 questions and scored 120. How many questions did you get right?

30. A 70-liter tank of seawater contains 11% salt. How many liters of freshwater (water with no salt) need to be added to change the salt concentration to 6%? Round your answer to the nearest hundredth.

31. A peanut butter factory makes 10-ounce and 18-ounce jars. In an hour, they manufacture 600 jars of peanut butter that contain 10,160 ounces of peanut butter. How many 18-ounce jars did they manufacture?

32. In still air, a bird flies at 36 miles per hour. With the wind, it travels 6 miles farther in 3 hours than it flies in 6 hours against the wind. How fast is the wind, in miles per hour? Round your answer to the nearest tenth.

33. A plane ride takes 4 hours from Seattle to Springfield and 3.8 hours headed back. Assuming the wind is blowing parallel to the plane in the same direction with a constant speed of 10 mph for both trips, what is the speed of the plane?

34. **MP 2, 4** A truck going 50 miles per hour set out on a 200-mile delivery at 6:00 A.M. Exactly half an hour later, a car left from the same place and traveled in the same direction as the truck. What was the speed of the car, in miles per hour, if it caught up to the truck at 8:00 A.M.? Round your answer to the nearest tenth.

Literal Equations

MODEL PROBLEMS

1. The equation $y = 3x + 5$ is of the form often used to graph lines. Solve it for x.

SOLUTION

Isolate x

$$y = 3x + 5$$
$$y - 5 = 3x + 5 - 5$$
$$y - 5 = 3x$$

Solve this equation for x. Subtract 5 from both sides to isolate the x-term.

Divide by the coefficient

$$\frac{y - 5}{3} = x$$

$$x = \frac{y - 5}{3}$$

Divide both sides by 3 to isolate x. State the equation with x on the left.

2. The equation $s = vt + 5t^2$ is a physics equation, with s standing for change in position, v for velocity, and t for time. Solve the equation for velocity.

SOLUTION

Isolate v

$$s = vt + 5t^2$$
$$s - 5t^2 = vt$$

Solve this equation for v. Subtract $5t^2$ from both sides so that the term with v is by itself on one side.

Divide by the coefficient

$$\frac{s - 5t^2}{t} = v$$

Divide both sides by t to solve for v.

State with variable on left

$$v = \frac{s - 5t^2}{t}$$

State the equation with the variable we are solving for on the left.

3. In the equation $3a + ax = 2b$, solve for a.

SOLUTION

Factor

$$3a + ax = 2b$$
$$a(3 + x) = 2b$$

To solve for a, first factor the expression on the left.

Divide by the coefficient

$$a = \frac{2b}{3 + x}$$

Divide both sides by the coefficient of a, $3 + x$, to solve for a.

PRACTICE

1. A student is designing a rectangular table. To experiment with values for length and perimeter of the table, the student wants to solve the formula for the width. Which best shows how to solve the formula for perimeter, $P = 2l + 2w$, for w?

A. $P - 2w = 2l$ C. $\dfrac{P - 2l}{2} = w$

B. $P - 2l = 2w$ D. $\dfrac{p - l}{2} = w$

2. It costs \$300 to buy materials to make candles. Each candle sells for \$15. If n represents the number of candles sold, which of the following represents the expression for the profits?

A. $15n - 300$

B. $300 - 15n$

C. $300 + 15n$

D. None of the above.

Practice Problems continue . . .

3. Lisa owns twice as many books as Jill. If Lisa owns b books, how many books does Jill own?

    A. $\dfrac{2}{b}$ C. $2b$

    B. $\dfrac{b}{2}$ D. b^2

4. If $x + y = 2$, what is $x - y$?

    A. -2

    B. 0

    C. 2

    D. There is not enough information.

5. Solve for a: $a - 9x = c$

6. Solve for x: $xy + z = 8w$

7. Solve for y: $8y - 7x + 9y = 112x$

8. Solve for y: $8y - 5x + 9y = 80x$

9. Solve for x: $7(x + 3a) = b$

10. Solve for x: $5(x + 6a) = b$

11. Solve for w: $\dfrac{w + 14}{x} = y$

12. Solve for w: $\dfrac{w + 11}{x} = y$

13. Solve for b: $bx + by = 18$

14. Solve for b: $bx + by = 12$

15. At Technic Music, the regular price of a music CD is d dollars. If all the music CDs are discounted 50% off regular price, how many music CDs can Brian purchase if he has r dollars?

16. If c construction workers can build a house in d days, how many days will it take m construction workers to build three identical houses? Assume the work rate for each construction worker is the same.

17. If the value of 10 ounces of gold is d dollars and an ounce of gold is equivalent to s ounces of silver, what is the value, in dollars, of 3 ounces of silver?

18. The relationship between the temperature in degrees Celsius C and degrees Fahrenheit F is given by the equation $C = \dfrac{5}{9}(F - 32)$.

Solve for F in terms of C.

19. The surface area of a right circular cylinder is given by the formula $SA = 2\pi r(r + h)$. Solve for the height h in the formula as a function of the surface area and radius.

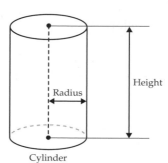

Cylinder

LESSON R.2

R.2 Linear Functions and Rate of Change

The Slope-Intercept Form of a Line

Slope is the rise over the run of a line. The rise is the vertical change between any two points on the line, and the run is the horizontal change between those same two points. The slope of a line can be calculated by the formula $\dfrac{y_2 - y_1}{x_2 - x_1}$. The formula uses variables with subscripts like y_1, which is read as "y sub 1." As usual, the variables x and y are the coordinates of the points.

When an equation is written $y = mx + b$, it is said to be written in **slope-intercept form**. The constant m is the slope of the line. The other constant in the equation is b, the y-intercept. An **intercept** is where a graph intersects an axis on the graph. The y-intercept is where the line intersects the y-axis, at the the point $(0, b)$. In the equation $y = 2x + 3$, $m = 2$ and $b = 3$.

1. Calculate the slope of the line in the graph.

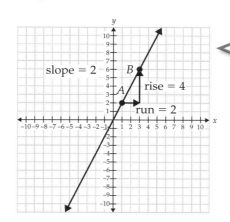

The line in the graph rises 4 between A and B, and it runs 2.

SOLUTION

Slope equals rise divided by run

$$\text{slope} = \frac{\text{rise}}{\text{run}}$$

Rise = 4
Run = 2

$$\text{slope} = \frac{4}{2}$$

$$\text{slope} = 2$$

Between A and B, the line travels from a y-coordinate of 2 to 6. That is a vertical change of +4. The rise from A to B is 4. The line travels from an x-coordinate of 1 to an x-coordinate of 3. That is a horizontal change of +2. The run from A to B is 2. The slope equals rise divided by run. The slope of this line is 2.

2. Calculate the slope of the line between points $(-1, 4)$ and $(2, 1)$ using the formula $\frac{y_2 - y_1}{x_2 - x_1}$.

The subscript 2 is used for point A and subscript 1 for point B.

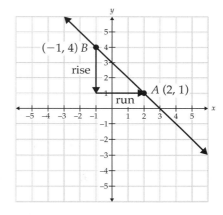

SOLUTION

Formula for slope

$$\frac{\text{rise}}{\text{run}} = \frac{\text{change in } y}{\text{change in } x} = \frac{y_2 - y_1}{x_2 - x_1}$$

This is the formula for slope. The slope equals the rise divided by the run. That is the change in y between two points divided by the change in x. Calculate the rise, or the change in y, by subtracting the y-coordinates. To calculate the run, or the change in x, subtract the x-coordinates of the two points.

Substitute the coordinates

$$\frac{y_2 - y_1}{x_2 - x_1} = \frac{1 - 4}{2 - (-1)}$$

Substitute the values stated above. The y-coordinates are in the numerator, and the coordinates of point A come first.

Do the operations

$$\frac{1 - 4}{2 - (-1)} = \frac{-3}{3} = -1$$

Now do the calculation. The slope is -1.

Model Problems continue . . .

3. Use the graph to identify m and b, and describe how they affect the line that they describe.

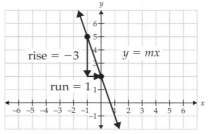

SOLUTION

$y = mx + b$ $y = -3x + 2$ You see an equation written in the form $y = mx + b$, with b equal to 2. The coefficient of x is m. In this equation, $m = -3$, because x is multiplied by -3.

m = slope $m = -3$ = slope   For an equation in this form, the slope of the line equals m, the coefficient of x. Since m equals -3, the slope equals -3. Between any two points on the line the ratio of the rise to the run is -3.

b is y-intercept y-intercept is 2   The value of b determines the y-intercept, or the value of y where the line crosses the y-axis. In the graph of $y = -3x + 2$, the line crosses the y-axis at 2.

4. Describe how a line is plotted on a graph when the slope is 3, -3, and -30.

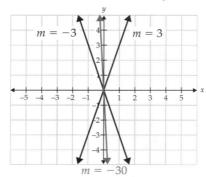

> By looking at the value of m in an equation of the form $y = mx + b$, you can determine the direction of the line, and whether it is steep or flat.

SOLUTION

m positive: line goes up from left to right $y = 3x$ When the slope is positive, like in the graph of $y = 3x$, the line goes up as you move from left to right. In other words, as x increases in value, so does y. When m is positive, the line goes up from left to right.

m negative: line goes down from left to right $y = -3x$ When the slope is negative, like in the graph of $y = -3x$, the line goes down from left to right. Its steepness is the same as $y = 3x$, but $y = -3x$ goes up from left to right.

The larger the absolute value of m, the steeper the line $y = -30x$ As the absolute value of m becomes larger, the line becomes steeper, like in the graph of $y = -30x$. It is steeper than the graph of $y = -3x$.

5. Graph the equation $y = \dfrac{3}{4}x - 2$.

> One way to graph an equation is to use its y-intercept and slope. First, plot its y-intercept. Then, move to the right for the run. Move up the rise (if the slope is positive) or down (if the slope is negative). Plot a second point there and draw a line through the points.

SOLUTION

y-intercept $y = \dfrac{3}{4}x + (-2)$ The y-intercept, where the line crosses the y-axis, is the constant added to the x-term. We restate subtracting 2 as adding -2, so the constant is being added. The y-intercept is the term added to the term with x, so -2 is the y-intercept.

Model Problems continue . . .

Plot the y-intercept	$(0, -2)$	This gives us one point to plot. The y-intercept is where the line intersects the y-axis.
slope $= \dfrac{\text{rise}}{\text{run}}$	slope $= \dfrac{3}{4}$	The slope is the coefficient of the x-term, which is $\dfrac{3}{4}$.
Add rise, run to point	$(0 + 4, -2 + 3) = (4, 1)$	Use the rise and run to determine a second point. The point $(0, -2)$ is our starting point. We rise 3 above -2 and run 4 to the right of 0.
Connect the points with a line	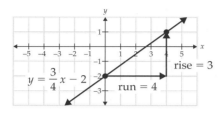	Two points make a line, so draw a line through them to graph the equation.

6. The points $(1, -7)$ and $(10, 8)$ are on a line. Find the equation for the line in slope-intercept form.

SOLUTION

Given	$(1, -7)$ and $(10, 8)$	The line runs through the points $(1, -7)$ and $(10, 8)$. Use these points to calculate the slope of the line.
Formula for slope	$m = \dfrac{y_2 - y_1}{x_2 - x_1}$	This is the equation for slope.
List coordinates using subscripts	$y_1 = -7, y_2 = 8$ $x_1 = 1, x_2 = 10$	These are the coordinates of the points.
Substitute	$m = \dfrac{y_2 - y_1}{x_2 - x_1} = \dfrac{8 - (-7)}{10 - 1}$	Substitute the values stated above.
Calculate m	$m = \dfrac{15}{9} = \dfrac{5}{3}$	Subtract and divide. The slope, m, is $\dfrac{5}{3}$.
Substitute $\dfrac{5}{3}$ for m	$y = mx + b$ $y = \dfrac{5}{3}x + b$	Since both points, $(1, -7)$ and $(10, 8)$, are solutions to the equation, substitute either one of these points into the equation $y = \dfrac{5}{3}x + b$, with the value of m calculated above. Then solve for b.
Substitute point on line	$-7 = \left(\dfrac{5}{3}\right)(1) + b$	Substitute the point $(1, -7)$ into the equation so far. Replace x with 1 and y with -7.
Solve for b	$-7 = \dfrac{5}{3} + b$ $b = -7 - \dfrac{5}{3} = -\dfrac{26}{3}$	Solve for b.
Write equation	$y = \dfrac{5}{3}x - \dfrac{26}{3}$	We calculated $m = \dfrac{5}{3}$ and $b = -\dfrac{26}{3}$. Replace m and b with those values in the slope-intercept form of the equation.

PRACTICE

1. The graph shows the function $y = mx + b$. According to the graph, which of the following is true?

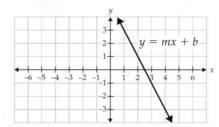

A. $m > 0, b > 0$ C. $m < 0, b < 0$
B. $m > 0, b < 0$ D. $m < 0, b > 0$

2. What is the slope of $y = 13x - 17$?

3. What is the slope of $y = -3x - 13$?

4. What is the y-intercept of $y = -3x + 14$?

5. What is the y-intercept of $y = -18x + 11$?

6. What is the y-intercept of $y = 3x + 6$?

7. Calculate the slope of the line that passes through $(3, -4)$ and $(1, 4)$.

8. Calculate the slope of the line that passes through $(5, -10)$ and $(3, 4)$.

Exercises 9–16: Graph each function.

9. $y = 6x + 8$

10. $y = 8x + 5$

11. $y = -8x - 8$

12. $y = -6x - 6$

13. $y = 3x - 9$

14. $y = \dfrac{1}{8}x - 9$

15. $y = \dfrac{5}{6}x + 7$

16. $y = \dfrac{8}{7}x - 10$

17. Graph the lines $y = -2x + 2$ and $y = -2x - 2$ on the same set of axes. What are the similarities and the differences of these graphs?

18. Graph $y = \dfrac{1}{2}x + 3$ and $y = -2x + 1$ on the same set of axes. What do you notice about the angle between the graphed lines? What is the relationship between the slopes of the lines?

19. MP 2, 4 Geoducks are a clam found on the northwest coast of the United States and southwest coast of Canada. They can live 150 years, and their shells can grow to 20 centimeters in length or more. A geoduck grows from 4 centimeters in length at age 10 years to 18 centimeters in length at age 100. Assuming it grows at a constant rate, write an equation in slope-intercept form that describes a geoduck's growth as a function of its age.

20. MP 2, 4 A company installed a computer system worth $15,000. After 8 years, the value of the system was estimated to be $2600. Assuming that the system depreciates linearly, write an equation in the form $P = mt + b$ showing the relationship of the worth, P, of the system and the time, t, in years.

Rate of Change

How quickly one quantity changes with respect to another is described by a ratio called the **rate of change**. A rate of change might describe how fast something changes with time, for example, how the vertical position of someone on an amusement park ride changes over time.

The rate of change measures how rapidly one quantity changes with respect to another. The slope of the graph equals the rate of change. A positive slope indicates a positive rate of change, and the greater the slope, the greater the rate of change. The quantities increase or decrease together. A negative slope means a negative rate of change. When one quantity increases, the other decreases, and vice versa.

We analyze the graph of Charlie on an amusement park ride. The graph on the right is his vertical position versus time. During part *A*, Charlie is rising on the amusement park ride. During part *B*, Charlie is on hold, waiting to be dropped. During part *C*, Charlie is dropped and falls back to his initial position.

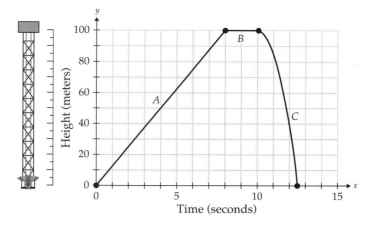

MODEL PROBLEM

Use the graph to answer the following questions.
a Describe Charlie's rate of change between 0–8 seconds, 8–10 seconds, and 10–12.5 seconds.
b Calculate Charlie's speed during his ascent.

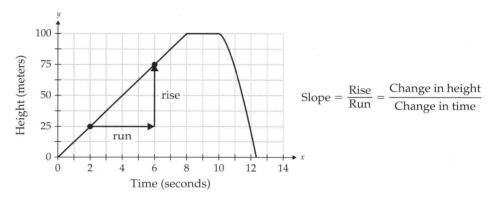

$$\text{Slope} = \frac{\text{Rise}}{\text{Run}} = \frac{\text{Change in height}}{\text{Change in time}}$$

SOLUTION

a

0 to 8 seconds	Constant rate	The slope equals the rate of change, or the speed. When Charlie is being pulled up, he rises at a constant speed.
8 to 10 seconds	Rate = 0	Charlie then gets 2 seconds of suspense, dangling before he falls. The graph is horizontal, which means the slope is 0.
10 to 12.5 seconds	Rate increases over time	As he falls toward the ground, he moves faster and faster. He accelerates. The curve becomes steeper as he approaches the ground. The absolute value of its slope at each time equals his speed at that time.

b

Formula for slope	$\text{Slope} = \dfrac{\text{rise}}{\text{run}}$	The slope of the line equals the rate of change.
Substitute values	$\text{Slope} = \dfrac{75 \text{ m} - 25 \text{ m}}{4 \text{ s}}$	Calculate the rise between two points. He rises from 25 meters to 75 meters in 4 seconds.
Solve	$\text{Slope} = 12.5 \text{ m/s}$	The rate of change is 12.5 m/s.

PRACTICE

1. The graph represents a boat's movement during the day. Which of the following is true, according to the graph?

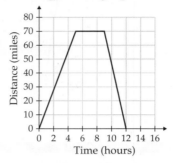

   A. The boat started and finished its trip in different ports.
   B. The boat changed its direction of sailing twice during the day.
   C. The average speed of the boat's three speeeds was 5 mph.
   D. The velocity of the boat was negative during the last 3 hours of its trip.

2. The graph shows Tim's savings growth during the year. Calculate the slope to find how much he saved each month.

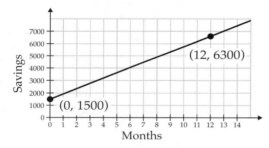

3. A graph of a car's distance from home along a straight road is shown.

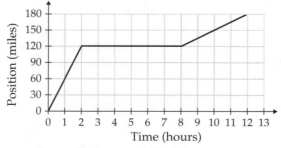

   a What is the car's speed from 0–2 hours?
   b What is the car's speed from 2–8 hours?
   c What is the car's speed from 8–12 hours?
   d When is the car moving fastest?

4. **MP 2, 4** You leave your house and walk toward school along a straight line at a constant speed. After walking for four minutes, you pause, looking for your hat. It takes you one minute to realize you dropped it and two minutes to walk back to it. You pick it up and head back to school, this time walking a bit faster so that you arrive at school eight minutes later. Draw a graph of the relationship of your distance away from home versus time. Although you do not have enough information to draw a line with a specific slope during some time periods, draw a graph that could accurately reflect your walk.

5. A graph of a marble's distance versus time is shown.

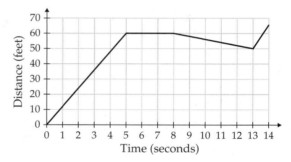

   a When is the marble's velocity negative?
   b What is the marble's velocity from 0 to 5 seconds?
   c What is the marble's velocity from 5 to 8 seconds?
   d What is the marble's velocity from 8 to 13 seconds?

6. Mr. Sheridan drives 196 miles in his car at a constant speed. He starts with a full tank of 13 gallons, and finishes with 6 gallons.

   a Draw a graph representing the amount of gasoline, g, in Mr. Sheridan's car as a function of mileage, m.
   b What does the slope of your line tell us about the efficiency of Mr. Sheridan's car?

Practice Problems continue . . .

7. The graph of the position of two friends with respect to time is shown.

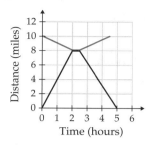

   a What is the speed of the slower friend in the first two hours of the trip?

   b What is the speed of the faster friend during the same time?

   c Explain the situation represented by the graphs. Use the friends' speeds, directions, and meeting time in your explanation.

8. Water is poured into a vase at a steady rate. Look at the graph showing the level of water in the vase as a function of volume of water added. Is the rate of change of the water level constant? If not, explain how it changes, and why.

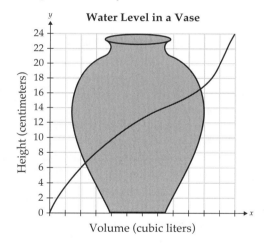

Water Level in a Vase

9. A group of students made an experiment: they poured water into vases of various shapes and measured the water level in each vase. (The same glass for pouring water was used for all.) They also drew a graph showing the water level, W, as a function of number of glasses poured, H. Analyze the rate of change of the water level in each graph and sketch the matching vase shape.

a
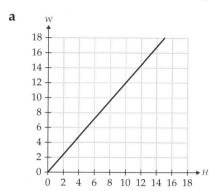

b
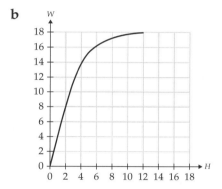

c
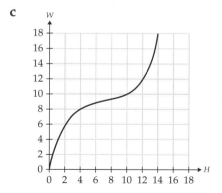

R.3 Functions

A **function** is a relation between two sets that takes an input from one set and supplies exactly one output from the other set. Different inputs can have the same output. The **domain** is the set of possible inputs. The **range** is the set of possible outputs.

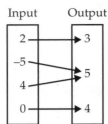

Input   Output

The output given by a function is usually written using the notation *f(x)*, which is pronounced "*f* of *x*," where *f* is the name of the function and *x* is the input. A function can be defined by a mathematical expression, such as 11 − 2*x*.

Mathematical expressions can impose limits on the domain and range. For a number to be part of the domain, it must, when substituted, create an expression with a defined value. For instance, the domain of the function $f(x) = \dfrac{4}{2 - x}$ is all real numbers except 2. Why? If $x = 2$, then the function is undefined since the denominator equals 0 in this case, and the result of dividing by zero is not defined.

An example of how an expression limits the range is the function $g(x) = x^2$. Its range is 0 and positive numbers. Why? The expression x^2 cannot be negative for a real number input.

MODEL PROBLEMS

1. What is $f(x) = 11 - 2x$ when $x = 3$?

Be careful: The expression *f*(3) does **not** mean multiply *f* by 3! The letter *f* here represents a function, not a number.

SOLUTION

$f(x)$ when $x = 3$

$f(x) = 11 - 2x$
$f(3) = 11 - 2 \cdot 3$
$f(3) = 11 - 6$
$f(3) = 5$

The function f assigns to each input x the value of $11 - 2x$. To evaluate a function means to calculate the output for a given input, such as 3. Subtract 6 from 11 to get 5. The value of the function $f(x) = 11 - 2x$ is 5 when $x = 3$.

2. a What is $g(3)$ when $g(x) = 2x^3 - 4$?
  b What is $g(-2)$ when $g(x) = 2x^3 - 4$?
  c State your answers from parts **a** and **b** as ordered pairs.

Letters other than *f* can represent a function: $g(x) = 2x^3 - 4$ and $h(y) = y + 2$ are functions as well.

SOLUTION

a Find $g(3)$

$g(x) = 2x^3 - 4$
$g(3) = 2(3)^3 - 4$

The function $g(x)$ is defined by the mathematical expression $2x^3 - 4$. To find the value of the function for the input $x = 3$, start by substituting 3 for x in the expression that defines the function.

Evaluate expression

$g(3) = 2 \cdot 27 - 4$
$g(3) = 50$

On the right, perform the operations: $2 \cdot (3)^3 - 4$. The result is 50.

Model Problems continue . . .

b Find $g(-2)$ $g(x) = 2x^3 - 4$
$g(-2) = 2(-2)^3 - 4$
$g(-2) = 2 \cdot (-8) - 4$
$g(-2) = -20$

Find $g(-2)$ by substituting -2 for x and evaluating the expression. The result is -20.

c State as ordered pairs $g(3)$: $(3, 50)$
$g(-2)$: $(-2, -20)$

The inputs and outputs can be represented as the ordered pairs $(3, 50)$ and $(-2, -20)$. The first coordinates in the ordered pairs are the input values, and the second coordinates are the output values of the function.

Graphs of Functions

The graph of a function is the result of plotting all the ordered pairs (x, y), where x, the horizontal coordinate, is any member of the domain of $f(x)$, and y, the vertical coordinate, equals the value of the function $f(x)$. The set of all vertical coordinates is the range. The vertical axis can be labeled $f(x)$ or y.

> You can determine the domain and range of a function by examining its graph. The set of x-values represents the domain, and the set of y-values represents the range.

MODEL PROBLEMS

1. Graph the linear function $f(x) = 3x - 1$.

SOLUTION

Plot first point $f(x) = 3x - 1$
$f(0) = 3(0) - 1 = -1$

To graph a function f, you can replace $f(x)$ with y, and graph the resulting equation. Evaluate the function f for $x = 0$ and find that it equals -1. State that as the ordered pair $(0, -1)$. Plot the point.

Plot second point $f(1) = 3(1) - 1 = 2$

Do the same for $x = 1$. The output of the function is 2. Plot the point $(1, 2)$.

Draw line

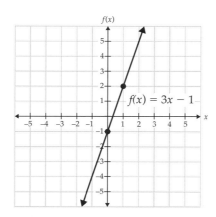

To graph the function, connect the points with a line.

Model Problems continue . . .

2. You see a graph representing the vertical location of a ball versus time. Its vertical location is measured on the vertical axis, and time is measured on the horizontal axis. The graph reflects the possible values for the domain and range. What are the domain and range of the function shown in the graph?

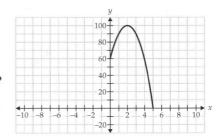

SOLUTION

Domain	From 0 to 5 $0 \le x \le 5$	Determine the domain first. The graph does not go to the left of the origin, or to the right of 5 on the x-axis, and there are function values for every value of x between 0 and 5. The domain of this function is restricted to the set of numbers from 0 to 5.
Range	From 0 to 100 $0 \le y \le 100$	The smallest y-value on the graph is 0 and the largest is 100, and every y-value between is represented on the graph. The range is the set of numbers from 0 to 100.

PRACTICE

1. Which table represents a function?

A.

x	2	2	2
y	1	5	7

B.

x	1	5	7
y	2	2	2

C.

x	1	1	7
y	2	5	7

D.

x	2	5	2
y	1	2	7

2. Which gives two points that lie on the graph of the function $f(x) = \frac{1}{2}x + 3$?

A. $(2, 4), (-2, 4)$

B. $\left(\frac{1}{2}, 3\right), \left(3, \frac{1}{2}\right)$

C. $(2, -2), (4, 2)$

D. $(2, 4), (4, 5)$

3. If $g(x) = -2x^3 + 3$, what is $g(-2)$?

A. -13

B. 19

C. 26

D. 67

4. Suppose y is directly proportional to x by a factor of k, i.e., $y = kx$. When $x = 5$ and $y = -25$, what is the proportionality constant k?

A. -5

B. $-\frac{1}{5}$

C. $\frac{1}{5}$

D. 5

5. $f(x) = 4x - 16$. What is $f(5)$?

6. $g(y) = 10y + 13$. What is $g(-2)$?

7. $f(z) = 4z^5 + 9$. What is $f(4)$?

8. $f(z) = 2z^3 - 20$. What is $f(-3)$?

Practice Problems continue . . .

Exercises 9–12: Give the domain and range for each function.

9.

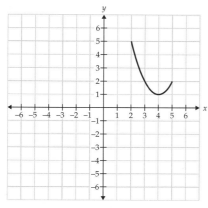

10.

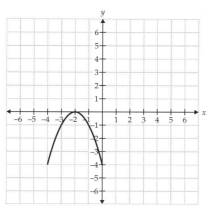

11.

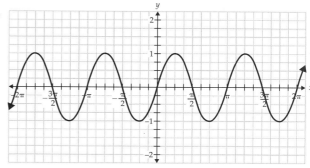

12.

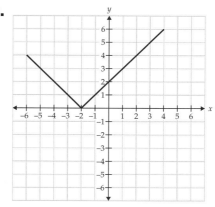

LESSON R.4

R.4 Solving Systems of Linear Equations and Inequalities

Solving Systems of Equations by Graphing

A **system of equations** is two or more equations with the same set of variables. The equations we will start working with are linear equations like those in the model problems. For a system with two variables, the solution is an ordered pair. The point of intersection of the lines is the solution to the system of equations.

A system of linear equations may have no solutions, one solution, or an infinite number of solutions. If the two lines are parallel, then they will never intersect and the system will have no solutions. If the two lines overlap, then every point on the lines is a solution. Since there are infinite number of points on a line, there are an infinite number of solutions.

1. Determine the number of solutions for each system of equations.

A

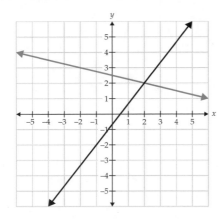

C

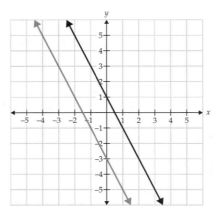

B

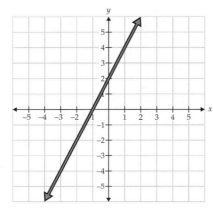

SOLUTION

Graph A has one solution because the lines represented by the system intersect at a single point. Graph B has an infinite number of solutions because both equations of the system represent the same line. Graph C has no solutions because the lines are parallel.

2. Solve $y = -x + 3$ and $y = x - 1$ by graphing.

SOLUTION

Graph each equation

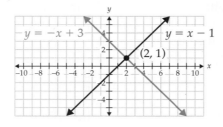

The first step in solving a system of equations by graphing is to graph each of the equations. Graph $y = x - 1$ and $y = -x + 3$.

Locate intersection

(2, 1)

Once the equations are graphed, see if they intersect. In the example, the lines intersect at (2, 1). The intersection is the solution.

PRACTICE

1. Which ordered pair is the solution to the system of equations?

    $-5x + 5y = -35; 10x - 5y = 80$

    A. $(0, 0)$ C. $(9, 2)$
    B. $(5, 5)$ D. $(9, 0)$

2. Which ordered pair is the solution to the system of equations?

    $y = x + 3; y = -x - 4$

    A. $\left(-\dfrac{7}{2}, -\dfrac{1}{2}\right)$ C. $(-4, -1)$
    B. $(-1, 2)$ D. $\left(-\dfrac{3}{2}, -\dfrac{1}{2}\right)$

3. Which ordered pair is the solution to the system of equations?

    $-6x + 7y = 25; 12x - 10y = -22$

    A. $(0, 0)$ C. $(4, 7)$
    B. $(7, 6)$ D. $(4, 0)$

4. When you graph the system of equations $x + y = -6$ and $y = ax + 3$, they intersect at $(-3, -3)$. What is a?

    A. -2 C. 2
    B. -1 D. 3

5. Use the graph to determine the solution to the system.

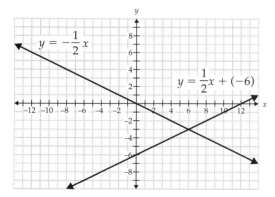

6. Use the graph to determine the solution to the system.

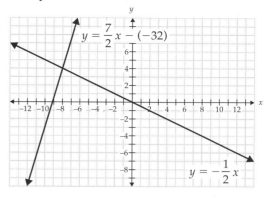

Exercises 7–9: Solve graphically and label the solutions.

7. $x - 2y = 6; 3x + 2y = -6$

8. $8x + 20y = 3; 4x + 10y = 32$

9. $x - y = 0; 2x + 3y = -5$

10. In a video game, you move two androids on a coordinate grid until they totally overlap. One android is moving along the line $y = 6x + 5$ and the other is moving along the line $y = 10x - 1$. At what point do the two androids meet?

Solving Systems by Elimination or Substitution

When solving a system of equations by elimination, you get rid of (or eliminate) one of the variables by adding equations, or equivalent equations, together. The result is a single equation with one variable, which you then solve.

Solving by substitution means solving one equation for a variable, then substituting the expression for that variable into the other equation. Finally, solve for the remaining variable and use that variable to find the other.

When solving by elimination or substitution, if the result is an equation that is not true, such as $5 = 4$, then the system has no solution. If the result is an equation that is always true, such as $3x = 3x$, then the system has an infinite number of solutions.

MODEL PROBLEMS

1. **a** Solve $4x + y = 7$ and $-4x + 5y = 11$ for y, using elimination by addition.
   b Use the value of y to find x.

SOLUTION

a Add equations together to eliminate a variable

$$\begin{array}{r} 4x + y = 7 \\ + \quad -4x + 5y = 11 \\ \hline 6y = 18 \end{array}$$

The idea behind elimination is to get rid of, or to eliminate, one variable. Add the equations together to achieve this. Line up the variables and the constants as we show. Add the equations. Since $0x$ equals 0, simplify the equation to $6y = 18$. The x-term is now eliminated.

> In a system of equations, if two variable terms are opposites, like $4x$ and $-4x$, add the equations to eliminate the variable. Or if two terms are identical, subtract to eliminate the variable.

Solve for variable

$$y = 3$$

Solve for the remaining variable by dividing both sides of the equation by 6, so $y = 3$.

b Replace y with 3 to find x

$$4x + y = 7$$
$$4x + 3 = 7$$

When we have solved for one variable, we can then solve for the other by substituting the solution into either equation. We chose $4x + y = 7$. Replace y with 3 in $4x + y = 7$.

$$4x = 4$$
$$x = 1$$

Solve for x by first subtracting 3 from both sides and then dividing both sides by 4, so $x = 1$.

State solution

$$(x, y) = (1, 3)$$

The solution to this system of equations stated as an ordered pair is $(1, 3)$.

Model Problems continue . . .

2. a Solve $x + 3y = -7$ and $3x + 6y = -9$ for x using elimination by multiplication and then adding.

   b Use the value of x to find y.

> The system of equations here is not as convenient. To eliminate a variable by adding the equations in this case, first multiply one equation by a constant to create terms that are opposites. Then add the equations.

SOLUTION

a Multiply to make coefficients opposite

$$-2(x + 3y) = (-2)(-7)$$

The first equation has $3y$ and the second has $6y$. Multiply the first equation by -2; the result will have a $-6y$ term. The coefficients of the y-terms will be opposites.

$$-2x - 6y = 14$$

Do the multiplication. Now $-6y$ is in the equation, which was our goal.

Add the equations

$$\begin{array}{r} -2x - 6y = 14 \\ +\quad 3x + 6y = -9 \\ \hline x = 5 \end{array}$$

Add the equation from the previous step to the second equation in the system. The y-terms cancel.

b Replace x with 5 to find y

$$x + 3y = -7$$
$$5 + 3y = -7$$
$$y = -4$$

Now solve for y by substituting 5 for x back into one of the original equations, so $y = -4$.

Solution

$$(x, y) = (5, -4)$$

Since $x = 5$ and $y = -4$, the solution to this system of equations is $(5, -4)$.

3. Solve $y - 4x = 12$ and $3x + y = -2$ by substitution.

SOLUTION

Solve equation for one variable

$$y - 4x = 12$$
$$y = 4x + 12$$

Solve this system using substitution. Solve $y - 4x = 12$ for y. Isolate y by adding $4x$ to both sides.

Substitute expression into other equation

$$3x + y = -2$$
$$3x + (4x + 12) = -2$$

Now substitute the expression for y from the previous step into the second equation. To do this, replace y with $4x + 12$. The result is an equation in one variable, x.

Solve equation

$$7x + 12 = -2$$
$$\frac{7x}{7} = \frac{-14}{7}$$
$$x = -2$$

Solve the equation by combining like terms and dividing by the coefficient.

Use value for variable to find the other

$$y - 4x = 12$$
$$y - 4 \cdot (-2) = 12$$
$$y + 8 = 12$$
$$y = 4$$

Use the value of x to find y. Replace x with -2 in the first equation in the system. Solve for y, so $y = 4$.

State solution

$$(x, y) = (-2, 4)$$

The solution is $(-2, 4)$. There are other similar ways to solve the system above. For instance, we could have solved the second equation for y and substituted.

Model Problems continue . . .

4. A bird flies the same distance in two hours with the wind as it flies against the wind in three hours. If there is no wind, the bird flies at 25 miles per hour. How fast is the wind?

  a Create a table to organize the information in the problem and create necessary equations.

  b Solve the equations from part **a** using substitution to find the wind speed.

SOLUTION

a w = wind

Downwind speed = $25 + w$

We use w to represent the speed of the wind. When the bird flies with the wind, we call it *downwind*. The problem says the bird flies at 25 miles per hour when there is no wind. Add w, the speed of the wind, to 25.

Upwind speed = $25 - w$

We call flying against the wind *upwind*. Its speed equals 25 minus the speed of the wind.

d = distance bird travels in one leg

distance = speed · time

We use d to represent the distance the bird travels. It travels the same distance both times. State the relationship of distance to speed and time: distance equals the product of speed and time.

Downwind

$d = (25 + w) \cdot 2$

Downwind, the bird benefits from the wind. The product of speed and time equals distance traveled.

Upwind

$d = (25 - w) \cdot 3$

Upwind, the bird fights the wind. The product of speed and time equals distance traveled.

Create table

	Speed	**Time**	**Distance = Speed · Time**
Downwind	$25 + w$	2	$d = (25 + w) \cdot 2$
Upwind	$25 - w$	3	$d = (25 - w) \cdot 3$

b Solve by substitution

$d = 2(25 + w)$
$d = 3(25 - w)$

Solve the equations. Using the commutative property, place the coefficients before the parentheses.

Set expressions for d equal

$2(25 + w) = 3(25 - w)$

Both the equations in the system are equal to d, so set these expressions for d equal. This is equivalent to substituting.

Simplify

$50 + 2w = 75 - 3w$

Simplify the equation. On the left side of the equation, distribute 2, and on the right side distribute 3. Then perform the multiplication.

Solve equation

$50 + 5w = 75$
$5w = 25$
$w = 5$

Combine the w terms by adding $3w$ to both sides. Combine the constants by subtracting 50 from both sides. Then divide by the coefficient, 5, to find w.

The wind's speed is 5 miles per hour. This means the bird flies at 30 miles per hour downwind and 20 miles per hour upwind. The problem said it flew the same distance downwind in two hours and in three hours upwind. With a little multiplication, we see that it flew 60 miles in both cases, which checks our solution.

1. An airplane flies from Detroit to Seattle in 6 hours against a headwind. The airplane then flies from Seattle to Detroit in 4 hours with a tailwind. The airplane flies at a constant speed of 550 miles per hour when there is no wind. If x represents the speed of the wind and d is the distance the plane flies, which system of equations best models the situation?

   A. $d = (550)(4); d = (550)(6)$
   B. $d = (550 - x)(4); d = (550 + x)(6)$
   C. $d = (550 + x)(4); d = (550 + x)(6)$
   D. $d = (550 + x)(4); d = (550 - x)(6)$

2. Samantha rides her bike 2.5 miles per hour faster than Lindsey. The two girls start cycling at the same point. Samantha gives Lindsey a 15-minute head start and catches up with her after cycling for 1 hour and 15 minutes. How fast did the two girls ride?

   A. 7 miles per hour for Lindsey and 2.5 miles per hour for Samantha
   B. 15 miles per hour for Lindsey and 17.5 miles per hour for Samantha
   C. 3.75 miles per hour for Lindsey and 6.25 miles per hour for Samantha
   D. 18 miles per hour for Lindsey and 20.5 miles per hour for Samantha

Exercises 3–14: Solve each system of equations.

3. $4x + 5y = 140; 3x - 5y = 105$

4. $4x + 4y = 56; 3x - 4y = 56$

5. $4x - 5y = -180; -4x - 4y = -180$

6. $2x - 3y = -36; -2x - 3y = -48$

7. $3x + 3y = -24; 3x + 5y = -6$

8. $5x + 2y = -40; 5x + 4y = -20$

9. $4x + 9y = 29; x = 5y - 87$

10. $6x + 4y = 88; x = 3y - 110$

11. $5x + y = 513; 7x - 10y = 171$

12. $5x + y = 69; 8x - 3y = 46$

13. $7x + 10y = -225; x + 5y = -75$

14. $6x + 7y = -328; x + 8y = -328$

15. The sum of two numbers is 123. Their difference is 37. What are the numbers?

16. The sum of two numbers is 91. Their difference is 13. What are the numbers?

17. Two robots participate in a joke contest. Each one is designed to produce a certain number of jokes per day. The two robots write for two days straight and a quarter of their jokes, 150, are accepted to the contest. One robot decides to keep working for an extra day and increases their total number of jokes written to 720. How many jokes did each robot write per day?

18. The same plane travels with the wind when it flies from Seattle to Spokane and against the wind on the return trip. What is the speed of the wind?

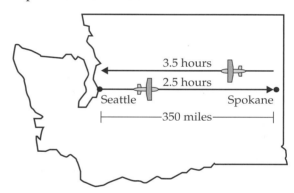

19. A pine tree is currently 9 feet tall and grows 6 inches every year. You plant a new variety of tree next to it that is 16 inches tall and grows 14 inches a year. When will the two trees be equal in height, and how tall will they be? Round the values to the nearest tenth.

20. At a restaurant, you bought only hamburgers and sodas. Based on the bill, how many hamburgers did you buy?

Alan's Burgers	
Hamburgers =	$4
Sodas =	$2
Total items purchased: 14	
Total =	$46

Practice Problems continue . . .

21. 3 plates and 6 bowls cost $78.00, and 6 plates and 4 bowls cost $91.20. How much does one plate cost? one bowl? Express your answer to the nearest tenth.

22. Is it possible to pay $100 using a total of 30 $5 and $1 bills? If yes, explain how; if not, explain why.

23. Sam is three times as old as Steve. In 3 years, he will be twice as old. How old is Steve today?

24. As part of a charity event, you and your friend have been sponsored to make a total of 912 free throws. You can make 8 free throws each minute, and your friend can make 5 free throws each minute. You start shooting on time, but your friend is 10 minutes late. How many minutes will it take to reach your goal?

25. A plane travels west from Chicago for 1 hour and 15 minutes before developing electrical system trouble that forces it to turn around. Because of a west wind, the return trip takes only 1 hour. The average ground speed of the plane is 450 mph without the wind. Find the speed of the wind in miles per hour (assuming it stays constant throughout the entire trip).

26. You can shovel the snow off your driveway in 2 hours by yourself. Your younger sister can do it in 3 hours by herself. How many hours would it take both of you, working together, to shovel the driveway? Round your answer to the nearest tenth.

Graphing Linear Inequalities

We show how to graph a linear inequality in two variables, such as $y > 3x + 2$.

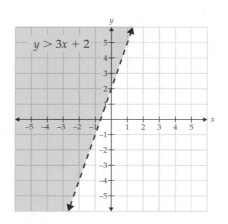

1. Graph boundary line

Temporarily change the inequality sign to an equals sign and graph the equation as a line. This is the **boundary line**.

2. Use test point to decide which side

Shade one side of the line or the other. To determine which side, choose a test point on one side. We chose the test point $(0, 0)$ to make the calculations easy.

3. Shade one side of line
- $(0, 0)$ not a solution
- Shade other side

Substituting the point $(0, 0)$ into the inequality and evaluating results in a false inequality. This means the solutions are on the other side of the boundary line. We shade that side.

4. Boundary line is
- Solid for $\leq$ or $\geq$
- Dashed for $<$ or $>$

If the inequality symbol is $\leq$ or $\geq$, make the boundary line solid to show points on the line are part of the solution. If the inequality is $<$ or $>$, make the boundary line a dashed line to show points on the line are not part of the solution.

Solving Systems of Linear Inequalities by Graphing

A **system of inequalities** is two or more inequalities with the same variables. In this section, we study systems of linear inequalities consisting of two linear inequalities involving two variables. A solution to this system is any ordered pair that makes both inequalities true.

 In this activity, solve several systems of inequalities.

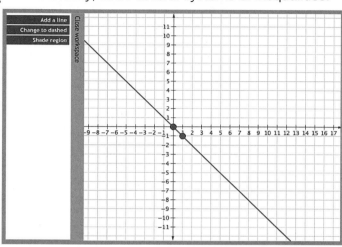

To solve a system of inequalities, graph each inequality and find the region where the solutions overlap.

MODEL PROBLEM

Solve $y \leq -\frac{1}{2}x + 3$ and $3y - 2x < -6$ by graphing.

SOLUTION

Graph first inequality	Boundary line is $y = -\frac{1}{2}x + 3$	Start with $y \leq -\frac{1}{2}x + 3$ and graph its boundary line as a solid line, since the inequality symbol is $\leq$.
Test point on one side of boundary	$0 \leq -\frac{1}{2}(0) + 3$	Since $(0, 0)$ is a solution to the inequality, the solutions are below the boundary line. Shade this region.
Graph second inequality	Boundary line is $y = \frac{2}{3}x - 2$	Then consider $3y - 2x < -6$ and graph its line, $y = \frac{2}{3}x - 2$, as a dashed line, since the inequality symbol is $<$. (We find the boundary line equation by changing the inequality to an equals sign and solving for y.)
Test point on one side of boundary	$3(0) - 2(0) \overset{?}{<} -6$ $0 \not< -6$	We tried $(0, 0)$ and it was *not* a solution to the inequality, so shade the other side of the line.
Solutions are in region of overlap	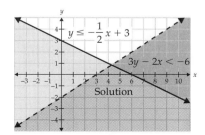	The solutions to the system are in the region where the solutions to the inequalities overlap. Any point in this region is a solution to both inequalities.

PRACTICE

Exercises 1–4: Determine which ordered pairs are solutions to the given system of inequalities. Select all that apply.

1. $y \geq -2x + 11$ and $y \leq 5x - 10$

    A. $(0, 0)$

    B. $(6, 0)$

    C. $(3, 5)$

    D. $(4, -2)$

    E. $(2, 10)$

    F. None of these.

2. $y < 6x - 2$ and $y \geq x + 3$

    A. $(1, 4)$

    B. $(0, 0)$

    C. $(2, 0)$

    D. $(0, 6)$

    E. $(3, 8)$

    F. None of these.

3. $y > x - 1$ and $y \leq x + 2$

    A. $(-3, 0)$

    B. $(-1, 1)$

    C. $(0, 0)$

    D. $(2, 1)$

    E. $(3, 0)$

    F. None of these.

4. $y > -4x + 5$ and $y < -4x - 3$

    A. $(-4, 0)$

    B. $(-1, 1)$

    C. $(0, 0)$

    D. $(0, 7)$

    E. $(1, 1)$

    F. $(2, 2)$

    G. None of these.

Exercises 5–10: Write the inequality or system of inequalities that matches the graph.

5.

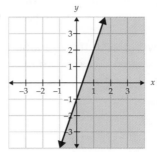

6.

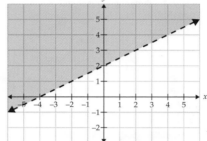

7.

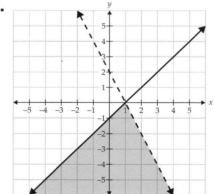

8.

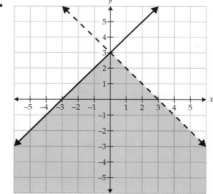

Practice Problems continue . . .

9.

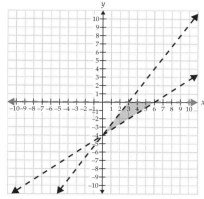

10.

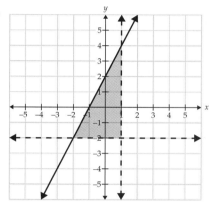

Exercises 11–18: Graph the inequality or system of inequalities.

11. $y < -\dfrac{3}{2}x - 2$

12. $y \geq \dfrac{3}{4}x + 1$

13. $y > -4x - 5; y < \dfrac{1}{4}x + 1$

14. $y \leq 2x - 5; y < -\dfrac{1}{2}x + 3$

15. $y \geq -3x; y \leq \dfrac{2}{3}x - 4$

16. $y < x - 3; y \geq -5x + 5$

17. $y > -\dfrac{2}{3}x - 2; y \leq \dfrac{5}{2}x + 5; y \leq -3x$

18. $y \leq \dfrac{3}{2}x - 4; y \leq -2x + 1; y \leq -\dfrac{1}{4}x - 4$

19. An algebra teacher is writing a 90-minute test. There will be two types of questions: multiple choice and open-ended. The multiple-choice questions each take 3 minutes to complete, and the open-ended questions each take 12 minutes to complete. There must be at least 3 open-ended questions, at least 10 multiple-choice questions, and the test should take no more than 84 minutes.

  a Write this scenario as a system of inequalities, using M for the number of multiple-choice problems and O for the number of open-ended problems.

  b Graph the system of inequalities that you found in part **a**. Put M on the horizontal axis and O on the vertical axis.

  c List the possible combinations that the teacher could use to write the test.

20. In the Algebra Hockey League, a team receives two points for a win and one point for a loss in overtime. There are no points awarded for a loss during regulation time. A team has 8 games to go in the season and needs more than 10 points to earn a bid to the playoffs.

  a Describe this situation with a system of inequalities, using W for the number of wins and L for the number of overtime losses.

  b Graph the system of inequalities that you wrote in part **a**. Put W on the horizontal axis and L on the vertical axis.

  c List the different possible ways (wins, losses, losses in overtime) that the team could make the playoffs.

R.5 Polynomial Operations

Power Rules

We state the rules for multiplying and dividing powers and raising powers to a power.

	Rule	Example	Description
Product rule	$x^m \cdot x^n = x^{m+n}$	$2^3 \cdot 2^2 = 2^{3+2} = 2^5$	To multiply two powers with the same base, *add the exponents*. For example, when multiplying 2^3 by 2^2, add the exponents 3 and 2 to get 5. The product is 2^5.
Quotient rule	$\dfrac{x^m}{x^n} = x^{m-n}$	$\dfrac{x^7}{x^4} = x^{7-4} = x^3$	To divide powers, *subtract the exponents*. When dividing x^7 by x^4, subtract 4 from 7 to get x^3.
Power of a power rule	$(x^m)^n = x^{m \cdot n}$	$(5^3)^4 = 5^{3 \cdot 4} = 5^{12}$	To raise 5^3 to the fourth power, *multiply exponents*. 5^3 to the fourth power equals 5^{12}.

MODEL PROBLEM

Simplify $\dfrac{a^4 \cdot a^2}{a}$ **Remember that $a = a^1$.**

SOLUTION

Apply product of powers rule $\quad \dfrac{a^{4+2}}{a^1} \quad$ Add the exponents to multiply in the numerator. Restate a as a^1 to make the next step clearer.

$\dfrac{a^6}{a^1}$

Apply quotient of powers rule $\quad a^{6-1} \quad$ To divide, subtract exponents.

a^5

PRACTICE

1. Simplify $2^{15} \cdot 2^{13}$ to a power of 2.

2. Simplify $7^{12} \cdot 7^{12}$ to a power of 7.

3. Simplify $\dfrac{6^{14}}{6^8}$ to a power of 6.

4. Simplify $\dfrac{11^{12}}{11^8}$ to a power of 11.

Exercises 5–14: Simplify.

5. $y^4 \cdot y^8$

6. $y^4 \cdot y^6$

7. $(x^3)^9$

8. $(x^7)^7$

9. $5r^4 \cdot 8r^{12} \cdot 5r^5$

10. $6r^7 \cdot 7r^9 \cdot 3r^6$

11. $\dfrac{a^{18}}{a^9}$

12. $\dfrac{a^{17}}{a^5}$

13. $\dfrac{z^6 z^{10}}{z^5}$

14. $\dfrac{z^6 z^{12}}{z^{14}}$

Products and Quotients to a Power

	Rule	Description
Power of a product rule	$(xy)^n = x^n y^n$	The power of a product rule states that to raise a product to a power, raise each factor to the power and multiply.
Power of a quotient rule	$\left(\dfrac{x}{y}\right)^n = \dfrac{x^n}{y^n}$	When $\dfrac{x}{y}$ is raised to the nth power, both the numerator and the denominator are raised to the nth power.

MODEL PROBLEMS

1. Simplify $(2x)^4$.

SOLUTION

Raise each factor to the power and multiply them

$2^4 x^4$
$16x^4$

To raise a product to a power, raise each factor to the power and multiply. Form 2 to the fourth power and multiply it by x to the fourth power. 2^4 can be written as 16.

2. Simplify $\left(\dfrac{w}{5}\right)^2$.

SOLUTION

Raise numerator and denominator to the power

$\dfrac{w^2}{5^2}$

To raise a quotient to a power, raise the numerator and the denominator to the power. Take the numerator, w, and square it to get w^2. Take the denominator, 5, and square it to get 5^2.

$\dfrac{w^2}{25}$

Simplify the expression by writing 5^2 as 25.

PRACTICE

1. Write $(6^8)^9$ as a power of 6.

2. Write $(7^7)^8$ as a power of 7.

3. Write $(3^6)^7$ as a power of 3.

4. Write $(5^7)^9$ as a power of 5.

Exercises 5–15: Simplify.

5. $(ab)^{15}$

6. $(ab)^{17}$

7. $(3t)^3$

8. $(2t)^3$

9. $\left(\dfrac{a}{b}\right)^{11}$

10. $\left(\dfrac{a}{b}\right)^5$

11. $\left(\dfrac{4}{c}\right)^4$

12. $\left(\dfrac{3}{c}\right)^3$

13. $\left(\dfrac{x}{yz}\right)^{18}$

14. $(2a^3b^4)^2$

15. $\left(\dfrac{3u^2}{v^5}\right)^3$

16. **MP 3** A student simplified the expression $(2x^4)^4$ to $2x^8$. What did the student do wrong? Justify your answer.

Zero and Negative Exponents

Any number (other than 0) to the 0 power equals 1. For instance, both 35^0 and $(-3.1)^0$ equal 1. Zero raised to any positive whole number is 0, while 0^0 and 0 raised to a negative exponent are undefined.

A negative exponent such as x^{-n} is the same as a positive exponent in the denominator. Stated as an equation: $x^{-n} = \dfrac{1}{x^n}$

> A number x raised to the power $-n$ equals the reciprocal of x raised to the power n.

MODEL PROBLEM

What does 2^{-5} equal?

SOLUTION

Reciprocal of power with positive exponent

$$x^{-n} = \frac{1}{x^n}$$

$$2^{-5} = \frac{1}{2^5}$$

A power with a negative exponent equals the reciprocal of the power with a positive exponent.

In the example, 2^{-5} equals its reciprocal, $\dfrac{1}{2^5}$.

PRACTICE

Exercises 1–4: Evaluate.

1. 388^0

2. 402^0

3. 396^0

4. 392^0

Exercises 5–16: Simplify. Write without negative exponents.

5. $4r^{-9}$

6. $3r^{-6}$

7. $\dfrac{4}{x^{-12}}$

8. $\dfrac{8}{x^{-6}}$

9. $\dfrac{3x^{-8}}{5y^{-17}}$

10. $\dfrac{5x^{-10}}{9y^{-13}}$

11. $x^{-2} \cdot x^{15}$

12. $x^{-2} \cdot x^{14}$

13. $(xy)^{-8}$

14. $(xy)^{-3}$

15. $(x^4 y^{-6})^{-4}$

16. $(x^6 y^{-5})^{-4}$

Exercises 17–19: Write without a fraction.

17. $\dfrac{6}{c^{11}}$

18. $\dfrac{7}{c^{10}}$

19. $\dfrac{3}{c^8}$

20. **MP 7** What must be true about x and a if $x^a = 0$?

21. **MP 7** What must be true about x and a if $x^a = 1$?

MP 3 Exercises 22–23: Explain why the statement is incorrect.

22. $x^{-4} = -x^4$

23. $5x^{-1} = \dfrac{1}{5x}$

Multiplying Polynomials

Since multiplying **polynomials** is a core skill in algebra, we review it before moving to more advanced topics.

MODEL PROBLEMS

1. Multiply $3x^2(5x^4 - 7x + 8)$.

> To multiply a **monomial**, distribute the monomial to each term in the polynomial. Then multiply the monomials.

SOLUTION

Distribute the monomial	$3x^2(5x^4 - 7x + 8)$ $(3x^2 \cdot 5x^4) + (3x^2 \cdot (-7x)) + (3x^2 \cdot 8)$	Distribute the $3x^2$, which means multiply every term in the polynomial by $3x^2$. (The term being subtracted, $7x$, is written as a negative.)
Multiply monomials in each term	$3 \cdot 5 \cdot x^2 \cdot x^4 + 3 \cdot (-7) \cdot x^2 \cdot x + 3 \cdot 8 \cdot x^2$ $15 \cdot x^2 \cdot x^4 + (-21) \cdot x^2 \cdot x + 24 \cdot x^2$	Each term is now a product of monomials. Rearrange the factors in each product monomial. Then multiply the coefficients.
Multiply the variables	$15x^{2+4} + (-21)x^{2+1} + 24x^2$ $15x^6 - 21x^3 + 24x^2$	To multiply the powers, add the exponents and keep the bases the same for each multiplication.

2. Multiply $(3x^2 + 4x)(5x - 2)$.

> We multiply two binomials using the distributive property as well. Each polynomial here is a **binomial**, a polynomial of two terms. Multiply by distributing each term in the first binomial.

SOLUTION

Distribute	$(3x^2)(5x - 2) + (4x)(5x - 2)$	Use the distributive property to multiply each term of $3x^2 + 4x$ by the other polynomial, $5x - 2$.
Multiply	$15x^3 - 6x^2 + \ldots$	Distribute the $3x^2$ across $5x - 2$, multiplying to get $15x^3 - 6x^2$.
	$15x^3 - 6x^2 + 20x^2 - 8x$	And then multiply $4x$ and $5x - 2$ to get the last two terms, $20x^2 - 8x$.
Write in standard form	$15x^3 + 14x^2 - 8x$	There are two like terms, $-6x^2$ and $20x^2$, which combine to $14x^2$. The answer is in the **standard form of a polynomial**.

Model Problems continue . . .

3. Multiply $(3x - 2)(2x - 7)$ using FOIL.

> FOIL stands for **First, Outer, Inner, Last.** Multiply the first terms of each binomial, then the outer terms, then the inner, and, finally, the last terms.

SOLUTION

| Multiply using FOIL: First, Outer, Inner, Last | $(3x - 2)(2x - 7)$ $3x \cdot 2x + 3x \cdot (-7) - 2 \cdot 2x - 2 \cdot (-7)$ $6x^2 - 21x - 4x + 14$ | Start by multiplying the first terms of the binomials, $3x$ and $2x$. The result is $6x^2$. Next, multiply the outer terms, $3x$ and -7. The result is $-21x$. Now the inner terms, -2 and $2x$, are multiplied to get $-4x$. Finally, multiply the last terms of the binomials, -2 and -7. |
| Simplify and combine like terms | $6x^2 - 25x + 14$ | Simplify each product and combine like terms. The first term, $6x^2$, has no like term. The two x-terms in the middle are like terms, and combine them to get $-25x$. The last term, 14, has no like terms. |

4. Multiply $(2x + 3) \cdot (2x^2 - 4x + 1)$.

SOLUTION

Distribute one polynomial across the other	$2x(2x^2 - 4x + 1) + 3(2x^2 - 4x + 1)$	The parentheses around $(2x^2 - 4x + 1)$ indicate that we should treat it as one factor. Distribute it across the other polynomial, meaning multiply $2x$ and 3 by $2x^2 - 4x + 1$.
Distribute the monomials across the polynomials	$2x \cdot 2x^2 + 2x \cdot (-4x) + 2x \cdot 1 + 3(2x^2 - 4x + 1)$ $2x \cdot 2x^2 + 2x \cdot (-4x) + 2x \cdot 1 + 3 \cdot 2x^2 + 3 \cdot (-4x) + 3 \cdot 1$	Distribute the monomial $2x$ across $2x^2 - 4x + 1$. Multiply each term in $2x^2 - 4x + 1$ by $2x$. Do the remaining distribution. Distribute the monomial 3 across $2x^2 - 4x + 1$.
Multiply the monomials	$4x^3 - 8x^2 + 2x + 6x^2 - 12x + 3$	Multiply the monomials.
Write in standard form	$4x^3 - 2x^2 - 10x + 3$	The second-degree terms, $-8x^2$ and $6x^2$, combine to $-2x^2$. Similarly, $2x$ and $-12x$ combine to $-10x$. The final answer is in standard form.

PRACTICE

Exercises 1–17: Multiply and state in standard form.

1. $(6x^2)(9x^5)$

2. $(6x^7)(13x^8)$

3. $(5x^6)(8x^8)(-3x^6)$

4. $8x(7x^4 + 12)$

5. $5x^5(9x^3 + 8x)$

6. $2x^4(7x^4 + 12x^3 + 4x)$

7. $3x^6(8x^4 + 12x + 4)$

8. $(7x^4 + 6)(6x^9 + 9)$

9. $(2x + 5)(6x^5 - 5)$

10. $(3x^6 - 7)(4x^6 - 6)$

11. $(6x + 7)(4x^7 - 7x)$

12. $(4x^4 + 6x)(6x^9 + 9x)$

13. $(5x + 4)^2$

14. $(6x - 4)^2$

15. $(6x + 2)(6x - 2)$

16. $(7x + 7)(7x - 7)$

17. $(6x^3 - 4)(8x^3 - 3)$

18. The side of the rectangle labeled W has a length of $7x + 2$, and the side of the rectangle labeled L has a length of $4x - 7$. Write an expression for the area of the rectangle.

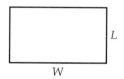

19. The area of an equilateral triangle with sides of length s is $\frac{\sqrt{3}}{4}s^2$. Write an expression for the area of an equilateral triangle with sides of length $\frac{x^3}{2}$.

LESSON R.6

R.6 Parabolas

The graphs of functions of the form $f(x) = ax^2$, such as $f(x) = -2x^2$, are **parabolas**. A parabola is a bowl-shaped curve. The variable a represents the coefficient of x^2.

Every parabola has an **axis of symmetry** that passes through the vertex. The **vertex** of a parabola of the form $f(x) = ax^2$ is at the origin. The y-coordinate of the vertex is the minimum or maximum value of the function. Each point on the parabola has a mirror image point across the axis of symmetry.

The value of a determines the direction in which the parabola opens.

> The value of *a* does not change the location of the vertex, but it does change the shape and direction of the parabola.

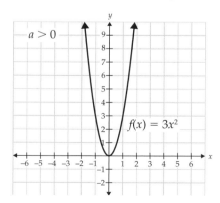

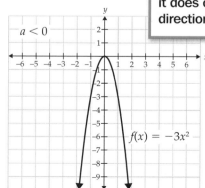

In the graph above, the coefficient of x^2 is 3. If $a > 0$, the parabola opens up.

In the graph above, the coefficient of x^2 is -3. If $a < 0$, the parabola opens down.

Graph $f(x) = -2x^2$.

SOLUTION

> To graph a parabola use some of its properties. Start by plotting its vertex, the highest or lowest point of a parabola.

Vertex   Vertex $= (0, 0)$ The vertex is the highest or lowest point of a parabola. When a parabola is of the form $f(x) = ax^2$, its vertex is at the origin, $(0, 0)$.

Axis of symmetry $x = 0$ For a parabola of this form, the axis of symmetry is the y-axis, or the line $x = 0$.

Each point mirrored across axis

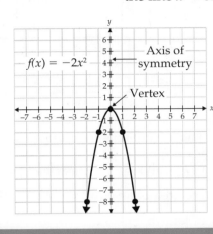

x	$f(x)$
0	0
2	-8
-2	-8
1	-2
-1	-2

To graph the parabola, substitute a value for x, evaluate and plot the point. For instance, if $x = 2$, the output of this function is -8. Since $x = 2$ and -2 are both 2 away from the axis, the output of the function is -8 for both inputs. We can calculate other points in the same fashion. Since $f(-1)$ is -2, $f(1)$ is also -2.

Translating Parabolas in Vertex Form

The function $f(x) = x^2$ is the parent function of the graphs of parabolas. Any parabola can be described with the function $f(x) = a(x - h)^2 + k$ where a, h, and k are constants. We call this the **vertex form for a parabola**.

The expression $f(x) = a(x - h)^2 + k$ is a polynomial expression when multiplied out. The constants h and k translate the function from the origin, and a changes the shape of the curve. As with other functions, k translates the graph vertically, and h translates it horizontally. The value of a and the location of the vertex determine the maximum or minimum value of a parabola of the form $f(x) = a(x - h)^2 + k$. The axis of symmetry is $x = h$.

To describe how the parabola translates, we locate its vertex using h and k.

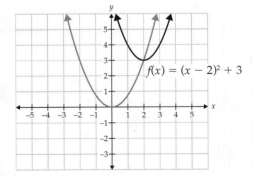

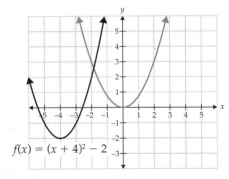

$f(x) = (x - 2)^2 + 3$
Vertex is $(2, 3)$

$f(x) = (x + 4)^2 - 2$
$f(x) = (x - (-4))^2 + (-2)$
Vertex is $(-4, -2)$

In this activity, experiment with translating a parabola.

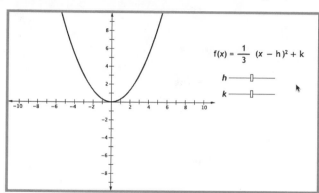

$f(x) = \dfrac{1}{3}(x - h)^2 + k$

h ———

k ———

> Go to **www.amscomath.com** to use the activity.

PRACTICE

1. Determine whether the parabola $y = \dfrac{1}{2}(x + 8)^2 - 5$ has a maximum or minimum value.

   A. Maximum
   B. Minimum

2. Determine whether the parabola $y = -2(x - 8)^2 + 16$ has a maximum or minimum value.

   A. Maximum
   B. Minimum

Exercises 3–8: For each of the parabolas, write the equation of the axis of symmetry.

3. $y = x^2$

4. $y = -2x^2$

5. $y = -2x^2 + 3$

6. $y = -2(x + 1)^2$

7. $y = -(x - 3)^2$

8. $y = 2(x - 1)^2 + 2$

Exercises 9–13: Determine if the parabola opens up or down.

9. $y = \dfrac{1}{2}x^2$

10. $y = -x^2$

11. $y = 2(x - 3)^2 + 1$

12. $y = -\dfrac{1}{4}(x + 1)^2 - 5$

13. $y = -3(x + 1)^2 + 8$

Exercises 14–15: Identify the coordinates of the vertex of each parabola.

14. $y = \dfrac{1}{2}(x - 6)^2 - 5$

15. $y = \dfrac{1}{3}(x + 2)^2 + 1$

16. Determine the y-value of the vertex of the parabola $y = -5(x - 9)^2 + 14$.

Chapter Content

Vocabulary

asymptote	line of best fit	residual
coefficient of determination	model	scatter plot
end behavior	objective function	structure of an equation
even function	odd function	transformation
feasible region	parent function	translation
limit	regression	trend line
linear programming		

LESSON 1.1

1.1 Functions

In Algebra 2, you will learn some additional functions, but you have a good collection of them already. Some of the functions you may have learned about:

- Linear functions: $f(x) = mx + b$
- Absolute value functions: $f(x) = |x|$
- Quadratic functions: $f(x) = x^2$
- Exponential functions: $f(x) = a^x$
- Piecewise functions: $f(x)$ has different definitions given the value of x

Along your mathematical journey, you may have learned additional functions, but the list above gives us plenty to discuss. We will use graphs to discuss these functions, since graphs provide a visual way to investigate the functions' properties.

Properties of Functions

Functions with Constant Slope

An important property of graphs with straight lines is that they have a constant slope. A linear function has one slope. Each straight line component of an absolute value function has a constant slope.

Linear function $f(x) = mx + b$	**Absolute value function** $f(x) = |x|$
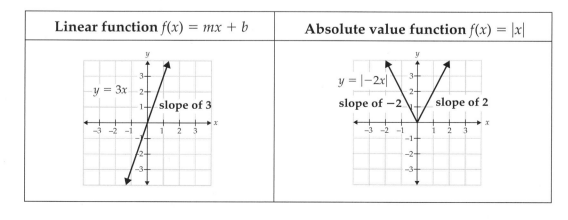	

Functions with Changing Slopes

The slopes of functions that are described by curved graphs are not constant. The steeper the curve, the greater the absolute value of the slope.

Quadratic function $f(x) = x^2$	Exponential function $f(x) = a^x$
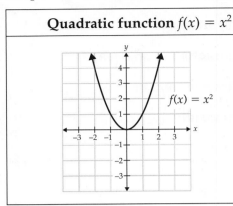	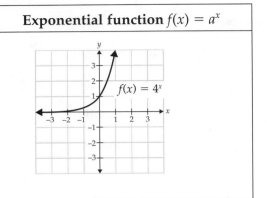

Average Rate of Change

In later courses, you may learn how to compute the exact slope at any point on a curve, but for now, you can calculate the average slope (or average rate) by connecting a pair of points on the curve. The diagram to the right shows how to calculate average slopes for $f(x) = x^2$. We compute them in three consecutive intervals; the slope of each segment is the average slope of the curve between the segment's endpoints. You can see how the average slope is steeper (greater) in the rightmost interval, from 0.1 to approximately 0.19, than in the two intervals to the left of it.

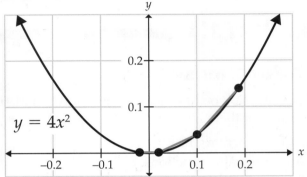

Symmetrical Functions

Some functions are symmetrical. If the graph is symmetrical, a line can be drawn, and for every point on one side of that line, another point can be found that is on the other side of and the same distance from that line. Or, to put it another way, the graph can be created by "reflecting" each point across a line, the graph's axis of symmetry.

Quadratic function $f(x) = x^2$	Absolute value function $f(x) = |x|$
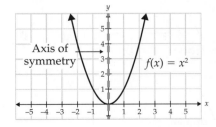	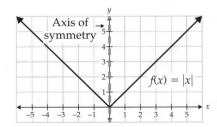
The graph of the parabola above is symmetrical about the vertical axis. You could create the side to the left of the origin by reflecting the side on the right about the y-axis.	The same applies to the absolute value function. The side to the left of the vertical axis is a mirror image of the side to the right.

Non-Symmetrical Functions

The graph of an exponential function is not symmetrical. There is no line that can be drawn where every point can be paired with another point an equal distance from that line. Put another way, there is no way to create this graph by a single reflection.

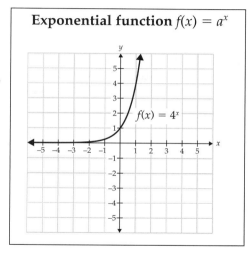

Exponential function $f(x) = a^x$

$f(x) = 4^x$

Continuous and Discontinuous Functions

Another property of a function that is shown by its graph is whether it is continuous or discontinuous. With a continuous graph, every point on the graph is adjacent to another point as you move in either direction. If it is discontinuous, there are gaps in the graph between some points.

Examples of continuous functions:

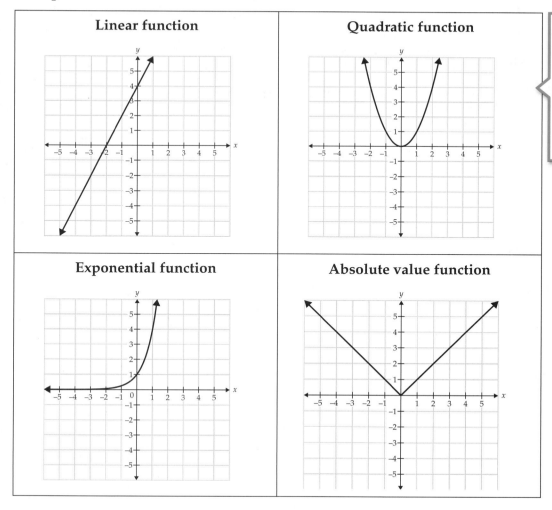

Linear function

Quadratic function

Exponential function

Absolute value function

> Many of the functions you study are continuous. Move a bit to the left or right on the graph, and you always find an adjacent point.

Examples of discontinuous functions:

Not all functions are continuous. One way to create a discontinuous graph is to simply define the graph not to be continuous, like the step function to the right. Later, you may study other functions with graphs that are discontinuous, such as the graph of the tangent function in trigonometry or rational functions.

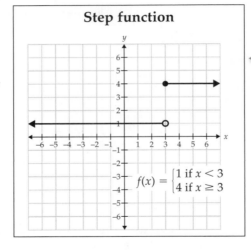

Step function

$$f(x) = \begin{cases} 1 \text{ if } x < 3 \\ 4 \text{ if } x \geq 3 \end{cases}$$

$$f(x) = \begin{cases} 1 \text{ if } x < 3 \\ 4 \text{ if } x \geq 3 \end{cases}$$
creates a gap as shown. The graph is not continuous at $x = 3$.

Piecewise Functions

Piecewise functions come in "pieces." They are defined by different expressions on different parts of the domain. Absolute value functions are continuous piecewise functions because they come in two pieces, the left and right sides. Step functions are discontinuous piecewise functions.

Domain and Range of Functions

Some functions have no restrictions to their *domain* (possible inputs) and *range* (possible outputs), while other functions do have restrictions. We use the structure and graph of the function to understand how this is possible.

The linear function $f(x) = 2x - 1$ has no limit to how positive or negative the inputs are, and the same applies to the outputs. The function is defined for every real number. The function has no restrictions.

Some functions have a restriction on their domains. For instance, the rational function $f(x) = \dfrac{1}{x}$ is not defined for 0 (since dividing by 0 is undefined), so 0 is not part of its domain.

Other functions have a restriction on their range. Examining the structure of $f(x) = x^2$, we know it will always have an output of zero or positive numbers since a real number squared cannot be negative. Using the graph of $f(x) = -x^2 + 3$, the vertex of the graph represents the greatest possible value of its range, which is 3 in this case.

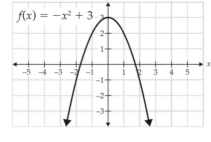

The ranges of certain functions approach but never quite reach another number. The line defined by this number, such as $f(x) = 0$, is called an **asymptote**. Exponential functions provide an example of this behavior. For instance, $f(x) = 3^x$ will approach 0 as the values of x become increasingly negative, but never equal zero. For example, if $x = -10$, then the function equals about 0.0000169, and if $x = -100$, the function equals about 1.9×10^{-48}. These are small and very, very small numbers, respectively, but they are not zero.

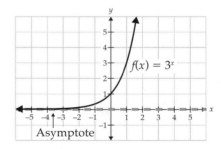

We can use the domain and range of a function to describe the **end behavior** of graphs. In the graph of $f(x) = 3^x$, as x becomes increasingly positive, $f(x)$ becomes increasingly large. In this case, we say the far right behavior of the graph approaches positive infinity. As x becomes increasingly negative, $f(x)$ approaches 0. In this case, we say the far left behavior of the graph approaches 0.

Real-World Limits on Domain and Range

The real world can also impose **limits** (or constraints) on the domain and range of functions. The parabola in the diagram to the right shows the vertical position of a model rocket launched from ground level, with time on the horizontal axis. Ground level is 3 meters above sea level. The domain is the time in seconds. Time cannot be negative, so the domain is 0 and positive numbers. The range is the height; in this case, its minimum value is 3 meters (we will assume the rocket does not plunge below Earth's surface upon impact).

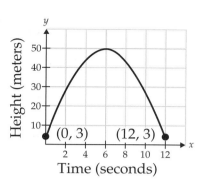

Translating Function Graphs

A **parent function** is the simplest form of a type of function and serves as a building block for more complex functions. For instance, $f(x) = x^2$ is a parent function, and $f(x) = -2x^2 + 5$ is an example of a child function. Other examples of parent functions include $f(x) = |x|$ and $f(x) = \sqrt{x}$. With parent functions, the variable has no coefficient, and there is no constant being added or subtracted.

A change of a relationship is called a **transformation**. If the change moves (shifts) the graph of a relationship without changing the shape of the graph, the transformation is a **translation**.

MODEL PROBLEMS

1. Graph $f(x) = x^2 + 3$.

SOLUTION

Identify parent function

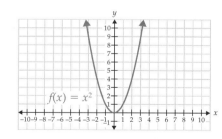

Given the original function $f(x) = x^2 + 3$, we identify the parent function $f(x) = x^2$ and graph it.

Constant is added to parent function

$f(x) = x^2 + 3$

The original function equals 3 added to the parent function.

Graph translates vertically by constant

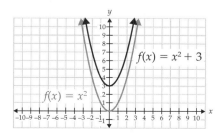

Adding +3 to the parent function results in translating the graph of the parent function vertically upward 3 units.

Model Problems continue . . .

2. Graph $f(x) = x^2 - 3$.

SOLUTION

Identify parent function

$f(x) = x^2$

The parent function of $f(x) = x^2 - 3$ is $f(x) = x^2$.

Constant is added to parent function

$f(x) = $ parent function $+ k$

Adding a positive constant k to a parent function translates it up k units.

Translates by k

$f(x) = x^2 - 3 = x^2 + (-3)$

Subtracting a positive constant from a parent function translates the graph of the parent function downward that many units. For example, subtracting 3 from the parent function translates its graph downward 3 units.

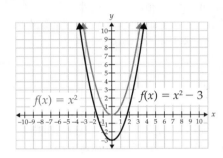

> *Adding* a positive constant to a parent function translates its graph *up* that many units. *Subtracting* a positive constant from a parent function translates its graph *down* that many units.

3. Graph $f(x) = |x - 3|$.

SOLUTION

Identify parent function

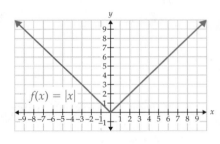

Start with the graph of its parent function, $f(x) = |x|$.

Constant is subtracted from input of function

$f(x - h)$
$f(x) = |x - 3|$

The function we wish to graph has 3 subtracted from the input of the parent function.

Graph translates horizontally by constant

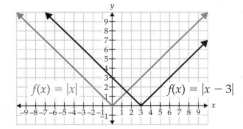

When a positive constant is subtracted from the input, the graph translates to the right by that amount. In general, subtracting h from the input of a function translates the graph of $f(x)$ to the right h units.

Model Problems continue . . .

4. Graph $f(x) = |x + 3|$.

SOLUTION

Identify parent function	$f(x) = |x|$	The parent function of $f(x) = |x + 3|$ is $f(x) = |x|$.
Constant is subtracted from input	$f(x - h)$	Subtracting h from the input of the function translates the graph of the function h units to the right.
Translates by h	$f(x) = |x + 3| = |x - (-3)|$	Add the constant. Restate it as subtraction. The graph moves -3 to the right, which is the same as 3 to the left.

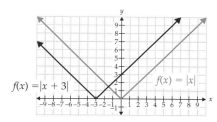

Subtracting a positive constant from the input of a function translates its graph to the *right* that many units. *Adding* a positive constant to the input of a function translates its graph to the *left* that many units.

5. Graph $f(x) = |x + 2| - 1$.

SOLUTION

Identify parent function	$f(x) = |x|$	The parent function of $f(x) = |x + 2| - 1$ is $f(x) = |x|$.
Compare to parent function	$f(x - h) + k$ $f(x - (-2)) - 1$	Negative two is subtracted from the input of the absolute value function. One is subtracted from the parent function.
Translates down 1, translates left by 2		The graph translates down by 1 since $k = -1$. Since the constant h is negative, the graph is translated to the left, here by 2 units.

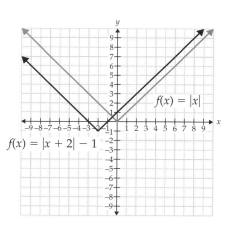

In this activity, translate functions up, down, left, and right to match parent functions.

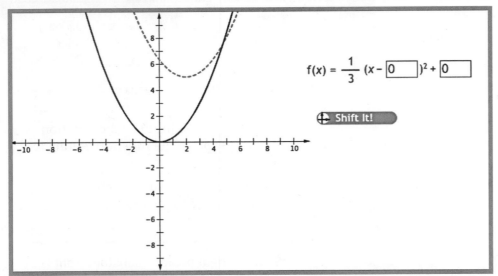

$$f(x) = \frac{1}{3}(x - \boxed{0})^2 + \boxed{0}$$

Shift It!

Go to **www.amscomath.com** to use the activity.

The graph is translated up or down depending on the value added to the output. It is translated left or right depending on the value added to the input.

Scaling Function Graphs

The last change we can make to a parent function is scaling. It is determined by the coefficient, either $f(x) = ax^2$, or $f(x) = (bx)^2$. The coefficient changes the scale of the graph, making it wider or narrower.

Examples of $f(x) = ax^2$:

We show $f(x) = x^2$, $g(x) = 3x^2$, and $h(x) = \frac{1}{2}x^2$. A coefficient greater than 1 stretches the function's output in the y-direction. A coefficient between 0 and 1 shrinks the output in the vertical direction. If a is negative, it reverses the direction of the graph and scales it.

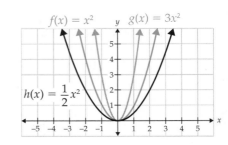

Examples of $f(x) = (bx)^2$:

We show $f(x) = x^2$, $g(x) = (2x)^2$, and $h(x) = \left(\frac{1}{2}x\right)^2$. A value greater than 1 shrinks the graph along the x-axis, making the graph steeper. A coefficient between 0 and 1 has the opposite effect. Changing the sign of b will not change the direction of this graph.

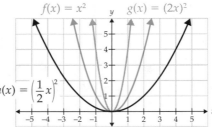

Odd and Even Functions

Even functions are symmetric with respect to the y-axis. This means that the graph coincides with a mirror image when reflected about the y-axis. An even function always has the same value for an input and its opposite. For example, if the output of an even function $f(-3)$ is 5, then the output of $f(3)$ is also 5. In general, if f is an even function, then $f(-x) = f(x)$ for all x-values in the domain of f. The function $f(x) = x^2$ is an example of an even function.

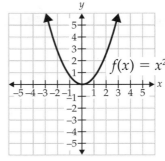

Odd functions are symmetric about the origin. In other words, if it is rotated 180° about the origin, the graph is unchanged. With an odd function, if you input the opposite of a value, the output is also the opposite. For instance, if $f(2) = 8$, $f(-2) = -8$. In general, if f is an odd function, then $f(-x) = -f(x)$ for all x-values in the domain of f. The function $f(x) = x^3$ is an example of an odd function.

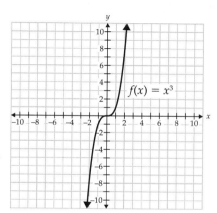

One way to remember this is that $f(x) = x^2$ has an even exponent, and it is an even function (as is $f(x) = x^4$, and so on). Similarly, $f(x) = x^3$ has an odd exponent, and it is an odd function.

PRACTICE

1. What is the domain of the function $f(x) = x^2 + 1$?

A. All positive numbers and 0
B. All numbers that are greater than or equal to 1
C. All negative numbers
D. All real numbers

2. What is the range of the function $f(x) = x^2 + 1$?

A. All positive numbers and 0
B. All numbers that are greater than or equal to 1
C. All negative numbers
D. All real numbers

3. What does the graph of $f(x + 4)$ look like compared to the graph of $f(x)$?

A. $f(x + 4)$ is shifted up 4 units
B. $f(x + 4)$ is shifted down 4 units
C. $f(x + 4)$ is shifted right 4 units
D. $f(x + 4)$ is shifted left 4 units

4. What does the graph of $f(x) + 4$ look like compared to the graph of $f(x)$?

A. $f(x) + 4$ is shifted up 4 units
B. $f(x) + 4$ is shifted down 4 units
C. $f(x) + 4$ is shifted right 4 units
D. $f(x) + 4$ is shifted left 4 units

5. What does the graph of $y = 3x^2 - 2$ look like compared to the graph of $y = 3x^2$?

A. It is shifted up 2 units
B. It is shifted down 2 units
C. It is shifted right 2 units
D. It is shifted left 2 units

6. What does the graph of $y = (x - 3)^2$ look like compared to the graph of $y = x^2$?

A. It is shifted up 3 units
B. It is shifted down 3 units
C. It is shifted right 3 units
D. It is shifted left 3 units

7. `MP 3` What is the domain and range of the function $g(x) = \dfrac{3}{x}$? Justify your reasoning.

8. `MP 3` What is the domain of the function below? What is the range of the function? Explain how you found the domain.

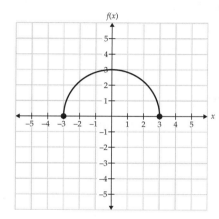

Practice Problems continue . . .

Exercises 9–10: State each function described by the graph. The function is of the form $f(x) = |x - h| + k$.

9.

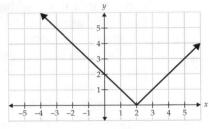

10.

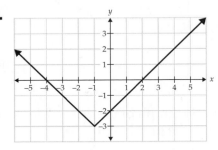

11. Find $f(0)$ for $f(x) = \begin{cases} 1 & \text{if } x < -1 \\ x & \text{if } x \geq -1 \end{cases}$.

12. If $f(x) = \begin{cases} x & \text{if } x \leq 0 \\ -x & \text{if } x > 0 \end{cases}$, what is $f(-3)$?

13. If $f(x) = \begin{cases} 5 & \text{if } x < 2 \\ 0 & \text{if } 2 \leq x \end{cases}$, what is $f(5)$?

14. What is $f(-2)$ if $f(x) = \begin{cases} x - 1 & \text{if } x < 3 \\ 0 & \text{if } x = 3 \\ 2x & \text{if } x > 3 \end{cases}$?

Exercises 15–19: Determine how the graph of $g(x)$ is shifted compared to the graph of $f(x)$.

15. $g(x) = 10^{x-3}$; $f(x) = 10^x$

16. $g(x) = \left(\dfrac{2}{3}\right)^{x+7}$; $f(x) = \left(\dfrac{2}{3}\right)^x$

17. $g(x) = 0.4^{2+x}$; $f(x) = 0.4^x$

18. $g(x) = a^{-5+x}$; $f(x) = a^x$

19. $g(x) = a^{b+x}$; $f(x) = a^x$; assume b is positive.

Exercises 20–21: Determine the exponential function of the form $f(x) = a^x$ from each of the graphs.

20.

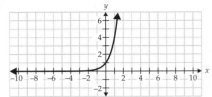

21.

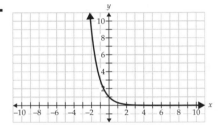

LESSON 1.2

1.2 Models

A **model** uses mathematical equations to describe the behavior of a system. Typically, a model is trying to determine if there is a relationship between an *independent variable* (typically on the horizontal axis) and a *dependent variable* (typically on the vertical axis). Models use data, which is often best analyzed when shown on a graph.

A **scatter plot** is a graph of a table of data. Scatter plots are a good starting point for analyzing data.

Example Model: Earnings and Education

We want to see if there is a relationship between how many years a U.S. resident has studied and how much money he or she earns. We want to see if more years of education might have an effect on how much a person earns. If a person has graduated from high school, we count 12 years of education. If the person has graduated from college, we count 16 years of education, and so on. We think a possible effect of more education is greater earnings. The possible cause is on the horizontal axis. We put weekly earnings on the vertical axis.

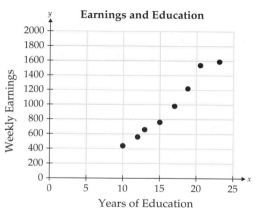

Spreadsheet and Graphing Calculator: Drawing a Scatter Plot

A graphing calculator can be used to draw scatter plots and perform other useful work. The first step is to enter data into the calculator. Use the table of values below representing a girl's growth.

Height (cm)	104	110	116	122	129
Mass (kg)	17.6	18.9	21.1	23.5	25.5

Spreadsheet

You can use a computer application called a *spreadsheet* to draw a scatter plot of these data values.

1. **Enter your data in columns.** Select data by dragging your mouse over the data in the columns.

2. **Create the scatter plot.** Using your spreadsheet program, select Chart. Choose the XY (Scatter) chart type and then click the Next button. Type a title for your graph and labels for the *x*- and *y*-axes.

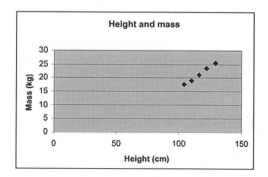

Graphing Calculator

1. **Set up editor.** Press [STAT], scroll down to **SetUpEditor** and press [ENTER] (or just press [5]), then press [ENTER] again. Press [STAT] again, and press [ENTER] or [1] to select **Edit**. The stat list editor is displayed.

2. **Enter data values.** Use the cursor keys to move to the first row under **L1**, type in the first data value, and press [ENTER]. Continue entering the other values, with one variable under **L1** and the other under **L2**. **L1** and **L2** correspond to *x* and *y*.

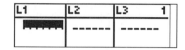

Directions continue . . .

3. **Set function graphing mode.** Press MODE, scroll down to **FUNC**, and press ENTER.

4. **Choose graph type and set options.** Press Y=. Press 2nd [STAT PLOT] (on the top row of the calculator), select **1** under **STAT PLOTS** and then press ENTER. Press ENTER to select **On** for **Plot1**. After **Type:** select the first icon, which is for scatter plots, and press ENTER. Scroll to the position following **Xlist:** and press 2nd [L1] to select list **L1** for the *x*-values for the graph. Scroll to the position following **Ylist:** and press 2nd [L2] to select list **L2** for the *y*-values for the graph. Scroll to the + icon after **Mark:** and press ENTER.

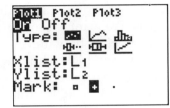

5. **Create scatter plot.** Press ZOOM and 9 (which selects **9:ZoomStat** from the ZOOM menu) to draw the scatter plot.

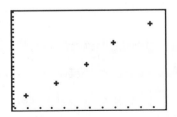

Modeling Data with Trend Lines

Example Model: Speed versus Time

We completed an experiment to determine the relationship between the speed of a bowling ball that is dropped and the elapsed time. We organized our information in the table of data, shown to the right. We measured the speed of the bowling ball at specific times. Each row of data is an ordered pair: (time, speed). Using the data, we created a scatter plot.

Time (s)	Speed (m/s)
0.4	2.1
1.0	4.5
1.6	8.1
2.3	12.0
3.0	15.5
3.5	16.8

The **trend line** in the scatter plot shows the relationship between two variables. In this case, the relationship is linear. It passes as close to the points on the graph as possible. The trend line can be used to predict points not on the line. As with any experiment, there is some error in our measurements.

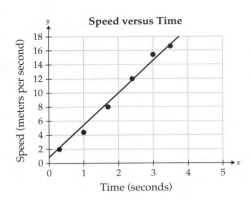

A linear model shows positive correlation when the trend line slope is positive. If the slope is negative, then the correlation is negative. If a line is not a good model, then there is no correlation.

Regression

How can we create a trend line? In the scatter plot to the right, we believe the trend line $y = 7x + 24$ can be used to predict the y-values for any x-values better than the trend line $y = 6.5x + 26$. How might we test that hypothesis? In other words, how do we evaluate a trend line?

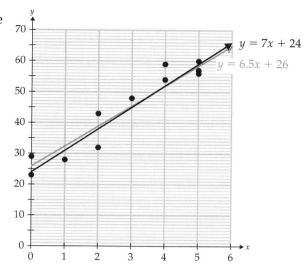

One way to determine whether a trend line is a good fit for the data is to measure the differences between the observed y-values (y(Data) in the table below) and the y-values on the trend line (y(Model)). These differences are called **residuals**. In other words, the residual tells us how far the observed value is from the expected value. When deciding between two trend lines, square the residuals and sum them. The sum that is closer to zero is a better choice.

x	y (Data)	y (Model) $y = 7x + 24$	Residuals	Residuals Squared	y (Model) $y = 6.5x + 26$	Residuals	Residuals Squared
2	43	38	5	25	39	4	16
5	57	59	−2	4	58.5	−1.5	2.25
4	54	52	2	4	52	2	4
2	32	38	−6	36	39	−7	49
5	60	59	1	1	58.5	1.5	2.25
0	23	24	−1	1	26	−3	9
3	48	45	3	9	45.5	2.5	6.25
2	32	38	−6	36	39	−7	49
5	56	59	−3	9	58.5	−2.5	6.25
4	59	52	7	49	52	7	49
1	28	31	−3	9	32.5	−4.5	20.25
0	29	24	5	25	26	3	9
Sum			2	208		−5.5	222.25

Computers (and calculators) can automate this process. They can use formulas to predict the equation of the trend line that is closest to the data points. A process for finding an equation that matches the data is called **regression**. If the model is a linear equation, the process is called *linear regression*.

In addition to providing an equation, a regression tool can state the **coefficient of determination**, called r^2. The coefficient of determination is a tool for determining the relationship between two variables. If the model is appropriate for the data, this provides a measure of how well the model fits the data.

> The coefficient of determination has values between 0 and 1. The closer r^2 is to 1, the better the model equation describes the data.

The graph on the right shows data about the relationship between the resistance and the length of a wire. The graph shows a very high correlation between resistance and length.

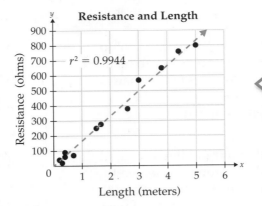

Resistance and Length

$r^2 = 0.9944$

A **line of best fit** is the best possible trend line for a set of data. It is the one with the highest coefficient of determination. Calculating a line of best fit with pencil and paper is time-consuming. Most mathematicians leave it to computers or calculators.

The graph on the right shows the Dow Jones Average, an average of stock prices, as the dependent variable against time as the independent variable. This trend line has a very low coefficient of determination, less than 0.1, so the year is a poor predictor of stock prices. There is no correlation between the line of best fit and the model.

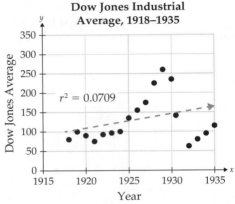

Dow Jones Industrial Average, 1918–1935

$r^2 = 0.0709$

Spreadsheet and Graphing Calculator: Linear Models

We show how to perform a linear regression to calculate the line of best fit and to calculate the coefficient of determination. We use the data from the following table, which shows the cost of an airplane ticket (in Chinese *yuan*) for flights from Shanghai to five cities and the distances to the cities.

City	Beijing	Hong Kong	Singapore	Mumbai	Sydney
Distance (km)	1067	1231	3795	5046	7852
Price (yuan)	1259	2009	4527	6028	10,426

Spreadsheet

1. **Choose trendline, equation, and coefficient.** In your spreadsheet program, make sure the chart is selected. Then choose **Add Trendline** from the **Chart** menu. The **Linear** option should be selected when the **Trend/Regression type** dialog opens. If not, select it.

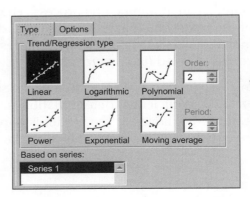

The instructions start assuming you have entered the data and created a scatter plot.

2. **Add the equation for the line.** Add the equation for the line and the coefficient of determination, r^2, by choosing the **Options** tab and checking the boxes labeled "Display equation on chart" and "Display R squared value on chart."

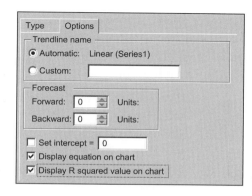

3. **Add trend line and format it.** Click **OK** to add the line. While the trend line is selected, you can choose **Selected Trendline** from the **Format** menu to change its appearance. To the right, we have formatted the line as a dashed green line. The spreadsheet program states the equation for the line as $y = 1.2851x - 31.4$ and gives the value for r^2 directly on the graph. Notice that the notation R^2 is used instead of r^2 for the coefficient of determination. Its value here, 0.9882, indicates a good fit of the line to the data.

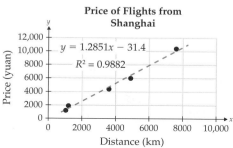

Graphing Calculator

1. **Turn on diagnostic option and choose linear regression.** Turn on the diagnostic mode in the calculator. Press [2nd] [CATALOG] to list all the operations available on the calculator, then scroll down to **DiagnosticOn** and press [ENTER] twice. Press [STAT] and scroll right to the **CALC** menu to see the regressions available on the calculator. Scroll to **4:LinReg($ax + b$)** and press [ENTER].

2. **Enter parameters for regression line.** Enter the parameters to tell the calculator what data to perform the calculation on. Set up the calculator's **L1** and **L2** lists with the data from the table as part of creating the scatter plot. Press [2nd] [L1] [,] and [2nd] [L2] [,] to enter these two lists after the **LinReg($ax + b$)** command. You need one more parameter. Press [VARS] and scroll right to **Y–VARS**, then press [ENTER]. On the following screen, press [ENTER] to choose **Y1** and add it after the **LinReg($ax + b$)** command.

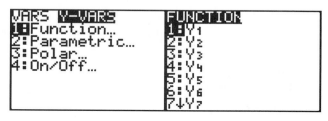

3. **Perform regression and plot line.** Press [ENTER] to execute the **LinReg($ax + b$)** command. Notice that the calculator expresses the equation for the line as $y = ax + b$. That is, the slope is indicated as a, not m. The equation for the line of best fit is $y = 1.2851x - 31.4$. Since $r^2 = 0.9882$, this line is a good fit for the data. To see the scatter plot with the line of best fit drawn, press [GRAPH].

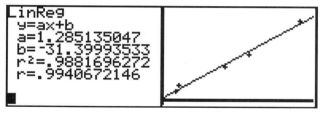

The slope of 1.2851 represents the increased ticket cost in yuan for every additional kilometer of flight distance. The change in the vertical coordinates divided by the change in the horizontal coordinates equals the slope.

PRACTICE

1. Select all the statements that apply. A trend line is a line that

   A. Passes close to the points on a scatter plot.

   B. Shows the relationship between one variable and another.

   C. Is used to predict points not shown on the plot.

   D. Always has a positive slope.

2. A positive correlation means

   A. All the points on the scatter plot lie on a line.

   B. As one value increases, the other decreases.

   C. As one value increases, the other increases.

   D. The trend line only crosses the positive axes.

Exercises 3–7: A researcher gives you graphs of data for various experiments. Based on the data, what type of linear correlation, if any, would you suggest the researcher further explore?

3.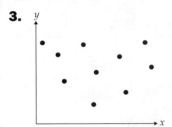

   A. Positive
   B. Negative
   C. None
   D. Not enough information

4.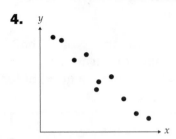

   A. Positive
   B. Negative
   C. None
   D. Not enough information

5.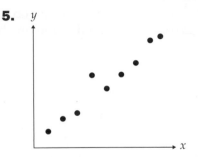

   A. Positive
   B. Negative
   C. None
   D. Not enough information

6.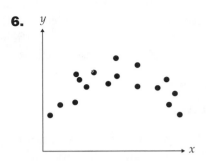

   A. Positive
   B. Negative
   C. None
   D. Not enough information

7. This graph shows (a) _____ correlation.

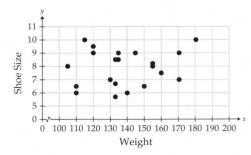

   A. Negative
   B. Positive
   C. None
   D. Not enough information

Practice Problems continue . . .

8. The graph shows the relationship between the retail cost of a bag of Rainier cherries and the weight. Approximately how much would Tara pay for 6 pounds of cherries?

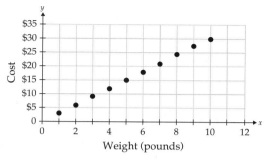

A. $12
B. $14
C. $16
D. $18
E. $20

9. Determine if there is a negative, positive, or no correlation between a child's age and height.

A. Positive
B. Negative
C. None
D. Not enough information

10. If there is no correlation in the data of a scatter plot, is it useful to sketch a trend line? Explain your reasoning.

11. Use a graphing calculator to create a scatter plot using the table of data below. Sketch the results.

Number of Eggs Produced by Iguanas of Various Body Weights

Weight (lb)	Number of Eggs
0.9	33
1.55	50
1.3	46
1	33
1.55	53
1.8	57
1.5	44
1.05	31
1.7	60

12. MP 6 The equation $y = 2.1x + 9.0$ is used to model some data. A y-value of 16.1 is measured at an x-value of 3.0. What is the squared residual at that value of x?

Exercises 13–15: Draw a scatter plot from the data. Then sketch a trend line and decide if the graph has a positive or negative linear correlation. State the equation that represents the trend line.

13. MP 2, 4, 5

x	y
1	5.7
2	7.2
3	9.5
4	10.5
5	12.8

14. MP 2, 4, 5

x	y
2	8
4	5
8	2
6	4
1	9
3	6
5	5
4	4

15. MP 2, 4, 5

x	y
1	31.5
2	29.1
3	17
4	18
5	9.9

Practice Problems continue . . .

16. Use the table of data to answer the
questions.

x	y
2.028	16.425
4.972	13.248
8.0	12.0
11.0	8.478
13.554	6.693

a Draw a scatter plot of the data set.
b Find a possible linear model for the data
using regression.

17. The table shows the heights of 10 fathers
and the heights of their adult sons in inches.

Fathers	Sons
70.25	71
62.5	64
67.5	66.5
74	72
68	67
64	64
69.75	70
72	73
65	64.5
61	62

a Draw a scatter plot of the data, with the
heights of the sons on the vertical axis
and the heights of the fathers on the
horizontal axis.
b Find a possible linear model for the data
using regression.
c Based on your model's equation, what
would you expect the height of the son to
be if the father is 76 inches tall?
d Based on your model's equation, what
would you expect the height of the son to
be if the father is 58 inches tall?
e What do you notice about the predicted
heights of sons whose fathers are either
extremely tall or extremely short?
f List at least two other factors that might
also be relevant in predicting a child's
final height.

18. An algebra class does an experiment in which
they pass a hula hoop around the room. The
table shows the number of people and the
time in seconds required to complete a pass.

People	Time
3	11.5
6	20.2
9	24.7
12	50.6
15	42.7
18	51.2
21	59.4
24	75.3
26	78.2

a Draw a scatter plot of the data and sketch
a trend line.
b The equation of the linear regression is
$t = 2.85p + 3.5$, where t is time in seconds
and p is people. Predict the time it would
take 20 people to complete the hula hoop
pass.
c Assuming the trend continues in a similar
manner for larger groups of people,
how long would it take for 100 people to
complete the pass? Round your answer to
the nearest second.

19. A student states: "A coefficient of
determination of $r^2 = 1.02$ was calculated
for a model of the relationship between the
students' rating of the teacher and class
attendance." Has the student correctly
applied regression to the data?

20. A group of high school students were
given two 20-point quizzes. The ordered
pairs that represent their scores for the two
quizzes are:

(7, 14), (10, 8), (13, 13), (18, 18), (16, 18),
(15, 12), (20, 18), (15, 16), (17, 16), (20, 14),
(14, 15), (14, 19), (10, 18), (15, 14), (19, 16),
(17, 20), (11, 9)

a Create a scatter plot for the data.
b Does the relationship between the
consecutive quiz scores appear to
be linear? If not, give some possible
explanations.

Practice Problems continue . . .

Practice Problems continued . . .

21. Several farmers in the same area varied
the amount of fertilizer on their fields and
obtained varied yields of their crop. The
results are shown in the table.

Fertilizer	Crop Yield
9	12.3
7.5	9.8
8.2	10
8.4	11.6
9.4	12.8
10.1	12.7
8	11.1
8.9	11.3
9.2	12.6

a Create a scatter plot for the data, with the
amount of fertilizer as the independent
variable.

b Calculate a linear regression equation for
the data.

c What is the meaning of the slope and
y-intercept in the equation?

• Multi-Part PROBLEM Practice •

MP 2, 3, 4, 5 Maya's class wanted to find out if different body
parts are proportional, so each student measured his or her
height and arm span. Their data is displayed to the right.

a Make a scatter plot, with height as the independent
variable.

b Find the equation for a trend line that best fits this data.
You may use a spreadsheet or graphing calculator to
help you.

c Is your equation a good predictor of arm span, given a
person's height? Why or why not?

d What would be the predicted arm span of a person
who is 80 inches tall?

Height (in)	Arm Span (in)
73	72
72	71
63.5	65
65.5	67.5
74	72
72	72
74	74
73	74.75
69	69
70	71
77	74.5
67.5	71
71	71
72	68
70	69
70	72
66	67
69	71
70	72
66	67
69	71
70	67.6

1.3 Working with Models

Real-world situations can be modeled with functions. We show several examples of real-world models in the problems below. In this book, the globe icon indicates that a problem is a real-world model.

MODEL PROBLEMS

1. **MP 2, 4** Economists use supply and demand curves. Supply increases with price, but demand decreases. The law of supply and demand says the price will reach a level where supply equals demand. The point where the two lines intersect is the price where supply equals demand, and it is the solution to the system.

What is the consumption of peanuts in a country if the supply can be calculated with the equation $Q = 0.4P + 60$ and the demand can be calculated with the equation $Q = 420 - 0.2P$? Q stands for quantity (in thousands of tons) and P is the price per ton.

SOLUTION

Graph the system of equations

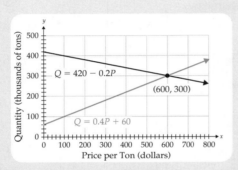

The solution to the system of equations is the point where the graphs of the two equations intersect.

Intersection is solution   (600, 300)   The graphs intersect at (600, 300). The price is per
               $600 per ton for 300,000 tons   ton while the quantity is in thousands of tons.

2. **MP 2, 4** A field-goal kicker kicks a football that follows a parabolic path. The height of the ball can be expressed as a function of the distance (expressed in yards) from where the ball was kicked using $h(x) = -\dfrac{1}{36}x^2 + \dfrac{5}{3}x$.

  a The kicker is 57 yards from the goalpost. Assuming the kick is on target, will the kick be high enough to make it over the goalpost? (The crossbar of the goalpost is 10 ft, or $3\dfrac{1}{3}$ yards, above ground.)

  b Find the maximum height of the ball.

SOLUTION

a Given $h(x) = -\dfrac{1}{36}x^2 + \dfrac{5}{3}x$ Start with the given function.

Substitute $h(x) = -\dfrac{1}{36}(57)^2 + \dfrac{5}{3}(57)$ The kicker is 57 yards from the goalpost. In this situation, $x = 57$. Substitute 57 into the function.

Evaluate $h(x) = -\dfrac{1}{36}(3249) + \dfrac{5}{3}(57)$ Use the order of operations to evaluate the function.
           $h(x) = -90.25 + 95$ At 57 yards, the ball is 4.75 yards above the ground,
           $h(x) = 4.75$ which is more than sufficient to clear the goalpost.

Model Problems continue . . .

b The vertex of the function is at (30, 25). The ball reaches a maximum height of 25 yards.

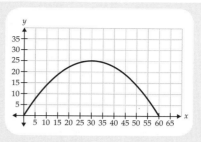

Linear Programming

Linear programming is a tool for solving problems with constraints modeled as linear inequalities. We can use linear programming to decide how many pies and cakes to make. There are constraints on how many pies and cakes we can make. For instance, perhaps we can only use an oven for 3 hours to make these pies and cakes.

Our goal is to make as much money as possible selling cakes and pies at a bake sale. So our profit is our **objective function**, which we want to maximize. More generally, we want to optimize the objective function, or find the best solution possible. "Optimize" might mean minimize, such as a solution that has least cost. When the constraint inequalities are graphed, the **feasible region** is the area on the graph in which the variables obey the constraints. This set of solutions to the inequalities represents all the possible choices we can make.

The vertices of the feasible region will always provide the maximum and minimum values for the objective function. When the value of the objective function is the same at adjacent vertices, it is also the same at all points on the connecting segment.

MODEL PROBLEMS

1. **MP 2, 4** Your class is participating in a bake sale where every item on sale must be baked at the sale. You sell cakes for $10 and pies for $6. Each class is allowed to use the oven for 3 hours. You can bake one pie or cake at a time. It takes 45 minutes to bake a cake and 30 minutes to bake a pie.

  a Determine the objective function and graph the feasible region.

  b Optimize the objective function.

SOLUTION

a Identify variables	s = sales x = cakes y = pies	State the objective function as an equation. Let s represent sales (that is, the amount of money we receive selling our cakes and pies). Let x represent the number of cakes we sell. Let y represent the number of pies we sell.
State as equation	$s = 10x + 6y$	Let's say we can sell cakes for $10 and pies for $6. That means our sales from cakes will equal $10x$. That means $6y$ is our sales from pies. The expression $10x + 6y$ is sales for both cakes and pies.

Model Problems continue . . .

Constraint	The oven	One limit is how long we can use the oven. We have 3 hours to use the oven and can only bake one pie or cake at a time.
State constraints as inequalities	$45x + 30y \leq 180$	It takes 45 minutes to bake a cake and 30 minutes to bake a pie. $45x$ is the number of minutes the oven is used to bake cakes. $30y$ is the amount of time we use the oven to bake pies. We have 3 hours of time to use the oven. Three hours equals 180 minutes. The amount of time we spend baking pies and cakes, $45x + 30y$, must be less than or equal to 180.
	$x \geq 0, y \geq 0$	The number of cakes, x, has to be 0 or positive. We cannot bake a negative number of cakes. State this constraint as $x \geq 0$. The same applies to pies. We can bake 0 pies or a positive number of pies, but not a negative number of pies.

Determine feasible region(s)

Feasible: A and B
Not feasible: C

Graph the constraint inequalities, shading the solution region. We have graphed a system of linear inequalities. The solution to these inequalities is the feasible region. Any solution to the system is a possible choice we can make. For instance, we have enough time to bake 2 cakes and 1 pie. We show that point as A. Or we can bake 0 cakes and 6 pies. We show that as point B. That's another solution to this system of inequalities. On the other hand, we cannot make 3 cakes and 4 pies. We show that as point C. That is outside the feasible region. It takes more time to bake them, 255 minutes, than we have.

> To help you bake as much as possible, map out a feasible region. The diagram shows a graph of your choices.

b Optimize objective function

$s = 10x + 6y$

We want to optimize the objective function. In particular, we want to maximize the dollar sales of pies and cakes. This objective function reflects that we get $10 per cake and $6 per pie.

Substitute values at vertices:
Vertex $(0, 0)$

$s = 10 \cdot 0 + 6 \cdot 0 = 0$

To optimize the function, substitute the values of the points at the vertices: Substituting the values for the vertex $(0, 0)$, we have 0 cakes and 0 pies, giving us $s = 10(0) + 6(0) = 0$ dollars.

> Optimizing an objective function may mean finding the maximum or the minimum value. For instance, if the relationships represented costs, then the solution would be $(0, 0)$ since that would minimize costs.

Vertex $(4, 0)$ $s = 10 \cdot 4 + 6 \cdot 0 = 40$

Choosing another vertex, $(4, 0)$, we have 4 cakes and 0 pies, giving us $40 in sales.

Vertex $(0, 6)$ $s = 10 \cdot 0 + 6 \cdot 6 = 36$

Using the values for the last vertex, $(0, 6)$, we have 0 cakes and 6 pies, resulting in $36 in sales.

Model Problems continue . . .

Solution   4 cakes, 0 pies   Since the vertex (0, 4) results in the highest value for sales, the optimized (maximum) sales occur if we bake 4 cakes and 0 pies. If you are skeptical, you can try other combinations of pies and cakes. For instance, how about 2 cakes and 3 pies? That is feasible since it is on the line on the graph, which means it can be done in 180 minutes. Sales for 2 cakes and 3 pies are $38. Our solution is better.

2. **MP 2, 4** A factory can make two types of snowboards, the Air and the Podium. The Air requires one employee-hour to manufacture and the Podium requires three employee-hours. The factory has 450 employee-hours of labor available each day. The factory has enough supplies on hand to build 300 Airs and 200 Podiums. Graph the daily manufacturing capabilities of the factory. Is it possible to build 140 Podiums and 120 Airs in a day?

SOLUTION

Choose variables	A = Airs P = Podiums	Choose variables to represent the number of Airs and Podiums.
Write inequalities about supplies	$A \le 300$ $P \le 200$	The factory has enough supplies to make at most 300 Airs and 200 Podiums. State these limits using inequalities.
State restrictions	$A \ge 0$ $P \ge 0$	State the restrictions that the factory cannot build a negative number of boards as inequalities.
Graph the inequalities about supplies and restrictions	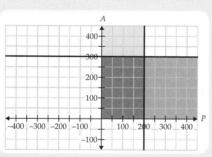	The factory is limited by supplies, so the inequalities must reflect that. If the factory were limited only by supplies, it could build any quantity of boards shown in the region $A \le 300$ and $P \le 200$.
Write statement about workers	$A + 3P \le 450$	The problem says it takes 3 times longer to build a Podium than an Air. Write an inequality for the total time it takes to make the boards.
Graph all inequalities	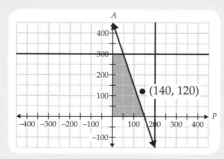	The possible outputs of the factory are in the shaded region, which is the feasible region for this situation. The question asked if the factory could build 140 Podiums and 120 Airs in a day. That point is outside the solution region, so it is impossible for the factory to do that. The factory cannot build 140 Podiums and 120 Airs in a day. It lacks enough employee-hours.

We show one of three similar activities below. In these activities, you must solve linear programming problems. Graph them, identify the feasible region, and then select the vertex that is the solution.

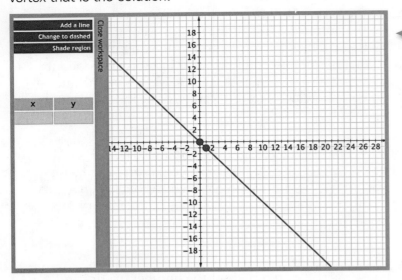

Go to **www.amscomath.com** to use the activities.

PRACTICE

1. What is the maximum value of the function $z = 10x + 7y$ on the indicated feasible region?

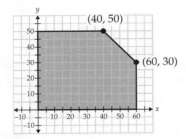

   A. 400
   B. 600
   C. 800
   D. 810

2. One of the spouts from a decorative fountain needs to be replaced. The spout is 1 foot above the water level. In order to match the other spouts, water coming out of the spout must reach a height of 15 feet at a distance of 4 horizontal feet from the spout, and it should reach the water level 8 horizontal feet from the spout. Write the equation of the parabola that describes the path of the water leaving the spout. Use x for the horizontal distance from the spout, and y as the height above the water.

3. In order to fence off a rectangular plot of land that is bordered on one side by a stone wall, a wooden fence is built along the other three sides. The contractor brought enough materials to build 200 yards of fence. What dimensions for the fence will make the largest area of the fenced plot?

4. Given the graph below, where do the two lines intersect?

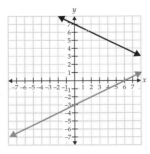

5. You can split all the wood in a woodpile in 5.5 hours. Your father can do it in 7 hours. You work for two hours together before you have to go to work and leave your father to finish the job himself. How many more hours will it take your father to finish the job alone? Round your answer to the nearest tenth of an hour.

Practice Problems continue . . .

6. To make a collage, Dina is placing a square piece of multicolored paper on top of a square of cardboard, as shown in the diagram below. The smaller square will be placed so that each of its corners is *a* inches from the nearest corner of the larger square. The side length of the larger square is 1 foot. What value of *a* should Dina choose so the multicolored square covers the smallest area?

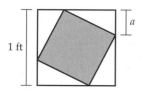

7. With the wind, which adds to her speed, a cyclist travels 85 miles in 5 hours. Against the wind, which subtracts equally from her speed, she travels 49 miles in 7 hours. How fast, in miles per hour, does she travel when there is no wind?

8. In the year 2004, it was estimated that there were about 260 adult bald eagles in Maine. In the year 2007, there were about 374 adult bald eagles. In the same time period, the adult loon population in Maine declined from about 2900 to about 2540 adults. If these rates remain the same, during what year would you estimate the populations of adult bald eagles to be the same as the population of adult loons? What is the population number of each when this occurs? Round the values to the nearest tenth.

9. A recipe calls for 2 cups of whole milk, which is about 4% fat. You have only 2% milk and half-and-half (which is about 11% fat). How much of each liquid should you use to create the correct amount of simulated whole milk? Round the values to the nearest tenth.

10. How many liters of a 3% salt solution and a 12% salt solution must be combined to obtain 46 liters of a solution that is 9% salt? Round the values to the nearest tenth.

11. One mixture of paint has 35% pigment. Another mixture has 10% pigment. If you want 11 gallons of paint that have 21% pigment, how many gallons of each mixture should you use, to the nearest tenth?

12. I'm twice as old as you were when I was as old as you are now. When you are as old as I am now, the sum of our ages will equal 63. How old is each of us now?

13. **MP 4** The following problem was first suggested by the famous Russian novelist, Leo Tolstoy: A team of workers has to mow two fields, one twice as large as the other. The team has been mowing the larger field for half of a day. Then the team splits in half: half of the workers stay and work on the rest of the larger field, while the other half starts mowing the smaller field. By the end of the first day, the larger field is done. The smaller field is finished by one worker mowing all of the next day. How many workers were in the team?

Exercises 14–17: Each graph reflects the feasible region for profits, and the purpose is to maximize profits.

14. The objective function is $z = 6x + 5y$. State the values that maximize profits as an ordered pair.

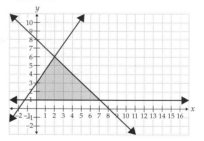

15. The objective function is $z = 8x + 10y$. State the values that maximize profits as an ordered pair.

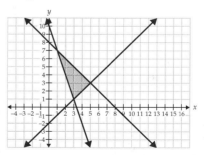

Practice Problems continue . . .

16. The objective function is $z = 7x + 2y$. State the values that maximize profits as an ordered pair.

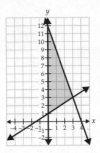

17. The objective function is $z = 5x + 8y$. State the values that minimize costs as an ordered pair.

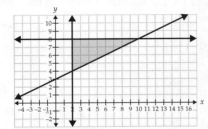

Exercises 18–21: Sketch the region determined by the constraints. State the maximum and minimum of the objective function, and where they occur.

18. Objective function: $z = 5x + 2y$

Constraints: $\begin{cases} x \geq 0 \\ y \geq 0 \\ x + y \leq 8 \end{cases}$

19. Objective function: $z = 4x + 0.5y$

Constraints: $\begin{cases} x \geq 0 \\ y \geq 0 \\ 2x + y \leq 6 \\ 3x + 2y \leq 10 \end{cases}$

20. Objective function: $z = 4x + 3y$

Constraints: $\begin{cases} x \geq 0 \\ 2y - x \leq 10 \\ x + 2y \geq 4 \\ 4x - y \leq 16 \end{cases}$

21. Objective function: $z = 0.5x + 0.35y$

Constraints: $\begin{cases} x \geq 0 \\ y \geq 0 \\ x + 2y \geq 4 \\ y + 2x \leq 8 \end{cases}$

22. The price of 82% nickel alloy is $11.31 per lb. The price of 92% nickel alloy is $12.80 per lb. Determine the blend of lowest cost of these two alloys if the percentage of nickel in it should be at least 90%. Hint: Let x stand for the fraction of 82% alloy, and y for the fraction of 92% alloy in each pound.

• Multi-Part PROBLEM Practice •

MP 2, 4 Hannah has 50 minutes to take an English test that has 20 multiple-choice questions and 20 short-answer questions. She knows she can answer a multiple-choice question in 1.5 minutes and a short-answer question in 2 minutes. Each correct multiple-choice answer receives 2 points, and each correct short-answer receives 3 points.

a Write the appropriate inequalities.

b Graph them to find the feasible region.

c Write the objective function for Hannah's scores.

d What are the maximum and minimum possible scores Hannah can receive?

1.4 Seeing Structure in Equations and Expressions

The Form of an Equation

An effective tool to solve problems is to look for the **structure of an equation**. *Structure of an equation* means the properties that enable you to recognize it as a form of an equation you know how to work with.

For instance, say you are asked to graph $6x - 3y = 12$ and also asked if and where the graph intercepts the y-axis. One way to solve this would be to graph points, substituting values for x, and computing y. A faster method is to recognize it as a linear equation. You can solve for y, getting $y = 2x - 4$. This matches it with another equation with structure, $y = mx + b$. The slope of this line is 2, and its y-intercept is -4. Your knowledge of the structure of equations makes for a fast, efficient way to answer the question, and even tells you the shape (a line) of the graph and its slope.

> Simplifying an equation or expression may reveal its structure.

MODEL PROBLEM

Describe the graph of $8y^2 = 128 - 8x^2$.

SOLUTION

Identify structure of the equation	$8y^2 = 128 - 8x^2$ $8x^2 + 8y^2 = 128$	The key to solving this problem is to recognize this is the equation of a circle, which has the form $x^2 + y^2 = r^2$, with r equaling the radius.
Divide	$x^2 + y^2 = 16$	Divide the equation by 8.
Write in standard form for a circle and identify properties	$x^2 + y^2 = 4^2$	Write constant as a square. The equation is a circle with its center at the origin. Its radius is 4. This means the circle will intercept axes at $(4, 0)$, $(0, 4)$, $(-4, 0)$, and $(0, -4)$, since all these points are 4 from the origin.

> Simplifying coefficients can help you see the form of an equation.

Structure and Factoring

Seeing the structure of an equation can help with factoring it as well. For instance, in factoring $3x^2 + 6x + 3$, look at the coefficients and see 3 is a factor of them all. Simplify the expression to $3(x^2 + 2x + 1)$. The expression in the parentheses is a perfect square, which can also factor to get $3(x + 1)^2$. This approach can enable us to factor expressions we might otherwise struggle with.

MODEL PROBLEMS

1. Identify the structure of the expression, $4x^4 - 4y^4$, and then factor.

SOLUTION

Identify structure of the expression	$4x^4 - 4y^4$	This is the difference of squares.
Factor	$4(x^4 - y^4)$	Factor out 4.
Identify structure of the expression	$4(x^2 - y^2)(x^2 + y^2)$	x^2 and y^2 are squared terms in a difference of squares.
Identify structure of the expression	$4(x - y)(x + y)(x^2 + y^2)$	We also recognize one more structure: a sum of two perfect squares, $(x^2 + y^2)$. That is an expression we *cannot* factor, so we know we are done there.

2. Solve $13 + 6x^2 - 20x - x^2 + 7 = 0$.

SOLUTION

Combine like terms	$13 + 6x^2 - 20x - x^2 + 7 = 0$
	$5x^2 - 20x + 20 = 0$
Factor	$5(x^2 - 4x + 4) = 0$
Identify the structure of the expression: Perfect square	$5(x - 2)^2 = 0$
Apply zero product property	$x - 2 = 0$
	$x = 2$

3. Factor $x^2 + (a + b)x + ab$ in terms of x.

SOLUTION

From factoring, we know the constant is the product of two constants, and the coefficient is the sum of those constants: $(x + a)(x + b)$.

Systems of Equations with More than Two Variables

Systems of equations can have more than two variables. The solutions to these systems are ordered sets of numbers, similar to ordered pairs. For example, any solution to a system with three variables will be an ordered triple of the form (x, y, z).

Systems with more than two variables are usually solved algebraically by elimination, substitution, or some combination of both. Solving by graphing is rarely a practical solution technique because an equation containing three or more variables is difficult to graph on a surface.

Like two-variable systems of equations, systems with more than two variables can have a finite number of solutions, an infinite number, or no solution. In order for a system to have a finite number of solutions, it needs to have at least as many equations as variables.

Solve the system of equations in three variables: $3x - y + 7z = 10$; $y - x = 3$; $z = y - 5$

SOLUTION

Solve second equation for y	$y - x = 3$ $y = x + 3$	We decide to substitute. We solve the second equation for y.
Substitute for y and z	$3x - y + 7z = 10$ $3x - (x + 3) + 7(y - 5) = 10$	We substitute the expressions for y and z into the first equation.
Substitute for y again	$3x - (x + 3) + 7((x + 3) - 5) = 10$	In order to solve the equation, we need to eliminate all but one variable. We do this by substituting for y again, which leaves x as the only variable in the equation.
Solve for x	$9x - 17 = 10$ $9x = 27$ $x = 3$	Combine like terms, isolate the variable, and then divide to find x.
Solve for y	$y - x = 3$ $y - (3) = 3$ $y = 6$	Substitute the value of x into the second equation, then solve for y.
Solve for z	$z = y - 5$ $z = (6) - 5$ $z = 1$	Substitute the value of y into the third equation, then solve for z.
Solution stated in ordered form	$(x, y, z) = (3, 6, 1)$	Solutions to systems with more than two variables can be stated in ordered form, as we show. The solution to this example is the ordered triple $(3, 6, 1)$.

PRACTICE

1. Which of the following sequences could be modeled by a linear function, $f(x) = mx + b$?

   A. 3, 6, 12, 24, ...   D. 3, 6, 9, 12, ...

   B. 3, 8, 13, 18, ...   E. 3, 12, 21, 30, ...

   C. 3, 6, 18, 72, ...

2. Which of the following sequences can be modeled by a function of the form $g(x) = a(b)^x$?

   A. 10, 20, 40, 80, ...

   B. 7, 2, −3, −8, ...

   C. −6, 12, −24, 48, ...

   D. 1, 3, 5, 7, ...

MP 7 Exercises 3–4: What do the equations have in common?

3. $y = 3x - 21$; $y = \frac{1}{2}x + 4$; $y = -\frac{2}{3}x - 1$

4. $y = x^2$; $y = 3x^2$; $y = -0.5x^2$

5. Could the equations $y = 2x - 5$ and $4x + y = -2$ be written so they have similar structure? Explain.

MP 6, 7 Exercises 6–7: Compare and contrast the structure of each set of equations or expressions.

6. $y = x + 1$ and $x + y = 1$

7. $x^2 - 81$ and $144 - y^2$

8. Write the expressions $5 + x$ and $3 + x$ in the form $x + a$. What property allows the expressions to be written in this form?

9. Write the equation $2x + y = 9$ in the form $y = mx + b$.

10. Identify the slope and the y-intercept of $2x - 3y = 6$.

11. Write an equation that has a similar form to $y = 3x + 1$.

Practice Problems continue . . .

12. MP 2, 3 Compare the graphs of the functions $y = \frac{1}{2}x - 1$ and $-x + 2y = -2$.

13. Compare the structure of the two expressions.

Expression 1	Expression 2
$3x - 4x + 9(2x + 1)$	$x^2 + 6(-2x + 1) - 3(7 + x^2)$

14. Compare the structure of the two expressions.

Expression 1	Expression 2
$-x - y$	$-(y + x)$

15. MP 3 Two students find the area of a circle with radius 5 cm. The students each used a different formula. Describe the validity of each student's work.

Student 1	Student 2
$A = \pi r^2$	$A = (r)(\pi)(r)$
$A = \pi(5)^2$	$A = (5)(\pi)(5)$
$A = 25\pi$	$A = 25\pi$

16. Describe the solution to the system of equations: $y = \frac{2}{5}x - 3; 2x - 5y = 15$

MP 7 Exercises 17–28: Solve each system of equations.

17. $a + 3b + c = 4; a = -4b; c = 5b$

18. $y = -z + 1; x + y = -3z - 3; x = z + 17$

19. $x = -1 - z; y = z + 9; z = 2x - 4y - 4$

20. $2x + y - 3z = -6; x = 2z; y = -4z$

21. $x = y; z = 2x + 1; 3x - y + z = 21$

22. $2a + 2b = 2; 2a + 2b + c = -5; 3a - 4c = 13$

23. $3x = y; -2x + 2y + 3z = 3; x = -z$

24. $3x + 3z = 0; 2x + y + 3z = 3; 2x + y = 6$

25. $2u = v; u + v = w + 1; 3u - v + w = 7$

26. $2z = x; x + 3y = z; 2x + 3y = 9$

27. $2z + 5 = x; x + 2 = y; 2x - y + 5z = 3$

28. $y = 2x - 2z; 3x + 2y - z = 12; z = x - 2$

Chapter 1 Key Ideas

1.1 Functions

- Linear functions have constant slope Absolute value functions have a constant slope in each straight line component. Functions with changing slope include quadratic and exponential functions.
- Symmetrical functions include quadratic and absolute value functions. Non-symmetrical functions include exponential functions.
- Continuous functions include linear, quadratic, exponential, absolute value, and piecewise functions. Non-continuous functions include piecewise and step functions, rationals, and tangents.
- Functions have a domain and range based on the possible inputs and outputs.
- A parent function is the simplest form of a function, and can be translated up or down, left or right, or be scaled.
- Adding a positive constant to a parent function translates its graph up by that many units. Subtracting a positive constant from a parent function translates its graph down by that many units.
- Subtracting a positive constant from the input of a function translates its graph to the right by that many units. Adding a positive constant to the input of a function translates its graph to the left by that many units.
- Scaling a function increases or decreases the inputs and outputs compared to the parent function. For example, a scaled function may look wider or more narrow compared to the parent function.

1.2 Models and 1.3 Working with Models

- Models are used to determine if there is a relationship between variables.
- Regression is used to determine the quality of a model's fit to the data.

1.4 Seeing Structure in Equations and Expressions

- The structure of an equation can show the properties of an equation.
- Systems with more than two variables can be solved by elimination, substitution, or some combination of both. Like two-variable systems of equations, systems with more than two variables can have one solution, an infinite number, or no solution. Any solution to a system with three variables will be an ordered triple of the form (x, y, z).

CHAPTER 1 REVIEW

1. What is the domain of the function $f(x) = 2x^2$?

A. All positive numbers and 0
B. All numbers that are greater than or equal to 2
C. All negative numbers
D. All real numbers

2. What is the range of the function $f(x) = 2x^2$?

A. All positive numbers and 0
B. All numbers that are greater than or equal to 2
C. All negative numbers
D. All real numbers

3. Choose the correct statement about the scatter plot of the data.

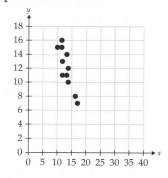

A. There is no linear correlation
B. There is a negative linear correlation
C. There is a positive linear correlation
D. There is a correlation, but it is not linear

4. Determine if there is a negative, positive, or no correlation between the number of hours someone spends practicing and their batting average.

A. Positive
B. Negative
C. No correlation
D. Not enough information

5. **MP 4** Lucy's mile run times versus the weight of her sneakers can be modeled with a line with an r^2 value of 0.8. Bill's mile run times can be modeled with a line with an r^2 value of 0.64. Assuming that a linear model is reasonable for both, whose run times are best modeled by their respective lines of fit?

A. Lucy's
B. Bill's
C. Not enough information

6. A scientist models the acceleration of a cart as a function of the net force on it. She obtains a set of data that is well-fitted by a line. Which of the following could be the r^2 value for the fit?

A. 96   C. -1
B. 0.04   D. 0.96

7. A regression equation for predicting y from x is found to be $y = 1.25x + 84.5$. What is the estimated change in the mean value of y when x increases by 3?

A. 3   C. 88.25
B. 1.25   D. 3.75

Chapter Review continues . . .

8. What is the domain and range of the function shown in the graph?

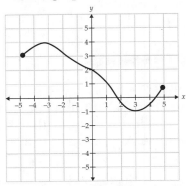

9. What does the graph of $y = (x + 2)^2 - 3$ look like compared to the graph of $y = x^2$?

10. What does the graph of $y = |x - 1| + 2$ look like compared to the graph of $y = |x|$?

Exercises 11–13: Sketch each function by creating a table with at least 5 data points.

11. $f(x) = 2^x$

12. $f(x) = 2^{x + 3}$

13. $g(x) = 0.5^{x - 2}$

14. **MP 7** A function that repeats its values in regular intervals is called *periodic*. Below is an example of a periodic graph. You can see that it repeats itself again and again. What is a relationship in nature that could be represented with a periodic graph?

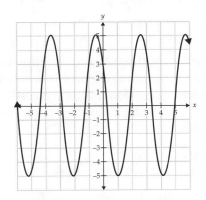

15. **MP 1, 2** A square is inscribed into a circle of radius R. Sketch the graph of the relationship between the area S of the square and the radius R of the circle.

16. **MP 5** A realtor wants to sell some riverfront lots. To set a fair price for them, he studies several similar riverfront lots nearby that were sold recently. The table shows the area of the lots (in hundreds of square feet) and their selling prices (in thousands of dollars).

Square Footage	Price
189	240
232	260
172	230
195	230
240	280
210	260
200	240
230	250
191	241
198	255

a Create a scatter plot for the data. Does it appear to have a linear trend?

b The coefficient of determination for the data is found to be equal to $r^2 = 0.673$. Explain what that means in terms of association of the price of the lot and its area.

c Calculate a regression line for the data.

17. A car dealer is placing orders for the delivery of next month's vehicles. He has made advance sales for 2 SUVs and 5 cars. Recent sales indicate he can expect to sell no more than 32 total vehicles a month. He makes a profit of $6400 on each SUV he sells and $1600 on each car. How many of each vehicle should he order?

18. An art studio has been contracted to supply a gallery with 60 vases each quarter. The studio produces two types of vases, hand-painted and plain. They can make only 50 plain vases each quarter. Similarly, they can create a maximum of 35 hand-painted vases each quarter. The studio makes a profit of $30 on each hand-painted vase and $10 on each plain vase. How many of each vase should they make to maximize their profits?

Chapter Review continues . . .

19. A farmer wants to sell his produce in two neighboring towns, A and B. He can grow up to 700 pounds of vegetables, but the demand for vegetables is at most 400 pounds in Town A, where he sells his produce at $3.25 per pound, and 600 pounds in Town B, where the price is $2.99 per pound. How much should the farmer sell in each town to maximize his profits?

20. Write the system of inequalities that describe a parallelogram with vertices at the points $(0, 0)$, $(0, -2)$, $(2, 0)$, and $(2, 2)$. Find the area of the figure.

21. Write a system of inequalities describing the right triangle shaded in the graph.

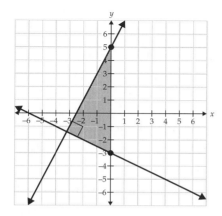

22. Will the objective function $z = x + y$ reach its maximum value on the region determined by the given constraints? Justify your answer.

Constraints: $\begin{cases} x \geq 0 \\ y \geq 0 \\ -x + y \leq 1 \\ -x + 2y \leq 4 \end{cases}$

23. You found a feasible region for the constraints in a linear programming problem. It turned out that the objective function reaches its maximum value at the adjacent vertices $(2, 5)$ and $(7, 3)$ of the region. Can you conclude that the objective function also has a maximum value at the points $(2.5, 4.8)$ and $(6.5, 3.2)$? Explain your reasoning.

24. **MP 4** A Christmas tree farm makes a profit of $40 on each Blue Spruce they plant and $30 on each Douglas Fir. They must plan the number of each type of tree to plant this year. They are under contract to grow at least 120 trees. To ensure adequate variety, they must plant a minimum of 20 of each tree. The farm has 3900 square feet of growing space. The Douglas Firs require 30 square feet per tree, and the Blue Spruces require 36 square feet per tree. How many of each kind of tree should they plant to maximize this year's profits?

25. Jacob takes a part-time job at a computer firm. He is paid $15 for fixing a computer on the spot, which requires 20 minutes of his time. He gets $60 for resolving computer problems over the phone, which takes 1 hour and 10 minutes each time. Jacob works 24 hours a week or less. What combination of activities at work will yield Jacob maximum revenue? Assume that he performs an integer number of fixes.

26. A printing company makes hardcover and paperback books. They make a profit of $8 for each hardcover book they sell and $3 for each paperback book. Their records show that they sell at least four times as many paperback books as hardcover books. Their printing presses can make a hardcover book in 6 minutes or a paperback book in 4 minutes. If the printing presses can run for 55 hours this week, how many of each type of book should they produce in a week to make the most profit?

27. Identify a circumstance or circumstances in a linear programming problem where a vertex might not be a solution to a real-world problem.

28. **MP 3** A fellow student claims that linear programming is just graphing a system of inequalities. Do you agree or disagree? Why?

Chapter Content

Vocabulary

complete the square	focus of the parabola	real numbers
complex conjugates	imaginary numbers	roots
complex numbers	perfect square trinomial	square root principle
difference of cubes	Pythagorean triple	standard form of the equation for a parabola centered at the origin
difference of squares	quadratic equation	sum of cubes
directrix	quadratic formula	zero-product property
discriminant	quadratic trinomial	zeros
factoring by grouping		

LESSON 2.1

2.1 Algebra 1 Review: Factoring Polynomials

To factor a polynomial means to write it as a product of polynomials (called *factors*) so that when the factors are multiplied together, they equal the original polynomial. A **quadratic trinomial** such as $x^2 + 7x + 12$ can be factored as a pair of *linear factors*: $(x + 4)$ and $(x + 3)$.

We will analyze trinomials like this by stating them in the form $x^2 + bx + c$:

> In general, the product of $x + m$ and $x + n$ is $x^2 + (m + n)x + mn$. The coefficient of x is $m + n$, and the constant c is the product mn.

MODEL PROBLEMS

1. Factor $x^2 + 7x + 12$.

SOLUTION

Create table: List factors of trinomial's constant and sums of constants in factors

Factors of 12	Sum
1, 12	13
2, 6	8
3, 4	7

List the factors of 12 in one column, and the sum of those factors in the other.

The factors of 12 are 1 and 12; 2 and 6; and 3 and 4.

Add the factors: $1 + 12 = 13$; $2 + 6 = 8$; $3 + 4 = 7$.

> A table lets you list the factors of the constant term in the trinomial, and sum them to determine what the constants in the binomial factors are.

Middle term coefficient equals sum of these constants

Middle term = $7x$
Coefficient = 7
$(x + 3)(x + 4)$

The coefficient of the middle term equals the sum of the factors. We use the factors 3 and 4, since their sum equals the coefficient of the middle term, 7. The polynomial factors are $x + 3$ and $x + 4$.

Model Problems continue . . .

2. Factor $x^2 + 4x - 5$.

SOLUTION

Create table:
List factors
of trinomial's
constant and sums

Factors of −5	Sum
1, −5	−4
−1, 5	+4

List the factors of
−5 in one column
and the sum of those
factors in the other.
The factors of −5 are +1 and −5, and −1 and +5.
Add the factors: $1 + (-5) = -4; -1 + 5 = 4$.

> Unlike the first trinomial quadratic
> we factored, this one has a
> negative constant, −5. The
> factors of a quadratic trinomial of
> this form will have constants with
> opposite signs (or, if you like, one
> added and one subtracted).

Middle term
coefficient equals
sum of these
constants

Middle term = $4x$
Coefficient = 4
$(x - 1)(x + 5)$

The coefficient of the middle term equals the sum of the
factors. Since the coefficient is +4, we use the factors −1
and +5. This means the polynomial factors are $x - 1$
and $x + 5$.

3. Factor $x^2 - 11x + 10$.

SOLUTION

Create table

Factors	Sum
−1, −10	−11
−2, −5	−7

List the factors of the
constant, 10, in one
column, and the sum
of those factors in the
other.

> The trinomial $x^2 - 11x + 10$ has
> a negative coefficient for *x* and a
> positive constant. Its factors will
> have two negative constants (or,
> if you like, both subtracted).

We want two negative numbers since we know their
product is positive and their sum is a negative number. We
therefore consider the factors −1 and −10, and −2 and −5.

Add the factors: $-1 + (-10) = -11; -2 + (-5) = -7$.

Middle term
coefficient equals
sum of these
constants

Middle term = $-11x$
Coefficient = −11
$(x - 1)(x - 10)$

The coefficient of the middle term in this case is −11, so we
choose the factors −1 and −10 since their sum is −11. This
means the polynomial factors are $x - 1$ and $x - 10$.

Special Product Patterns

When some binomials are multiplied, their products have a pattern. It can be
helpful to know these to speed multiplication.

Description	Product Patterns	Example
The square of a binomial sum	$(a + b)^2 = a^2 + 2ab + b^2$	$(x + 4)^2 = x^2 + 8x + 16$
The square of a binomial difference	$(a - b)^2 = a^2 - 2ab + b^2$	$(x - 3)^2 = x^2 - 6x + 9$
The product of the sum and difference of two terms	$(a + b)(a - b) = a^2 - b^2$	$(x + 2)(x - 2) = x^2 - 4$

Proving identities like those on the previous page is a direct application of the FOIL method.

FOIL stands for First, Outer, Inner, Last and provides a sequence for multiplying terms.

Derive the square of a binomial sum.

Start with $A + B$	$A + B$
Square	$(A + B)(A + B)$
Multiply using FOIL	$A^2 + AB + AB + B^2$
Combine like terms to get a **perfect square trinomial**	$A^2 + 2AB + B^2$

Derive the product of the sum and difference of two terms.

Start with $(A + B)(A - B)$	$(A + B)(A - B)$
Multiply using FOIL	$A^2 - AB + AB + B^2$
Simplify to get a **difference of squares**	$A^2 - B^2$

MODEL PROBLEMS

1. Simplify $(2x^2 + x)^2$.

SOLUTION

Square of binomial sum pattern	$(a + b)^2 = a^2 + 2ab + b^2$	$(2x^2 + x)^2$ follows the pattern for the square of a binomial sum.
Identify values	$a = 2x^2, b = x$	To apply the pattern, identify the values of a and b in this example: $a = 2x^2$ and $b = x$.
Substitute and simplify	$(2x^2)^2 + 2(2x^2)(x) + (x^2)$ $4x^4 + 4x^3 + x^2$	Substitute the values for a and b into the pattern and simplify.

2. Simplify $(3x + y)(3x - y)$.

SOLUTION

Pattern for product of sum and difference of two terms	$(a + b)(a - b) = a^2 - b^2$	The pattern for the product of the sum and difference of two terms can be applied here.
Identify values	$a = 3x, b = y$	To apply the pattern, identify the values of a and b in this example, $3x$ and y.
Substitute and simplify	$(3x)^2 - (y)^2$ $9x^2 - y^2$	Substitute the values of a and b into the pattern and simplify.

Model Problems continue . . .

3. Factor $4x^2 - 25$.

> When you recognize a pattern, you can use it to factor. For instance, in model problem 3, you can recognize the expression as a difference of squares.

SOLUTION

One square subtracted from another	$4x^2 - 25$	*Difference of squares* refers to a polynomial that has two terms, one perfect square subtracted from another. The polynomial $4x^2 - 25$ is a difference of perfect squares, since $4x^2$ is the square of $2x$, and 25 is 5 squared.
The factors are:	$(2x \quad)(2x \quad)$	A difference of two squares is the product of two binomials. The binomial factors start with the square root of the first term of the polynomial being factored, so $2x$ is the first term here.
• The square root of the first term		
• Plus and minus square root of second term	$(2x + 5)(2x - 5)$	The square root of the second term is then added and subtracted, so 5 is added to and subtracted from $2x$.

4. Factor $x^2 - 4x + 4$.

SOLUTION

Perfect square trinomial	$x^2 - 4x + 4$	The trinomial in this problem has the middle term subtracted. A perfect square trinomial like this factors as $(A - B)(A - B)$.
Identify variables	$A = \sqrt{x^2} = x$ $B = \sqrt{4} = 2$	The expression A is the square root of the first term, which is x. The expression B is the square root of the last term, which is 2.
Substitute and simplify	$2AB = 4x$	Multiply 2, A, and B to get $4x$, the middle term subtracted in the original expression.
State factors	$x^2 - 4x + 4 = (x - 2)(x - 2)$	The factors are both $A - B$, which here means the factorization is $x - 2$ times $x - 2$.

Structure and Factoring

Now we consider slightly more complicated factoring problems. The key to factoring them is to see within them the structure of a polynomial that we can factor.

MODEL PROBLEMS

1. Factor $-x^2 - 8x + 9$.

SOLUTION

Factor out -1	$-(x^2 + 8x - 9)$	How do we factor a polynomial where the term with the highest degree is negative? It's often easiest to factor out -1 and then find binomial factors.
Factor remaining polynomial	$-(x + 9)(x - 1)$	Factor the remaining trinomial. We do not show the steps here, but you could factor this by making a list of the factors of 9.

Model Problems continue . . .

2. Factor $4x^4 + 20x^3 + 24x^2$.

SOLUTION

Factor out greatest common factor	$4x^2(x^2 + 5x + 6)$	The number 4 is the greatest common factor of all the coefficients, and x^2 is the highest common power of x. Factor out $4x^2$, which is the greatest common factor.

> Removing the greatest common factor from a polynomial first can help you factor it. The *greatest common factor* has the greatest common coefficient and the greatest common power of each variable.

Factor remaining polynomial	$4x^2(x + 2)(x + 3)$	We do not show the steps here, but the remaining polynomial, $x^2 + 5x + 6$, can be factored as $x + 2$ times $x + 3$. This completes the factoring.

3. Factor $2(z - 12) + z^2$.

SOLUTION

Distribute first	$2(z - 12) + z^2$ $2z - 24 + z^2$	First distribute the 2 across the parentheses.
State in standard form	$z^2 + 2z - 24$	Rearrange the polynomial so that it is in standard form.
Create table		Now this is looking like a trinomial that can be factored. List the factors of the constant term, -24, in one column, and the sum of those factors in the other column.

Factors of -24	Sum
$-1, 24$	23
$1, -24$	-23
$-2, 12$	10
$2, -12$	-10
$-3, 8$	5
$3, -8$	-5
$-4, 6$	2
$4, -6$	-2

Choose correct sum	$-4 + 6 = 2$	To find which of these 8 pairs of possible factors is correct, add them. Remember that they must add to the coefficient, 2 in this case, of the middle term of the trinomial. The correct pair is -4 and 6.
Write out factors	$(z - 4)(z + 6)$	The two binomial factors are $z - 4$ and $z + 6$.

Factoring by Grouping

In **factoring by grouping**, you create groups of terms in a polynomial that you can factor, so that the groups then have a common factor. Then you apply the distributive property to factor out the common factor. This method is typically used when there are four terms in the polynomial.

MODEL PROBLEM

Factor $4x^4 + 16x - 5x^3 - 20$.

SOLUTION

Rewrite polynomial in groups you can factor	$(4x^4 + 16x) + (-5x^3 - 20)$	Notice that there is a common factor of $4x$ in the first two terms and another common factor of -5 in the last two terms. Since there are common factors in both the first two terms and last two terms, we rewrite the polynomial in two groups, so that each group has a common factor.
Factor out greatest common factors	$4x(x^3 + 4) + (-5)(x^3 + 4)$	Factor out the greatest common factor from each group. In the first group, $4x$ can be factored out. And in the second group, -5 can be factored out. The minus sign does not have to be factored out, but by factoring out -5 we get a common factor, $x^3 + 4$, in both groups.
Apply distributive property	$(4x - 5)(x^3 + 4)$	Since the common factor $x^3 + 4$ is multiplied by $4x$ and by -5, use the distributive property and multiply it by $4x - 5$.

PRACTICE

Exercises 1–22: Factor.

1. $x^2 - 25$

2. $x^2 - 289$

3. $4x^2 - 49$

4. $25x^2 - 36$

5. $100x^2 - 121$

6. $x^2 + 12x + 36$

7. $x^2 + 14x + 49$

8. $x^2 - 20x + 100$

9. $x^2 - 14x + 49$

10. $9x^2 + 42x + 49$

11. $16x^2 + 24x + 9$

12. $121x^2 + 22x + 1$

13. $169x^2 + 26x + 1$

14. $x^2 + 3x - 40$

15. $x^2 - 2x - 80$

16. $x^2 - 3x - 18$

17. $x^2 - 8xy + 15y^2$

18. $x^2 - 10xy + 16y^2$

19. $x^2 - 17xy + 70y^2$

20. $-3x^2 - 15x + 18$

21. $-5x^2 - 20x + 60$

22. $x^2 - 2(7x - 12)$

23. **MP 1, 2** Write as the product of two binomials: $x^2 + 4(5x + 16)$

24. **MP 1, 2** Write as the product of two binomials: $x^2 + 5(4x + 15)$

2.2 Polynomial Patterns

Factoring Sums and Differences of Cubes

The polynomial $x^3 + 27$ is the sum of perfect cubes, and $x^3 - 8$ is the difference of perfect cubes. A polynomial is called a **sum of cubes** if its terms are two perfect cubes that are added, and a **difference of cubes** if it is one perfect cube subtracted from another.

Sum of cubes $A^3 + B^3$	$(A + B)(A^2 - AB + B^2)$	The sum of two perfect cubes equals the two factors multiplied together.
Difference of cubes $A^3 - B^3$	$(A - B)(A^2 + AB + B^2)$	The difference of two perfect cubes equals the factors multiplied together.

MODEL PROBLEM

MP 7 Factor $27y^6 - 125$.

SOLUTION

Identify cubes
$A^3 = 27y^6 = (3y^2)^3$
$A = 3y^2$
$B^3 = 125 = 5^3$
$B = 5$

$27y^6 - 125$ is a difference of cubes, since each term is a perfect cube. Use a formula to factor it. Set A^3 equal to $27y^6$, which is the cube of $3y^2$. Set B^3 equal to 125, which is 5 cubed. B is equal to 5.

Substitute
$(A - B)(A^2 + AB + B^2)$
$(3y^2 - 5)(9y^4 + 15y^2 + 25)$

State the formula and the terms just calculated, then substitute. Perform the operations.

PRACTICE

1. Three students attempt to factor the expression $x^2y^2 - m^2n^2$.

Student 1: $(x - y)(m + n)$
Student 2: $(xy + mn)(xy - mn)$
Student 3: $(xy - mn)(xy + mn)$

Which best describes who factored the expression correctly?

A. Student 1 only
B. Student 2 only
C. Students 2 and 3
D. Student 3 only

Exercises 2–3: Write as a polynomial in standard form.

2. $[(7x + 3) - x^3]^2$

3. $[(6x + 8) - x^4]^2$

Exercises 4–22: Factor completely.

4. $7x^6 - 21x^5$

5. $42x^9 - 147x^7$

6. $x^4 + 10x^2 + 21$

7. $x^4 + 13x^2 + 22$

8. $x^3 + 5x^2 - 24x$

9. $11x^3 + 44x^2 + 33x$

10. $125x^3 + 64$

11. $27x^3 + 512$

12. $343x^3 + 64$

13. $27x^3 + 1000$

14. $64y^3 - 125$

Practice Problems continue . . .

15. $8y^3 - 125$

16. $216y^3 - 343$

17. $64y^3 - 729$

18. $64x^3 + 27$

19. $216x^3 + 64$

20. $64x^3 + 125$

21. $125x^3 + 216$

22. $z^{12} - 27$

23. MP 3, 7 Show that
$(a + b)^3 = a^3 + 3a^2b + 3ab^2 + b^3$.

24. MP 2, 6 If the sum of the squares of a positive number and its reciprocal is equal to 2, what is the sum of the cubes of that number and its reciprocal equal to?

25. MP 2, 6 Jackie thought of two consecutive natural numbers and told Yan that the difference of their cubes was 331. Yan figured out Jackie's numbers. What numbers did he get?

Factoring Two-Variable Polynomials

In the model problems below, we show an example that requires us to factor a polynomial with two variables. The key to our approach is to see how the structure of this polynomial relates to a polynomial we already know.

MODEL PROBLEMS

MP 7 Exercises 1–4: Factor each expression.

1. $x^4 + 2x^2y^2 + y^4$

SOLUTION

Perfect square trinomial
$x^4 + 2x^2y^2 + y^4$
$A^2 + 2AB + B^2$
$A = x^2, B = y^2$
$(x^2)^2 + 2(x^2)(y^2) + (y^2)^2$

The first step in factoring $x^4 + 2x^2y^2 + y^4$ is to recognize that it is a perfect square trinomial. It happens that instead of x and y being the terms that are squared, it is x^2 and y^2. Write the expression to emphasize that it is a perfect square trinomial.

Use perfect square identity
$A^2 + 2AB + B^2 = (A + B)^2$
$(x^2)^2 + 2(x^2)(y^2) + (y^2)^2 = (x^2 + y^2)^2$

Use the identity, with A in this case being x^2 and B being y^2.

2. $4m^8 - n^8$

SOLUTION

Difference of squares
$(2m^4)^2 - (n^4)^2$
$(A + B)(A - B)$
$A = 2m^4, B = n^4$

Factor $4m^8 - n^8$ by recognizing that it is the difference of two squares. In this case, the two squared terms are $2m^4$ and n^4.

Use difference of squares identity
$A^2 - B^2 = (A + B)(A - B)$
$(2m^4)^2 - (n^4)^2 = (2m^4 + n^4)(2m^4 - n^4)$

We take advantage of the fact that the result of raising a power to a power is the product of those exponents of those powers. Use the difference of squares identity, with A in this case being $2m^4$ and B being n^4.

Model Problems continue . . .

3. $x^2 + 5xy + 4y^2$

SOLUTION

Determine how to factor and determine sign	$x^2 + 5xy + 4y^2 = (x + \ldots y)(x + \ldots y)$	An important thing to observe is that this polynomial follows the basic pattern created by multiplying two binomials together: There are three terms, the two outer terms include a variable squared, and the middle term has both variables multiplied together. In this case, we consider two binomials that each have an x-term and a y-term. Since all terms are positive, the two binomials are sums of positive terms.

Create table

Factors of 4	Sum
1, 4	5
2, 2	4

List the factors of the coefficient of the last term in one column, and the sum of those factors in the other column. We only need to consider all positive factors since all terms in the original polynomial are positive. Make a list of the possible positive factors of 4, the coefficient of y^2. Since the sum of the factors must equal the coefficient, 5, of the middle term of the original trinomial, we use 1 and 4.

Write out factors $(x + 1y)(x + 4y) = (x + y)(x + 4y)$ Write out the factors.

4. $m^4 - 8m^2 + 15$

SOLUTION

Determine how to factor $m^4 - 8m^2 + 15 = (m^2 + \ldots)(m^2 + \ldots)$ The polynomial in the model problem is similar to a quadratic that is the square of a binomial sum. We decide to try to factor this into two binomials, each with an m^2 term and a constant term.

> Even though this polynomial is not quadratic, we can factor it into two binomials. We first recognize that it is in the form $x^2 + bx + c$ with $x = m^2$.

Determine signs $(m^2 - \ldots)(m^2 - \ldots)$ Since the middle term of the expression is negative and the constant term is positive, both constant terms of the binomial factors must be negative.

List factors of constant
$15 = -1 \cdot (-15)$
$15 = -3 \cdot (-5)$
Make a list of the negative factors of 15.

List sums of factors
$-1 + (-15) = -16$
$-3 + (-5) = -8$
Since the sum of the factors must equal the coefficient, -8, of the middle term of the trinomial, consider the sums of each pair of factors. The factor pair, -3 and -5, add to -8.

Write out factors $(m^2 - 3)(m^2 - 5)$ Write out the two binomials with the pair of factors whose product is the constant, 15, and whose sum is the coefficient, -8, of the middle term.

PRACTICE

MP 7 Exercises 1–26: Factor.

1. $x^2 + 8xy + 15y^2$

2. $x^2 + 11xy + 24y^2$

3. $24xy + 104x - 15y - 65$

4. $6xy + 26x - 15y - 65$

5. $10xy + 35x + 8y + 28$

6. $15xy + 35x + 12y + 28$

7. $8x^3 - 12x^2 + 34x - 51$

8. $16x^3 - 14x^2 + 152x - 133$

9. $119x^3 + 136x^2 + 21x + 24$

10. $65x^3 + 52x^2 + 15x + 12$

11. $x^2 + 12xy + 32y^2$

12. $x^2 + 11xy + 28y^2$

13. $x^2 + 14xy + 48y^2$

14. $x^2 + 9xy + 20y^2$

15. $x^2 + 12xy + 35y^2$

16. $x^2 + 5xy + 6y^2$

17. $x^2 + 10xy + 21y^2$

18. $x^2 + 7xy + 10y^2$

19. $x^2 + 13xy + 42y^2$

20. $x^2 + 15xy + 56y^2$

21. $40xy + 136x - 35y - 119$

22. $4xy + 26x - 10y - 65$

23. $6xy + 34x - 15y - 85$

24. $20xy + 35x + 16y + 28$

25. $16xy + 56x + 6y + 21$

26. $21xy + 49x + 12y + 28$

LESSON 2.3

2.3 Patterns and Equations

Algebra 1 Review: The Square Root Principle

The **square root principle** states that the solutions of $x^2 = k$ are the positive square root and negative square root of the constant $k \geq 0$.

> The square root principle applies when a squared quantity is equal to some constant. Solve equations by taking the positive and negative square roots of the constant, provided the constant is greater than or equal to zero.

MODEL PROBLEMS

1. What are the two solutions to $x^2 = 49$?

SOLUTION

Square root principle   If $x^2 = k$, then $x = \sqrt{k}$ **or** $x = -\sqrt{k}$

The square root principle says that if x^2 equals a constant k, then the solutions are the square root of k and the negative of the square root of k.

Apply the square root principle
$$x^2 = 49$$
$$x = 7, -7$$

The solutions are the positive and negative square roots of the constant. Here, the solutions are 7 and -7, the positive and negative square roots of 49.

Model Problems continue . . .

2. Find the two solutions to $3x^2 = 39$ using the square root principle.

SOLUTION

Put equation into form $x^2 = k$	$3x^2 = 39$ $x^2 = 13$	Divide both sides of the equation by 3 to cancel the coefficient of x^2. The result is the equation $x^2 = 13$, which can be solved using the square root principle.
Find square roots	$x = \sqrt{13}, -\sqrt{13}$	The solutions are the positive and negative square roots of 13.

3. Solve $(x - 3)^2 = 25$ using the square root principle.

SOLUTION

Square root principle	$x - 3 = \sqrt{25} = 5 \textbf{ or}$ $x - 3 = -\sqrt{25} = -5$	The two solutions can be found by taking the square root of the left side and the positive and negative square roots of the right side. The result is two linear equations.
Solve first equation	$x - 3 = 5$ $x = 8$	The first equation can be solved by adding 3 to each side. The solution is 8.
Solve second equation	$x - 3 = -5$ $x = -2$	The second equation can also be solved by adding 3 to each side. The solution is -2.
State solutions	$x = 8, -2$	The two solutions to the quadratic equation are 8 and -2.

> The square root principle can be applied any time one side of the equation is a constant and the other side is a perfect square expression.

Algebra 1 Review: The Zero-Product Property

The **zero-product property** states: If the product of factors is zero, then at least one of the factors must be zero. For instance, if $5x = 0$, x must be 0. The solutions are called the **roots**, or **zeros**, of the equation.

> The zero-product property states that when a product is 0, at least one of its factors must be 0. You can set each factor equal to 0 and solve to find the solutions to the equation.

Zero-Product Property
If $ab = 0$, then $a = 0$ or $b = 0$.

A **quadratic equation** is one that can be written with a quadratic polynomial on one side of the equation and 0 on the other side. The standard form of a quadratic equation is $ax^2 + bx + c = 0$, where $a \neq 0$.

1. Find the solutions to $x^2 + 4x - 5 = 0$ using the zero-product property.

> The solutions to the equation will cause the expression on the left, $x^2 + 4x - 5$, to equal zero. This is why they are called *zeros* of that expression.

SOLUTION

Factor trinomial	$(x - 1)(x + 5) = 0$	Factor the trinomial.
Zero-product property	$x - 1 = 0$ ***or*** $x + 5 = 0$	Since the product of the two factors equals 0, the zero-product property states that at least one of them must equal 0. Set each factor equal to zero to find out what values of x will make the factor equal 0.
Solve first equation	$x - 1 = 0$ $x = 1$	Solve the resulting linear equations. The solution to the first equation is 1.
Solve second equation	$x + 5 = 0$ $x = -5$	The solution to the second equation is -5.
State solutions	$x = 1, -5$	The solutions to the quadratic equation are 1 and -5.

2. Find the solutions to $4x^2 - 8x = 0$ using common variable factors.

SOLUTION

Factor	$4x^2 - 8x = 0$ $4x(x - 2) = 0$	Factor out the common factor of $4x$ on the left side of the equation.
Zero-product property	$4x = 0$ ***or*** $x - 2 = 0$	Using the zero-product property, set each factor equal to 0 and solve.
Solve first equation	$4x = 0$ $x = 0$	The solution to the first equation is 0.
Solve second equation	$x - 2 = 0$ $x = 2$	The solution to the second equation is 2.
State solutions	$x = 0, 2$	The two solutions to the quadratic equation are 0 and 2.

3. Solve $x^2 + 4x - 6 = -1$ by factoring.

SOLUTION

State equation in standard form for a quadratic equation	$x^2 + 4x - 6 + 1 = -1 + 1$ $x^2 + 4x - 5 = 0$	To apply the property, zero must be on one side of the equation, so write the equation in standard form.
Factor	$(x + 5)(x - 1) = 0$	Factor the expression on the left side of the equation. Its factors are $x + 5$ and $x - 1$.
Zero-product property	$x + 5 = 0$ ***or*** $x - 1 = 0$	Since the product of the two factors equals 0, the zero-product property states that at least one of them must equal 0. Set each factor equal to zero to find out what values of x will make the factor equal 0.

Model Problems continue . . .

Solve first equation	$x + 5 = 0$ $x = -5$	Solve each of the resulting linear equations. The solution to the first equation is -5.
Solve second equation	$x - 1 = 0$ $x = 1$	The solution to the second equation is 1.
State solutions	$x = -5, 1$	The two solutions to the equation are -5 and 1.

4. Solve $(x - p)(x + m) = 0$ for x. Which could be a solution to the equation?
  A. $-p$
  B. x
  C. $-m$
  D. m

SOLUTION

A. Substituting $x = -p$ into the equation does not make one of the factors equal to 0.
B. The student does not understand how to solve for x.
C. **Correct answer.** Using the zero-product property, $x + m = 0$ or $x - p = 0$. Therefore, $x = -m$ or $x = p$.
D. Substituting $x = m$ into the equation does not make one of the factors equal to 0.

PRACTICE

Exercises 1–20: Solve.

1. $4x(x - 12) = 0$

2. $(5f + 4)(6f - 5) = 0$

3. $b^2 + 9b + 18 = 0$

4. $5x(x - 11) = 0$

5. $(7a + 4)(4a - 8) = 0$

6. $x^2 + 8x + 12 = 0$

7. $z^2 + 7z + 10 = 0$

8. $5x^2 + 55x = 0$

9. $x^2 + 12x + 35 = 0$

10. $x^2 + 10x + 24 = 0$

11. $x^2 - 11x + 28 = 0$

12. $x^2 - 7x + 12 = 0$

13. $x^2 - 10x + 24 = 0$

14. $x^2 + 19x + 78 = 0$

15. $7x^2 + 63x = 0$

16. $x^2 - 8x + 15 = 0$

17. $x^2 + 7x + 10 = 0$

18. $3x^2 + 18x = 0$

19. $x^2 + 20x + 99 = 0$

20. $4x^2 + 20x = 0$

21. MP 2 Write a quadratic equation which has the solutions -1 and -4.

22. MP 1, 7 Could an even number be a solution to the quadratic equation $3x^2 - 19x + 7 = 0$? Why or why not?

Using Structure in Expressions to Solve an Equation

When we recognize the structure of an expression, we can use some methods we already know for solving an equation involving it.

MODEL PROBLEMS

1. Solve $x^2 + 8x + 16 = 11$.

> You could try solving this equation by using the zero-product property, but after you write the equation in standard form, you will get a trinomial that does not factor. One way to solve this problem is to notice that the left side of the equation is a perfect square trinomial.

SOLUTION

Factor and write as square	$x^2 + 8x + 16 = 11$ $(x + 4)^2 = 11$	Factor the left side to write it as a squared expression.
Apply square root principle	$x + 4 = \sqrt{11}$ **or** $x + 4 = -\sqrt{11}$	Since the equation is in the necessary form, we may apply the square root principle to take the positive and negative square roots.
Solve first equation	$x + 4 = \sqrt{11}$ $x = -4 + \sqrt{11}$	Solve the first equation by subtracting 4 from both sides. x is by itself on the left side of the equation. On the right side is $-4 + \sqrt{11}$.
Solve second equation	$x + 4 = -\sqrt{11}$ $x = -4 - \sqrt{11}$	Solve the second equation similarly.
State solutions	$x = -4 \pm \sqrt{11}$	The two solutions are stated in a compact form, where the ± symbol means to add and subtract the square root of 11 from -4.

> The expression $a \pm b$ is short for the two expressions $a + b$ and $a - b$.

2. Solve $(2x + 1)^2 - 3(2x + 1) - 4 = 0$.

SOLUTION

Substitute	$y^2 - 3y - 4 = 0$	Substitute y for $2x + 1$, and state the quadratic equation using that substitution.
Factor	$(y - 4)(y + 1) = 0$	Factor the trinomial.
Apply zero-product property	$y - 4 = 0$ **or** $y + 1 = 0$ $y = -1, 4$	Apply the zero-product property and solve the equations.
Substitute $2x + 1$ for y	$2x + 1 = 4$ $2x + 1 = -1$	Substitute, returning to $2x + 1$.
Solve	$x = \dfrac{3}{2}$ $x = -1$	Solve the equations.
State solutions	$x = \dfrac{3}{2}, -1$	And state the solutions.

Model Problems continue . . .

Model Problems *continued*

3. **MP 1, 2, 4** You are given a square picture and are curious how the area would change as the same length is added to one dimension and subtracted from another. Hint: Use an identity to answer this question.

SOLUTION

Area = s^2

Area = s^2
Area = $(s + b)(s - b)$

The area of a square is the length of a side squared. We want to calculate what happens if we take two sides of the square which are opposite each other, increase their lengths by the same amount, and shorten the other two sides by that same amount. Use b for the change.

Use identity

$(s + b)(s - b) = s^2 - b^2$
The area shrinks by b^2

Use the identity to determine the new area. The area shrinks by b^2. Whether the original square has sides of 120 inches or 10 inches, if you reduce two sides by 2 inches and lengthen the other two sides by those 2 inches, the area will be reduced by 4 square inches. The reduced area always equals b^2.

Factoring and Identities

Polynomial expressions can be used to generate **Pythagorean triples**. To do so, use the equation $(x^2 + y^2)^2 = (x^2 - y^2)^2 + (2xy)^2$. In short, the equation is of the form $c^2 = a^2 + b^2$, where $a = x^2 - y^2$, $b = 2xy$, and $c = x^2 + y^2$, which is to say, it is true for a Pythagorean triple.

> A *Pythagorean triple* is a set of three integers that satisfies the Pythagorean theorem.

You can pick two integer values of x and y, such as 11 and 2, and substitute them into the expression on the right of the equation. If you choose those values, you get 117 for $x^2 - y^2 = a$, 44 for $2xy = b$, and 125 for $x^2 + y^2 = c$. It's a triple!

How do we know this expression is true for any values (that it is an identity)? We prove it below.

Prove: $(x^2 + y^2)^2 = (x^2 - y^2)^2 + (2xy)^2$	
$(x^2 + y^2)^2 = (x^2 - y^2)^2 + (2xy)^2$	Given
$(x^2 + y^2)^2 - (x^2 - y^2)^2 = (x^2 - y^2)^2 + (2xy)^2 - (x^2 - y^2)^2$	Subtract $(x^2 - y^2)^2$
$(x^4 + 2x^2y^2 + y^4) - (x^4 - 2x^2y^2 + y^4) = (2xy)^2$	Do the operations
$4x^2y^2 = (2xy)^2$	Combine like terms
$(2xy)^2 = (2xy)^2$	Factor

PRACTICE

Exercises 1–26: Solve.

1. $x^2 + 3x - 57 = 3x + 7$

2. $x^2 + 2x - 41 = 2x + 8$

3. $x^2 + 4x - 75 = 4x + 6$

4. $x^2 + 7x - 45 = 7x + 4$

5. $5x^2 = 320$

6. $5x^2 = 80$

7. $6x^2 - 12 = 90$

8. $3x^2 + 21 = 126$

9. $(x + 2)^2 = 81$

10. $(x + 4)^2 = 81$

11. $(x - 12)^2 = 25$

12. $(x - 11)^2 = 25$

13. $x^2 + 4x + 4 = 11$

14. $x^2 + 6x + 9 = 10$

15. $x^2 + 16x + 64 = 37$

16. $x^2 + 12x + 36 = 33$

17. $x^2 + 10x + 25 = 10$

18. $x^2 + 10x + 25 = 15$

19. $x^2 + 18x + 81 = 34$

20. $x^2 + 16x + 64 = 34$

21. $x^2 - 16x + 64 = 20$

22. $x^2 + 14x + 49 = 5$

23. $x^2 + 24x + 144 = 100$

24. $x^2 - 10x + 25 = 8$

25. $x^2 + 18x + 81 = 7$

26. $x^2 + 8x + 16 = 10$

27. `MP 1, 7` For which values of m do the solutions to the equation $3x^2 + m^2x - 4mx + m - 1 = 0$ have the same absolute values, but opposite signs?

28. `MP 1, 2` Find x in terms of b: $7x^2 + 17bx + 6b^2 = 0$

29. `MP 3` Explain why the equation $x^2 - y^2 = 30$ doesn't have any integer solutions.

LESSON 2.4

2.4 Algebra 1 Review: The Quadratic Formula

Completing the Square

To **complete the square** means to add a constant to a binomial like $x^2 + 6x$ to create a perfect square trinomial. To do this, take half the coefficient of the x-term, square it, and add. A perfect square trinomial is a polynomial like $x^2 + 6x + 9$ that results from squaring another binomial, in this case, $(x + 3)^2$.

1. Add a constant to $x^2 + 10x$ to make it a perfect square.

SOLUTION

Take half of coefficient of x	$\dfrac{10}{2} = 5$	To determine what to add to create a perfect square trinomial, first take half of the coefficient of x. In this example, half of 10 is 5.
Square it	$5^2 = 25$	The square of 5 is 25.
Add to binomial	$x^2 + 10x + 25$	Add the result of the previous step to the other two terms. This completes the square.
Check your solution	$(x + 5)^2 = (x + 5)(x + 5)$ $(x + 5)^2 = x^2 + 5x + 5x + 5^2$ $(x + 5)^2 = x^2 + 10x + 25$	

> Note that the coefficient of the squared term must be 1, such as x^2, as opposed to, say, $3x^2$, for you to apply this method. Shortly, we will discuss how to complete the square when the coefficient does not equal 1.

2. What constant added to $x^2 - 8x$ makes the resulting trinomial a perfect square?

SOLUTION

Find half the coefficient of x	half the coefficient of x is -4	Start by finding half the coefficient of x. The coefficient is negative.
Square it	$(-4)^2 = 16$	Square -4. A negative number squared is positive.
Add to binomial	$x^2 - 8x + 16$	Add the result of the previous step to the original binomial. The resulting trinomial is a perfect square.
Check your solution	$(x - 4)^2 = (x - 4)(x - 4)$ $(x - 4)^2 = x^2 - 4x - 4x + (-4)^2$ $(x - 4)^2 = x^2 - 8x + 16$	

3. What constant added to $x^2 - 11x$ makes the resulting trinomial a perfect square? Hint: The constant is not an integer.

SOLUTION

Find half the coefficient of x	half the coefficient of x is $\dfrac{-11}{2}$	Start by finding half the coefficient of x. The coefficient is negative.
Square it	$\left(\dfrac{-11}{2}\right)^2 = \dfrac{121}{4}$	Square both the numerator and denominator of the fraction. A negative number squared is positive.
Add to binomial	$x^2 - 11x + \dfrac{121}{4}$	Add the result of the previous step to the original binomial. The resulting trinomial is a perfect square.
Check your solution	$\left(x - \dfrac{11}{2}\right)^2 = \left(x - \dfrac{11}{2}\right)\left(x - \dfrac{11}{2}\right)$ $\left(x - \dfrac{11}{2}\right)^2 = x^2 - \dfrac{11}{2}x - \dfrac{11}{2}x + \left(\dfrac{11}{2}\right)^2$ $\left(x - \dfrac{11}{2}\right)^2 = x^2 - 11x + \dfrac{121}{4}$	

Model Problems continue . . .

4. Rewrite $3x^2 + x = 2$ by completing the square so that the left side is a binomial square.

> In the equation $3x^2 + x = 2$, the coefficient of the x^2 term is 3, not 1. The coefficient of x^2 must be 1 in order to complete the square.

SOLUTION

Divide by 3, coefficient of x^2

$$3x^2 + x = 2$$

$$x^2 + \frac{1}{3}x = \frac{2}{3}$$

To complete the square, the x^2 term should have a coefficient of 1. Divide this equation by 3 so that is the case.

Complete the square

$$x^2 + \frac{1}{3}x + \frac{1}{36} = \frac{2}{3} + \frac{1}{36}$$

$$x^2 + \frac{1}{3}x + \frac{1}{36} = \frac{24}{36} + \frac{1}{36}$$

$$x^2 + \frac{1}{3}x + \frac{1}{36} = \frac{25}{36}$$

The coefficient of the x-term is $\frac{1}{3}$.

Half of that is $\frac{1}{6}$, and the square

of $\frac{1}{6}$ is $\frac{1}{36}$. We add $\frac{1}{36}$ to each side of the equation so the

left side is a perfect square trinomial.

Factor

$$\left(x + \frac{1}{6}\right)^2 = \frac{25}{36}$$

Factor the left side of the equation to write it as a binomial squared.

PRACTICE

Exercises 1–17: What constant should be added to each expression to complete the square?

1. $x^2 - 10x$

2. $x^2 + 4x$

3. $x^2 + 16x$

4. $x^2 + x$

5. $x^2 + 5x$

6. $x^2 + 3x$

7. $x^2 + 8x$

8. $x^2 - 14x$

9. $x^2 + 2x$

10. $x^2 + 18x$

11. $x^2 + 20x$

12. $x^2 - 22x$

13. $x^2 - 16x$

14. $x^2 + 30x$

15. $x^2 - 9x$

16. $x^2 - x$

17. $x^2 - 11x$

Exercises 18–26: Rewrite the equation by completing the square so that the left side is a binomial squared.

18. $x^2 + 4x = 12$

19. $x^2 - 8x = -7$

20. $x^2 - 10x = 11$

21. $x^2 + 2x = 3$

22. $x^2 + 14x = -40$

23. $x^2 - 16x = -48$

24. $2x^2 - 5x - 7 = 0$

25. $2x^2 + 12x + 9 = 0$

26. $3x^2 + 4x - 12 = 0$

The Quadratic Formula

The **quadratic formula** can be used to solve any quadratic equation. The formula requires that the equation be written in standard form. It can be derived by completing the square, as you may recall from Algebra 1.

Quadratic Formula

$$x = \frac{-b \pm \sqrt{b^2 - 4ac}}{2a} \text{ for } ax^2 + bx + c = 0, \text{ when } a \neq 1$$

> The quadratic formula contains the ± symbol, which means you add and subtract the square root.

MODEL PROBLEMS

1. Solve $3x^2 + 2x - 1 = 0$ using the quadratic formula.

SOLUTION

Identify a, b, and c

$$3x^2 + 2x - 1 = 0$$
$$a = 3, b = 2, c = -1$$

The quadratic formula uses a, the coefficient of x^2; b, the coefficient of x; and c, the constant term. The constant term, c, is -1 because of the subtraction, $a = 3$, and $b = 2$.

Apply the quadratic formula

$$x = \frac{-b \pm \sqrt{b^2 - 4ac}}{2a}$$

$$x = \frac{-2 \pm \sqrt{2^2 - 4(3)(-1)}}{2(3)}$$

Substitute a, b, and c in the quadratic formula. Replace b with 2 in all cases; replace a with 3; and replace c with -1.

Evaluate

$$x = \frac{-2 \pm \sqrt{16}}{6} = \frac{-2 \pm 4}{6}$$

Start under the radical, which simplifies to the square root of 16, which is 4.

Add

$$x = \frac{-2 + 4}{6} = \frac{2}{6} = \frac{1}{3}$$

Now deal with the ± in the numerator. It means add and subtract 4. First add -2 and 4 to get 2 in the numerator. Simplify the fraction to get $\frac{1}{3}$.

Subtract

$$x = \frac{-2 - 4}{6} = \frac{-6}{6} = -1$$

Subtract 4 from -2 to get -6. Simplify $\frac{-6}{6}$ to get -1.

State solutions

$$x = \frac{1}{3}, -1$$

There are two solutions, $\frac{1}{3}$ and -1.

Model Problems continue . . .

2. Solve $10x^2 - 12 = -7x$.

SOLUTION

State in standard form

$$10x^2 + 7x - 12 = 0$$

Restate the original equation in standard form by adding $7x$ to both sides. The trinomial is now set equal to 0.

> To apply the quadratic formula, the equation must be in standard form.

Identify a, b, and c

$$a = 10, b = 7, c = -12$$

Identify a, b, and c for this quadratic equation. c is negative since it is subtracted.

Substitute

$$x = \frac{-b \pm \sqrt{b^2 - 4ac}}{2a}$$

$$x = \frac{-7 \pm \sqrt{7^2 - 4(10)(-12)}}{2(10)}$$

Substitute a, b, and c into the quadratic formula.

Evaluate

$$x = \frac{-7 \pm \sqrt{49 - (-480)}}{20}$$

$$x = \frac{-7 \pm \sqrt{529}}{20}$$

$$x = \frac{-7 \pm 23}{20}$$

Multiply under the radical, subtract a negative, and then take the square root of 529.

State solutions

$$x = \frac{4}{5}, -\frac{3}{2}$$

Add and subtract 23 and simplify the fractions to get the solutions.

3. Solve $2x + 4\sqrt{x} - 1 = 0$.

SOLUTION

Substitute y for $\sqrt{x}$

$$2y^2 + 4y - 1 = 0$$

Substitute y for $\sqrt{x}$, and state the quadratic equation resulting from that substitution.

Solve with quadratic formula

$$y = \frac{-4 + \sqrt{24}}{4} \text{ or}$$

$$y = \frac{-4 - \sqrt{24}}{4}$$

$$y \approx 0.225, -2.225$$

Solve the equation using the quadratic formula.

Substitute $\sqrt{x}$ for y using the first solution

$$\sqrt{x} \approx 0.225$$
$$x \approx 0.505$$

Substitute and solve.

Substitute $\sqrt{x}$ for y using the second solution

$$\sqrt{x} \approx -2.225$$
No real solution

No real number has a negative number as its square root, so $\sqrt{x} \approx -2.225$ does not result in a real solution to the original equation.

State solution

$$x \approx 0.505$$

The equation has only one real solution.

Model Problems continue . . .

MODEL PROBLEMS *continued*

4. **MP 2, 4** A bank pays interest compounded annually on savings accounts. If the amount in a savings account grows from $1000 to $1060.90 in two years, what is the interest rate?

> The formula for compound interest calculations is $A = P(1 + r)^N$, where P is the principal, or original amount; r is the interest rate for a period of time; and A is the amount in the account after N periods of time.

SOLUTION

Compound interest formula	$A = P(1 + r)^N$	Start with the formula for compound interest.
Substitute values	$1060.90 = 1000(1 + r)^2$	Enter the values stated in the problem. P is the original amount in the account, $1000; A$ is the current amount, $1060.90; and N is the number of years, which is 2.
Expand square and distribute	$1060.90 = 1000(1 + 2r + r^2)$ $1060.90 = 1000 + 2000r + 1000r^2$	Square the binomial and distribute 1000.
Write in standard form	$1000r^2 + 2000r - 60.90 = 0$	Swap the sides of the equation, put the terms of the polynomial in descending order, and subtract 1060.90 from each side to put the equation in standard form.
Use quadratic formula	$r = \dfrac{-b \pm \sqrt{b^2 - 4ac}}{2a}$ $r = \dfrac{-2000 \pm \sqrt{2000^2 - 4(1000)(-60.90)}}{2 \cdot 1000}$ $r = \dfrac{-2000 \pm 2060}{2000}$	Restate the quadratic formula here, using r instead of x, since r is the variable in the equation. Substitute and simplify.
Evaluate and state solution	$r = -2.03$ or 0.03 $r = 3\%$	Evaluate two possible values. Add and subtract 2060. The negative solution does not make sense since negative interest is not what you expect a bank to offer. The solution is 3%.

Graphing Calculator: The Quadratic Formula

1. Naming the program. Press PRGM. Scroll over to the **NEW** tab. Press ENTER and name your program by pressing the keys below the green letters on the keypad. For this example, we named the program **QUADFORM**.

```
EXEC EDIT NEW
1:Create New
```

2. Move to screen to write program. Press ENTER once more to go to the screen where we will be writing the body of the program.

```
PROGRAM:QUADFORM
:
```

Directions continue . . .

3. Find catalog of symbols and functions. The next step is writing the program. The full program is shown in step 4, so you can refer to it to check whether your program will work properly. The first line is **Disp** $Ax^2 + Bx + C = 0$. **Disp** can be found by pressing [2nd] then the number zero. Scroll down until you reach **Disp** then press [ENTER]. When the calculator comes to the word **Disp** in a program, it will display whatever follows on the same line. If there are quotes around some text, it will print the text. Otherwise, it will interpret the rest of the line as a math problem, and will print the solution of the problem.

```
CATALOG          ⊞
 DependAuto
 det(
 DiagnosticOff
 DiagnosticOn
 dim(
▶Disp
 DispGraph
```

> The catalog has all the symbols and functions that the calculator can interpret, so if you forget where one is located, you can always look in the catalog.

4. Write the program. Press [ALPHA] followed by [+] which will create the first quotation mark around the text that will be displayed. The $Ax^2 + Bx + C$ can be written by pressing [ALPHA] followed by the keys corresponding to the various letters in the equation. The equal sign can be found either in the catalog or by pressing [2nd] then [MATH]. This followed by the number zero and another quotation mark will end the first line of code. This line will display the equation on the screen when the user executes the program.

```
PROGRAM:QUADFORM
:Disp "AX²+BX+C=
0"
```

Press [ENTER] to get to the next line, where we will be writing **Prompt** *A, B, C*. This line of code will ask the user for three inputs that correspond to the coefficients of the different terms in the quadratic equation. **Prompt** can be found in the catalog, and the letters can be written using the [ALPHA] key. The [,] key can be found above the [7] in the keypad.

```
:Prompt A,B,C
```

The next line in the program is $B^2 - 4AC \rightarrow D$. This part of the quadratic formula is called the *discriminant*, so we store it as the variable *D*. You can write the program without calculating *D* first, but doing so makes the code easier to read later. The two new symbols are ^{2} and $\rightarrow$, which can be found on the [x²] and [STO▶] keys on the left side of the keypad.

```
:B²-4AC→D
```

The next line in the program is **Disp** $(-B + \sqrt{(D)})/(2A)$. To find the square root symbol, press [2nd] then [x²]. Notice that there are not any quotation marks surrounding the expression in this line because we want the calculator to print a single number instead of the expression.

```
:Disp (-B+√(D))/
(2A)
```

The next line in the program is Disp $(-B - \sqrt{(D)})/(2A)$.

```
:Disp (-B-√(D))/
(2A)
```

The next four lines are DelVar followed by *A, B, C,* or *D*, which deletes the variable from the calculator's memory once the program has finished running. DelVar can be found by scrolling through the catalog.

```
:DelVar A
:DelVar B
:DelVar C
:DelVar D
```

5. Execute the program. Press [2nd] then [MODE] to quit out of the program. Press [PRGM] to access the programs menu where you can choose which program to run. If you have more than one program stored, scroll through using the up and down arrow keys until you get to the **QUADFORM** program and press [ENTER] twice to start running the program.

6. Using the program. In order to test the program, we have picked a quadratic equation $x^2 - 2x - 3 = 0$ that we know has two different real answers. Since we already have the program running, we can just put the three coefficients into the calculator, with each followed by pressing $\boxed{\text{ENTER}}$. After entering the final number and pressing $\boxed{\text{ENTER}}$, the two answers, 3 and -1, should be displayed in the bottom right corner of the screen.

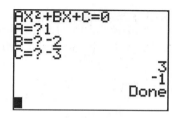

7. Answers that are not real. Not all quadratics have real answers. The calculator shows an error if there are no real answers. The next step covers how to adjust your calculator settings so that you won't see this error.

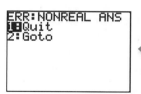

We discuss answers that are not real in the next lesson.

8. Fixing the error message. If you get the error above, as you would if you plugged in the quadratic equation $-x^2 + 4x - 13 = 0$, perform the following steps: Press $\boxed{\text{ENTER}}$ to quit the program. Press $\boxed{\text{MODE}}$ and scroll down and to the right until the cursor is blinking over **a + b*i*** and press $\boxed{\text{ENTER}}$. This allows the calculator to print imaginary numbers as answers to the program.

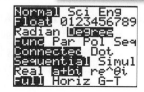

Press $\boxed{\text{2nd}}$ then $\boxed{\text{MODE}}$ to get out of the settings menu and run the program as you did before. Try plugging the quadratic equation above back into the program. This time, the answers should be $2 - 3i$ and $2 + 3i$. If the solutions are irrational, the calculator will approximate the solutions as decimals rather than their correct radical counterparts. You can now have your calculator solve quadratics, even if they do not have real answers.

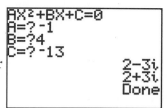

PRACTICE

1. What is the sum of the solutions to the equation $z^2 - 80z + 1200 = 0$?

    A. 40   C. -40

    B. 80   D. -100

2. If the sum of two consecutive positive integers is 29 smaller than their product, then the smaller of the numbers is

    A. 11   C. 6

    B. 12   D. 7

3. If the equation $ax^2 + 9x - 2 = 0$ has only one real solution, then a is equal to

    A. 8   C. $-\dfrac{9}{8}$

    B. $-\dfrac{1}{8}$ D. $-\dfrac{81}{8}$

Exercises 4–16: Solve.

4. $x^2 + 11x + 28 = 0$

5. $x^2 + 11x + 18 = 0$

6. $x^2 - 13.5x + 38 = 0$

7. $x^2 - 13.5x + 42.5 = 0$

8. $4x^2 + 13.5x + 11 = 0$

9. $10x^2 + 108.5x + 85 = 0$

10. $27x^2 - 63.75x + 28.875 = 0$

11. $56x^2 - 104.75x + 44.625 = 0$

12. $3x^2 + 7x + 3 = 0$

13. $4x^2 + 15x + 3 = 0$

14. $5x^2 + 11x + 5 = 0$

15. $4x^2 + 14x + 5 = 0$

16. $6x^2 + 12x + 4 = 0$

17. **MP 4** A ball is launched vertically upward at 19.6 meters per second from a 102.9-meter-tall building. The height of the ball is modeled by the function $f(t) = -4.9t^2 + 19.6t + 102.9$. How many seconds after launch does the ball strike the ground?

Practice Problems continue . . .

18. **MP 4** A pumpkin is launched vertically upward at 24.5 meters per second by a catapult mounted on a 29.4-meter-tall wall. The height of the pumpkin is modeled by the function $f(t) = -4.9t^2 + 24.5t + 29.4$. How many seconds after launch does the pumpkin strike the ground?

19. **MP 2, 4** The perimeter of a rectangle is 40 yards. Find the lengths of its sides if the total area of the squares constructed on two adjacent sides of this rectangle is equal to 208 square yards.

20. **MP 2, 4** Two roads come out of a village at a right angle and lead to two train stations. The direct distance between the stations is 37 miles, but it would take 47 miles going through the village. How far is it from the village to each of the stations?

21. A field-goal kicker kicks a football that follows a parabolic path. The height of the ball can be expressed as a function of the distance (expressed in yards) from where the ball was kicked using $h(x) = -\dfrac{1}{36}x^2 + \dfrac{5}{3}x$.

a Find the maximum height of the ball.

b He is 57 yards from the goalpost. Assuming the kick is on line, will the kick be high enough to make it over the goalpost? (The crossbar of the goalpost is 10 ft, or $3\dfrac{1}{3}$ yards, above ground.)

22. **MP 4, 6** One of the spouts from a decorative fountain needs to be replaced. The spout is 1 foot above the water level. In order to match the other spouts, water coming out of the spout must reach a height of 15 feet at a distance of 4 horizontal feet from the spout, and it should reach the water level 8 horizontal feet from the spout. Write the equation of the parabola that describes the path of the water leaving the spout. Use x for the horizontal distance from the spout, and y as the height above the water.

• Multi-Part PROBLEM Practice •

MP 2, 4 The height of a ball, at any time, t, thrown vertically upward into the air is determined by $s(t) = -16t^2 + v_0 t + s_0$, where v_0 = initial velocity in feet per second, s_0 = initial height in feet, and t = time in seconds. Mark is standing on the edge of a 50-foot-high cliff when he throws a ball into the air with a vertical speed of 35 feet per second. Assume that Mark releases the ball about 5 feet above the ground.

a Write an equation to represent the height of the ball at any time.

b After how many seconds does the ball hit the ground? Round your answer to the nearest tenth of a second.

c You should have gotten 2 answers for part **b**. How did you decide which answer was the correct one, and what is the meaning of the second answer?

d After how many seconds will Mark see the ball pass him going down, at the same height he released it? Round your answer to the nearest tenth of a second.

2.5 Imaginary and Complex Numbers

Real numbers are numbers that can be found on the number line. So, what other types of numbers are there? The answer comes in discussing the square root of negative numbers. We start with the opposite case—the square of any real number, either positive or negative, is positive. For instance, $(-3)^2 = 9$. This means the square root of a positive number is a real number.

But what about the square root of a negative number? For instance, there is no real number equal to the $\sqrt{-1}$. In other words, there is no real number x where $x^2 = -1$. This means negative numbers *do not* have square roots in the set of real numbers. However, in the set of **complex numbers**, negative numbers *do* have square roots. Use i to represent the square root of -1, so $i = \sqrt{-1}$.

We summarize these ideas below:

One **imaginary number** is the square root of -1. Its symbol is i.	• Imaginary numbers $\quad$ Examples: $i = \sqrt{-1}$ $\quad\quad\quad\quad -i = -\sqrt{-1}$
Multiplying i by any real number other than 0 results in another imaginary number.	• Products of real number and i $\quad$ Examples: $7i, -7i, i\sqrt{2}, \dfrac{i}{3}$
Represent the square root of any negative number using i.	• Used to express roots of negative numbers $\quad$ Example: $\sqrt{-17} = \sqrt{17} \cdot \sqrt{-1}$ $\quad\quad\quad \sqrt{-17} = i\sqrt{17}$
Radicals with negative radicands can be simplified using imaginary numbers.	• Simplifying an imaginary number $\quad$ Example: $\sqrt{-16} = \sqrt{16} \cdot \sqrt{-1}$ $\quad\quad\quad \sqrt{-16} = \sqrt{4 \cdot 4} \cdot \sqrt{-1}$ $\quad\quad\quad \sqrt{-16} = 4i$

If an imaginary number is added to a real number, such as $3 + 2i$, the result is a complex number. Real numbers are part of the set of complex numbers, with imaginary numbers, that produce a negative number when squared, another part of that set. The complex number system is important because the solutions to any equation studied in algebra can be written as complex numbers.

> Imaginary numbers combined with real numbers make the number system complete, since they handle the case of the square roots of negative numbers, similar to how irrational numbers handle the square roots of numbers which are not perfect squares.

Complex numbers contain all the real numbers like 4, and all the "pure" imaginary numbers like i. The sum of a real number and a "pure" imaginary number, such as $2 + 3i$, is also a complex number.	• Complex numbers Examples: 4, i, $2 + 3i$

Every complex number can be written in a standard form as a sum with a real part and an imaginary part. The standard form is $c = a + bi$ where a and b are real numbers, with a being the real part and b the imaginary part.	• Standard form: $c = a + bi$
	   Example: $2 + 3i$
	      real part = 2
	      imaginary part = 3

A real number can be stated as a subset of complex numbers. Since the imaginary part is 0, just write 4.	• Real numbers are a subset of complex numbers Example: $4 = 4 + 0i$

Adding and Subtracting Complex Numbers

To combine complex numbers, combine the real parts and imaginary parts. All of the properties of numbers, such as the associative, commutative, and distributive properties, can be applied to complex numbers.

MODEL PROBLEMS

1. Add $(3 + 4i) + (2 - i)$.

SOLUTION

Add like terms

$(3 + 4i) + (2 - i)$
$(3 + 2)$

Add the real parts. The real part of the first complex number is 3, and 2 is the real part of the second complex number.

> We state the addition of complex numbers using variables. The real numbers are summed, as are the coefficients of i:
> $(a + bi) + (c + di) = (a + c) + (b + d)i$

Add imaginary parts

$(3 + 2) + (4 - 1)i$

Now add the imaginary parts as coefficients of i. The coefficients are 4 and -1, since i is subtracted in the second complex number.

Simplify

$5 + 3i$

Simplify the expression. The real numbers sum to 5, and $4 - 1$ equals 3. The sum is $5 + 3i$.

2. Subtract $(8 + 3i) - (2 + 3i)$.

SOLUTION

Subtract like terms and simplify

$8 + 3i - 2 - 3i$
$(8 - 2) + (3 - 3)i$
$6 + 0i$
6

Like adding, subtracting complex terms is an exercise in combining like terms. Subtract the real parts, getting 6. Then subtract the imaginary parts by subtracting the coefficients of i. In this case, we get $0i$, so the result is 6.

> We use variables to summarize the process of subtracting complex numbers:
> $(a + bi) - (c + di) = (a - c) + (b - d)i$

Multiplying Complex Numbers

You multiply complex numbers as you would multiply binomials. For example, use FOIL to multiply complex numbers.

MODEL PROBLEM

Multiply $(4 + 2i)(5 + 3i)$.

SOLUTION

Multiply using FOIL	$4{\cdot}5 + 4 \cdot 3i + 2i{\cdot}5 + 2i \cdot 3i$ $20 + 12i + 10i + 6i^2$	Multiply these two complex numbers as binomials. Use FOIL to write the products and do the multiplications.
Apply the property of i	$20 + 12i + 10i + 6(-1)$ $20 + 12i + 10i - 6$	Replace i^2 with -1.
Combine like terms	$14 + 22i$	Subtract 6 from 20 and add the coefficients of i. The result is $14 + 22i$.

> The product of complex numbers $a + bi$ and $c + di$ is $(ac - bd) + (ad + bc)i$.

PRACTICE

Exercises 1–5: Describe each number using the terms real, imaginary, and complex. Some numbers may be described by multiple terms.

1. $2i$

2. $1 + i$

3. $4 + i\sqrt{7}$

4. $\sqrt{-15}$

5. $\sqrt{-25}$

Exercises 6–11: State with i. Remove perfect squares from radicals when possible.

6. $\sqrt{-81}$

7. $\sqrt{-9}$

8. $-\sqrt{-16}$

9. $-\sqrt{-36}$

10. $\sqrt{-10}$

11. $\sqrt{-17}$

MP 7 Exercises 12–39: Simplify.

12. $(5 + 4i) + (2 - 2i)$

13. $(2 + 5i) + (1 + 3i)$

14. $(4 - 6i) + (2 + 3i)$

15. $(1 + 4i) + (3 - i)$

16. $(2 - 7i) + (5 - 10i)$

17. $(4i + 7) + (1 - 2i)$

18. $(6 + 3i) + (3i - 4)$

19. $(8i + 9) + (2 + 3i)$

20. $(8 + 7i) - (5 + 3i)$

21. $(13 + 6i) - (4 + 3i)$

22. $(7 + 8i) - (7 + 2i)$

23. $(4 + 3i) - (1 - 4i)$

24. $(5 - 3i) - (6 + i)$

25. $(14 + 3i) - (5 - 7i)$

26. $(11 - 5i) - (10 - 11i)$

27. $(8i - 1) - (12 + 6i)$

28. $(9 - 5i) - (11i + 7)$

29. $(1 + i) - (7 - 3i)$

30. $(5 + 2i)i$

31. $(6 - 2i)i$

32. $i(5 + 3i)$

33. $2i(5 + 6i)$

34. $(6 + 2i)(1 + 8i)$

35. $(3 + 4i)(5 + 2i)$

36. $(4 + i)(3 + 5i)$

37. $(5 - 2i)(6 + 3i)$

38. $(10 + 3i)(1 - 5i)$

39. $(7 - 5i)(3 - 2i)$

Optional: Complex Conjugates

Complex conjugates are complex numbers with the same real parts, and imaginary parts that are opposites: $a + bi, a - bi$. For example, the complex numbers $5 + 2i$ and $5 - 2i$ are complex conjugates because they have opposite imaginary parts. The expressions are identical except that the imaginary part is added in one expression and subtracted in the other. The product of complex conjugates is a real number equal to $a^2 + b^2$, since both a and b are real numbers.

> Complex conjugates occur as a result of the quadratic formula. If the **discriminant** of the quadratic formula ($b^2 - 4ac$) is negative, the solution will be a complex conjugate pair. Why? Because the $\sqrt{b^2 - 4ac}$ term is added and subtracted to and from a real term.

Derive: $a^2 + b^2$ (Formula for Multiplying Complex Conjugates)

Formula for complex conjugates	$(a + bi)(a - bi)$
Multiply the expressions using FOIL	$a^2 - abi + abi - b^2i^2$
Combine like terms	$a^2 - b^2i^2$
Replace i^2 with -1	$a^2 - b^2(-1)$
Simplify	$a^2 + b^2$

MODEL PROBLEM

Multiply $5 + 2i$ by its complex conjugate.

SOLUTION

Identify complex conjugate

$5 - 2i$

$(5 - 2i)(5 + 2i) = ?$

Take the opposite of in $a + bi$ to find the complex conjugate $a - bi$. In this case, the complex conjugate of $5 + 2i$ is $5 - 2i$.

Multiplying complex conjugates

$(5 - 2i)(5 + 2i)$

$5^2 + 2^2$

$25 + 4$

29

The product of a pair of complex conjugates equals the sum of the square of their real part and the square of either imaginary part. Apply the rule here. Square $a = 5$ and $b = 2$ and add the results. The product of the complex conjugates is the real number 29.

PRACTICE

1. Which of the following pairs are complex conjugates? Select all that apply.

A. $5 + 4i$ and $-5 - 4i$
B. $2 - i$ and $2 + i$
C. $6 + 8i$ and $8i + 6$
D. $9 + 2i$ and $9 - 2i$

Exercises 2–6: Find the complex conjugate of each expression.

2. $15 + 7i$

3. $2 + 6i$

4. $8 - 4i$

5. $3 - 11i$

6. $25 - 25i$

MP 8 Exercises 7–13: Multiply each expression by its complex conjugate and state the result.

7. $3 + 5i$

8. $8 + 2i$

9. $3 + 6i$

10. $2 - 7i$

11. $4 - 3i$

12. $1 - i$

13. $-3 + 2i$

Factoring Identities and Complex Numbers

Factoring identities can be extended using complex numbers. For instance, $x^2 - y^2 = (x + y)(x - y)$. With complex numbers, we can extend this to $x^2 + y^2 = (x - yi)(x + yi)$.

MODEL PROBLEM

a Factor $9x^2 - 4$.
b Factor $9x^2 + 4$.
c Compare the factors for parts **a** and **b**.

SOLUTION

a Difference of squares
$$9x^2 - 4$$
$$(3x + 2)(3x - 2)$$

This is a difference of squares. Factor it with all real factors.

b Sum of squares
$$9x^2 + 4$$
$$(3x + 2i)(3x - 2i)$$

This is a sum, not difference, of squares. Factor it using complex numbers.

Check
$$(3x + 2i)(3x - 2i)$$
$$9x^2 + 6xi - 6xi - 4i^2$$
$$9x^2 - 4(-1)$$
$$9x^2 + 4$$

Check the factoring. Multiply the terms. The $6xi$ terms cancel out. Square i, which is -1. Subtracting the product of 4 and -1 is equivalent to adding 4. Note that the factors are complex conjugates, as they must be. It checks.

c The factors of $9x^2 - 4$ are real factors. The factors of $9x^2 + 4$ are complex.

PRACTICE

1. Which of the following expressions is equal to $16x^2 + 64$?

A. $(8x + 4i)(8x - 4i)$
B. $(16x + 4i)(x - 4i)$
C. $(4x + 8i)(4x - 8i)$
D. $(4x + 4i)(8x - 8i)$

2. Factor the expression $4x^2 + 81$ using complex factors.

3. Multiply and simplify $(3x + 5i)(3x - 5i)$.

4. What are the complex factors of the expression $100x^2 + y^2$?

5. $x + 7i$ is one factor of the expression $x^2 + 49$. What is the other factor?

6. $3x + 3i$ is one factor of the expression $9x^2 + 9$. What is the other factor?

7. $5x + 10i$ is one factor of the expression $25x^2 + 100$. What is the other factor?

8. $3x + 7i$ is one factor of the expression $9x^2 + 49$. What is the other factor?

9. $3x + 8i$ is one factor of the expression $9x^2 + 64$. What is the other factor?

10. $4x + 3i$ is one factor of the expression $16x^2 + 9$. What is the other factor?

11. a Complete the table by multiplying and simplifying the expressions. Write the products in standard form.

	Product
$(x + i)(x - i)$	
$(x + 1)(x - 1)$	
$(2x + 3i)(2x - 3i)$	
$(2x + 3)(2x - 3)$	

b Compare the products for the expressions that have complex numbers to the products that do not have complex numbers.

Practice Problems continue . . .

Exercises 12–16: Factor using complex numbers.

12. $25x^2 + 4$

13. $\dfrac{1}{4}x^2 + \dfrac{1}{9}y^2$

14. $\dfrac{1}{16} + \dfrac{1}{25}x^2$

15. $3x^2 + 27$

16. $72 + 2y^2$

17. MP 3, 7 Dan factored $x^2 + 121$ into $(x + 11)(x - 11)$. Describe his mistake and give a correct factorization using complex factors.

18. MP 6 Show that the factors of $49x^2 + 225$ are $(7x + 15i)(7x - 15i)$.

LESSON 2.6

2.6 Solutions of Quadratic Equations

Graphs and the Number of Solutions to a Quadratic

We show two methods to determine the number of solutions to quadratic equations:

Equation	Number of x-intercepts		Factoring
$4x^2 + 5x + 1 = 0$	Since the graph has two x-intercepts, the equation has two real solutions. 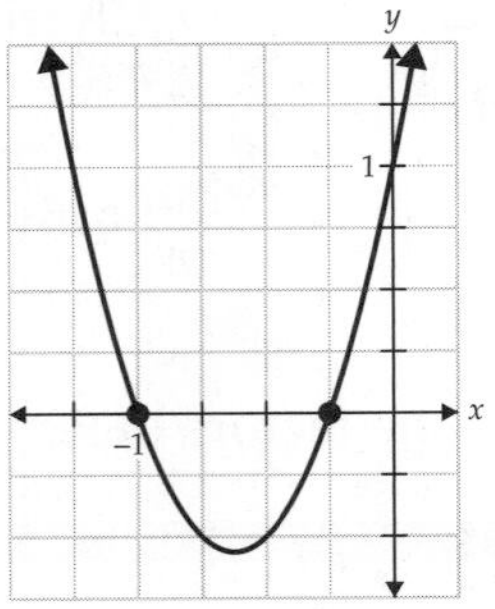		The factors of $4x^2 + 5x + 1 = 0$ are $(4x + 1)(x + 1)$. Using the zero-product property, the equation has two solutions.
$4x^2 + 4x + 1 = 0$	The graph shows the equation has one solution, since there is one x-intercept. 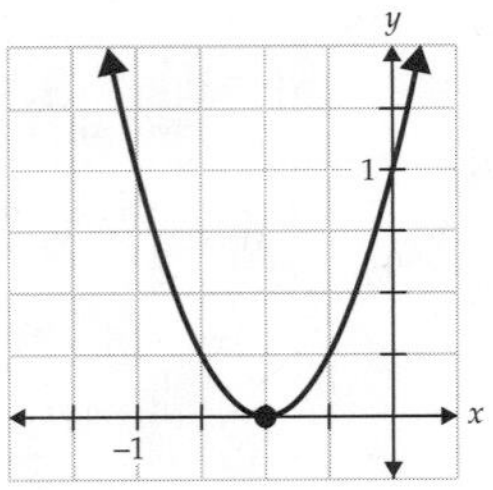		$4x^2 + 4x + 1 = 0$, is the perfect square $(2x + 1)^2$. Setting $2x + 1$ equal to zero results in only one solution to the equation.
$4x^2 + 3x + 1 = 0$	The graph shows the equation has no real solutions, since it never intersects the x-axis, which means it has no x-intercepts. 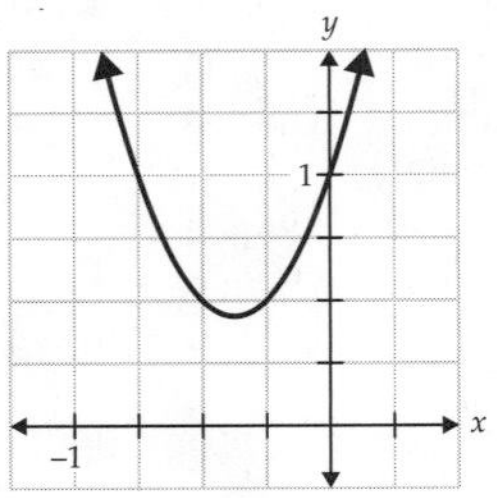		The polynomial, $4x^2 + 3x + 1 = 0$ cannot be factored. If you use the quadratic formula to try to solve it, you will see that it has no real solutions.

Graphing Calculator: Graphing Quadratic Equations

1. Enter the equation. Use $\boxed{Y=}$ to get to the equation entry screen. We want to graph $y = 2x^2 - 12x + 19$. Enter the equation into one of the Y variable lines, in this case, Y1.

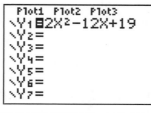

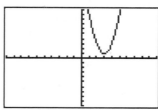

> If we complete the square, $y = 2x^2 - 12x + 19$ can be written as $y = 2(x - 3)^2 + 1$. That represents a parabola with vertex at the origin that is translated 3 to the right and up by one, which matches the graph. The graph does not cross the x-axis, so there are no real solutions to this quadratic equation.

2. Graph the equation. To get an image, graph the function using the standard graphing window of $-10 < x < 10$ and $-10 < y < 10$. Press $\boxed{\text{ZOOM}}$ **6:ZStandard**. If the graph does not display correctly, change the window using the $\boxed{\text{WINDOW}}$ or other $\boxed{\text{ZOOM}}$ commands.

The Discriminant

If you want to determine the number and type of solutions to a quadratic equation, you can use the *discriminant*. With the quadratic formula $x = \dfrac{-b \pm \sqrt{b^2 - 4ac}}{2a}$, the expression under the radical, $b^2 - 4ac$, is called the *discriminant* of the quadratic equation. The expression under the radical determines if solutions are complex (if the expression is negative) or real (if the expression is zero or positive).

Equation	Discriminant
$4x^2 + 5x + 1 = 0$	$b^2 - 4ac > 0$ If the discriminant is positive, there are two x-intercepts and therefore two real solutions. For example: $4x^2 + 5x + 1 = 0$ $b^2 - 4ac = (5)^2 - 4 \cdot 4 \cdot 1 = 9$
$4x^2 + 4x + 1 = 0$	$b^2 - 4ac = 0$ If the discriminant equals 0, there is one solution. For example: $4x^2 + 4x + 1 = 0$ $b^2 - 4ac = (4)^2 - 4 \cdot 4 \cdot 1 = 0$
$4x^2 + 3x + 1 = 0$	$b^2 - 4ac < 0$ If the discriminant is negative, there are no real solutions. For example: $4x^2 + 3x + 1 = 0$ $b^2 - 4ac = (3)^2 - 4 \cdot 4 \cdot 1 = -7$

> This can be explained using complex numbers. Remember that the discriminant is under a radical, $\sqrt{b^2 - 4ac}$. In this case, we have $\sqrt{b^2 - 4ac} = \sqrt{-7} = \sqrt{7}\sqrt{-1} = i\sqrt{7}$.

Complex Solutions to Quadratic Equations

A quadratic equation may not have real numbers as solutions. There are several algebraic ways to determine the complex solutions to quadratic equations: the square root principle, factoring, and the quadratic formula.

MODEL PROBLEMS

1. Determine the complex solutions to the quadratic equation $x^2 + 1 = 0$ using the square root principle, factoring, and the quadratic formula. Compare and contrast the solutions for each method.

SOLUTION

Square Root Principle

Isolate the variable	$x^2 = -1$	Subtract 1 from both sides to isolate the variable.
Take square root of both sides	$x = \sqrt{-1}$ or $-\sqrt{-1}$	Take the square root of both sides, and consider both positive and negative roots.
Use definition of imaginary number	$x = i$ or $-i$	Substitute using the definition of imaginary numbers. Check the solutions: $i^2 + 1 = 0$, $-1 + 1 = 0$. And checking the second solution: $(-i)^2 + 1 = 0$, $-1 + 1 = 0$.

Factoring

$x^2 + 1 = 0$ is the sum of two perfect squares and factors as $(x + i)(x - i) = 0$. The solutions are $x = i$ or $-i$.

Quadratic Formula

Identify a, b, and c	$a = 1, b = 0, c = 1$	Identify a, b, and c for this quadratic equation. b is 0 since there is no x-term.
Substitute	$x = \dfrac{-b \pm \sqrt{b^2 - 4ac}}{2a}$	Substitute a, b, and c into the quadratic formula.
	$x = \dfrac{-(0) \pm \sqrt{(0)^2 - 4(1)(1)}}{2(1)}$	
Evaluate	$x = \dfrac{0 \pm \sqrt{0 - 4}}{2}$	Do the operations and remove the perfect square from the radical.
	$x = \dfrac{0 \pm \sqrt{-4}}{2}$	All three methods arrive at the same answer: $x = i$ or $-i$.
	$x = \dfrac{\pm 2\sqrt{-1}}{2}$	
	$x = \pm \sqrt{-1}$	
	$x = \pm i$	

Model Problems continue . . .

2. Solve $2x^2 - 4x + 7 = 0$.

SOLUTION

Identify a, b, and c	$a = 2, b = -4, c = 7$	Identify a, b, and c for this quadratic equation. b is negative since it is subtracted.
Substitute	$x = \dfrac{-b \pm \sqrt{b^2 - 4ac}}{2a}$	Substitute a, b, and c into the quadratic formula.
	$x = \dfrac{-(-4) \pm \sqrt{(-4)^2 - 4(2)(7)}}{2(2)}$	
Evaluate	$x = \dfrac{4 \pm \sqrt{16 - 56}}{4}$	Multiply under the radical, subtract, and then pause. The equation has the square root of a negative number. $\sqrt{-40}$ is not a real number. This equation has no real solutions.
	$x = \dfrac{4 \pm \sqrt{-40}}{4}$	
Simplify	$x = \dfrac{4 \pm \sqrt{4}\sqrt{-10}}{4}$	Factor out the perfect square in the radicand and express the square root of -10 as imaginary number.
	$x = \dfrac{4 \pm 2\sqrt{-10}}{4}$	
	$x = 1 \pm \dfrac{\sqrt{-10}}{2}$	
	$x = 1 + \dfrac{i\sqrt{10}}{2}, 1 - \dfrac{i\sqrt{10}}{2}$	

3. Is $-1 + 2i$ a solution to $x^2 + 2x + 5 = 0$?

SOLUTION

Substitute and evaluate	$(-1 + 2i)^2 + 2(-1 + 2i) + 5 = 0$ $(1 - 4i - 4) - 2 + 4i + 5 = 0$ $0 = 0$	To see if $-1 + 2i$ is a solution, substitute and then evaluate. The two sides of the equation are equal, so $-1 + 2i$ is a solution to this equation.

4. Write an equation with $2 + i$ and $2 - i$ as solutions.

SOLUTION

State solutions	$x = 2 + i$ **or** $x = 2 - i$	These two complex numbers are solutions to the equation, so set them equal to x.
Use the zero-product property	$x - (2 + i) = 0$ **or** $x - (2 - i) = 0$ $[x - (2 + i)][(x - (2 - i)] = 0$	The zero-product property says that each factor of the left side of the equation consists of x minus one of the solutions, for both solutions. State two factors, and multiply them.
Perform multiplication	$(x - 2 - i)(x - 2 + i) = 0$ $x^2 - 4x + 4 - i^2 = 0$ $x^2 - 4x + 5 = 0$	Do the multiplication. Multiply each term in the first factor by each term in the second, and then combine like terms.

PRACTICE

1. The equation $x^2 - 5x + 2p = 0$ has only one real solution. What is p equal to?

A. No such p exists
C. $\dfrac{8}{25}$

B. $\dfrac{25}{8}$
D. 25

2. Graph the equations $y = 3x^2 - 5x - 2$ and $y = -7$. What do the graphs indicate about the solutions to the equation $3x^2 - 5x - 2 = -7$?

A. The horizontal line intersects the parabola in two places, so there are two real solutions to the equation.

B. The horizontal line intersects the parabola only at the vertex, so there is one real solution to the equation.

C. The horizontal line does not intersect the parabola, so there are two real solutions to the equation.

D. The horizontal line does not intersect the parabola, so there are no real solutions to the equation.

3. Sara is solving a quadratic equation where $ax^2 + bx + c = 0$ and $b^2 = 4a$. Sara says that if c is less than or equal to 1, the equation has two real solutions. Which statement best describes Sara's explanation?

A. She is correct because the discriminant will be real.

B. She is correct because the discriminant will be a perfect square.

C. She is wrong because the discriminant can be imaginary.

D. She is wrong because the discriminant can be zero.

4. Which of the following is true about the equation $x^2 + x + 2 = 0$?

A. There is one real root.

B. There are two distinct real roots.

C. There are two distinct complex roots.

D. There is one pure imaginary root.

5. If a quadratic equation's discriminant is -2, how many real solutions does it have?

A. 0
C. 2

B. 1
D. More than two

6. If the discriminant is zero, how many times does the graph of a quadratic equation intersect the x-axis?

A. 0
C. 2

B. 1
D. More than twice

7. How many real solutions does $-9x^2 + 6x - 1 = 0$ have?

A. 0
C. 2

B. 1
D. More than two

8. How many real solutions does $3x^2 - 12x + 2 = 0$ have?

A. 0
C. 2

B. 1
D. More than two

9. How many times does the graph of $f(x) = 3x^2 + 2x + 7$ cross the x-axis?

A. 0
C. 2

B. 1
D. More than twice

10. Which of the following is true about the equation $4x^2 + 4x + 1 = 0$?

A. The discriminant is zero.

B. The discriminant is positive.

C. The discriminant is negative.

D. Not enough information to tell.

11. Find the number of solutions by calculating the discriminant of $5x^2 + 4x + 2 = 0$.

A. No real solutions

B. One real solution

C. Two real solutions

D. Not enough information to tell

12. What are the solutions to $x^2 - 2x + 3 = 0$?

A. $1 + i\sqrt{2}, 1 - i\sqrt{2}$

B. $2 + 22i, 2 - 22i$

C. $-2 + 22, -2 - 22$

D. $1 + 42i, 1 - 42i$

13. Find a such that $(4 - 3i)a = 1$.

A. $4 + 3i$
C. $\dfrac{4}{25} - \dfrac{3}{25}i$

B. $\dfrac{1}{4} - \dfrac{1}{3}i$
D. $\dfrac{4}{25} + \dfrac{3}{25}i$

Practice Problems continue . . .

Practice Problems continued . . .

14. **MP 1, 2** On the graph of the function $y = x^2$, find the point with the smallest sum of coordinates.

15. **MP 2** Find the length of the longest segment parallel to the y-axis and lying inside the figure that is bounded by the graphs of $y = 5 - x^2$ and $y = x^2 - 3$. Sketch the figure.

16. The graphs of the functions $y = x^2 + 4x - 2$ and $y = (x + 2)^2 - 7$ are each intersected by the line $x = c$. What is the distance between the points of intersection of this line with the two graphs? Sketch the graphs.

17. Solve $\left(x - \frac{1}{x}\right)^2 - 3\left(x - \frac{1}{x}\right) - 4 = 0$, letting $y = x - \frac{1}{x}$.

18. **MP 1, 2** Can different quadratic equations of the type $ax^2 + bx + c = 0$ have the same solutions? If not, explain why not. If so, explain what the graphs of the equations will have in common and sketch the graphs.

19. State the x-intercepts of the quadratic function $f(x) = x^2 + 12x + 32$.

20. State the x-intercepts of the quadratic function $f(x) = x^2 + 5x + 6$.

21. State the x-intercepts of the quadratic function $f(x) = 28x^2 - 51x + 20$, to the nearest hundredth.

22. How many times does the graph of $f(x) = 4x^2 + 20x + 25$ intersect the x-axis?

Exercises 23–24: Find the discriminant.

23. $y = 4x^2 + 8x - 6$

24. $y = 4x^2 + 7x - 5$

Exercises 25–29: For each equation, find the discriminant and identify the number of real solutions.

25. $-4x^2 + 24x - 36 = 0$

26. $\frac{1}{2}x^2 + 5x - 12 = 0$

27. $x^2 - 7x + 15 = 0$

28. $-4x^2 + 3x + 3 = 0$

29. $64x^2 - 49 = 0$

30. How do we use the value of the discriminant to determine the number of real solutions of a quadratic equation? State the rule.

31. Write a function $f(x)$ for which the equation $f(x) = 0$ has no real solutions.

32. Find all k such that the function $y = x^2 - 2(k - 1)x + 2k + 1$ has two x-intercepts.

33. Find n such that the equation $(2n - 1)x^2 - 2(n + 1)x + \frac{1}{2}n = 0$ has only one real solution.

34. Show that if a and c have different signs, the equation $ax^2 + bx + c = 0$ always has different real solutions.

35. Solve $x^2 + 10x + 29 = 0$ using the quadratic formula.

36. **MP 3, 7** Give a general form of a quadratic equation that has only one real solution. Explain your reasoning.

Exercises 37–40: Determine if the complex number is a solution to the quadratic equation. If it is, determine the other solution.

37. Equation: $x^2 + 4x + 8 = 0$; Root: $-2 + 2i$

38. Equation: $x^2 - 12x + 37 = 0$; Root: $6 + i$

39. Equation: $x^2 + 8x + 21 = 0$; Root: $4 - i\sqrt{5}$

40. Equation: $x^2 - 9x + 25 = 0$; Root: $\frac{9}{2} + \frac{i\sqrt{19}}{2}$

Exercises 41–45: State each quadratic equation with leading coefficient 1 and the complex numbers as solutions.

41. $3i, 4 - 3i$

42. $i + 2, i - 2$

43. $5 + i\sqrt{3}, 5 - i\sqrt{3}$

44. $8 + 15i, 8 - 15i$

45. $-3 + 4i, -3 - 4i$

Exercises 46–49: Find all solutions to each equation.

46. $x^4 - 81 = 0$. Hint: First find the real solutions, then use them to write binomials that you can factor out of the original polynomial. Find the complex solutions to the quotient polynomial using the quadratic equation.

Practice Problems continue . . .

47. $x^3 - 8 = 0$

48. $x^3 + 1 = 0$

49. $x^3 + 8i = 0$

50. **MP 1, 7** What clues might you look for in a quadratic equation to determine whether there is/are:

  a One real root?

  b Two real roots?

  c Two complex roots?

51. **MP 7, 8** Consider the equation $y = x^2 - 3x + 3$.

  a Use the discriminant to determine how many roots there are to this equation and what kind they are.

  b Find the exact roots to the equation.

  c Find the roots to the nearest hundredth.

LESSON 2.7

2.7 Modeling with Quadratic Functions

Spreadsheet and Graphing Calculator: Modeling with Quadratic Functions

Some scatter plots suggest relationships between variables that are not linear. Using a spreadsheet or graphing calculator, you can determine a best-fit quadratic equation model for this set of data using *quadratic regression*. Quadratic regression determines the best values for the constants a, b, and c in the equation $y = ax^2 + bx + c$.

Spreadsheet

1. Create scatter plot. In a spreadsheet, start by entering the data and creating a scatter plot.

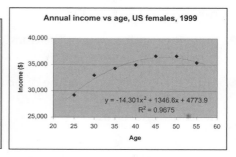

2. Use quadratic regression. Make sure the chart is selected, and then choose **Add Trendline** from the **Chart** menu. To do a quadratic regression, choose the **Polynomial** option under **Trend/Regression type** and leave the **Order** set at 2 (for quadratic). You can add the model equation and the coefficient of determination r^2 using the **Options** tab.

Graphing Calculator

1. Create scatter plot. Start by entering the data and creating a scatter plot. See the directions in chapter 1.

2. Use quadratic regression. Choose quadratic regression instead of linear regression. To do this, press STAT and then scroll right to the **CALC** menu.

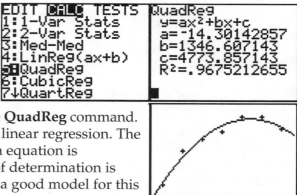

Scroll down to **5:QuadReg** and press ENTER to set up the **QuadReg** command. Then enter the parameters and do the regression as for linear regression. The calculator displays the results as shown. The regression equation is $y = -14.301x^2 + 1346.6x + 4773.9$, and the coefficient of determination is $r^2 = 0.9675$. Since r^2 is close to 1, the equation might be a good model for this data.

In this activity, you can work with both quadratic regression and artillery. What equation describes the range of a cannon as a function of the elevation angle? Create a table and then use a spreadsheet or graphing calculator to determine a quadratic equation in the form $y = ax^2 + bx + c$ and the value of r^2.

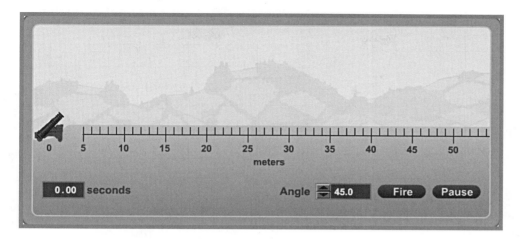

MODEL PROBLEM

 MP 2, 4 Use the data of age and income earned by U.S. females in 1999 to answer the following questions.

a Create a scatter plot.

b Use the scatter plot to describe the relationship between age and income.

c Determine the function model that best fits the data.

d Use the function model to determine the maximum amount of money females earned in 1999?

Age	Income
25	$29,663
30	$33,108
35	$34,096
40	$36,072
45	$38,643
50	$38,599
55	$37,815

SOLUTION

a
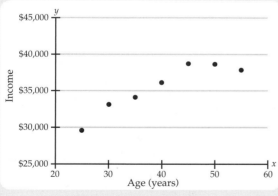

b The scatter plot relates annual income and age. In 1999, income increased as age increased, up until about age 50. After the age of 50, income decreased.

c It does not look like a line would make for a good linear model because the data points rise and then fall back again. This suggests a quadratic equation like $y = ax^2 + bx + c$ would make a better model than a linear equation. The equation from the regression is $y = -11.96x^2 + 1242.4x + 6064.4$. The r^2 is 0.966, which is high.

d To find the maximum value for the function, we need to find the vertex of the parabola. According to the quadratic regression model, the maximum amount females earned in 1999 was approximately $38,300 at around age 52.

PRACTICE

1. Find the best-fit quadratic equation for the data in the table and the coefficient of determination.

x	1	2	3	4	5	6	7	8	9
y	12	16	18	19	20	21	19	16	11

2. **MP 5, 8** Which type of equation most closely models the data in the table: linear or quadratic? Explain. Then use a graphing calculator or spreadsheet to find a best-fit equation.

x	y
8	450
10	509
14	611
15	650
16	591
19	402

3. Find a quadratic model that best fits the data using a graphing calculator.

x	0.2	0.4	0.6	0.8	1.0	1.2	1.4	1.6	1.8
y	4.7	6.5	6.8	7.1	7.9	8.1	12.3	16.1	20.9

4. Find a linear and quadratic model of best fit for the data in the table. Using the coefficient of determination, decide which model best fits the data.

x	y
0	0.56
1	1.89
2	2.91
3	5.06
4	8.11

5. The data in the table show the number of people riding a commuter train at different times of the day. Find a quadratic equation of best fit for the data.

Time	4	5	6	7	8	9	10
Number of People	20	40	70	80	70	50	30

6. **MP 4, 5** The table gives the population of Hawaii for different years. Determine the best-fit quadratic equation for the population of Hawaii for a given year. (Use 0 to represent 1900.)

Year	Population
1900	154,001
1950	499,794
1990	1,108,229
2000	1,211,537
2004	1,262,840
2006	1,285,000
2007	1,283,388

7. **MP 4, 5** The table states the price of gold for the first 20 trading days of 2009. Determine the best-fit quadratic equation for the price of gold on a given trading day.

Day	Price	Day	Price
0	$874.50	10	$833.75
1	$853.50	11	$833.00
2	$848.25	12	$853.25
3	$848.50	13	$849.25
4	$855.75	14	$860.00
5	$847.25	15	$875.75
6	$827.00	16	$910.25
7	$826.50	17	$897.50
8	$821.50	18	$895.25
9	$810.00	19	$892.25

Practice Problems continue . . .

8. The table shows the number of toy block sets sold over several weeks.

Week	Number Sold
1	1500
2	1650
3	1800
4	1920
5	2060
6	2300
7	2200
8	2090
9	1980
10	1800

a Find the best-fit quadratic equation for the data.

b Find and interpret the coefficient of determination, r^2, for the quadratic model.

c A student says a linear model would better fit the data because for the first seven weeks, the number of toys sold increases. The linear model of best fit has a coefficient of determination of 0.558. Based on this, does a linear equation appear to best model the data?

9. Use the tables to answer the questions.

Table 1: The path of a football thrown in the air for two seconds.

Time (s)	0	0.4	0.6	1	1.2	1.6	1.8	2.0
Height (m)	2	4.5	5.3	5.8	5.6	4.0	2.8	1.2

Table 2: The path of a football thrown in the air that meets a gust of wind at 1.6 seconds.

Time (s)	0	0.4	0.6	1	1.2	1.6	1.8	2.0
Height (m)	2	4.5	5.3	5.8	5.6	5.8	6.0	5.8

a Find the best-fit quadratic equation for Table 1.

b Find the best-fit quadratic equation for Table 2.

c For which table does a quadratic model better fit the data? How do you know?

d Graph the equations of best fit for both tables. Compare and contrast the graphs with relation to the path of the football.

10. **MP 3** Consider the data in the table.

x	2	4	6	8	10	12	14	16	18
y	4	16	36	64	100	152	200	300	412

Meredith says the equation of best fit for the table is $y = x^2$ because more than half of the data points fit this equation exactly. April uses a graphing calculator to find a quadratic equation of best fit. Find April's equation and decide which equation better fits the data. Explain your reasoning.

MP 2, 4 The students in Ms. May's physics class launched air rockets at various angles to determine the optimum angle for reaching the farthest distance. Here is one group's data:

Launch Angle (degrees)	Distance Traveled (yards)
10°	58
15°	80
30°	126
35°	136
40°	141
45°	141
50°	139
55°	132
60°	120

a Make a scatter plot of the data.
b Find the equation of a quadratic equation that best matches the data.
c Is your equation a good representation of the data? Why or why not?
d Use the equation to predict the distance a rocket launched at an angle of 75° would travel.

LESSON 2.8

2.8 Parabolas at the Origin

Geometric Definition of a Parabola

A basic type of parabola can be described by a quadratic equation of the form $y = ax^2$. A parabola of this form has its vertex at the origin, opens up or down, and has the y-axis as its axis of symmetry.

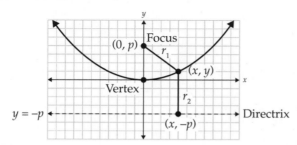

A parabola can also be described geometrically using a line and a point:

Set of points equidistant from a fixed point as it is from a fixed line	$r_1 = r_2$	A parabola is the set of all points in a plane where each point is the same distance from a point as it is from a line. We call these two distances r_1 and r_2.
Point is focus	$(0, p)$	The point the distance is measured from is called the **focus of the parabola**. With a parabola that opens up and with its vertex at the origin, the focus is at $(0, p)$.
Line is directrix	$y = -p$	The line is called the **directrix**. With a parabola that opens up and with its vertex at the origin, it is the line $y = -p$.

We derive an equation for a parabola from its geometric definition. We start with a parabola that opens up with its vertex at the origin.

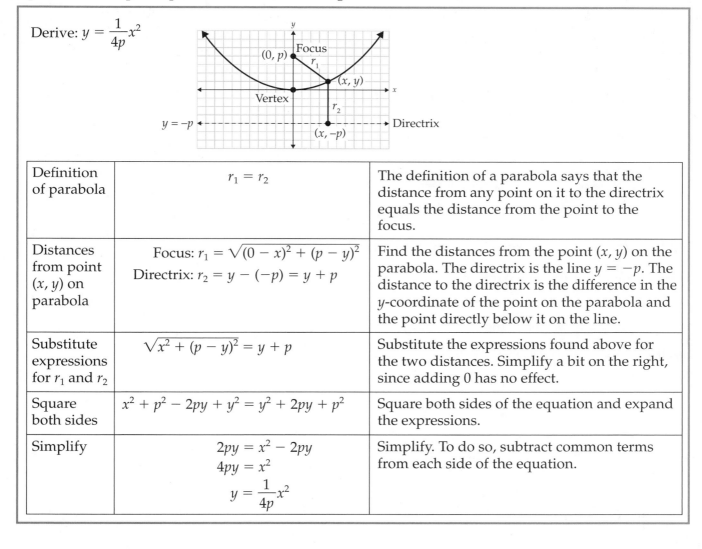

Derive: $y = \dfrac{1}{4p}x^2$

Definition of parabola	$r_1 = r_2$	The definition of a parabola says that the distance from any point on it to the directrix equals the distance from the point to the focus.
Distances from point (x, y) on parabola	Focus: $r_1 = \sqrt{(0 - x)^2 + (p - y)^2}$ Directrix: $r_2 = y - (-p) = y + p$	Find the distances from the point (x, y) on the parabola. The directrix is the line $y = -p$. The distance to the directrix is the difference in the y-coordinate of the point on the parabola and the point directly below it on the line.
Substitute expressions for r_1 and r_2	$\sqrt{x^2 + (p - y)^2} = y + p$	Substitute the expressions found above for the two distances. Simplify a bit on the right, since adding 0 has no effect.
Square both sides	$x^2 + p^2 - 2py + y^2 = y^2 + 2py + p^2$	Square both sides of the equation and expand the expressions.
Simplify	$2py = x^2 - 2py$ $4py = x^2$ $y = \dfrac{1}{4p}x^2$	Simplify. To do so, subtract common terms from each side of the equation.

The activity shows the focus and directrix, which define the parabola. The parabola can open up, down, left, or right.

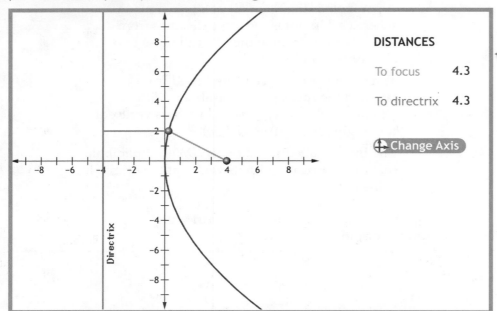

DISTANCES

To focus   4.3

To directrix   4.3

⊕ Change Axis

The distances to the focus and to the directrix are always equal for any point on the parabola.

Graphing a Parabola at the Origin

The equation for a parabola, $y = \dfrac{1}{4p}x^2$, can be used to

determine some of its important properties. The constant p can be positive or negative. Its sign determines whether the parabola opens up or down $\left(\text{for } y = \dfrac{1}{4p}x^2\right)$ or right or

left $\left(\text{for } x = \dfrac{1}{4p}y^2\right)$. These equations are in the **standard**

form of the equation for a parabola centered at the origin.

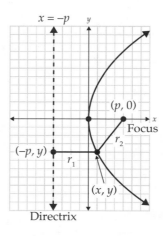

In this activity, you will move the focus, and you will see the equation and the value of p change.

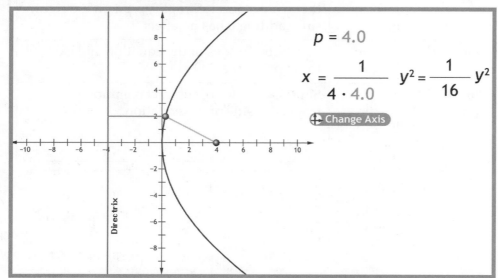

$p = 4.0$

$$x = \dfrac{1}{4 \cdot 4.0} \quad y^2 = \dfrac{1}{16} y^2$$

⊕ Change Axis

In this activity, enter the coordinates of the focus and the equation of the directrix and see how they affect the parabola's graph.

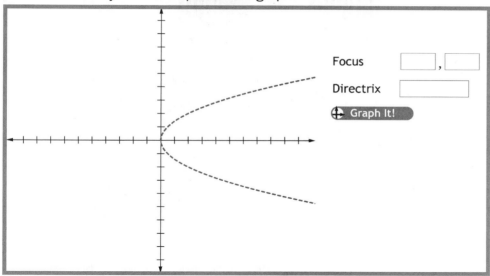

Focus [   ] , [   ]

Directrix [   ]

⊕ Graph It!

We summarize some key properties of parabolas located at the origin:

Equation	Vertex	Axis of Symmetry	Orientation
$y = \dfrac{1}{4p}x^2, p > 0$	$(0, 0)$	Vertical	Up
$y = \dfrac{1}{4p}x^2, p < 0$	$(0, 0)$	Vertical	Down
$x = \dfrac{1}{4p}y^2, p > 0$	$(0, 0)$	Horizontal	Right
$x = \dfrac{1}{4p}y^2, p < 0$	$(0, 0)$	Horizontal	Left

MODEL PROBLEMS

1. Parabola H is defined by the equation $y = \dfrac{1}{16}x^2$, and parabola G is defined by the equation $x = -y^2$. Select the true statement.

   A. Parabola H would have a vertical axis of symmetry, and parabola G would have a horizontal axis of symmetry.
   B. Parabola H would be steeper (more rapidly changing curve) than parabola G.
   C. Both A and B are true.
   D. Neither A nor B is true.

SOLUTION

The answer is A. With y equal to an expression with a squared x-term, it is a vertical parabola, and its axis of symmetry is vertical, which makes the first half of answer A true. With x equal to a squared y-term, parabola G would be a horizontal parabola (opening to the left due to the negative sign). Its axis of symmetry would be horizontal. Parabola H is not steeper than parabola G, since its coefficient has a lesser absolute value, so statement B is false. That makes answer C false, and D is false since statement A is true.

Model Problems continue . . .

2. **MP 2, 5, 7** Graph $x = -\dfrac{1}{8}y^2$ using properties determined from its equation.

SOLUTION

Calculate p	$4p = -8, p = -2$	The squared term is multiplied by $-\dfrac{1}{8}$. This means $4p = -8$, so $p = -2$.
Determine axis of symmetry	x-axis since y is squared	y is squared so this will be a horizontal parabola.
Calculate directrix and focus	directrix: $x = -p = 2$ focus: $(p, 0) = (-2, 0)$	The vertex is at the origin. The directrix is a vertical line since the parabola is horizontal. Write the equation for the directrix. It is $x = -p$, which is $x = 2$.

Graph

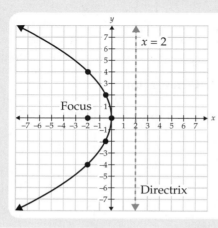

x	y
0	0
$-\dfrac{1}{2}$	2
-2	4
$-\dfrac{1}{2}$	-2
-2	-4

Plot points and then draw the curve. Note that we can use the symmetry of the parabola to help us. The x-values are the same for $y = 4$ and $y = -4$.

3. State the equation for the graph shown.

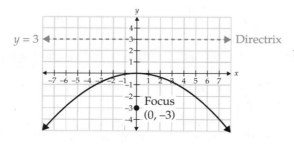

> With this problem, we can see where the focus and directrix are. We use that information to calculate p and then state the parabola's equation.

SOLUTION

Focus	$(0, p)$ $p = -3$	The focus is at $(0, p)$ for a vertical parabola. Since the focus of this parabola is at $(0, -3)$, $p = -3$.
Substitute into equation	$y = \dfrac{1}{4p}x^2$ $y = \dfrac{1}{4(-3)}x^2$ $y = -\dfrac{1}{12}x^2$	Since the parabola is vertical, the x-term is squared. Substitute the value of p. Then simplify by multiplying.

Model Problems continue . . .

4. **MP 4** An antenna, like the one to the right, reflects signals from distant sources such as orbiting satellites to a receiver on a pole in front of the dish. A cross-section of the antenna is a parabola. The parabola causes the reflected signals to concentrate at the focus of the parabola, where the receiver is located. Parabolic antennas are superior to spherical ones, which focus the signal less precisely.

Reflectors with parabolic cross-sections, including parabolic troughs, are also used to concentrate solar energy in order to generate electricity. In the photo to the right, you see one being assembled. The stated goal of the company financing the system is to build 20,000 reflectors, each capable of producing about 150 kilowatts of power.

Use the graph to state an equation for the reflector and calculate the reflector's diameter, which is its horizontal distance across the reflector at its focus. The diameter of a parabola is also called the *latus rectum*.

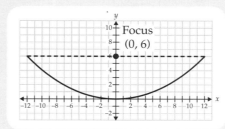

> The *focal length* is the distance from the vertex to the focus.

SOLUTION

Substitute p into parabola equation	$y = \dfrac{1}{4p}x^2$ $y = \dfrac{1}{4p}x^2 = \dfrac{1}{4 \cdot 6}x^2 = \dfrac{1}{24}x^2$	State an equation for the parabolic reflector described by the graph.
To find radius, solve equation for x	$24y = x^2$ $x = 2\sqrt{6y}$	The radius at the focus is the horizontal distance from the focus to the reflector. To calculate the radius, solve the equation for x.
Substitute	$x = 2\sqrt{6y} = 2\sqrt{6 \cdot 6} = 12$ diameter $= 2x = 24$ units	Substitute. The radius at the focus is 12 units. Double the radius to calculate the diameter, which is 24 units.

Model Problems continue . . .

5. **MP 2, 3, 4** The function $f(t) = -0.5(t - 9)^2 + 12$ describes the vertical position of a ball on the moon's surface over time, with t representing time in seconds, and $f(t)$ the position in meters. The function is only used to describe the time when the ball is at the level of the moon (0 meters) or higher.

    a Graph this function, showing only the time the ball is above the surface of the moon (which is at 0 meters).

    b What are the approximate domain and range of the function?

    c Show how a line can be used to estimate the times when the ball is 5 meters high.

    d Using the concept of an inequality, highlight the parts of the graph that represent when the ball is 5 meters or lower. Explain your reasoning.

SOLUTION

    a

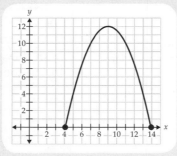

    b The domain is from about 4 seconds to about 14 seconds—that is when the ball is above the earth. The range is 0 to 12 meters. The maximum height 12 is the vertex, which can be determined from the k, the $+12$, that is added to the function.

    c

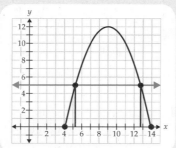

    d

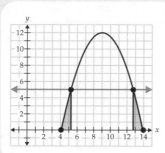

        The ball is 5 meters or lower when $4 \le x \le 5.2$ and $12.8 \le x \le 14$. Between $5.2 < x < 12.8$, the ball is above 5 meters.

PRACTICE

Exercises 1–6: For each equation, determine in which direction the parabola opens.

1. $y = -5x^2$

    A. Opens up   C. Opens left
    B. Opens down   D. Opens right

2. $y = 3x^2$

    A. Opens up   C. Opens left
    B. Opens down   D. Opens right

3. $x = 3y^2$

    A. Opens up   C. Opens left
    B. Opens down   D. Opens right

4. $x = -5y^2$

    A. Opens up   C. Opens left
    B. Opens down   D. Opens right

5. $y = -2x^2$

    A. Opens up   C. Opens left
    B. Opens down   D. Opens right

6. $y = -3x^2$

    A. Opens up   C. Opens left
    B. Opens down   D. Opens right

7. The receiver of a parabolic television dish antenna is located at the focus. The cross section of the reflector is modeled by $y = \dfrac{1}{14}x^2$ (in feet). What is the distance from the lowest point on the reflector to the receiver?

    A. 7 ft   C. 14 ft
    B. 3.5 ft   D. 28 ft

8. A parabola's focus is at $\left(0, -\dfrac{5}{4}\right)$ and its directrix is at $y = \dfrac{5}{4}$. What is the equation for the parabola? State your answer in the standard form of an equation for a parabola at the origin.

9. A parabola has an equation $y = \dfrac{3}{8}x^2$. Where is its focus?

10. A parabola has an equation $y = \dfrac{7}{4}x^2$. Where is its focus?

11. A parabola has an equation $y = \dfrac{5}{16}x^2$. Where is its focus?

12. A parabola's focus is at $(0, 2)$ and its directrix is at $y = -2$. What is the equation for the parabola?

13. A parabola's focus is at $\left(0, -\dfrac{1}{12}\right)$ and its directrix is at $y = \dfrac{1}{12}$. What is the equation for the parabola?

14. A parabola has an equation $y = 2x^2$. Where is its focus?

15. [MP 4] A parabolic trough collects solar energy. The mirrored trough has a parabolic cross-section. Its focus is shown on the graph. Write an equation for the trough with its vertex at the origin.

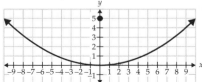

16. What is the vertex of the parabola described by $y = -ax^2$?

Exercises 17–20: Find the vertex, axis of symmetry, and directrix of the parabolas.

17. $y = 4x^2$

18. $y = 3x^2$

19. $x = -2y^2$

20. $x = 3y^2$

Practice Problems continue . . .

Exercises 21–22: Graph the equations. Draw and label the focus and directrix for each parabola.

21. $y = \frac{1}{4}x^2$

22. $x = -y^2$

Exercises 23–24: State the equation for each parabola.

23. Focus at $(-9, 0)$ and directrix is $x = 9$.

24. Focus at $(0, 8)$ and directrix is $y = -8$.

Exercises 25–27: Each parabola described has its vertex at the origin. State the equation of each parabola in standard form and graph it.

25. The focus of the parabola is $\left(0, \frac{5}{4}\right)$.

26. The focus of the parabola is $(-3, 0)$.

27. The directrix of the parabola is $y = \frac{3}{4}$.

28. MP 3 Does any parabola intersect its directrix? If so, give an example of such a parabola. If not, explain why not.

29. MP 3 Dina wants to find the directrix of a parabola which has its vertex at the origin and its focus on the horizontal axis. She writes the equation for the directrix in the form $y = a$. Will this be a correct equation for the directrix?

30. MP 3 Prove that the equation for a horizontal parabola can be written $x = \frac{1}{4p}y^2$, where $(p, 0)$ is the focus and $x = -p$ is the directrix.

Chapter 2 Key Ideas

2.1 Algebra 1 Review: Factoring Polynomials

- To factor a polynomial means to state it as a product of polynomials.

2.2 Polynomial Patterns

- A polynomial is called a *sum of cubes* if its terms are two perfect cubes which are added, and a *difference of cubes* if it is one perfect cube subtracted from another.

2.3 Patterns and Equations

- If you know that the product of two numbers is 0, you know that at least one of the factors must be 0. This is called the *zero-product property*.

2.4 Algebra 1 Review: The Quadratic Formula

- One technique for solving quadratic equations uses a method called *completing the square*. To complete the square means to add a constant to a binomial to create a perfect square trinomial.
- Any quadratic equation can be written in the standard form $ax^2 + bx + c = 0$. The solutions to a quadratic equation in standard form can be calculated using the quadratic formula,

$$x = \frac{-b \pm \sqrt{b^2 - 4ac}}{2a}.$$

2.5 Imaginary and Complex Numbers

- Because the square of a real number is never negative, negative numbers do not have square roots in the real numbers. However, real numbers are a subset of a set called the *complex numbers*, and negative numbers do have square roots in the complex numbers. In the complex number system, $\sqrt{-1}$ exists and mathematicians use the symbol i to represent it.

- Adding and subtracting complex numbers is like adding and subtracting binomials in that you combine like terms. You combine the real parts and the imaginary parts (the coefficients of i) separately. To multiply square roots with negative radicands, restate the factors using i.

- Complex conjugates are complex numbers with the same real parts, and imaginary parts that are opposites.

2.6 Solutions of Quadratic Equations

- The expression under the radical in the quadratic equation, $b^2 - 4ac$, is called the *discriminant* of the quadratic equation. It determines how many real number solutions the quadratic equation has.

- The x-intercepts of the parabola $f(x) = ax^2 + bx + c$ are the real solutions to the quadratic equation $ax^2 + bx + c = 0$ because these are the points representing the real numbers for which the value of the function is zero. We can find the x-intercepts by setting $f(x)$ equal to 0 and solving.

- Equations can have complex numbers as solutions. If the discriminant of a real-coefficient quadratic equation is negative, the equation has complex solutions.

2.7 Modeling with Quadratic Functions

- To check if a model is sufficiently adequate, use quadratic regression.

2.8 Parabolas at the Origin

- A parabola is defined geometrically as the set of points which are equidistant from a point called the *focus* and a line called the *directrix*.

- A parabola with the y-axis as its axis of symmetry, a focus at $(0, p)$, and the directrix of $y = -p$, is defined with the formula $y = \dfrac{1}{4p}x^2$. If p is positive, the parabola will open up. If p is negative, it will open down. If the variables x and y are switched, the parabola is horizontal rather than vertical and has the x-axis as its axis of symmetry, its focus at $(p, 0)$, and the directrix of $x = -p$. In this case, the parabola will open right if p is positive and left if p is negative.

CHAPTER 2 REVIEW

1. **MP 2** Solve the equation $(x + 3)^2 = a$ using the square root principle. If it is given that a is a positive real number, which best describes the solution(s) to the equation?

   A. One real solution
   B. Two real solutions
   C. Only negative solutions
   D. Only non-real solutions

2. **MP 2** To solve a quadratic equation, a student graphs the function. Determine the discriminant of the quadratic equation.

   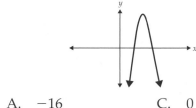

   A. -16 C. 0
   B. -5 D. 16

Chapter Review continues . . .

Exercises 3–6: Factor.

3. $x^8 + 12x^4 + 36$

4. $x^6 + 8x^3 + 16$

5. $343x^3 + 216$

6. $125x^3 + 216$

7. Find the formula for the square of a sum of three numbers a, b, and c. Justify your answer.

8. **MP 1** The square of the sum of two consecutive positive numbers is 112 greater than the sum of their squares. What are those numbers?

Exercises 9–12: Solve.

9. $7x^2 + 70x + 147 = 0$

10. $9x^2 - 16 = 0$

11. $4x^2 - 64 = 0$

12. $9x^2 - 25 = 0$

13. **MP 3** Explain why the quadratic equation $3x^2 - 18x + 10 = 0$ cannot have a negative number as a solution.

14. For which values of m are the solutions to the equation $x^2 - (5m^2 - 4m)x + 25m^2 - 16 = 0$ equal to zero?

15. Dorothy says she found solutions to the quadratic equation $3x^2 + 18x + 10 = 0$. "Are they positive or negative?" asked her friend Xavier. "Both are positive," said Dorothy. "Sorry, but there must be some mistake in your calculations!" Xavier exclaimed. How did he know that?

16. **MP 4** Two riders start at the same point and begin moving away from each other along two roads that form a right angle. The riders' speeds are 12 mph and 16 mph. When will the distance between the riders be equal to 80 miles?

17. Find the value of a such that the equation $(a + 1)x^2 + 6x + 3 = 0$ has only one real solution. Find this solution. Graph if necessary.

18. Graph the points (x, y) such that the equation $2t^2 + 4(x - 3)t + 2y = 0$ has only one real solution for t.

19. For which values of m do the graphs of the functions $y = x^2 - mx + 4$ and $y = x^2 - 19x + 9$ not intersect? Graph if necessary.

20. Show that the quadratic equation $ax^2 + bx + c = 0$, where $a \neq 0$, has two different real solutions of the same sign if $a \cdot c > 0$ and $b^2 - 4ac > 0$.

Exercises 21–22: Multiply.

21. $(5 + 4i)(7 - i)$

22. $(6 + 2i)(2i - 4)$

Exercises 23–24: Determine the complex conjugate of each expression.

23. $-3 + 4i$

24. $-12 - 3i$

25. Multiply $-6 - i$ by its complex conjugate and state the result.

Exercises 26–27: Solve.

26. $5 = 2x - ix$

27. $13 = -3x - 2ix$

28. Draw a diagram showing the relationships between the following types of numbers: complex, imaginary, real, rational, and irrational.

Exercises 29–30: For each equation, find the discriminant and identify the number of real solutions.

29. $-4x^2 + 24x - 36 = 0$

30. $\frac{1}{2}x^2 + 5x - 12 = 0$

31. A parabola's focus is at $(0, 5)$ and its directrix is at $y = -5$. Find the y-coordinates of the points on the parabola with the x-coordinates 10 and -10.

32. A parabola's focus is at $\left(0, -\frac{3}{2}\right)$ and its directrix is at $y = \frac{3}{2}$. What is the equation for the parabola? State your answer in the standard form of an equation for a parabola at the origin.

Cumulative Review
for Chapters 1-2

1. This graph shows _____ correlation.

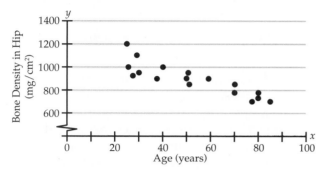

 A. Negative
 B. Positive
 C. No

2. The graph shows the relationship between the retail cost of a bag of Rainier cherries and the weight. Approximately how much would Tara pay for 9 pounds of cherries?

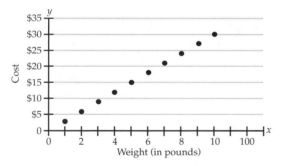

 A. $15
 B. $17
 C. $24
 D. $27
 E. $30

3. Determine if there is a negative, positive, or no correlation between the number of siblings someone has and their grade in school.

 A. Positive
 B. Negative
 C. No Correlation

4. Researchers found that there was a negative correlation between the mean SAT scores of high school seniors in each state and the percentage of graduates in each state who took the test. Which of the following must be correct?

 A. The SAT scores are higher in states where the percentage of graduates who took the test is higher.
 B. There is no association between the SAT scores in the state and the percentage of graduates who took the test.
 C. The SAT scores tend to be higher in states where the percentage of graduates who took the test is lower.
 D. The SAT scores tend to be lower in states where the percentage of graduates who took the test is lower.

5. If its discriminant is positive and real, how many times does the graph of a quadratic function cross the x-axis?

 A. Zero times
 B. Once
 C. Twice
 D. More than two times

6. The solutions to $x^2 + 4x + 5 = 0$ are

 A. $i, -i$
 B. $-2 + i, 2 - i$
 C. $-4 + 2i, 4 - 2i$
 D. $-2 + 2i, -2 - 2i$

7. What is the domain of the function $f(x) = x$? Justify your reasoning.

8. What is the range of the function $f(x) = x$? Justify your reasoning.

9. What does the graph of $f(x - 4) + 2$ look like compared to the graph of $f(x)$?

10. What does the graph of $f(x + 3) - 7$ look like compared to the graph of $f(x)$?

11. **MP 2, 3** Alejandro is collecting data to make a scatter plot. He wants to collect data that will show a negative correlation. If one of his variables is daily temperature, name another variable that could result in a scatter plot with a negative correlation.

12. **MP 5, 6** Calculate the linear regression equation for the data. Round all values to the nearest thousandth.

Standing Height	Kneeling Height
58	44
70	53
66	50
67	50
64	48
73	55
62	47
64	48
68	51
66	50

13. **MP 2, 7** A researcher analyzed data on the costs of producing an online test preparation program. She found the line of best fit to be $c = 90{,}000 + 15.95n$, where c is the total cost (in dollars) of serving n students. Interpret the meaning of the two numbers in this equation.

14. **a** Given the constraints $x + 3y \leq 15$; $2x + y \leq 10$; $x \geq 0$; $y \geq 0$; and that the objective function $z = x + y$ has a maximum value of $z = 7$, graph the corresponding relationship between x and y for this maximum.

    b Use the graph from part **a** to determine the point in the feasible region that yields the maximum value of the objective function. Explain how you arrived at your answer.

15. **MP 1** A juice plant produces apple juice and applesauce from 70,000 pounds of apples per day. To produce a can of juice, 1 pound of apples is needed, while only one-third of a pound is needed to produce a can of sauce. The cans are packed into boxes, 24 cans per box. The storage facilities only allow for 2000 boxes of juice and 6500 boxes of sauce a day. The plant sells a box of juice for $18, and a box of applesauce for $9. How many pounds of apples should be used for each type of product to maximize the plant's revenues?

16. Tina counts on her energy bars to provide some calories and vitamins in her diet. She wants to get at least 400 calories, 60 units of vitamin A, and 70 units of vitamin C per day from the bars. She likes two types of energy bars: Coolbar, which costs $1.15 per bar, and Extrabar, which costs $1.05 per bar. The Coolbar provides 80 calories, 10 units of vitamin A, and 30 units of vitamin C. The Extrabar provides 80 calories, 15 units of vitamin A, and 10 units of vitamin C. How many bars of each kind should Tina eat to minimize the cost and meet her dietary requirements? How much will her bars cost per day?

Exercises 17–22: Factor.

17. $z^{12} - 64$

18. $z^{12} - 125$

19. $z^{12} - 8$

20. $20x^4 + 100x^3 + 120x^2$

21. $512y^3 - 343$

22. $64y^3 - 125$

Exercises 23–24: Solve.

23. $x^2 - 8x + 16 = 64$

24. $x^2 + 12x + 36 = 14$

25. What is the complex conjugate of $-5 + 6i$?

Exercises 26–28: Graph each function.

26. $y = 6x - 1 - 3x^2$

27. $y = (2 - x)(x - 6)$

28. $y = x^2 - 4x + 4$

29. Find the discriminant and identify the number of real solutions: $x^2 - 7x + 15 = 0$

30. A parabola has a vertex at the origin and opens upward. What is the equation of the directrix if the focus point is $(0, 7)$?

31. A parabola's focus is at $(0, -2)$ and its directrix is at $y = 2$. What is the equation for the parabola?

Chapter 3 Polynomials

Chapter Content

Vocabulary

cubic equation	fundamental theorem of algebra	quartic equation
Descartes' rule of signs	linear factorization theorem	remainder theorem
factor theorem	multivariable polynomial	synthetic division

LESSON 3.1

3.1 Multivariable Polynomials

A polynomial like $3x^2 + 2x$ has just one variable, x. In chapter 2, you factored polynomials such as $5x^3y^2 + 2x^4y + yz$, called **multivariable polynomials**. In this section we add, subtract, and multiply multivariable polynomials.

MODEL PROBLEMS

1. What is the degree of the multivariable monomial $5x^3y^2$?

SOLUTION

Degree = sum of powers of all variables

$5x^3y^2$
$3 + 2 = 5$
Degree is 5

> Many of the same principles discussed for one-variable polynomials still apply. What is different? To calculate the degree of a monomial, you have to add the powers of all the variables.

The degree of a multivariable monomial is the sum of the powers of all the variables. The power of the variable x is 3, and the power of the variable y is 2. The sum of these powers is $3 + 2 = 5$. The degree of the monomial $5x^3y^2$ is 5.

2. What is the degree of the multivariable polynomial $5x^3y^2 + 2x^4y + yz$?

SOLUTION

Compute degrees of each term to determine largest

$5x^3y^2$ degree is $3 + 2 = 5$
$2x^4y$ degree is $4 + 1 = 5$
yz degree is $1 + 1 = 2$

Calculate the degree of each term in the polynomial by adding the powers in each term. The degree of the first term is 5, since the sum of the powers is $3 + 2$. Calculate the degrees of the other terms by summing their powers.

Largest degree is degree of polynomial

Degree is 5

The largest degree of any term is 5, so the degree of the polynomial is 5.

> The degree of a polynomial is the largest degree of any of the terms.

Combining Like Terms in Multivariable Polynomials

Like terms must have exactly the same variables *and* the same power of each variable. When there is more than one variable, compare the exponents of each variable.

Both single and multivariable polynomials can be simplified by combining like terms. To combine, you add or subtract the coefficients of the like terms.

MODEL PROBLEMS

1. Which terms of the polynomial $5xy^2 - 2xy^2 + 3x^3y + x^2z$ are like terms?

SOLUTION

$5xy^2$ and $-2xy^2$ are like terms — Like terms have the same variables to the same powers. Apply the test to the first two terms, $5xy^2$ and $-2xy^2$. Both have x to the first power, and y to the second, and no other variables. Since they have the same variables to the same powers, they are like terms.

$3x^3y$ has no like terms — The term $3x^3y$ is the only term with x^3 in it. Other terms have the variable x, but not to the third power. This means it has no like terms.

x^2z has no like terms — The term x^2z is the only one with the variable z. This means there are no like terms to this term.

2. Combine the like terms of $5xy^2 - 2xy^2 + 3x^2y$.

SOLUTION

Identify like terms $\quad 5xy^2 - 2xy^2 + 3x^2y \quad$ The first two terms have xy^2 as their variable factors, so they are like terms. The third term has no like terms, since $3x^2y$ has the same variables x and y, but to different powers than the other terms.

Combine like terms $\quad 3xy^2 + 3x^2y \quad$ Combine the like terms $5xy^2$ and $-2xy^2$ by adding the coefficients. Since $5 + (-2) = 3$, the combined term is $3xy^2$. The simplified polynomial is written in standard form.

> The standard form of a polynomial is written in descending degree order. In a multivariable polynomial, write the terms in descending degree order of one of the variables.

PRACTICE

Exercises 1–3: For each polynomial, determine which type of polynomial it is: monomial, binomial, or trinomial.

1. $3x + y^2$

2. $12x^2zy^5$

3. $10x^2 + xy - 7z$

Exercises 4–9: Determine the degree of each expression.

4. $2x^2y$

5. $15x^4y^2z$

6. $2y^2z^3$

7. $14x^3 + 3y^2 + 5x^2y^4$

Practice Problems continue . . .

Practice Problems continued . . .

8. $2x^3y^6 + 4y^7 - 8xy$

9. $5y^5z - 13z + 10$

Exercises 10–16: Determine whether the monomials are like terms. Then add the monomials and write the sum in standard form.

10. $3x^2y$ and x^2y

11. $4x^3z$ and $4x^3$

12. $11xz^8$ and $-2xyz^8$

13. $5x^4y^3z$ and $-2x^4y^3z$

14. $27yz$ and $37yz$

15. xyz^2 and xyz^2

16. $15x^6y^2z$ and $7x^6yz^2$

Exercises 17–30: Combine any like terms.

17. $7xy + 5xy$

18. $5x^2y - 7x^2y$

19. $11xy^3 + 6xy^3$

20. $5x + 7x^2z - 2x^2z$

21. $13x^2y^2 + 2x^2y^2 + xy$

22. $9xz^3 - 3xz^3 + xz^3$

23. $4y^3z^2 + 5y^3z^2 - 17$

24. $13xyz + 2xyz - 3yz$

25. $5xz^2 + 11x - 2xz^2$

26. $-2x^4y^5 + 13xy - 7x^4y^5$

27. $5x^2y^2 + 5x^3y^3$

28. $9xy + 3yz + 3xz$

29. $4x^2 - 2xy - 2xy - y^2$

30. $3x^2 + xy - 6xy - 2y^2$

Evaluating Multivariable Polynomials

To evaluate a multivariable polynomial, replace each variable with that variable's value. Then follow the order of operations to evaluate the polynomial.

MODEL PROBLEMS

1. Evaluate $5xy^2 + 2x^2y + 3xy$ when $x = 3$ and $y = -1$.

SOLUTION

Substitute for x	$5(3)y^2 - 2(3)^2y + 3(3)y$	We choose to substitute for x first.
Substitute for y	$5(3)(-1)^2 - 2(3)^2(-1) + 3(3)(-1)$	Substitute for y.
Do the operations	$5(3)(1) - 2(9)(-1) + 3(3)(-1)$ $15 - (-18) + (-9)$ $15 + 18 - 9$ 24	Using the order of operations, first apply exponents. Next multiply, then add and subtract left to right to get 24.

2. Simplify $5xy^2$ when $x = 2$.

SOLUTION

| Substitute known values | $5xy^2$ $5(2)y^2$ | Substitute the given value, $x = 2$. |
| Multiply | $10y^2$ | Simplify. |

> With multivariable polynomials, only some of the values of the variables may be known. You can evaluate or simplify the polynomial using the known variables. The values we do not know stay in the polynomial as variables.

PRACTICE

Exercises 1–28: Evaluate and simplify.

1. $x^3 - 4xy$ for $x = 2, y = 5$

2. $2xy - x^2z$ for $x = 1, y = 3, z = -2$

3. $5xyz - 3xy^2$ for $x = 5, y = 2, z = 3$

4. $3x^2y^2 + 2xz^2$ for $x = -2, y = 4, z = 6$

5. $3x^3 - y^2 + xz - 10$ for $x = 2, y = 3, z = 10$

6. $8y^2z - 4x + 6z^2$ for $x = 5, y = -2, z = 10$

7. $5x^2 - 6y + 3z^2y - 76$ for $x = 0, y = 4, z = -5$

8. $xyz - xy - xz + yz$ for $x = 3, y = 4, z = 5$

9. $\frac{1}{2}x^3z - \frac{3}{2}yz + xy^2 + 5$ for $x = 3, y = -1,$ $z = 2$

10. $4x^2z - 3y^2z - xy$ for $x = 5, y = -2, z = 7$

11. $3x^2y$ for $x = 10$

12. $11x + 3yx$ for $x = 3$

13. $-9xy + 6z + 1$ for $x = 2, z = 4$

14. $x^2y + 2yz$ for $z = 8$

15. $8x - 2xy^2 + xz$ for $x = 5, y = -4$

16. $5 + 2xz^2 + x$ for $x = 3$

17. $4x - 2xy + 7yz$ for $x = -3, y = 4$

18. $11z^2 + 8y + 10xyz$ for $y = 5$

19. $-8 + 5xy + z^3y^2$ for $x = 3, z = -2$

20. $x^3 + 3xy^2 + 3x^2y + y^3$ for $y = 5$

21. $3x + 7xy^2 + y^2$ for $y = -1$

22. $7xyz - 3xy$ for $x = 3, z = -2$

23. $4x^2y - 5yz^3 + 2$ for $x = 5, z = 2$

24. $6xy^2 + 3xz - y^2z$ for $x = 2, y = -2$

25. $-3xy^2 + 5x^2z + 3z$ for $x = 3$

26. $4xyz - 6xz + y^3 + 1$ for $y = 2$

27. $4x^3z + 5yz - yx$ for $x = -1, y = 4$

28. $x^3y - xyz - 6xy + 8y$ for $x = 3$

Operations with Multivariable Polynomials

You can perform operations with multivariable polynomials the same way you do polynomials in one variable.

MODEL PROBLEMS

MP 7 Exercises 1–2: Simplify.

1. $(2x^2y + 3x + 9) + (-x^2y + 5y - 2x - 11)$

SOLUTION

Write polynomial in descending order for x

$(2x^2y + 3x + 9) + (-x^2y + 5y - 2x - 11)$

$2x^2y - x^2y + 3x - 2x + 5y + 9 - 11$

Remove the parentheses and write the polynomial in descending order for the variable x.

> You can subtract multivariable polynomials by determining the additive inverse of each term of the subtracted polynomial, and then adding the resulting polynomials.

Combine like terms

$x^2y + x + 5y - 2$

Combine like terms, $2x^2y$ and $-x^2y$ to get x^2y. Combine the like terms $3x$ and $-2x$ to get x. Combine the constants 9 and -11 to get -2. The resulting polynomial has no like terms and is in descending order, so we are done.

Model Problems continue . . .

2. $(5a^2 + ab)(3a - 2ab)$

SOLUTION

Multiply using FOIL $(5a^2 + ab)(3a - 2ab)$

$(5a^2)(3a) + (5a^2)(-2ab) + (ab)(3a) + (ab)(-2ab)$

Start by multiplying the first term of each binomial, $5a^2$ and $3a$. Multiply the outer terms $5a^2$ and $-2ab$ and add their product to the first product. Do the same with the inner terms and the last terms of the binomials, adding their products to the expression.

> To multiply multivariable binomials using FOIL, multiply the First, Outer, Inner, and Last terms of the binomials. Simplify the monomial products by multiplying the coefficients and the variables in each term, and combine like terms.

Simplify products $15a^3 - (10a^3b) + 3a^2b - 2a^2b^2$

Simplify the result by multiplying the first terms, $(5a^2)(3a)$, the outer terms, $(5a^2)(-2ab)$, the inner terms, $(ab)(3)$, and the last terms, $(ab)(-2ab)$. Add the products and simplify.

PRACTICE

Exercises 1–8: Simplify.

1. $(3xy + 7x^2 - 11) + (xy^2 + 3x^2 + 1)$

2. $(5xz + xyz - 3x^2y^2 + y) + (3z + 5xz - 2xyz + 4y)$

3. $(4ab + 7c^2 + 8ac - a^2b) + (3b + a^2b + ab - b^2)$

4. $(6xy^2 - 5x^2y + 3x + 4) + (8x^2 - 4xy^2 - 3x + 6)$

5. $(3xz - 4x^2 - 6yz - 1) - (1 + 6yz + 2x^2 + 3xy)$

6. $(5u^2 + 3v^2 - 6u + 11v) - (u^2v + 3uv - 2u + 11)$

7. $(xyz + 3xz - 10z + 1) + (4xyz + 7xy + 3z + y)$

8. $(5y^2z^2 + 7yz^2 + x^2 - y) - (yz^2 + 3x^2 + 4y + z)$

Exercises 9–17: Multiply and combine like terms.

9. $(xy + y)(y - z)$

10. $(2x + y)(x - 2y)$

11. $(2xy - z)(x^2z + y^2)$

12. $(3yz + 5z)(2x + 4y)$

13. $(y^2z + 6xz)(2xz + y^3)$

14. $(xy - 10z^2)(xy + 2z^2)$

15. $(4y - 15x)(2yx + 6x)$

16. $(xz - 3yz)(2xz + yz)$

17. $(7x^2y - z)^2$

18. **MP 3, 6** Mark was given the expression $(3xz^2 + x)(yz - 2y)$ to simplify in standard form. Review his work and correct the errors he made, with an explanation as to what he did wrong. Write the correct answer.

Step 1	$(3xz^2 + x)(yz - 2y)$
Step 2	$3xyz^2 + xyz - 2yx - 6xyz^2$
Step 3	$-3xyz^2 + xyz - 2yx$

LESSON 3.2

3.2 Dividing Polynomials

Long Division of Polynomials

In this section, we divide polynomials using long division. It parallels the method used with the long division of numbers, and many of us use calculators these days instead of long division, so we provide a quick overview of the process.

MODEL PROBLEM

Divide 288 by 12.

SOLUTION

Divide 12 into 28	$12\overline{)288}$	Start by dividing 12 into 28, the first two digits of 288.
Multiply divisor by partial quotient	$\begin{array}{r} 2 \\ 12\overline{)288} \\ 24 \end{array}$	We can divide 12 into 28 twice, since 2 times 12 is 24. Write 24 under 28.
Subtract	$\begin{array}{r} 2 \\ 12\overline{)288} \\ -24 \\ \hline 48 \end{array}$	Subtract 24 from 28. The result is 4, which is smaller than 12. Bring down the next digit, the second 8, to create a new number, 48 (which happens to be divisible by 12 in this example).
Repeat	$\begin{array}{r} 24 \\ 12\overline{)288} \\ -24 \\ \hline 48 \\ 48 \\ \hline 0 \end{array}$	Now, repeat. Dividing 48 by 12, the result is 4, this time with no remainder. Write 48 under 48 and subtract. The result is 0 of course, since there is no remainder.

The same process is applied in polynomial division, where you start with the leading term, the one with the greatest power. This means you should also write the polynomials in standard form.

MODEL PROBLEMS

1. Divide $2x^2 + 5x + 3$ by $x + 1$.

SOLUTION

Divide $x + 1$ into $2x^2 + 5x + 3$ $x + 1\overline{)2x^2 + 5x + 3}$ Write the problem in the long division format.

> When a fraction has a polynomial in its numerator or denominator, it is called a *rational expression*, which is a topic in chapter 4.

Model Problems continue . . .

Divide leading terms

$$x + 1 \overline{)2x^2 + 5x + 3}$$ with $2x$ above the bar

Start by dividing the leading terms, x divided into $2x^2$, and write the quotient $2x$ above the division bar.

Multiply divisor by partial quotient

$$\begin{array}{r} 2x \\ x + 1 \overline{)2x^2 + 5x + 3} \\ 2x^2 + 2x \end{array}$$

Multiply $x + 1$ by $2x$ to get $2x^2 + 2x$.

Subtract

$$\begin{array}{r} 2x \\ x + 1 \overline{)2x^2 + 5x + 3} \\ -(2x^2 + 2x) \\ \hline 3x \end{array}$$

Next subtract like terms to get $3x$.

Repeat

$$\begin{array}{r} 2x + 3 \\ x + 1 \overline{)2x^2 + 5x + 3} \\ -(2x^2 + 2x) \\ \hline 3x + 3 \\ -(3x + 3) \\ \hline 0 \end{array}$$

Bring down the 3, then divide the leading terms, x divided into $3x$, to get 3. Multiply $x + 1$ by 3 to get $3x + 3$. Subtract, and get a remainder of 0. With a remainder of 0, we are done. This completes the long division.

2. Divide $x^3 - 1$ by $x - 1$.

SOLUTION

> Remember to insert terms with zero as coefficients for "missing" powers, such as the $0x^2$ term in our example.

Divide

$$\begin{array}{r} x^2 \\ x - 1 \overline{)x^3 + 0x^2 + 0x - 1} \end{array}$$

Use 0 as a placeholder for terms not present in the polynomial. Start by dividing the leading terms. Divide x into x^3 and write the quotient x^2 above the division bar.

Multiply divisor by partial quotient and then subtract

$$\begin{array}{r} x^2 \\ x - 1 \overline{)x^3 + 0x^2 + 0x - 1} \\ -(x^3 - x^2) \\ \hline x^2 + 0x - 1 \end{array}$$

Multiply $x - 1$ by x^2. Write the product below the terms with the same degree. You can see why the 0 terms help.

Subtract these terms, then bring down the next terms.

Repeat until done

$$\begin{array}{r} x^2 + x + 1 \\ x - 1 \overline{)x^3 + 0x^2 + 0x - 1} \\ -(x^3 - x^2) \\ \hline x^2 + 0x - 1 \\ -(x^2 - x) \\ \hline x - 1 \\ -(x - 1) \\ \hline 0 \end{array}$$

Divide the leading terms. Divide x into x^2 to get x. Then multiply $x - 1$ by x, and subtract.

Divide x into x to get 1. Then multiply $x - 1$ by 1. Subtract, and get a remainder of 0.

Model Problems continue . . .

3. Divide $2x^3 - 51x + 5$ by $x - 5$.

SOLUTION

Divide leading terms, multiply divisor by partial quotient, then subtract

$$\begin{array}{r} 2x^2 \\ x-5{\overline{\smash{\big)}\,2x^3 + 0x^2 - 51x + 5}} \\ \underline{-(2x^3 - 10x^2)} \\ 10x^2 - 51x \end{array}$$

Start by dividing the leading terms. Divide $2x^3$ by x and write the quotient $2x^2$ above the division bar.

Multiply $x - 5$ by $2x^2$. The first term is $2x^3$. This is written below the $2x^3$ term of the dividend. Next multiply -5 by $2x^2$ and write that product below the $0x^2$ term.

Subtract and bring down $-51x$.

Repeat

$$\begin{array}{r} 2x^2 + 10x - 1 \\ x-5{\overline{\smash{\big)}\,2x^3 + 0x^2 - 51x + 5}} \\ \underline{-(2x^3 - 10x^2)} \\ 10x^2 - 51x \\ \underline{-(10x^2 - 50x)} \\ -x + 5 \\ \underline{-(-x + 5)} \\ 0 \end{array}$$

The division is continued by dividing the leading terms, multiplying, and subtracting. The remainder is 0, which means the polynomial divides evenly.

PRACTICE

1. **MP 8** If $2x^2 + 2x - 8$ is the quotient when $x + 3$ divides $P(x)$, which of the following is the quotient when $2x + 6$ divides $P(x)$?

A. $x^2 + x - 4$

B. $2x^2 + 2x - 8$

C. $4x^2 + 4x - 16$

D. There is not enough information

2. **MP 7** Which of the following could be the value of k if $x - 2$ divides $3x^3 + kx^2 - kx - 2$ evenly, with a zero remainder?

A. -11 C. 8

B. -8 D. 11

Exercises 3–15: Divide.

3. $(x^2 + 7x + 12) \div (x + 3)$

4. $(x^2 + 14x + 48) \div (x + 6)$

5. $(x^2 - 11x + 28) \div (x - 7)$

6. $(x^2 - 15x + 50) \div (x - 10)$

7. $(x^2 - 14x + 33) \div (x - 11)$

8. $(20x^2 + 64x + 48) \div (5x + 6)$

9. $(9x^2 + 42x + 49) \div (3x + 7)$

10. $(x^4 + 18x^3 + 116x^2 + 312x + 288) \div (x + 6)$

11. $(x^4 + 18x^3 + 119x^2 + 342x + 360) \div (x + 6)$

12. $(x^4 + 18x^3 + 71x^2 - 258x - 1512) \div (x - 4)$

13. $(x^4 + 15x^3 + 33x^2 - 371x - 1470) \div (x - 5)$

14. $(36x^2 - 36) \div (6x + 6)$

15. $(16x^2 - 81) \div (4x + 9)$

16. Use long division to factor $x^3 + 8x^2 + 5x - 14$. The polynomial has a factor of $x - 1$.

17. **MP 2, 3** Suppose $ax + b$ evenly divides the polynomial $P(x)$. Explain how to find a solution to the equation $P(x) = 0$.

18. If $d(P)$ is the degree of a polynomial P, write an equation that relates $d(Divisor)$, $d(Dividend)$, and $d(Quotient)$.

19. **MP 2** Write a 4th-degree polynomial in standard form $ax^4 + bx^3 + cx^2 + dx + e$ that divides by $x + 9$ evenly (with a remainder of 0).

Practice Problems continue . . .

Practice Problems continued . . .

20. Find a such that $2x + 5$ will be a factor of $4x^3 + 8x^2 + ax + 30$.

21. If $x - 1$ is a factor of $x^{101} + kx^3 - 5$, what is the value of k?

22. A rectangle has an area A of $5x^5 - 19x^4 - 36x^3 + 36x^2 - 39x + 45$ and a length L of $x - 5$. What is the width of the rectangle?

W	A

L

Long Division of Polynomials with Remainder

The remainder can be expressed as a fraction, such as $\dfrac{2}{2x + 1}$. It is the remainder divided by the divisor.

MODEL PROBLEMS

1. **MP 1** Divide $2x^2 + 5x$ by $2x + 1$.

SOLUTION

Divide until degree of remainder less than degree of divisor

$$\begin{array}{r} x + 2 \\ 2x + 1 \overline{)2x^2 + 5x} \\ -(2x^2 + x) \\ \hline 4x + 0 \\ -(4x + 2) \\ \hline \text{remainder } -2 \end{array}$$

This is the result of the first two steps in the long division. The quotient is $x + 2$.

There is no like term for 2, so add a 0 to subtract from. Subtract, and get a remainder of -2. The degree of this constant is 0, which is less than the degree of the divisor $2x + 1$, which is 1. This completes the long division.

> Here, the division has a remainder that is not 0. When the degree of the remaining terms is less than the degree of the divisor, the division process stops.

Remainder is rational expression

$$\dfrac{2x^2 + 5x}{2x + 1} = x + 2 - \dfrac{2}{2x + 1}$$

We can write the result of the division using a rational expression to represent the remainder. The numerator is the remainder, -2, and the denominator is the divisor, $2x + 1$. Another way to write the result of the division would be $(2x + 1)(x + 2) - 2$.

2. Jan divides a quadratic polynomial using long division with a divisor of $x - a$. Which remainder indicates that $x - a$ is a factor of the polynomial?

  A. x C. 0

  B. a D. 2

SOLUTION

A. Any remainder means that $x - a$ is not a factor.

B. Again, any remainder means the $x - a$ is not a factor.

C. **Correct answer.** When performing long division, a remainder of 0 indicates that the divisor is a factor of the dividend.

D. Any remainder means that $x - a$ is not a factor.

Synthetic Division

Synthetic division provides an efficient way to divide polynomials. It can be used when the divisor is of the form $x - c$, such as $x - 5$. To introduce the concept of synthetic division, we show how to divide $2x^3 - 51x + 5$ by $x - 5$ using both synthetic and long division. This model problem is intended to give you a sense of how synthetic division works.

MODEL PROBLEMS

1. Use synthetic division and long division to divide $2x^3 - 51x + 5$ by $x - 5$. Are the answers the same?

SOLUTION

Synthetic Division

Use additive inverse of constant term as synthetic divisor

$$5 \rfloor$$

The synthetic divisor is 5, the opposite of the constant term in the binomial divisor.

Write coefficients of dividend

$$2x^3 + 0x^2 - 51x + 5$$
$$\downarrow \quad \downarrow \quad \downarrow \quad \downarrow$$
$$5 \rfloor \; 2 \quad 0 \quad -51 \quad 5$$

Write the coefficients of the polynomial dividend to represent the synthetic dividend. Remember to put in zero as a placeholder for any power of x not present in the polynomial dividend.

Bring down first coefficient

$$5 \rfloor \; 2 \quad 0 \quad -51 \quad 5$$
$$\underline{}$$
$$\quad 2$$

Bring down the first coefficient, 2.

Multiply synthetic divisor by first term in quotient

$$5 \rfloor \; 2 \quad 0 \quad -51 \quad 5$$
$$\quad \quad {}_{\cdot 5} \nearrow 10$$
$$\underline{}$$
$$\quad 2$$

Multiply the first coefficient, 2, by the synthetic divisor, 5, to get 10.

Add

$$5 \rfloor \; 2 \quad 0 \quad -51 \quad 5$$
$$\quad \quad \quad 10$$
$$\underline{}$$
$$\quad 2 \quad 10$$

Add the result to the next coefficient, 0, to get $0 + 10 = 10$.

Model Problems continue . . .

Multiply synthetic divisor by second term in quotient

$$
\begin{array}{r|rrrr}
5 & 2 & 0 & -51 & 5 \\
  &   & 10 & 50 & \\
\hline
  & 2 & 10 & -1 &
\end{array}
$$

Repeat the process, multiplying the synthetic divisor by 10 to get 50 and add it to -51 to get -1.

Multiply synthetic divisor by third term in quotient

$$
\begin{array}{r|rrrr}
5 & 2 & 0 & -51 & 5 \\
  &   & 10 & 50 & -5 \\
\hline
  & 2 & 10 & -1 & 0
\end{array}
$$

Multiply the synthetic divisor by the third term in the quotient, -1, to get -5. Add that to 5 and get 0.

Terms are coefficients of dividend and remainder

$$
\begin{array}{r|rrrr}
5 & 2 & 0 & -51 & 5 \\
  &   & 10 & 50 & -5 \\
\hline
  & 2 & 10 & -1 & 0
\end{array}
$$

$2x^2 + 10x - 1$, remainder 0

All the terms in the bottom row, except the last one, are the coefficients of the dividend. The last term, 0, is the remainder. The first number, 2, is the coefficient of x^2; 10 is the coefficient of x; and -1 is the constant term in the quotient. (The highest power of x in the quotient is one less than the highest power of the dividend.)

> Note that this process works only for divisors that are linear polynomials with a leading coefficient of 1, as in $x - 5$.

Long Division

Divide using long division

$$
\require{enclose}
\begin{array}{r}
2x^2 + 10x - 1 \\
x - 5 \enclose{longdiv}{2x^3 + 0x^2 - 51x + 5} \\
\underline{-(2x^3 - 10x^2)} \\
10x^2 - 51x \\
\underline{-(10x^2 - 50x)} \\
-x + 5 \\
\underline{-(-x + 5)} \\
0
\end{array}
$$

Divide the leading terms, multiply, subtract, and repeat. Both synthetic division and long division produce the same expression.

Model Problems continue . . .

2. Divide $4x^4 + 11x^3 - 19x^2 + x - 14$ by $x + 4$ using synthetic division.

SOLUTION

Additive inverse is synthetic divisor; write coefficients of dividend

$$4x^4 + 11x^3 - 19x^2 + x - 14$$

$$\underline{-4\,|}\quad 4 \quad 11 \quad -19 \quad 1 \quad -14$$

The divisor is $x + 4$, so use the additive inverse of $+4$, which is -4, as the synthetic divisor. State the coefficients of the dividend.

Multiply synthetic divisor by first term in quotient

$$\underline{-4\,|}\quad 4 \quad 11 \quad -19 \quad 1 \quad -14$$
$$\qquad\qquad -16$$
$$\cdot\,(-4)$$
$$\qquad 4 \quad -5$$

Bring down the first coefficient, 4. Multiply 4 by -4, get -16, and add that to 11 to get -5.

Multiply synthetic divisor by second term in quotient

$$\underline{-4\,|}\quad 4 \quad 11 \quad -19 \quad 1 \quad -14$$
$$\qquad\qquad -16 \quad 20$$
$$\qquad 4 \quad -5 \quad 1$$

Multiply -5 by -4 to get 20. Add that to -19 to get 1.

Multiply synthetic divisor by third term in quotient

$$\underline{-4\,|}\quad 4 \quad 11 \quad -19 \quad 1 \quad -14$$
$$\qquad\qquad -16 \quad 20 \quad -4$$
$$\qquad 4 \quad -5 \quad 1 \quad -3$$

Multiply 1 by -4 to get -4, add that to 1, and get -3.

Multiply synthetic divisor by fourth term in quotient

$$\underline{-4\,|}\quad 4 \quad 11 \quad -19 \quad 1 \quad -14$$
$$\qquad\qquad -16 \quad 20 \quad -4 \quad 12$$
$$\qquad 4 \quad -5 \quad 1 \quad -3 \quad -2$$

Multiply -3 by -4 to get 12, and add that to -14 to get -2.

Terms are coefficients of dividend and remainder

$$\underline{-4\,|}\quad 4 \quad 11 \quad -19 \quad 1 \quad -14$$
$$\qquad\qquad -16 \quad 20 \quad -4 \quad 12$$
$$\qquad 4 \quad -5 \quad 1 \quad -3 \quad -2$$
$$4x^3 - 5x^2 + x - 3, \text{ remainder } -2$$

All the terms but the last one are coefficients, and the last term is the remainder.

> Remember the first term of the quotient must be one degree lower than the dividend.

Model Problems continue . . .

3. Divide $3x^4 + 10x^3 + 5$ by $x + 3$ using synthetic division.

SOLUTION

Additive inverse is synthetic divisor; write coefficients of dividend

$$3x^4 + 10x^3 + 0x^2 + 0x + 5$$
$$\downarrow \quad \downarrow \quad \downarrow \quad \downarrow \quad \downarrow$$
$$-3\rfloor \quad 3 \quad 10 \quad 0 \quad 0 \quad 5$$

The divisor is $x + 3$, so use the additive inverse of $+3$, which is -3, as the synthetic divisor. State the coefficients of the dividend. Note that there are two 0's, since 0 is the coefficient of the x^2 and x-terms.

Multiply synthetic divisor by first term in quotient

$$-3\rfloor \quad 3 \quad 10 \quad 0 \quad 0 \quad 5$$
$$\cdot (-3) \nearrow \quad -9$$
$$3 \quad 1$$

Bring down the first coefficient in the divisor, 3. Multiply -3 by 3, get -9, and add that to 10 to get 1.

Multiply synthetic divisor by second term in quotient

$$-3\rfloor \quad 3 \quad 10 \quad 0 \quad 0 \quad 5$$
$$-9 \quad -3$$
$$3 \quad 1 \quad -3$$

Multiply -3 by 1 to get -3. Add that to 0 to get -3.

Multiply synthetic divisor by third term in quotient

$$-3\rfloor \quad 3 \quad 10 \quad 0 \quad 0 \quad 5$$
$$-9 \quad -3 \quad 9$$
$$3 \quad 1 \quad -3 \quad 9$$

Multiply -3 by -3 to get 9, add that to 0, and get 9.

Multiply synthetic divisor by fourth term in quotient

$$-3\rfloor \quad 3 \quad 10 \quad 0 \quad 0 \quad 5$$
$$-9 \quad -3 \quad 9 \quad -27$$
$$3 \quad 1 \quad -3 \quad 9 \quad -22$$

Multiply -3 by 9 to get -27, and add that to 5 to get -22.

Terms are coefficients of dividend and remainder

$$-3\rfloor \quad 3 \quad 10 \quad 0 \quad 0 \quad 5$$
$$-9 \quad -3 \quad 9 \quad -27$$
$$3 \quad 1 \quad -3 \quad 9 \quad -22$$

All the terms but the last are coefficients, and the last term is the remainder.

$$3x^3 + x^2 - 3x + 9, \text{ remainder } -22$$

Dividing Expressions Using a Computer Algebra System

A computer algebra system is a software program that solves algebra problems. These tools can also solve more complex mathematical problems and are used by engineers and scientists around the world.

Below is a computer algebra system showing the input and output for dividing two polynomials: $8x^7 - 24x^6 + 38x^5 + 44x^3 - 60x^2 + 90x - 40$ divided by $4x^5 + 3x^3 - x^2 + 7x - 5$. It shows first the quotient as Out[1] and the remainder as Out[2]. The remainder can be written as a rational expression, the remainder divided by the divisor. All it takes is a few brief commands, and the program does the polynomial long division that would take a good amount of time to do by hand.

```
In[1]:= PolynomialQuotient[
          8 x^7 - 24 x^6 + 38 x^5 + 44 x^3 - 60 x^2 + 90 x - 40, 4 x^5 + 3 x^3 - x^2 + 7 x - 5, x]

Out[1]= 8 - 6 x + 2 x²

In[2]:= PolynomialRemainder[
          8 x^7 - 24 x^6 + 38 x^5 + 44 x^3 - 60 x^2 + 90 x - 40, 4 x^5 + 3 x^3 - x^2 + 7 x - 5, x]

Out[2]= 4 x + 20 x⁴
```

PRACTICE

1. What is the remainder when $x^3 + 8x^2 + 7x$ is divided by $x + 6$?

   A. -546 C. 30

   B. -30 D. 546

2. Which of the following polynomials has a remainder of 1 when divided by $x + 2$, $x + 3$, and $x + 5$?

   A. $x^3 + 10x^2 + 31x + 29$

   B. $x^3 + 10x^2 + 31x + 30$

   C. $x^3 + 10x^2 + 31x + 31$

   D. None of the above

Exercises 3–9: Find the remainder using long division.

3. $(x^2 + 14x + 42) \div (x + 6)$

4. $(x^2 + 13x + 31) \div (x + 9)$

5. $(x^2 + 14x + 43) \div (x + 9)$

6. $(x^2 + 16x + 57) \div (x + 9)$

7. $(x^2 + 6x + 15) \div (x + 4)$

8. $(x^2 + 10x + 32) \div (x + 6)$

9. $(x^2 + 8x + 23) \div (x + 4)$

10. In the context of the division of polynomials, what can you say about the degree of the remainder compared to the degree of the divisor?

11. MP 2 Dividing a polynomial by $x - 1$ gives $x^2 + 8x + 1$ with a remainder of 7. What is this polynomial?

12. Dividing a polynomial by $x - 1$ gives $x^2 + 4x + 1$ with a remainder of 8. What is this polynomial?

Exercises 13–17: Use synthetic division.

13. Divide $6x^3 - 3x^2 + 4x - 1$ by $x - 1$.

14. Divide $-4x^3 - 5x^2 + 2x + 2$ by $x + 1$.

15. Divide $2x^4 + 3x^3 - x^2 + x + 4$ by $x + 2$.

16. Divide $-2x^5 + 30x^3 - 140$ by $x + 4$.

17. Divide $-2x^4 + 50x^2 - 3$ by $x - 5$.

18. MP 7 An important note for the synthetic division algorithm requires that the coefficient of the linear divisor is 1. How can we modify the linear divisor $ax + b$ so that we can use synthetic division?

Practice Problems continue . . .

Practice Problems continued . . .

19. **MP 7** From the synthetic division, write the polynomials that would replace P, D, Q, and R in the equation $P = QD + R$.

$$\begin{array}{r|rrrr} 3 & 2 & -5 & 3 & -7 \\ & & 6 & 3 & 18 \\ \hline & 2 & 1 & 6 & 11 \end{array}$$

20. **MP 3** Keith used the synthetic division algorithm to divide the polynomial expression $2x^3 - x^2 - 20x + 3$ by the linear divisor $x + 3$. His solution steps are shown below:

$$\begin{array}{r|rrrr} 3 & 2 & -1 & -20 & 3 \\ & & 6 & 15 & -15 \\ \hline & 2 & 5 & -5 & 12 \end{array}$$

He concludes $\dfrac{2x^3 - x^2 - 20x + 3}{x + 3} =$

$2x^2 + 5x - 5$ with a remainder 12. Is his solution correct? If not, explain.

LESSON 3.3

3.3 Remainder and Factor Theorems

The Remainder Theorem

The **remainder theorem** states:

For a polynomial $P(x)$, the value $P(c)$ equals the remainder when $P(x)$ is divided by $x - c$.

In other words, if you evaluate a polynomial $P(x)$ for $x = 5$, the result equals the remainder when the same polynomial is divided by $x - 5$.

We prove the remainder theorem:

Divide $P(x)$ by $x - c$	$P(x) = Q(x) \cdot (x - c) + R(x)$	Write the dividend, $P(x)$, as a product of the quotient, $Q(x)$, times the divisor, $x - c$, plus a remainder polynomial $R(x)$.
Degree of $R(x)$ is less than degree of $x - c$	$P(x) = Q(x) \cdot (x - c) + R$	To be a remainder, $R(x)$ must have a degree less than that of the divisor $x - c$, which has degree 1. That means the degree of $R(x)$ is 0, so it is a constant. Let R represent this constant remainder, and we replace $R(x)$ with R.
Evaluate $P(c)$	$P(c) = Q(x) \cdot (c - c) + R$ $P(c) = Q(x) \cdot 0 + R$ $P(c) = 0 + R$ $P(c) = R$	Substitute c for x to evaluate $P(c)$. The factor $x - c$ becomes 0, and the result is that $P(c)$ equals the remainder R. This proves the theorem.

MODEL PROBLEMS

1. MP 7 **a** Evaluate $P(x) = 3x^3 - 13x^2 + 15x - 7$ for $x = 2$.

b Calculate the remainder of $3x^3 - 13x^2 + 15x - 7$ divided by $x - 2$ using synthetic division.

SOLUTION

a Substitute and evaluate

$P(x) = 3(2)^3 - 13(2)^2 + 15(2) - 7$
$P(x) = 24 - 52 + 30 - 7$
$P(x) = -5$

Substitute 2 for x and evaluate. When $x = 2$, the value of the polynomial is -5.

b Use synthetic division to calculate remainder

$$\begin{array}{r|rrrr} 2 & 3 & -13 & 15 & -7 \\ & & 6 & -14 & 2 \\ \hline & 3 & -7 & 1 & -5 \end{array}$$

Use synthetic division to divide. The remainder is -5. This is the same value as evaluating the function for $x = 2$. The value of the polynomial for $x = 2$ is -5, which is the remainder when the polynomial is divided by $x - 2$.

2. Evaluate $P(x) = 5x^4 + 10x^3 - 7x + 1$ for $x = -2$ using the remainder theorem.

SOLUTION

> Remember, if $x = c$ is a zero, then $x - c$ is a factor.

Use synthetic division to find the remainder

$$\begin{array}{r|rrrrr} -2 & 5 & 10 & 0 & -7 & 1 \\ & & -10 & 0 & 0 & 14 \\ \hline & 5 & 0 & 0 & -7 & 15 \end{array}$$

With $x = -2$, the divisor is $x + 2$, so the synthetic divisor is -2. The remainder is 15. This means the value of the function is 15 when $x = -2$.

Check

$P(-2) = 5(-2)^4 + 10(-2)^3 - 7(-2) + 1$
$P(-2) = 80 - 80 + 14 + 1$
$P(-2) = 15$

Check by evaluating the function for $x = -2$. As the theorem states, the value of the function is the same as the remainder just calculated.

The Factor Theorem

The roots of a polynomial function are the values that make the function equal to 0. The root (or zero) of $f(x) = x - 2$ is 2, since that value of x makes the function equal 0. It turns out there is a relationship between the roots of a polynomial function and the factors of a function. We state this concept with the **factor theorem**:

> A polynomial $P(x)$ has $x - r$ as a factor if and only if $P(r) = 0$.

> The factor theorem makes explicit the link between roots and factors. The factor theorem follows from the remainder theorem because whenever the remainder is 0, the divisor is a factor of a polynomial.

Examples:

• If $P(3) = 0$, then $x - 3$ is a factor of $P(x)$.

If the value of a polynomial function is 0 when $x = 3$, then $x - 3$ is a factor of that polynomial.

• If $x - 3$ is a factor of $P(x)$, then $P(3) = 0$.

The converse is also true. If $x - 3$ is a factor of the polynomial $P(x)$, then $P(3) = 0$.

• If $P(4) \neq 0$, then $x - 4$ is <u>not</u> a factor of $P(x)$.

If a polynomial is not equal to 0 for the value 4, then $x - 4$ is not a factor of that polynomial.

1. Find the roots of $x^3 - 2x^2 - 15x = 0$.

SOLUTION

Factor	$x(x + 3)(x - 5) = 0$	To solve a polynomial equation, such as $x^3 - 2x^2 - 15x = 0$, factor the polynomial and then use the zero-product property. First, factor the polynomial on the left.
Zero-product property	$x = 0$ **or** $x + 3 = 0$ **or** $x - 5 = 0$ $x = 0 \qquad x = -3 \qquad x = 5$	Set each factor equal to 0 and solve for x. The solution to the first equation is 0; the solution to the second equation is -3; and the solution to the third equation is 5.
State solutions	$x = 0, -3, 5$	The solutions to the polynomial equation are 0, -3, and 5.
Solutions are roots of polynomial	$P(0) = 0^3 - 2(0)^2 - 15(0) = 0$ $P(-3) = (-3)^3 - 2(-3)^2 - 15(-3) = 0$ $P(5) = 5^3 - 2(5^2) - 15(5) = 0$	The solutions to the equation $x^3 - 2x^2 - 15x = 0$ are the roots of the polynomial $P(x) = x^3 - 2x^2 - 15x$. If you substitute a solution into the polynomial, the value of the polynomial is 0.
Relationship of roots and factors	Since 5 is a root, $x - 5$ is a factor	As our example demonstrates, if r is a root of the polynomial equation, then $x - r$ is a factor of the polynomial.

2. Use the factor theorem to determine if $x - 4$ is a factor of $P(x) = x^3 - 3x^2 - x + 5$.

SOLUTION

Evaluate polynomial for $x = 4$	$P(4) = (4)^3 - 3(4)^2 - 4 + 5$ $P(4) = 64 - 48 - 4 + 5 = 17 \neq 0$ $x - 4$ is not a factor	The factor theorem says that if $x - r$ is a factor, then the polynomial should equal 0 when $x = r$. Here, r is 4, so evaluate the function for $x = 4$. Since the result is not 0, $x - 4$ is not a factor.

3. Is $x + 6$ a factor of $P(x) = 6x^3 + 31x^2 - 27x + 18$?

SOLUTION

Evaluate function for $x = -6$	$P(-6) = 6(-6)^3 + 31(-6)^2 - 27(-6) + 18$ $P(-6) = -1296 + 1116 + 162 + 18 = 0$ $x + 6$ is a factor	r is -6, so evaluate the function for $x = -6$. Since the result equals 0, $x + 6$ is a factor.

Model Problems continue . . .

4. State a polynomial equation that has solutions 3, 2, and -1.

SOLUTION

Apply factor theorem	$(x - 3), (x - 2), (x - (-1))$	The factor theorem states that these three polynomials must be factors of the polynomial in the equation.
Multiply and set equal to 0	$(x - 3)(x - 2)(x + 1) = 0$ $x^3 - 4x^2 + x + 6 = 0$	Write a polynomial equation with the product of the factors on the left and 0 on the right. Restate the subtraction of a negative number as addition in the third factor, and then multiply. There are more possible solutions to this question. If we multiplied the original polynomial by a constant such as 4, the equation would have the same solutions.

5. Solve the equation $x^3 + 7x^2 + 16x + 12 = 0$. One solution is -3.

SOLUTION

> If a number is a solution, such as -3 in model problem 5, then it can be used as the synthetic divisor to help factor the polynomial completely. Why? We can restate $x = -3$ as $x + 3 = 0$, with $x + 3$ a factor of the equation. The opposite of 3 is the synthetic divisor, which means -3 is the synthetic divisor.

Use synthetic division	$\begin{array}{r|rrrr} -3 & 1 & 7 & 16 & 12 \\ & & -3 & -12 & -12 \\ \hline & 1 & 4 & 4 & 0 \end{array}$	Since -3 is a solution, we use -3 as the synthetic divisor. Use synthetic division. Since the final term is 0, there is no remainder, which confirms that $x + 3$ is a factor.
State quotient and factor	$(x + 3)(x^2 + 4x + 4) = 0$ $(x + 3)(x + 2)^2 = 0$	Use the quotient coefficients from the synthetic division to factor the polynomial as the product of $x + 3$ and a quadratic polynomial. Factor the quadratic as a perfect square.
State solutions	$x = -3, -2$	Setting each factor equal to 0, state the solutions.

PRACTICE

1. Is $x + 2$ a factor of $P(x) = -3x^3 + 4x - 16$?

   A. Yes

   B. No

   C. Not enough information to tell

2. Is $x - 4$ a factor of $P(x) = 5x^4 - 12x^3 - 128x$?

   A. Yes

   B. No

   C. Not enough information to tell

3. Which of the following is a factor of $f(x) = 3x^3 + 23x^2 - 18x - 80$?

   A. $x + 2$ C. $x - 8$

   B. $x + 8$ D. $x + 80$

4. What is the remainder when $f(x) = 5x^3 + 4x^2 - 12x - 15$ is divided by $x - 2$?

   A. -17 C. 17

   B. -15 D. 32

Exercises 5–12: Use the remainder theorem to state the remainder.

5. $(x^4 + 10x + 5) \div (x + 2)$

6. $(2x^3 - 5x^2 + 3x - 1) \div (x - 3)$

7. $(4x^4 - 2x^3 - 52x^2 - 15x) \div (x - 4)$

8. $(x^6 + x^4 + x^2 + 1) \div (x + 3)$

9. $(5x^5 + 4x^4 + 3x^3 + 2x^2 + x) \div (x + 1)$

Practice Problems continue . . .

10. $(-2x^5 - x^4 + 2x^2 + 4x + 8) \div (x - 2)$

11. $(x^4 - 2x^3 - 3x + 4) \div (x - 3)$

12. $(2x^4 + x^2 - 1) \div (x - 2)$

13. Use synthetic division and the remainder theorem to find $P(-9)$ if $P(x) = -x^5 - 8x^4 - 82x^2 - 11x - 11$.

14. Use synthetic division and the remainder theorem to find $P(3)$ if $P(x) = -x^6 + 5x^4 - 2x + 10$.

15. Determine the remainder when $6x^3 - 3x + 20$ is divided by $x + 5$ by applying the remainder theorem (in other words, do not use long or synthetic division).

16. Determine the remainder when $-2x^5 + 4x^3 + 8x^2 + x$ is divided by $x + 3$ by applying the remainder theorem (in other words, do not use long or synthetic division).

Exercises 17–18: Determine whether the expressions are factors of the polynomial function.

17. $f(x) = 2x^3 + 3x^2 - 2x - 3$; expression $x + 1$

18. $f(x) = x^3 - 3x^2 - 24x - 28$; expression $x - 7$

19. For the expression $x^3 - 7x - 6$, if $x - 3$ is a factor, what is $P(3)$?

Exercises 20–24: State the other solutions to the equation.

20. $x^3 + 9x^2 + 6x - 56 = 0$; $x = 2$ is one root

21. $x^3 - 8x^2 + 11x + 20 = 0$; $x = -1$ is one root

22. $x^3 - 4x^2 - 4x + 16 = 0$; $x = 4$ is one root

23. One solution to $x^3 + 4x^2 - 19x + 14 = 0$ is 2.

24. One solution to $x^3 - 4x^2 - 37x + 40 = 0$ is 8.

Exercises 25–26: State a polynomial equation for which the leading coefficient is 1, given the solutions in each problem. Expand and simplify the polynomial.

25. Solutions: -3, 4, and 1

26. Solutions: 5, -3, and -1

Exercises 27–30: State a polynomial that has the roots given and 1 as the leading coefficient.

27. Roots: 1, 7, and -4

28. Roots: 3, 4, and 5

29. Roots: -7, -4, and -3

30. Roots: 2, 3, and -3

Exercises 31–32: State the solutions to the equation.

31. $x^3 + 4x^2 + x - 6 = 0$

32. $3x^3 - 8x^2 - 5x + 6 = 0$

33. **MP 6** You are told that the function $P(x) = x^3 + 10x^2 + 29x + 20$ has three real roots and are asked to factor it.

   a What coefficient or constant in the polynomial will be most useful in determining possible factors? Explain your answer.

   b What can you conclude about the signs (positive or negative) of the roots of the given function? Explain your answer.

   c Based on your answers to parts **a** and **b**, make a chart of all potential factors, and their corresponding roots, of the function.

   d Choose one possible factor from your list and determine if it is a factor of the polynomial.

34. **MP 3, 7** Polly says the expression $x + 3$ is a factor of the function $P(x) = x^3 - 11x^2 + 4x + 60$ because when she evaluated $P(3)$, the result was 0. What mistake did Polly make?

35. **MP 3** Explain two different ways to determine if the number 5 is a root of the polynomial $P(x)$.

3.4 Solving Polynomial Equations Algebraically

Solving Cubic Equations

A polynomial equation where the highest value of a variable is a cube is called a **cubic equation**. Although there is a formula for solving any cubic equation, it is very complicated and we will not show it. However, some cubic equations can be solved by factoring, as we show in the model problems.

MODEL PROBLEMS

1. **MP 7** **a** Factor $2x^3 + 3x^2 - 2x = 0$.

       b Use the zero-product property to create equations, then solve them.

SOLUTION

> When the terms of a cubic all have a common factor of x, solve the equation by factoring out the x and then factoring the remaining polynomial or applying the quadratic formula.

a Factor out common factor x $x(2x^2 + 3x - 2) = 0$ The terms on the left side all have the common factor x.

    Factor resulting quadratic $x(2x - 1)(x + 2) = 0$ Factor the remaining quadratic polynomial.

b Zero-product property $x = 0$ *or* $2x - 1 = 0$ *or* $x + 2 = 0$ The equation states that the product of three factors is equal to 0. Use the zero-product property to solve the equation, by setting each of the three factors equal to 0.

    Solve first equation $x = 0$ The first equation already states that x is 0.

    Solve second equation $2x - 1 = 0$ $2x = 1$ $x = \dfrac{1}{2}$ To solve the second equation, add 1 to each side and divide by 2. The solution to the second equation is $\dfrac{1}{2}$.

> You might think that a faster way to solve $2x^3 + 3x^2 - 2x = 0$ is by dividing both sides by x first. If you did this, you would then miss one of the solutions, $x = 0$.

    Solve third equation $x + 2 = 0$ $x = -2$ The solution to the third equation is -2.

    Solutions $x = 0, \dfrac{1}{2}, -2$ The cubic equation has three solutions: 0, $\dfrac{1}{2}$, and -2.

2. Solve $2x^2(x + 1) = 6x$.

SOLUTION

Multiply $2x^3 + 2x^2 = 6x$ To start, multiply out the left side.

Standard form $2x^3 + 2x^2 - 6x = 0$ Then subtract $6x$ from both sides, leaving 0 on the right.

Factor $2x(x^2 + x - 3) = 0$ Factor out the common factor, $2x$. What remains is a quadratic trinomial, which cannot be factored.

Zero-product property $2x = 0$ *or* $x^2 + x - 3 = 0$ Apply the zero-product property, by setting each factor equal to 0. The result is two equations, one linear and one quadratic.

Model Problems continue . . .

Solve first equation	$2x = 0$ $x = 0$	The solution to the linear equation is 0.
Solve second equation	$x = \dfrac{-1 \pm \sqrt{1^2 - 4 \cdot 1 \cdot (-3)}}{2 \cdot 1}$ $x = \dfrac{-1 \pm \sqrt{13}}{2}$	Since the second equation cannot be factored, we use the quadratic formula instead.
Solutions	$x = 0, \dfrac{-1 + \sqrt{13}}{2}, \dfrac{-1 - \sqrt{13}}{2}$	The cubic equation has three solutions.

Solving Quartic Equations

A polynomial equation where the highest power of the variable is four is a **quartic equation**. As with cubic equations, there is a general formula for solving quartic equations, but it is even more complicated than the very complicated formula for cubic equations.

Some quartic equations can be solved by reducing them to quadratic equations, and solving them as you would any quadratic equation. This approach is worth trying when the quartic equation does not contain terms to the third or first powers (x^3 or x). By substituting y for x^2 temporarily, the equation can be treated as a quadratic equation in y. This approach works when the x is raised to powers where one is double the other.

MODEL PROBLEM

MP 7 **a** Write in standard form and factor $x^4 - 3x^2 = 4$.

b Solve the equation using the zero-product property.

SOLUTION

a Write in standard form

$x^4 - 3x^2 - 4 = 0$ Subtract 4 from each side of the equation.

Replace x^2 with y

$y^2 - 3y - 4 = 0$ Substitute $x^2 = y$, so $x^4 = y^2$. The result is a quadratic equation in y.

Factor polynomial in y

$(y + 1)(y - 4) = 0$ Factor quadratic equation in y.

Put x^2 back in place of y

$(x^2 + 1)(x^2 - 4) = 0$ Now that the polynomial in y has been factored, put x^2 back in place of y.

Factor again

$(x^2 + 1)(x - 2)(x + 2) = 0$ Factor the difference of squares.

b Zero-product property

$x^2 + 1 = 0$ **or** $x - 2 = 0$
 or $x + 2 = 0$ Set each factor equal to 0 separately.

Solve first equation

$x^2 + 1 = 0$
 $x^2 = -1$
 $x = -i, i$ There is no real number that solves the first equation. Remember that the square root of -1 is equal to i.

Solve second and third equations

$x - 2 = 0$ $x + 2 = 0$
 $x = 2$ $x = -2$ Solve for x in the second and third equations.

Solutions

$x = -i, i, 2, -2$ The only real-number solutions are 2 and -2. The imaginary solutions are $-i$ and i.

PRACTICE

Exercises 1–24: Solve.

1. $5x^3 + 37x^2 + 42x = 0$

2. $5x^3 + 47x^2 + 84x = 0$

3. $8x^3 - 46x^2 + 63x = 0$

4. $15x^3 - 70x^2 + 80x = 0$

5. $3x^3 + 13x^2 + 3x = 0$

6. $4x^3 + 9x^2 + 5x = 0$

7. $3x^3 + 11x^2 + 3x = 0$

8. $6x^3 - 7x^2 + 2x = 0$

9. $4x^3 - 8x^2 + 3x = 0$

10. $5x^3 - 8x^2 + 3x = 0$

11. $x^4 - 20x^2 = 125$

12. $x^4 - 5x^2 = 36$

13. $x^4 - 9x^2 = 112$

14. $x^4 - 3x^2 = 54$

15. $x^4 - 23x^2 = 468$

16. $x^4 - 27x^2 = 324$

17. $x^4 - 14x^2 = 275$

18. $x^4 - 40x^2 = 441$

19. $5x^5 - 75x^3 = -250x$

20. $3x^5 - 48x^3 = -180x$

21. $5x^5 - 45x^3 = -70x$

22. $3x^5 - 27x^3 = -54x$

23. MP 1, 7 $x^6 + 9x^3 + 8 = 0$

24. $(x^2 - 2x)2 - 3x^2 + 6x = 4$

25. MP 2, 7 Solve $x^3 - x^2 + ax + 16 = 0$ if one of the solutions of the equation is equal to -4.

26. Solve $x^4 + x^3 - 4x^2 + x + 1 = 0$ by dividing both sides by x^2, and letting $y = x + \dfrac{1}{x}$.

Exercises 27–29: Justify each answer.

27. If m is a solution to the equation $ax^4 + bx^2 + c = 0$, then explain why $-m$ is also a solution to that equation.

28. MP 2, 3 If m is a nonzero solution to the equation $ax^4 + bx^3 + cx^2 + bx + a = 0$, then explain why $\dfrac{1}{m}$ is also a solution to that equation.

29. MP 3, 7 Explain why the equation $2x^4 + 3x^2 + 1 = 0$ has no real solutions.

30. MP 2, 6 The sum of the squares of a positive number and its reciprocal is equal to $\dfrac{17}{4}$. Find the number.

31. The solutions to the equation $x^4 + bx^2 + c = 0$ are 2 and $2\sqrt{2}$. Write the equation with possible values of b and c (there is more than one possible answer).

32. MP 1, 2 The product of 4 consecutive positive integers is equal to the difference between 10 times the product of the smallest and the greatest of them and 16. Find the smallest of these integers. Hint: Combine the first and the last terms in the product and substitute with a new variable.

LESSON 3.5

3.5 Finding Zeros of Polynomial Functions

In this section, we focus on the graphs of cubic polynomials, such as $P(x) = x^3 - 2x^2 - 6x + 6$, and quartic polynomials, such as $P(x) = 5x^4 - 3x^2 + 1$. The domains of these functions are the set of real numbers. The graphs of these functions are continuous—they have no gaps—and like the graphs of all functions, they pass the vertical line test.

The graphs of cubic and quartic functions are curves, not straight lines. Polynomials of the first degree (linear equations), $P(x) = ax + b$, have straight-line graphs. Polynomials of the second degree (quadratic equations), $P(x) = ax^2 + bx + c$, have parabolic graphs. The graphs of higher-degree polynomials have more complicated shapes.

Graphing Polynomial Functions by Plotting Points

To graph and analyze a polynomial function by plotting points:

1. Graph by plotting points.

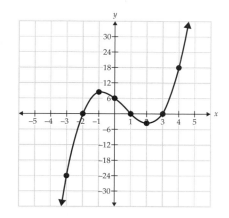

x	$P(x)$
-3	-24
-2	0
-1	8
0	6
1	0
2	-4
3	0
4	18

A polynomial function, such as $P(x) = x^3 - 2x^2 - 5x + 6$, can be graphed by plotting points. Calculate some points, plot them, and draw a curve through them.

2. Identify x-intercepts.

The x-intercepts are at -2, 1, and 3. The x-intercepts of the graph are the real zeros of the polynomial, since at these locations the value of the function is 0. We can use graphs to approximate zeros. When the graph crosses the x-axis, the value of the function must change from positive to negative, or vice versa.

3. Describe end behavior.

As x goes toward negative infinity, y also goes toward negative infinity. As x goes toward positive infinity, y also goes toward positive infinity.

The polynomial above has three distinct real zeros because it intersects the x-axis at three points. Cubic equations are not required to have three real roots. If the graph above intersected the x-axis once, the polynomial would have only one real zero, and if it intersected the x-axis twice, it would have two real zeros.

 In this activity, graph polynomial functions to calculate roots.

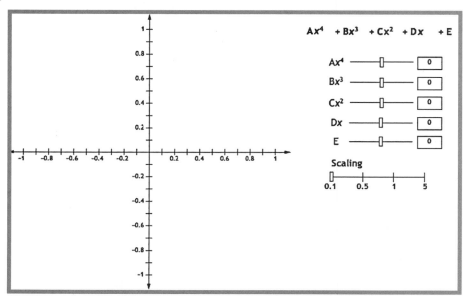

1. Determine the number of real zeros of each quartic poynomial.

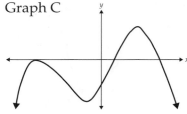

Quartic equations can have up to four real zeros.

Graph A

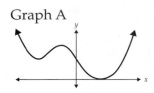

Graph C

Graph B

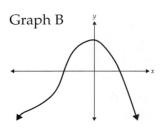

Graph D

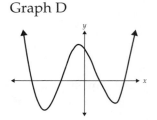

SOLUTION

Graph A One real zero. The number of x-intercepts of the graph of a polynomial equals the number of distinct real zeros of the polynomial. Graph A has one x-intercept, so the polynomial has one real zero.

Graph B Two real zeros. Since Graph B has two x-intercepts, the polynomial has two distinct real zeros.

Graph C Three real zeros. Graph C intersects the x-axis three times, so it has three real zeros.

Graph D Four real zeros. Graph D crosses the x-axis four times, so it has four real zeros.

2. Find the positive real zeros of $P(x) = x^3 + x^2 - 2x - 2$.

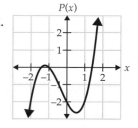

SOLUTION

Iterate to find roots

x	$P(x)$
0	-2
1	-2
1.1	-1.659
1.2	-1.232
1.3	-0.713
1.4	-0.096
1.5	0.625
2	6

The function crosses the x-axis between integers. Iterate solutions: try values, and use them to determine the next trials.

Trying values and noting when these values cause the value of the function to change sign is one way to estimate zeros.

When it changes sign, we have found two points between which the graph must pass through the x-axis. The graph crosses the x-axis between 1 and 2.

Employ the same idea with the tenths, and find that the value of the function changes sign between 1.4 and 1.5, and closer to 1.4. The process above could be continued, with values between 1.4 and 1.5 evaluated to determine the root to the nearest hundredth. The estimate above is close, and shows both the benefits and limits of estimation.

Model Problems continue . . .

3. **MP 3** Graph A and Graph B both represent the polynomial function $P(x) = x^3 + 15x^2 + x + 15$. They are viewed through different windows, showing different ranges and domains. Explain how the Graph B view changes one's view of the nature of the function's graph.

Graph A

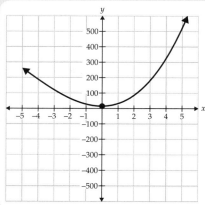

Graph B

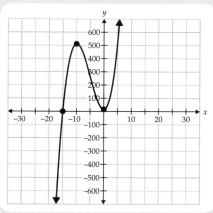

SOLUTION

Graph A displays the function from -5 to 5, while Graph B displays the function from -30 to 30. Graph A looks like a parabola and seems to have no zeros (since it does not cross the x-axis).

In Graph B, we show a larger domain of the same function and see a different shape for the graph. We see a zero where the graph crosses the x-axis at -15. It also seems like there might be a zero near $x = 0$. $x = 0$ is not a zero of the polynomial since $P(0) = 15$. It can be shown that the polynomial's relative minimum near $x = 0$ is at $x \approx -0.03345$, and the value of the polynomial there is $P(-0.03345) \approx 14.98$. Graph A shows the region near $x = 0$ in more detail and indicates that the relative minimum is above the x-axis.

We also get a more accurate view of the end behavior of the graph to the left of the origin in Graph B; it will become increasingly negative as x becomes more negative, since the cube term will be negative, and it will dominate the output.

Graphing Calculator: Graphing Polynomial Functions

We use a calculator to analyze $y = 4x^3 - 41x^2 - 551x - 260$. In addition to finding its zeros and describing end behavior, we also analyze the function for its relative minimums and maximums. Relative minimums and maximums are low and high points on a section of the graph.

> Graphing a polynomial function can be a useful way to determine its zeros, even when the zeros are irrational. This is particularly true in the era of graphing calculators, which can quickly produce a graph of a polynomial.

1. Enter function. Press [Y=] to get to the equation entry screen, and type the above polynomial into a Y variable line.

```
Plot1  Plot2  Plot3
\Y1▪4X^3-41X²-55
1X-260
\Y2=
\Y3=
\Y4=
\Y5=
\Y6=
```

Directions continue . . .

Directions continued . . .

2. Graph the function. To graph, press ZOOM 6:ZStandard, and graph the function using the graphing window of $-20 < x < 20$ and $-8000 < y < 4500$.

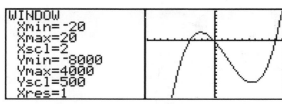

3. Find the intercepts. Press 2nd TRACE 2:Zero. Use the ◄ and ► keys to move the cursor to the left and right of each x-intercept. Press ENTER. Move the cursor so it is close to the same x-intercept and press ENTER.

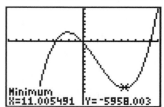

4. Finding the relative minimums. Press 2nd TRACE 3:Minimum to find the relative minimum of the polynomial. Use the ◄ and ► keys to move the cursor so it is to the left and right of each relative minimum. Press ENTER. Use the ◄ and ► keys to move the cursor close to the relative minimum. Press ENTER.

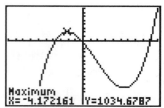

5. Finding the relative maximums. Press 2nd TRACE 4:Maximum to find the relative maximum of the polynomial. Use the ◄ and ► keys to move the cursor to the left and right of each relative maximum. Press ENTER. Use the ◄ and ► keys to move the cursor close to the relative maximum. Press ENTER.

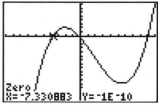

MODEL PROBLEM

MP 5, 6 Now that we have graphed the function $y = 4x^3 - 41x^2 - 551x - 260$ on a graphing calculator, complete an analysis based on the end behavior, x- and y-intercepts, domain and range, relative minimum and maximum, and the intervals the function increases and decreases. (We show one image of the graphed function to the right, but you should graph it on your own to complete your analysis or use the images above.)

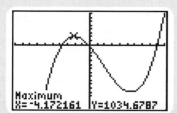

SOLUTION

End behavior: As x goes toward negative infinity, y also goes toward negative infinity. As x goes toward positive infinity, y also goes toward positive infinity.

x-intercepts (zeros): $x \approx -7.33$, $x \approx -0.49$, $x \approx 18.07$

Domain and range: All real numbers

y-intercept: -260

Relative minimum: $x \approx 11$ and $y \approx -5958$

Relative maximum: $x \approx -4.17$ and $y \approx 1034.68$

Increases on about $x > 11$ and $x \leq -4.17$

Decreases on about $-4.17 \leq x \leq 11$

158 Chapter 3: Polynomials

Graphing Polynomial Functions Using Zeros

Another way to get an accurate view of a polynomial exists if you can calculate its zeros. We use $P(x) = 3x^3 - 12x$ as an example. Factor the expression to get $(3x)(x^2 - 4)$. Recognize the second factor as a difference of squares, $(x + 2)(x - 2)$. Using the zero-product property, the roots are 0, 2, and -2. Plot those 3 points, some adjacent points and the points in between, to arrive at the graph to the right.

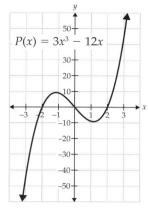

Considering the structure of the function, we would expect the function output to become increasingly negative as x becomes more negative, since the cubed term will dominate the output. For instance, if we substitute for $x = -1000$ into the two parts of the function, $3x^3 \rightarrow 3(-1000)^3$ is far greater than $12x \rightarrow 12(-1000)$. And as x becomes more positive, the output will become more positive, if we use similar analysis. So the directions of the endpoints in the graph will be maintained.

MODEL PROBLEM

MP 1, 6, 7 Graph $f(x) = -(x^2 + 2x + 1)(x^2 + 9)$ and analyze the end behavior of the function.

SOLUTION

Analyze structure of expression	$\begin{aligned} f(x) &= -(x^2 + 2x + 1)(x^2 + 9) \\ &= -(x^4 + 9x^2 + 2x^3 + 18x + x^2 + 9) \\ &= -(x^4 + 2x^3 + 10x^2 + 18x + 9) \end{aligned}$	Analyze the structure of the expression. It is a quartic expression (multiplying the two x^2 expressions will yield x^4). Then factor the expression.

Factor $\qquad = -(x + 1)(x + 1)(x^2 + 9)$

Factor the expression. The expression $(x^2 + 2x + 1)$ is a perfect square.

Use zero-product property

$$-(x + 1) = 0 \qquad x + 1 = 0 \qquad x^2 + 9 = 0$$
$$-x - 1 = 0 \qquad\qquad x = -1 \qquad x^2 = -9$$
$$x = -1 \qquad\qquad\qquad\qquad\qquad x = -3i, 3i$$

Using the zero-product property for the first two factors, we obtain from each that -1 is a zero. The third factor does not contribute real zeros. Using the zero-product property, $x^2 = -9$, and no real number when squared equals -9.

Analyze end behavior

x	y
-3	-72
-2	-13
-1	0
0	-9
1	-40
2	-117
3	-288

We consider the appearance of the graph at its endpoints: the leading term is $-x^4$, and as x becomes increasingly positive or negative, that term will become more negative. So we would expect the endpoints to point down as we move from the origin.

Graph

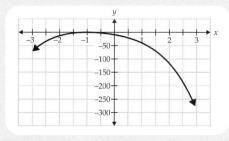

When we graph the function from $x = -3$ to $x = 3$, we get a graph that meets our description.

Fundamental Theorem of Algebra

The **fundamental theorem of algebra** states:

> Every single-variable polynomial function of degree $n \geq 1$ has at least one zero in the set of complex numbers.

This theorem says that a function like $P(x) = x^2 + 2x + 1$ has at least one complex zero. The function has one zero at -1 since $P(-1) = (-1)^2 + 2(-1) + 1 = 1 - 2 + 1 = 0$.

The fundamental theorem can be shown to be true for a general degree-two polynomial, $P(x) = ax^2 + bx = c, a \neq 0$, by considering the quadratic formula, $x = \dfrac{-b \pm \sqrt{b^2 - 4ac}}{2a}$. The formula shows that there are two zeros when the discriminant, $b^2 - 4ac$, does not equal zero and one zero when the discriminant equals zero. But in no case does it lack zeros altogether.

> Remember, the set of complex numbers includes real numbers. For instance, the number -1 is a complex number $(-1 + 0i)$. Similarly, the number $3i$ is complex $(0 + 3i)$.

Linear Factorization Theorem

The **linear factorization theorem** states even more information than the fundamental theorem of algebra:

> A polynomial of degree $n \geq 1$ has n complex zeros. A zero that occurs k times counts as k zeros.

> In other words, the number of zeros = degree of polynomial.

For example, $P(x) = 3x^3 + 30x^2 + 75x$ will have 3 zeros since the degree of the polynomial is 3 (its leading term has a power of three). It turns out that it has three zeros $(0, -5,$ and $-5)$, which means $(x - 0)$, $(x + 5)$, and $(x + 5)$ are factors. Note that -5 appears twice as a zero. A zero that appears k times has a *multiplicity* of k. The zero -5 has a multiplicity of 2, and the zero 0 has a multiplicity of 1.

We provide a table below of some polynomials, their degrees, and zeros. We also show the factors of the polynomial. Each zero corresponds to a linear factor of the form $x - r$, where r is a number in the form $a + bi$.

	Degree	Zeros	Factors
$x - 2 = 0$	1	2	$x - 2$
$x^2 + 9 = 0$	2	$-3i, 3i$	$x + 3i, x - 3i$
$x^3 + 6x^2 + 11x + 6 = 0$	3	$-1, -2, -3$	$x + 1, x + 2, x + 3$
$s^4 - 16 = 0$	4	$-2, 2, -2i, 2i$	$s + 2, s - 2, s + 2i, s - 2i$

MP 6 Consider the polynomial $P(x) = Ax^m + Bx$. Which statement best describes the polynomial $P(x)$?

A. The polynomial has 2 zeros because there are two terms, Ax^m and Bx.
B. The polynomial has m factors because the degree of the polynomial is m.
C. The polynomial has degree A because the leading coefficient is A.
D. The polynomial's graph can cross the x-axis a maximum of $(A + B)$ times.

SOLUTION

A. The number of terms does not determine the number of zeros in a polynomial.
B. **Correct answer.** The linear factorization theorem states that the degree of the polynomial indicates the number of zeros, which is the same as the number of factors.
C. The leading coefficient does not indicate the degree of the polynomial.
D. The graph can cross a maximum of m times because the degree of the polynomial is m.

Summary of Finding Zeros of Polynomial Functions

You now have several ways to think about polynomials and their factors, solutions, zeros, and x-intercepts. We provide a summary below of the tools that you have to determine the zeros of a polynomial function.

Method	Example	Explanation
Factors and zero-product property	$x^2 + 3x + 2 = 0$ $(x + 2)(x + 1) = 0$ $(x + 2) = 0$ $(x + 1) = 0$ Solutions are $-2, -1$	Factor $x^2 + 3x + 2$. Use the zero-product property to find that the solutions are -2 and -1. We could also think of this as an application of the factor theorem.
Zeros follow from factor theorem	Factors: $[x - (-2)][x - (-1)]$ Zeros are $-2, -1$	Use the factor theorem to say that if $(x - r)$ is a factor, then r is a zero of the polynomial.
Graph	x-intercepts are solutions	Graph the polynomial and its x-intercepts; the zeros of the function are where it crosses the x-axis.
Linear factorization theorem	$P(x) = x^2 + 3x + 2$ Must have 2 zeros	The linear factorization theorem tells us how many zeros a polynomial has.

PRACTICE

1. Which of the following statements best describes the zeros of the quartic polynomial function graphed?

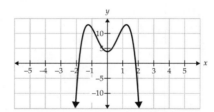

- A. There are 4 real zeros.
- B. There are 4 complex zeros.
- C. There are 3 real zeros and 1 complex zero.
- D. There are 2 real zeros and 2 complex zeros.

2. Which of the following polynomial functions does this graph best represent?

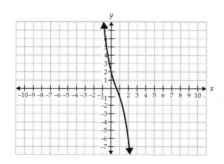

- A. $f(x) = -x^3 + 2x^2 - 4x + 2$
- B. $f(x) = x^3 + 3x^2 - 2x + 1$
- C. $f(x) = -x^3 + 5x^2 - 2x$
- D. $f(x) = -x^3 - x^2 + 3x - 4$

3. **MP 2** Mark analyzes a polynomial $P(x)$ and makes the following table of values.

x	3	4
$P(x)$	0.12	−1.6

Which of his statements is true about $P(x)$?

- A. The polynomial has a zero at $x = 3$ and $x = 4$.
- B. The polynomial has a zero between $x = 3$ and $x = 4$.
- C. The polynomial has factors $x - 0.12$ and $x + 1.6$.
- D. The polynomial has at least 2 x-intercepts.

4. The graph of a polynomial function never passes through the x-axis but passes through the y-axis once. How many real zeros does it have?

5. The graph of a polynomial function passes through the x-axis three times and the y-axis once. How many real zeros does it have?

Exercises 6–9: Use each graph to determine the number of real zeros of the function.

6.

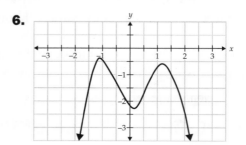

7.

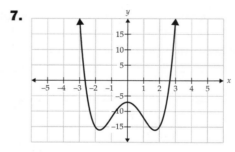

8.

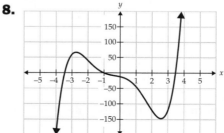

9.

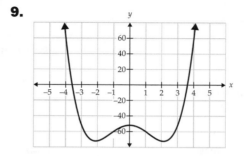

Practice Problems continue . . .

10. Use the graph of the polynomial function $f(x) = x^3 + x^2 - 3x - 3$ to approximate its real zeros, to the nearest tenth.

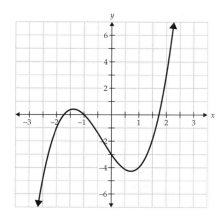

Exercises 11–13: Use iteration to determine the real zeros, to the nearest tenth.

11. $P(x) = x^4 - 6x^2 - 7$

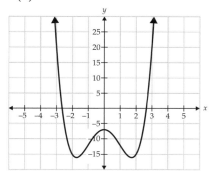

12. $P(x) = x^5 + x^4 - 11x^3 - 11x^2 - 12x - 12$

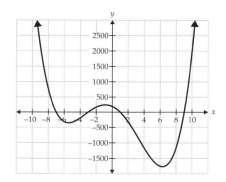

13. $P(x) = x^4 - 9x^2 - 52$

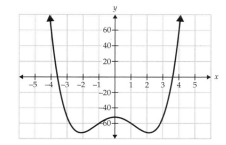

14. Find the cubic polynomial with leading coefficient 1 that has the zeros shown in the graph.

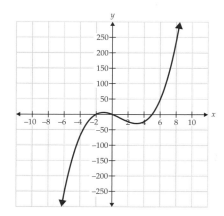

15. Find the quartic polynomial with leading coefficient 1 that has the zeros shown in the graph.

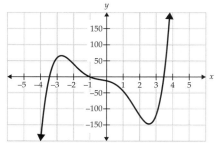

16. A student sees a graph of a cubic polynomial that passes through the x-axis three times. She then factors the polynomial and concludes it has the factors $x^2 + x + 1$ and $x - 1$. Can she be right? Why?

17. A polynomial whose graph is a straight line can have how many real zeros? Give an example for each answer you state.

18. A local maximum is the point where the graph of a polynomial function reaches its highest value within a restricted area or domain. For the polynomial $P(x) = x^3 + 8x^2 + 12x - 6$, a local maximum occurs between $x = -5$ and $x = -4$.

   a Use iteration to find the coordinates of the local maximum, to the nearest tenth.

   b Graph the function for the domain $-6 \leq x \leq -2$, and label the local maximum.

Practice Problems continue . . .

Practice Problems continued . . .

19. a Given the function $y = x^3 + 6x^2 - 5x - 4$, make a table of values of y for integer values of x in the domain $-3 \le x \le 3$.

   b Based on the values in your table, how many times will the graph of the function cross the x-axis in the given domain?

   c Graph the function for the stated domain and use it to check your answer to part **b**.

20. MP 3 Explain how to find a zero of the polynomial function $P(x)$ if you know $P(1) = -2$ and $P(2) = 5$.

21. Write a polynomial that has no real zeros.

22. Eric says because the graph of a polynomial function crosses the x-axis three times, it has three real zeros and must be a third-degree polynomial. What mistake did Eric make in his reasoning?

Exercises 23–24: Find the real zeros of the polynomial, to the nearest tenth over the interval given, using a calculator.

23. $f(x) = x^4 - 2x^3 - x^2 - 2x + 1$ from $x = -3$ to $x = 3$

24. $f(x) = x^4 + x^3 - 7x^2 - 8x - 2$ from $x = -3$ to $x = 3$

Exercises 25–32: Use a calculator to graph the function and state its real zeros.

25. $f(x) = 2x^3 + x^2 + x - 1$ from $x = -2$ to $x = 2$

26. $f(x) = x^4 - x^3 - x + 1$ from $x = -2$ to $x = 2$

27. $f(x) = x^3 + 3x^2 - x - 3$ from $x = -4$ to $x = 4$

28. $f(x) = x^3 - x^2 - 4x + 4$ from $x = -3$ to $x = 3$

29. $f(x) = 2x^3 + 3x^2 - 2x - 3$ from $x = -2$ to $x = 2$

30. $f(x) = x^4 + x^3 - 6x^2 - 4x + 8$ from $x = -3$ to $x = 3$

31. $f(x) = 2x^4 - 11x^3 + 16x^2 - x - 6$ from $x = -4$ to $x = 4$

32. $f(x) = 4x^3 + 4x^2 - x - 1$ from $x = -2$ to $x = 2$.

33. What are the zeros of $P(x) = x^3 + x^2 - 4x - 4$?

34. What are the zeros of $P(x) = 2x^3 - 5x^2 - 2x + 5$? Round to the nearest tenth.

35. What are the zeros of $P(x) = 2x^3 + 3x^2 - 11x - 6$? Round to the nearest tenth.

36. Investigate the properties of the graphs of fifth-, sixth-, seventh-, and eighth-degree polynomials. How are these graphs related to those of third- and fourth-degree polynomials?

37. A quartic polynomial can have zero real roots, and its graph will never cross the x-axis. Is this also true for a cubic polynomial? Explain your reasoning.

38. MP 2, 7 A third-degree polynomial has three real roots. The roots are consecutive odd integers, and their sum is three.

   a Find the roots, and write an equation for the polynomial function with these roots and a leading coefficient of 1.

   b Graph the polynomial function you wrote in part **a** for the domain $-2 \le x \le 4$.

3.6 Optional: Descartes' Rule of Signs

René Descartes was a French philosopher, writer, scientist, and mathematician. He contributed a theorem about the number of zeros of a polynomial with real coefficients called **Descartes' rule of signs**.

To illustrate the rule, consider the polynomial, $P(x) = 3x^5 - 2x^3 - 2x^2 + 7x - 5$, in standard form. You then count the number of times the sign changes from "plus" to "minus," or from "minus" to "plus."

There are three variations in signs. The first variation in sign is between the positive sign for the first term and the minus sign for the second term. There is no variation between the second and third terms, since they are both subtracted. There is a change between the third and fourth terms because the third term is subtracted, and the fourth term is added. And again between the fourth and fifth terms there is a change in sign. Note that there is a "missing" term, that there is no term to the fourth power. This is fine. You just skip any terms that are not present.

$$\overset{1}{\overset{\frown}{3x^5} - 2x^3} \overset{2}{-} \overset{3}{\overset{\frown}{2x^2 + 7x} - 5}$$

> The number of variations of sign between adjacent terms of $P(x)$ is used in Descartes' rule.

Descartes' rule also requires us to consider the variations in sign for the polynomial $P(-x)$.

Calculating variations in sign for $P(-x)$ given $P(x)$:

1. Substitute $-x$ for x and simplify

$$P(x) = 3x^5 - 2x^3 - 2x^2 + 7x - 5$$
$$P(-x) = 3(-x)^5 - 2(-x)^3 - 2(-x)^2 + 7(-x) - 5$$
$$P(-x) = -3x^5 + 2x^3 - 2x^2 - 7x - 5$$

Replace x with $-x$ and simplify. In this example, we use $P(x) = 3x^5 - 2x^3 - 2x^2 + 7x - 5$.

2. Determine number of variations in sign

$$P(-x) = \overset{1}{\overset{\frown}{-3x^5} + 2x^3} \overset{2}{-} 2x^2 - 7x - 5$$

There are two variations in sign.

With variation in sign explained, we state Descartes' rule of signs for a polynomial $P(x)$:

> The number of positive real zeros of the polynomial $P(x)$ equals the number of variations of sign, or is fewer by an even integer.
>
> To calculate the number of negative zeros, first write the polynomial $P(-x)$. Then the rule is the same as for the positive real zeros: The number of negative real zeros equals the number of variations in sign, or is fewer by an even integer.

> Descartes' rule enables you to calculate the number of possible positive and negative real zeros of a polynomial function.

Sometimes Descartes' rule, combined with the linear factorization theorem about the number of zeros, can give quite specific information about the nature of zeros.

1. How many positive real zeros can $P(x) = 5x^4 + 2x^3 - 4$ have? How many negative real zeros? How many complex zeros?

SOLUTION

Variations in sign of $P(x)$

$$\overset{1}{\overset{\frown}{P(x) = 5x^4 + 2x^3 - 4}}$$

There is one variation in sign for $P(x)$. Since there must be that number of positive real zeros, or that number minus an even integer, there must be exactly one positive real zero. (There cannot be $1 - 2 = -1$ positive real zeros.)

Variations in sign of $P(-x)$

$$\overset{1}{\overset{\frown}{P(-x) = 5x^4 - 2x^3 - 4}}$$

Apply Descartes' rule for $P(-x)$. Again, there is one variation in sign. This means there is exactly one negative real zero.

Roots | One positive real
One negative real
Two complex

The polynomial has degree 4. The linear factorization theorem states there must be 4 zeros. One zero is a positive real, one is a negative real, so the other two must be a conjugate pair of complex numbers.

2. How many positive real zeros does $P(x) = x^4 + x^3 - x^2 + x - 2$ have? How many negative real zeros?

SOLUTION

Variations in sign of $P(x)$

$$\overset{1 \quad 2 \quad 3}{\overset{\frown \frown \frown}{P(x) = x^4 + x^3 - x^2 + x - 2}}$$

There are three variations in sign for $P(x)$. Since there must be that number of zeros, or that number minus two, there can be three or one positive zeros.

Variations in sign of $P(-x)$

$$\overset{1}{\overset{\frown}{P(-x) = x^4 - x^3 - x^2 - x - 2}}$$

Apply Descartes' rule for $P(-x)$. There is one variation in sign. This means there is exactly one negative real zero.

Zeros | Three positive real and one negative real
or
One positive real, one negative real, and two complex

There must be four zeros. There can be three positive real zeros and one negative real zero, or one positive real zero, one negative real zero, and two complex zeros. It turns out the polynomial $P(x) = x^4 + x^3 - x^2 + x - 2$ factors as $(x - 1)(x + 2)(x + i)(x - i)$, so there is one positive real zero, one negative real zero, and two complex zeros.

PRACTICE

Exercises 1–6: How many positive zeros can the equations have? How many negative?

1. $-x^3 + x^2 - x + 1 = 0$

2. $4x^4 + 2x^3 - x + 1 = 0$

3. $5x^4 + 4x^3 + 3x^2 + 2x + 1 = 0$

4. $x^7 - x^5 + x^3 + x^2 - x = 0$

5. $-3x^4 - 3x^2 - 5 = 0$

6. $2x^4 - 3x^3 + 4x^2 + 5x - 6 = 0$

7. Fill in the table describing the possible combinations for the zeros of $P(x) = -x^6 + 2x^3 - 3x + 2$.

Number of Zeros

Positive Real	Negative Real	Complex
☐	1	☐
☐	☐	4

8. Fill in the table describing the possible combinations for the zeros of $P(x) = x^8 - 4x^5 - 3x^3 + x^2 - 7x + 12$.

Number of Zeros

Positive Real	Negative Real	Complex
☐	☐	4
2	☐	☐
0	☐	☐

9. Fill in the table describing the possible combinations for the zeros of $P(x) = -3x^5 + 9x^4 - 7x^3 - 3x^2 - 19$.

Number of Zeros

Positive Real	Negative Real	Complex
☐	☐	2
☐	1	☐

10. How many zeros does $P(x) = (x^3 - 4)^2 + 7x$ have?

11. How many zeros does $P(x) = 7x - 3x^4 + x^3$ have?

12. How many zeros does $P(x) = (x + 2)^3 - x^5$ have?

13. Write a fourth-degree polynomial function that has zeros of 5, −3, 2, and 0.

14. **MP 2, 3** Carlotta says the polynomial function $P(x) = (x^3 - 4x)^2 - 3x + 11$ will have three zeros because the largest exponent in the function is three.

   a What mistake did Carlotta make in her reasoning?

   b How many zeros does the polynomial actually have?

15. **MP 2, 7** The product of four consecutive integers is 7920. Use x to represent the smallest integer.

   a Write a polynomial function in standard form to model this situation, where the zeros of the function are the possible values of x.

   b Determine the minimum number of real solutions for x, and explain your reasoning.

16. Write a polynomial expression of degree three, which can be shown by Descartes' rule of signs to have exactly one negative and two complex zeros.

17. **MP 1, 7** The polynomial $P(x) = x^4 - 16x^3 + 94x^2 - 240x + 225$ has 2 distinct, real zeros, each with a multiplicity of two. Find the zeros.

3.7 Transformations of Polynomial Functions

With transformations of polynomials, we can apply the same rules as for functions of the form $f(x) = a(x - h)^n + k$. We graph $f(x) = x^3 - 20x$ and $g(x) = x^3 - 20x + 7$. As expected, $g(x)$ is obtained by translating $f(x)$ up by 7, since $k = 7$.

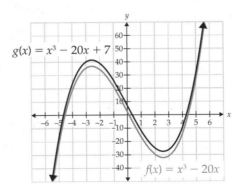

The leading coefficient of a polynomial, $f(x) = ax^n$, determines the end behavior of the function. For example, if the leading coefficient is positive, such as $f(x) = x^3$, the function decreases as x goes toward negative infinity, and increases as x goes toward positive infinity. If the leading coefficient of a polynomial is negative, such as $g(x) = -x^3$, the graph is flipped about the y-axis. The function increases as x goes toward negative infinity, and decreases as x goes toward positive infinity.

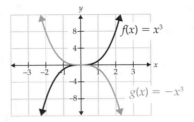

MODEL PROBLEM

Graph $f(x) = x^4$ and $g(x) = (x + 2)^4 + 3$. Compare and contrast the graphs. Identify h and k and use them in your comparison.

SOLUTION

In the transformation from $f(x)$ to $g(x)$, $h = -2$ and $k = 3$. The graph of $g(x)$ is shifted 2 to the left (because $h = -2$) and up 3 (because $k = 3$) compared to the graph of $f(x)$.

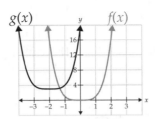

PRACTICE

1. A graph of a polynomial function is shown. Which of the following statements is true of the graphed function?

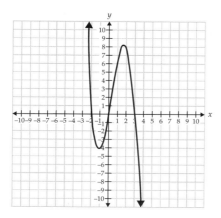

- A. The degree is odd; the leading coefficient is positive.
- B. The degree is even; the leading coefficient is positive.
- C. The degree is odd; the leading coefficient is negative.
- D. The degree is even; the leading coefficient is negative.

2. What does the graph of $x^3 - 5$ look like compared to the graph of x^3?

- A. $x^3 - 5$ is graph of x^3 translated left 5.
- B. Not enough information to tell.
- C. $x^3 - 5$ is graph of x^3 translated up 5.
- D. $x^3 - 5$ is graph of x^3 translated down 5.

3. The function $g(x) = x^5 + 7x^4 + 8x^3 - 16x^2 + 2$ has five x-intercepts. If the graph is shifted 2 units to the left, how many x-intercepts will there be?

- A. 3
- B. 5
- C. 7
- D. 0

4. A student wants to shift the function $f(x) = x^2 + (x - 3)^2$ vertically up 4 units and left 3 units and write it in standard form. Identify in which step the error occurred.

Step 1: $f(x) = x^2 + (x - 3)^2 = 2x^2 - 6x + 9$

Step 2: $g(x) = 2(x - 3)^2 - 6(x - 3) + 9 + 4$

Step 3: $g(x) = 2x^2 - 12x + 18 - 6x + 18 + 9 + 4$

Step 4: $g(x) = 2x^2 - 18x + 49$

5. What is the value of k that will translate $g(x) = 2x^4 + 3x^2 - 6x - 4 + k$ up 4 units from $f(x) = 2x^4 + 3x^2 - 6x - 9$?

6. Graph $f(x) = x^4 + 5x^2 + x + 7$ and $g(x) = x^4 + 5x^2 + x + 4$, then describe the transformation from $f(x)$ to $g(x)$.

7. Sketch the graphs of the functions $y = x^2$ and $y = x^4$ on the same set of axes. What are the differences and similarities in these graphs?

8. Sketch the graphs of the functions $y = x^3$ and $y = x^5$ on the same set of axes. What are the differences and similarities in these graphs?

9. Sketch both sides of the equation as separate functions and solve graphically: $x^4 = 2x - x^2$. State the solutions.

10. MP 7 Describe what happens to the graph of the polynomial function $f(x) = x^3 - 2x^2 - 5x + 6$ when the sign of each coefficient is reversed.

11. MP 7 Describe what happens to the graph of the polynomial function $f(x) = x^3 + x^2 - 17x + 15$ when x is replaced with $-x$.

12. Consider the parent function $y = x^3$ and the function $y = (x - h)^3 + k$. Describe the kind of values of h and k that move the parent function to the right and down.

13. Consider $f(x) = (x + 2)(x + 9)(x - 8)$ and $h(x) = (x - 1)(x + 6)(x - 11)$. Describe the transformation that occurs from $f(x)$ to $h(x)$.

14. Describe three transformations that change $y = x^5$ into $y = -(x + 2)^5 + 3$.

15. Kaitlin wants to write a function that is shifted 6 units vertically down from the function $f(x) = x^5 + 3x^4 + 2x^3 + x$. She writes the function $g(x) = 6x^5 + 3x^4 + 2x^3 + x$. Is Kaitlin correct? Explain your answer.

16. The function $g(x) = x^2 + 17$ has no x-intercepts. State a single transformation that will produce a function $h(x)$ with two x-intercepts.

Practice Problems continue . . .

Practice Problems continued . . .

17. The function $g(x) = -(x - 5)^2 - 6$ has no x-intercepts. State a single transformation that will produce a function $h(x)$ with one x-intercept.

18. A student wants to shift the graph of $f(x) = 2x^3 + 2x$ up by 1 unit and obtains the function $g(x) = 2x^3 + 6x^2 + 8x + 4$. What did the student do wrong, and what is the correct $g(x)$?

19. Find the cubic polynomial with leading coefficient -1 that has the roots shown in the graph.

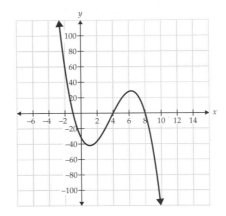

LESSON 3.8

3.8 Modeling with Polynomial Functions

Spreadsheet and Graphing Calculator: Modeling Polynomial Functions

Polynomial functions can be used to model real-world situations. As a water tank is being emptied, the height of the remaining water is measured every ten minutes. The table provides the numbers and the scatter plot gives you a visual sense of the data.

The scatter plot does not appear to be linear. Since the points do not rise and fall (or fall and rise), it also does not appear to be quadratic. It turns out that this data can be modeled by a *cubic regression*. In a cubic regression, the data points are modeled with a cubic function. You can use a spreadsheet or a graphing calculator to do the cubic regression.

Time Elapsed (minutes)	Height of Water in Tank (meters)
0	7
10	4.42
20	3.27
30	3.09
40	2.85
50	2.11
60	0

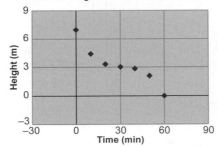

Measure of Height of Water in Tank Over Time

Spreadsheet

In a spreadsheet, start by entering the data and creating a scatter plot. Make sure the chart is selected, and then choose **Add Trendline** from the **Chart** menu. To do a polynomial regression, choose the **Polynomial** option under **Trend/Regression type**. Choose an order of 3 to reflect the cubic polynomial. You can add the model equation and the coefficient of determination, r^2, using the **Options** tab.

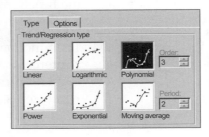

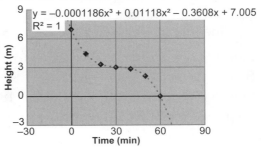

Measure of Height of Water in Tank Over Time

$y = -0.0001186x^3 + 0.01118x^2 - 0.3608x + 7.005$
$R^2 = 1$

170 Chapter 3: Polynomials

Graphing Calculator

Start by entering the data and creating a scatter plot. Then, choose cubic regression. To do this, press [STAT] and then scroll right to the **CALC** menu. Scroll down to **6:CubicReg** and press [ENTER] to set up the **CubicReg** command. Then enter the parameters and do the regression as for linear regression.

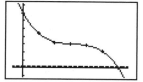

The calculator shows an r^2 of 0.9998037497. For comparison, a linear regression of these points results in $r^2 = 0.881$, and a quadratic regression gives $r^2 = 0.889$. The cubic regression is a better fit for the data since the r^2 value is the highest.

MODEL PROBLEM

MP 2, 4, 5, 7 A student is choosing between two animal population models. The numbers used are in thousands of animals, and the time is in years. One model uses the population formula $p = 0.1t^3 + 0.25t^2 - 0.9t + 2$. The other model sets the population equal to one plus the absolute value of time minus one. The models are for zero to 2.5 years.

    a Graph the models.

    b What population do the models start with?

    c At what time(s) do the models show identical populations?

    d Which model has the population closest to extinction?

    e Which model shows the greatest rate of change?

    f Which model shows the largest population at the end?

    g Discuss the constraints of the domain and range of the model.

SOLUTION

a   Graph

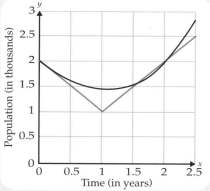

First, graph the absolute value expression $d = |t - 1| + 1$. It has values of 1 for h and 1 for k, so we translate the graph one to the right and one up from the origin compared to the parent function. The domain is 0 to 2.5 years. Next, graph the polynomial function $d = 0.1t^3 + 0.25t^2 - 0.9t + 2$.

b   Starting populations   2000 animals   The models show identical populations at 0 years. Both have 2000 animals then.

c   Graphs show identical populations   0 years, about 1.6 years, about 2.1 years   The model graphs show identical populations three times: at 0 years, about 1.6 years, and about 2.1 years.

d   Population extinct when $p = 0$ The population is closest to extinction when it is closest to 0. The absolute value function has the lowest value, 1000.

e   Rate of change   The polynomial function has a greater rate of change than the absolute value function between about 1.5–2.5 years. The average slope is greatest between those points.

Model Problem continues . . .

f Greatest value?　The polynomial function has a greater value at 2.5 years.

g Domain and range　Both expressions have a value of 2 when $t = 0$. You can see this from the graph or evaluate the expressions. The domain of the function is from 0 (since time cannot be negative) to 2.5 years, since the model is described as having that upper limit. The theoretical range has to be zero or positive—there cannot be a negative number of animals. The models predict a range from about 1000 to 2900 animals.

PRACTICE

1. A researcher is comparing two different models, $p = 2|t - 2| + 2$ and $p = 0.2t^3 - 0.3t^2 - 1.7t + 6$, for representing a population of prairie dogs over a four-year period. The two models, which express the prairie dog population in thousands, are shown on the graph below. In both models, the starting value for t is 0 and the ending value is 4.

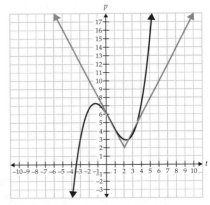

a What is the starting population for both models?

b What is the lowest population predicted by the absolute value model?

c Which model predicts a larger population after three years?

d After four years, which model predicts a larger population?

2. The polynomial function $y = x^3 - 4x^2 + 13$ models the number of students requesting tutoring at a university during a six-month period. The model is appropriate for $x = 0$ to $x = 6$, where x is the number of months and y is the number of students in hundreds. How many students requested tutoring when $x = 1$?

3. The functions $p = -5|x - 2| + 5$ and $p = -\dfrac{1}{3}x(x - 3)(x + 3)$ represent possible models showing the population of gray wolves in a state park over the course of about three decades. The absolute value model has a domain $1 < x < 3$ and the polynomial model has a domain $0 < x < 3$, where x is the number of decades since 1960. The population, p, is given in tens of wolves. For example, $p = 4$ represents 40 wolves. Which function depicts the highest population of wolves during the given time period? Explain how you know from looking at the graph.

4. A person dives off a springboard 7 feet above the surface of the water into a pool. Two possible models to describe the height, y, of the diver above the surface of the water are $y_1 = 2x^3 - 12x^2 + 16x + 7$ and $y_2 = -2|x - 1.5| + 10$. The domain for both models is $0 \le x \le 3$, where x is the time in seconds, and the height is measured in feet above the surface of the water. Decide which of the models better describes the height of the diver over time. Explain your reasoning.

5. The models $P_A = x^3 - x^2 - 2x + 3$ and $P_B = x^2$ show the population of two species of animals from $x = 0$ to $x = 2$ years. The populations are in thousands. At one point during the two years, the populations of the two species were the same. What was the population of each species when this occurred?

Practice Problems continue . . .

6. The function $p(x) = -2x^3 + 6x^2 + 2$ models the price of a stock over a four-month period of time.

    a Sketch the graph of the function. Choose an appropriate domain and range.

    b Describe what happens to the price of the stock between months 2 and 4.

7. A student plots the data of a population of animals housed in shelters over a period of 4 years, as shown below. The student will use her graphing calculator to find an equation that best fits the data. She has the choice of finding a linear, quadratic, or cubic equation. Which model do you think the student should start with? Explain your choice.

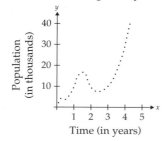

8. The population (in hundreds) of honeybees in an experimental hive can be modeled by the function $p = 0.01x^3 - 0.02x^2 + 1.55$ for 0 to 10 months. What is the population of the hive at the beginning of the experiment and at 10 months?

9. The graph of a data set from an experiment is shown below, along with two possible models. Katie is unsure which model best fits the data, so she plots another value from her experiment, shown by the "X" in the figure. Knowing this, which model best fits the data? Explain.

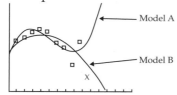

10. Consider the graphs below of linear and polynomial models for the data points in an experiment. Which model is best for the data points? Explain your answer.

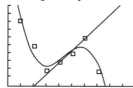

11. The price of gold fluctuates each month, as shown in the table.

Month	Price ($)
1	8.1
2	8.5
3	9
4	8.3
5	7.9
6	7.5
7	6
8	5.8
9	5.9
10	6.5
11	7.1
12	8.3

    a Create a scatter plot of the data using a spreadsheet or graphing calculator.

    b Find a polynomial model to fit the data.

12. The equation $p = x^3 + 2x^2 + 5$ gives the population of a rural town over a 20-year period, with x in years, starting at $x = 0$. Use the model to find the population of the town after 15 years.

13. **MP 2, 3, 4** An investment banker records the price of two different stocks over the course of 5 months. The prices are in dollars and the time is in months. The first stock is modeled by $p = 2|t - 3| + 4$. The second stock is modeled by $p = t^3 - 5t^2 + 4t + 9$.

    a Sketch a graph of the functions to show the price of the stocks. Choose an appropriate domain and range.

    b At $t = 0$ months, which stock had a lower value? What was the value, in dollars?

    c During the first 3 months, which stock reached a higher value?

    d During the first 4 months, how many times were the prices of the two stocks equal? How can you tell this from the graph?

    e An investor purchases both stocks when the prices are the same just after 3 months. Based on the future trends shown in the graph, which stock appears to be the better investment? Explain your answer.

Practice Problems continue . . .

14. The functions represent the distances from home for two people during a day. The distance, y, is in miles and the time, x, is in hours.

Marlen: $y = x(x - 4)(x - 5)$

Truman: $y = -3|x - 2| + 8$

a   Sketch graphs of the functions together on the same set of axes. Choose an appropriate domain and range. Consider only this part of the graphs for the next three questions.

b   At $x = 0$, how far is each person away from home?

c   Over the course of the day, who travels farther from home? How do you know?

d   Who returns home first? Explain how you know from the graph.

15. **MP 2, 4, 5** A realtor tracks the price of two houses over two years. The models represent the prices of the two houses from $x = 0$ to $x = 2$ years and the prices, y, are in tens of thousands of dollars.

House 1: $y_1 = 4x^3 - 12x^2 + 8x + 4$

House 2: $y_2 = 8x^3 - 24x^2 + 16x + 5$

a   When the realtor started tracking the prices, which house had a higher price? What was the price of the more expensive house?

b   Two times during the two-year period, the prices of the houses were the same. Find the approximate number of months when the prices were the same. Give your answer as a whole number between 0 and 24.

c   Which house price fluctuated the most during the two years? Explain your answer.

d   According to the models, which house would have been a better investment?

e   Sketch a graph of the models on the same axes, using an appropriate window for the two-year period of time.

• Multi-Part PROBLEM Practice •

MP 2, 4 The population of a bacteria sample is represented in the table on the right.

a   Make a scatter plot of the data.

b   Find a polynomial equation that best fits the data. Use the r-squared value to decide which degree polynomial is the closest fit. Discuss possible solutions.

c   Use your equation to predict the number of bacteria that will be present after 6 days and after 10 days.

Day	Number of Bacteria
0	28
1	132
2	217
3	336
4	525
5	818

3.9 Solving Systems of Polynomial Equations

Solving Polynomial Systems Graphically

A system of equations can be solved graphically by noting the location of the intersections of the graphs of the equations. We solve the system

$\dfrac{x^2}{16} - \dfrac{y^2}{25} = 1$ and $x^2 + y^2 = 16$ by graphing.

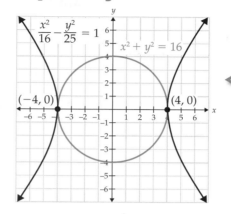

The solution to a system of equations, whether it is a complex system or not, is always the point(s) of intersection.

1. Graph hyperbola.	$\dfrac{x^2}{16} - \dfrac{y^2}{25} = 1$	Graph the hyperbola. The hyperbola intersects the x-axis at 4 and -4.
2. Graph circle.	$x^2 + y^2 = 16$	The circle is centered at the origin with a radius of 4.
3. Solutions are intersection points.	$(4, 0)$ and $(-4, 0)$	Note the intersection points. These are the solutions.

MODEL PROBLEM

Solve the system $x^2 + y^2 = 25$ and $y = \dfrac{4}{3}x$, given the graph of $x^2 + y^2 = 25$.

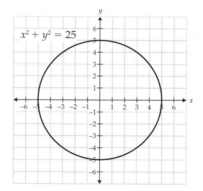

SOLUTION

Graph line

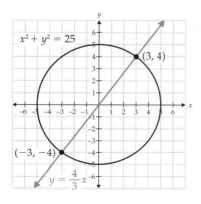

The line passes through the origin and has a slope of $\dfrac{4}{3}$.

Solutions $(3, 4)$ and $(-3, -4)$ Note the intersection points. These are the solutions.

Graphing Calculator: Solving a System of Polynomial Equations

We can use a calculator to solve a system of polynomial equations, $y = x^3 + 8x^2 - 101x - 468$ and $y = 2x^2 + 6x - 108$. We do this by graphing the two equations and noting their intersection points.

1. **Enter equation.** Use $\boxed{Y=}$ to get to the equation entry screen, and type the polynomials into separate Y variable lines.

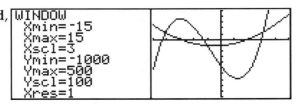

2. **Graph the equation.** To graph, press $\boxed{ZOOM}$ **6:ZStandard**, and graph the function using the graphing window of $-15 < x < 15$ and $-1000 < y < 500$.

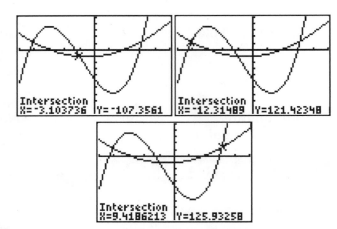

3. **Find the intersections.** Use $\boxed{2nd}$ $\boxed{TRACE}$ **5:Intersect** to find the solutions. You can use the $\boxed{◄}$ and $\boxed{►}$ keys to move the cursor so it is near the intersection point, and then press $\boxed{ENTER}$. The intersection points for $y = x^3 + 8x^2 - 101x - 468$ and $y = 2x^2 + 6x - 108$ are $x \approx -12.31$ and $y \approx 121.42$; $x \approx -3.10$ and $y \approx -107.36$; and $x \approx 9.42$ and $y \approx 125.93$.

MODEL PROBLEM

MP 5 Solve $y = 3x - 5$ and $x^2 + y^2 = 25$ using a graphing calculator. (This is a line and a circle.)

SOLUTION

We must first solve the second equation for y in terms of x.

$$x^2 + y^2 = 25$$
$$y^2 = 25 - x^2$$
$$y = \pm\sqrt{25 - x^2}$$

Enter equations

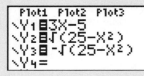

Graph the equations. Find the points of intersection. The solutions to $y = 3x - 5$ and $x^2 + y^2 = 25$ are $x = 3$, $y = 4$, and $x = 0$, $y = -5$.

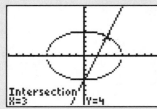
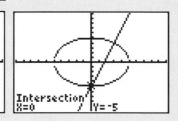

Solving Polynomial Systems Algebraically

> Solving more complex systems of equations by substitution or elimination uses the same process as solving less complex systems of equations by substitution or elimination.

You can also solve a complex system of equations algebraically using substitution or elimination.

MODEL PROBLEMS

1. Solve the system $y = 4x$ and $\dfrac{x^2}{8} - \dfrac{y^2}{256} = 1$ by substitution.

SOLUTION

Substitute
$$\frac{x^2}{8} - \frac{(4x)^2}{256} = 1$$
Substitute $4x$ for y in the quadratic equation, based on the equation $y = 4x$.

Solve for x
$$\frac{x^2}{8} - \frac{16x^2}{256} = 1$$
Solve the resulting equation. x equals positive or negative 4.

$$\frac{2x^2}{16} - \frac{x^2}{16} = 1$$

$$\frac{x^2}{16} = 1$$

$$x^2 = 16$$

$$x = \pm 4$$

Substitute and solve for y
$$y = (4)(4) = 16$$
$$y = (4)(-4) = -16$$
Substitute the values for x back into the first equation and see that y equals 16 or -16.

State solutions $(4, 16)$ and $(-4, -16)$
State the two solutions. The two solutions mean the graphs intersect at two points.

2. Solve the system $3x^2 + 4y^2 = 91$ and $x^2 + y^2 = 25$ by elimination.

SOLUTION

Eliminate one variable
$$\begin{array}{r} 3x^2 + 4y^2 = 91 \\ -\,(3x^2 + 3y^2 = 75) \\ \hline y^2 = 16 \end{array}$$
Multiply the second equation by 3, and then subtract the equations.

Solve $\qquad y = \pm 4$
There are two solutions for y, $+4$ or -4.

Substitute and solve for x
$$x^2 + 4^2 = 25$$
$$x^2 + (-4)^2 = 25$$
$$x^2 = 9$$
$$x = \pm 3$$
Substitute $+4$ or -4 into one of the equations, and see that x can equal $+3$ or -3.

State solutions $(3, 4), (3, -4), (-3, 4), (-3, -4)$
State the solutions as ordered pairs. Note that both values of x are assigned to each value of y. The four solutions mean the two graphs intersect in four locations.

PRACTICE

Exercises 1–10: Solve by graphing. State the solutions.

1. $y = x^2; y = 4x - 3$

2. $y = x^2 - 5; y = -6x - 15$

3. $x^2 + y^2 = 169; y = 5$

4. $x^2 + y^2 = 25; x^2 - 8x + 19 = y$

5. $x^2 + y^2 = 36; 4x^2 + y^2 = 144$

6. $y = -\dfrac{1}{x}; y = -4x$

7. $y = \dfrac{1}{x}; x^2 + y^2 = 2$

8. $y = \dfrac{1}{4}x^2 - 4; x^2 + y^2 = 16$

9. $4x^2 + y^2 = 16; y = -2x + 4$

10. **MP 2, 6** $x^2 - 16y^2 = 64; y = \dfrac{x}{3}$

Exercises 11–20: Solve algebraically.

11. $y = x^2 + x; y = -11x - 35$

12. $x^2 + y^2 = 16; y = -x$

13. $x^2 + y^2 = 25; y = \dfrac{1}{9}x^2 - 5$

14. $y = x^2 + 4; x^2 + y^2 = 1$

15. $x^2 - y^2 = 9; y = \dfrac{1}{2}x + \dfrac{3}{2}$

16. $x^2 + 9y^2 = 36; y = \dfrac{x^2}{18} - 2$

17. $y = \dfrac{4}{x}; x^2 + y^2 = 8$

18. $x^2 + 4y^2 = 45; 4x^2 + y^2 = 45$

19. $x^2 - y^2 = 16; x^2 + y^2 = 34$

20. $y^2 - x^2 = 4; x = y^2 - 4$

21. **MP 1, 2, 7** When a two-digit number is divided by the product of its digits, the quotient is $2\dfrac{2}{3}$. The sum of the number and the number written with the same digits, but in the reverse order, is 110. Find the number. (Hint: Write the number as $10x + y$, where x and y are its digits.)

22. **MP 1, 2, 7** A two-digit number is 22 more than the difference of the squares of its digits. Also, the difference of the number and the number written with the same digits, but in the reverse order, is equal to 54. Find the number.

• Multi-Part PROBLEM Practice •

MP 6, 7 Consider $x^2 + y^2 = 169$ and $y = -\dfrac{2}{3}x + 13$.

a Describe the graph of each equation.

b By observing the characteristics of each graph, what point do you know will be a solution to this system of equations? Why?

c Graph both equations on the same coordinate plane, by hand.

d Algebraically find the point(s) of intersection of the two graphs (i.e., the solution(s) to the system of equations). Explain why you do not need to use the quadratic formula to solve this equation.

Chapter 3 Key Ideas

3.1 Multivariable Polynomials

- Add and subtract multivariable polynomials by combining like terms.

3.2 Dividing Polynomials

- Polynomials can be divided in a fashion similar to long division of numbers.
- Synthetic division provides an efficient way to divide polynomials. It can be used when the divisor is of the form $x - c$.

3.3 Remainder and Factor Theorems

- The remainder theorem states that for a polynomial $P(x)$, the value of the function $P(c)$ equals the remainder when $P(x)$ is divided by $x - c$.
- The factor theorem states that the polynomial $P(x)$ has $x - r$ as a factor if and only if r is a root of the equation $P(x) = 0$.

3.4 Solving Polynomial Equations Algebraically

- A polynomial equation where the variable appears to the third power and no higher is called a *cubic equation*. Some cubic equations can be solved by factoring.
- A polynomial equation where the variable appears to the fourth power and no higher is called a *quartic equation*. Some quartic equations can be solved by reducing them to quadratic equations, and solving them as you would any quadratic equation.

3.5 Finding Zeros of Polynomial Functions

- The real zeros of a polynomial can be estimated from the x-intercepts of its graph.
- The fundamental theorem of algebra states that every polynomial function of degree $n \geq 1$ has at least one complex zero. The linear factorization theorem on the number of roots follows from the fundamental theorem of algebra, and states that every polynomial function of degree $n \geq 1$ with complex coefficients has n complex zeros.

3.6 Optional: Descartes' Rule of Signs

- Descartes' rule of signs enables you to calculate the number of possible positive and negative real roots of a polynomial function using the number of variations of sign of the polynomial.

3.7 Transformations of Polynomial Functions

- Like other functions you have seen, polynomial functions can be translated horizontally or vertically, or rotated.

3.8 Modeling with Polynomial Functions

- Polynomial functions can be used to model situations.
- Cubic regression can be used to determine if a cubic polynomial model is the best fit.

3.9 Solving Systems of Polynomial Equations

- Systems of polynomial equations can be solved both algebraically and graphically, just like systems of linear equations. The intersection point(s) on the graph are the solutions to the system.

CHAPTER 3 REVIEW

1. Divide $f(x) = 3x^3 + 6x^2 - x + 4$ by $x + 2$.

A. $3x^2 + 5$

B. $3x^2 - 1 + \dfrac{6}{x - 2}$

C. $3x^2 - x + 6$

D. $3x^2 - 1 + \dfrac{6}{x + 2}$

2. Is $x + 6$ a factor of $P(x) = -x^4 + 4x^3 + 432$?

A. Yes

B. No

C. Not enough information to tell

3. Is $x - a + b$ a factor of
$x^3 + (b - a)x^2 - a^2x - a^2(b - a)$?

A. Yes

B. No

C. Not enough information to tell

Exercises 4–6: Divide.

4. $(-3x^4 + 5x^2 - x - 4) \div (x + 3)$

5. $(x^2 + 11x + 30) \div (x + 5)$

6. $(x^4 + 15x^3 + 33x^2 - 371x - 1470) \div (x - 5)$

7. Find the remainder: $(x^2 + 9x + 25) \div (x + 6)$

8. **MP 2, 7** Write a fifth-degree polynomial in standard form $ax^5 + bx^4 + cx^3 + dx^2 + ex + f$ that divides by $x - 3$ evenly (with a remainder of 0).

Exercises 9–12: Use the remainder theorem to state the remainder.

9. $(x^5 - 25x^3 + 7) \div (x + 5)$

10. $(x^4 - x^2 + x - 5) \div (x - 1)$

11. $(4x^5 + x^4 + x^2 + 1) \div (x - 2)$

12. $(x^6 - 2x^4 + 3x^2 - 4) \div (x - 1)$

Exercises 13–14: State a polynomial that has the zeros given below and 1 as the leading coefficient.

13. Roots: 6, −2, and 3

14. Roots: −5, 1, and −1

15. Write a polynomial function with three distinct prime zeros.

Exercises 16–21: Determine how many linear factors there are for each polynomial.

16. $x^5 + 3x^3 - 1$

17. $x^4 - x^3 + x^2 - x$

18. $b^6 - 3b^3 + b^2 - b + 2$

19. a^8

20. $u^3 - 2u^2 + u - 1$

21. $v^{101} - v^{67} + v^2 + 3$

22. Factor $x^3 + (b - a)x^2 - a^2x - a^2(b - a)$.

23. a Evaluate the function
$P(x) = x^3 - 3x^2 - 6x + 8$ for all integers from −3 to 5. Record your answers in a table headed with x, $P(x)$.

   b Based on your table, what are the zeros of the function?

   c What happens to the sign value of the function on either side of each zero?

24. Use the graph of the polynomial function $f(x) = 2x^3 - x^2 - 10x + 5$ to approximate its real zeros, to the nearest tenth.

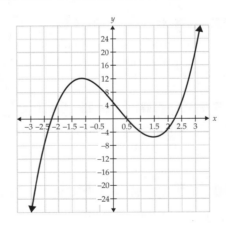

Chapter Review continues . . .

25. `MP 7` Consider a polynomial of the form $P(x) = Ax^3 + Bx^2 + Cx + D$.

    a State which value(s) would need to be changed, and by what amount, to shift the graph of the polynomial up by 5 units.

    b State which value(s) would need to be changed, and by what amount, to shift the graph of the polynomial to the right by 2 units.

26. `MP 3, 7` Two zeros of a polynomial are $3 - 2i$ and $1 + i$. What is the lowest possible degree of the polynomial, and how do you know?

27. `MP 3, 7` Is it possible to have a polynomial of odd degree that has no real zeros? Explain your reasoning.

28. `MP 2, 7` Consider the polynomial $x^n - 5^n$, where n can be any positive integer. Without knowing the value of n, state a factor of the polynomial.

Cumulative Review

for Chapters 1–3

1. Which of the following is equivalent to $(x + y)^2$?

- A. $x^2 + 2xy + y^2$
- B. $x + 2xy + y^2$
- C. $x^2y^2 + 2y + 2x$

2. **MP 2** If $x^3 + 2x^2 - 3x - 5 = 0$ and $x = m$ is a solution, which is true about the polynomial $P(x) = x^3 + 2x^2 - 3x - 5$?

- A. $P(m) = 0$
- B. $P(m) = m$
- C. $(x + m)$ is a factor
- D. $(x - 0)$ is a factor

3. A student analyzes the graphs of two polynomials from a system of equations.

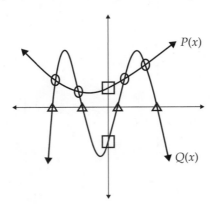

Which of the student's statements is incorrect?

- A. The circles and rectangles together represent the zeros of $P(x)$.
- B. The circles represent the solutions to the system of equations.
- C. The triangles represent the zeros of $Q(x)$.
- D. The rectangles represent the y-intercepts of $P(x)$ and $Q(x)$.

4. Which of the following could be the coordinates of an x-intercept of the graph of a function?

- A. $(-1, 2)$
- B. $(0, -1)$
- C. $(5, 0)$
- D. $(2, -1)$

5. The solutions to $x^2 - 4x + 5 = 0$ are

- A. $i, -i$
- B. $-2 + i, 2 - i$
- C. $-4 + 2i, 4 - 2i$
- D. $-2 + 2i, -2 - 2i$

Exercises 6–10: Write as a polynomial in standard form.

6. $(5x + 2)^2$

7. $(5x - 8)^2$

8. $(7x + 3)(7x - 3)$

9. $[(6x + 6) - x^5]^2$

10. $(6z^7x - 3x^4z^6)^2$

Exercises 11–14: Factor.

11. $x^2 - 22x + 121$

12. $16xy + 104x - 14y - 91$

13. $16x^3 - 20x^2 + 68x - 85$

14. $33x^3 + 44x^2 + 12x + 16$

Exercises 15–19: Divide.

15. $(x^2 + 13x + 40) \div (x + 5)$

16. $(x^2 - 11x + 24) \div (x - 8)$

17. $(25x^2 + 65x + 40) \div (5x + 5)$

18. $(20x^2 + 53x + 35) \div (4x + 5)$

19. $(36x^2 - 81) \div (6x + 9)$

20. Use synthetic division and the remainder theorem to find $P(-5)$ if $P(x) = 2x^4 + 7x^3 + 70x + 8$.

21. Determine the remainder when $-3x^4 + x + 19$ is divided by $x + 7$ by applying the remainder theorem (in other words, do not use long or synthetic division).

22. State a polynomial equation for which the leading coefficient is 1 and the solutions are -4, 9, and 1. Expand and simplify the polynomial.

23. **MP 3, 7** Under what circumstances will evaluating a polynomial function for $P(x)$ produce the exact same polynomial function as evaluating for $P(-x)$? Why does this occur?

24. How many real solutions does the quadratic equation $7x^2 + 4x + 10 = 0$ have?

Exercises 25–26: Solve.

25. **MP 5, 6** $(4p - 2)^2 - 10(4p - 2) + 21 = 0$

26. $p^4 - 4p^2 - 45 = 0$

27. Solve the system of equations. $y = x - \dfrac{1}{x}$; $\left(x - \dfrac{1}{x}\right)^2 - 3\left(x - \dfrac{1}{x}\right) - 4 = 0$

28. Find the x-intercepts of the graph of $f(x) = x^2 + 7x + 12$.

29. **MP 3, 8** Show that the quadratic equation $ax^2 + bx + c = 0$, where $a \neq 0$ has two different positive solutions if $a \cdot c > 0$, $a \cdot b < 0$, and $b^2 - 4ac > 0$.

30. **MP 4** Yummy Flakes Breakfast Cereal is increasing the size of the boxes it uses to package its cereal. The formula $V = lwh$ is used to calculate the volume of a box with a given length, width, and height.

a The existing boxes have a length of 10 inches, a width of 6 inches, and a height of 8 inches. Sketch one of the existing boxes and label the dimensions. Then calculate the volume of the box.

b For the new boxes, each dimension will be increased by some unknown amount, represented by x. Make a sketch of one of the new boxes. Using x, label each dimension with an expression representing its length.

c Write a polynomial function that could be used to calculate the volume of the new boxes for any value of x.

d The company decided the volume of each new cereal box will be 936 cubic inches. Explain how you could use the function you wrote in part **c**, and the factor theorem, to find the value(s) of x. (Note: You do not need to factor the function, just explain the steps you would follow.)

e Based on the scenario above, should you consider values of x that are negative to be valid solutions? Why or why not?

Chapter Content

Vocabulary

closed system

complex rational expression

extraneous solution

least common denominator

least common multiple

rational expression

reciprocal function

<hr>

LESSON 4.1

4.1 Multiplying and Dividing Rational Expressions

Simplifying Rational Expressions

A **rational expression** is an expression that can be written as the quotient of two polynomials. They can be written with a fraction bar, such as $\dfrac{x^4 + 2x - 5}{4x + 7}$, or division symbol, such as $(x^4 + 2x - 5) \div (4x + 7)$.

As with numeric fractions, you can simplify, multiply, and divide rational expressions. To *simplify a rational expression* means to perform operations so that there are no common factors in the numerator and denominator.

Operations with rational expressions are part of a closed system. In a **closed system**, the result of an operation is of the same type as the initial terms or factors. In other words, adding, subtracting, or multiplying any two rational expressions results in another rational expression. Dividing a rational expression by any rational expression other than zero also results in a rational expression.

> Remember, the horizontal bar of a fraction is a grouping symbol. Do the operations in the numerator and in the denominator **before** the division.

A common error in simplifying rational expressions involves canceling incorrectly. For example, in $\dfrac{5x^2 - 1}{5x^2 + 4}$, $5x^2$ is in both the numerator and denominator, but it is not a common factor. $5x^2$ is a term added to -1 in the numerator and to 4 in the denominator. You can only cancel common factors, not terms that are added.

MODEL PROBLEMS

1. Simplify $\dfrac{x^2 - 2x - 8}{x^5 - 4x^4}$.

SOLUTION

Factor
$$\dfrac{x^2 - 2x - 8}{x^5 - 4x^4} = \dfrac{(x + 2)(x - 4)}{x^4(x - 4)}$$
Factor out the common factor x^4 in the denominator.

Cancel common factors
$$\dfrac{(x + 2)\cancel{(x - 4)}}{x^4\cancel{(x - 4)}} = \dfrac{(x + 2)}{x^4}$$
Cancel the common factor of $x - 4$. Since we canceled out the common factor $x - 4$, the simplified expression is equivalent to the original expression, *except* for $x = 4$, since that value of x makes the denominator 0 (which would make the original expression undefined).

Model Problems continue . . .

2. **MP 1, 7** Simplify $\dfrac{x(x + 7) - (2x - 6)}{-x^2 + 9}$.

SOLUTION

Write numerator as polynomial	$\dfrac{x(x + 7) - (2x - 6)}{-x^2 + 9}$ $\dfrac{x^2 + 5x + 6}{-(x^2 - 9)}$	Simplify the numerator to write it as a polynomial. Factor out -1 in the denominator.
Factor the numerator and denominator	$\dfrac{(x + 2)(x + 3)}{-(x - 3)(x + 3)}$	Factor the numerator and denominator.
Cancel the common factor	$\dfrac{(x + 2)\cancel{(x + 3)}}{-(x - 3)\cancel{(x + 3)}}$ $\dfrac{x + 2}{-(x - 3)} = -\dfrac{x + 2}{x - 3}$	Cancel the common factor. The simplified expression is equivalent to the original expression *except* when $x = -3$, which would result in an undefined expression.

> From this point forward, when we simplify a rational expression, we will assume the variable does not equal a value that causes the original expression to be undefined, unless we say otherwise.

3. **MP 7** For what values of m and p does the rational expression, $\dfrac{(x + m)(x - p)}{x^2 - 2x - 15}$, simplify to 1?

A. $m = -2, p = -15$
B. $m = 3, p = 5$
C. $m = -3, p = -5$
D. $m = 5, p = 3$

SOLUTION

A. The denominator does not factor into $(x - 2)(x + 15)$.

B. **Correct answer**. The denominator factors into $(x + 3)(x - 5)$, therefore if $m = 3$ and $p = 5$, the rational expression is $\dfrac{(x + 3)(x - 5)}{(x + 3)(x - 5)} = 1$.

C. For $m = -3$ and $p = -5$, the rational expression is $\dfrac{[x + (-3)][x - (-5)]}{(x + 3)(x - 5)} = \dfrac{(x - 3)(x + 5)}{(x + 3)(x - 5)} \neq 1$.

D. For $m = 5$ and $p = 3$, the rational expression is $\dfrac{(x + 5)(x - 3)}{(x + 3)(x - 5)} \neq 1$.

PRACTICE

1. What does $\dfrac{(x^2 - 10x + 25)(x + 2)}{5x(x^2 - 3x - 10)}$ equal?

A. $\dfrac{x + 2}{5x}$

B. $\dfrac{(x + 5)(x + 2)}{5x}$

C. $\dfrac{1}{5x}$

D. $\dfrac{x - 5}{5x}$

Exercises 2–18: Simplify.

2. $\dfrac{2x^3 + 8x^2 - 10x}{x^2 + 2x - 3}$

3. $\dfrac{3x^3 + 15x^2 + 18x}{x^2 + x - 6}$

4. $\dfrac{2x^3 - 12x^2 + 16x}{x^2 - 3x - 4}$

Practice Problems continue . . .

5. $\dfrac{7(x-3)}{(-3+x)}$

6. $\dfrac{36x-72}{-6x+12}$

7. $\dfrac{40(4x-x^2)}{5(-8x-2x^2)}$

8. $\dfrac{72x^2-576x}{8x-64}$

9. $\dfrac{4x^2+8x}{x}$

10. $\dfrac{7x^2+9x}{x}$

11. $\dfrac{49x^3+21x}{7x}$

12. $\dfrac{100x^3+40x}{10x}$

13. $\dfrac{x^2+8x+12}{x+2}$

14. $\dfrac{x^2+8x+15}{x+3}$

15. $\dfrac{3-x}{7(x-3)}$

16. $\dfrac{2-x}{7(x-2)}$

17. $\dfrac{8x^2+56x+80}{8x+16}$

18. $\dfrac{7x^2+42x+56}{7x+14}$

Exercises 19–21: For what value(s) of x is each expression undefined?

19. $\dfrac{4x^2+6x+13}{x-3}$

20. $\dfrac{3x^2+5x+9}{x-5}$

21. $\dfrac{3x^2}{-24x^4-141x^3+18x^2}$

Multiplying Rational Expressions

The process of multiplying rational expressions is the same as multiplying numeric fractions, such as $\dfrac{5}{2}\cdot\dfrac{3}{4}=\dfrac{5\cdot3}{2\cdot4}=\dfrac{15}{8}$. Multiply the numerators together for the numerator and multiply the denominators together for the denominator.

> $\dfrac{a}{c}\cdot\dfrac{b}{d}=\dfrac{ab}{cd}$ for any fraction.

When multiplying, you should multiply the constants and variables; for instance, $3x\cdot2x^2=6x^3$. In some cases, you may choose not to multiply binomials or expressions; for instance, you can multiply $\dfrac{3x}{x+2}\cdot\dfrac{2x(x+1)}{x-1}$ and end with $\dfrac{6x^2(x+1)}{(x+2)(x-1)}$. This is called the *factored form*, and it makes later operations, such as solving an equation, easier.

MODEL PROBLEMS

1. Multiply $\dfrac{x+3}{x^2}\cdot\dfrac{4}{x-2}$.

SOLUTION

Multiply numerators and denominators

$$\dfrac{x+3}{x^2}\cdot\dfrac{4}{x-2}=\dfrac{(x+3)4}{x^2(x-2)}$$

Multiply the numerators and denominators.

Distribute

$$\dfrac{(x+3)4}{x^2(x-2)}=\dfrac{4x+12}{x^3-2x^2}$$

Distribute the 4 in the numerator, and distribute the x^2 in the denominator.

Model Problems continue . . .

2. Multiply $\dfrac{x+1}{4x} \cdot \dfrac{8x}{x^2-1}$.

SOLUTION

Multiply	$\dfrac{x+1}{4x} \cdot \dfrac{8x}{x^2-1}$	When multiplying rational expressions, check for common factors and cancel them before multiplying.
	$\dfrac{8x(x+1)}{4x(x^2-1)}$	
Cancel common factors	$\dfrac{2 \cdot \cancel{4x} \cdot (x+1)}{\cancel{4x} \cdot (x^2-1)}$	The factor $4x$ is common to both numerator and denominator, so we cancel it.
	$\dfrac{2(x+1)}{x^2-1}$	
Factor denominator	$\dfrac{2(x+1)}{(x+1)(x-1)}$	The denominator is factored as the difference of two squares.
Cancel common factors	$\dfrac{2\cancel{(x+1)}}{\cancel{(x+1)}(x-1)}$	The expression has a common factor in the numerator and denominator; cancel it.
	$\dfrac{2}{x-1}$	

PRACTICE

Exercises 1–18: Simplify, if possible.

1. $\dfrac{3x}{x+7} \cdot \dfrac{x+7}{x^2-11x}$

2. $\dfrac{x-9}{x^2+6x} \cdot \dfrac{8x}{x-9}$

3. $\dfrac{4x}{2x-3} \cdot \dfrac{2x-3}{x^2+5x}$

4. $\dfrac{x^2+9x+18}{x^2-25} \cdot \dfrac{x+5}{x+3}$

5. $\dfrac{x^2-8x+15}{x^2-16} \cdot \dfrac{x+4}{x-3}$

6. $\dfrac{x+7}{x-3} \cdot \dfrac{x+8}{x+7}$

7. $\dfrac{x+4}{x-5} \cdot \dfrac{x+7}{x+4}$

8. $\dfrac{10(x-3)}{x+9} \cdot \dfrac{x-5}{2(x-3)}$

9. $\dfrac{10(x-5)}{x+7} \cdot \dfrac{x-8}{2(x-5)}$

10. $\dfrac{6x^3+6x^2}{4} \cdot \dfrac{8x}{x^2(x+1)}$

11. $\dfrac{5x^3+5x^2}{3} \cdot \dfrac{6x}{x^2(x+1)}$

12. $\dfrac{x+5}{6x} \cdot \dfrac{6(5-x)}{x^2-25}$

13. $\dfrac{x^2+7x+12}{x^2+10x} \cdot \dfrac{5x^2}{x^2-6x-40}$

14. $\dfrac{x^2+7x+12}{x^2+8x} \cdot \dfrac{4x^2}{x^2-6x-40}$

15. $\dfrac{x^2}{5} \cdot \dfrac{2x}{x+6}$

16. $\dfrac{x+5}{x-6} \cdot \dfrac{x+8}{x+5}$

17. $\dfrac{10(x-3)}{x+9} \cdot \dfrac{x-6}{2(x-3)}$

18. $\dfrac{7x^3+7x^2}{3} \cdot \dfrac{6x}{x^2(x+1)}$

Dividing Rational Expressions

Dividing rational fractions starts with the concept that division by a fraction is equivalent to multiplication by its reciprocal. This is often stated as "invert the divisor and multiply." For instance, the quotient $\frac{1}{3} \div \frac{4}{5}$ is equivalent to

$$\frac{a}{b} \div \frac{c}{d} = \frac{a}{b} \cdot \frac{d}{c} = \frac{ad}{bc}$$

the product $\frac{1}{3} \cdot \frac{5}{4}$, which equals $\frac{5}{12}$. The same process can be used to divide rational expressions. For instance, to perform the operation $\dfrac{\left(\dfrac{3x+1}{7}\right)}{\left(\dfrac{5x-2}{12}\right)}$, invert the

divisor and multiply to get $\dfrac{(3x+1) \cdot 12}{7 \cdot (5x-2)}$.

In a **complex rational expression** the numerator or denominator, or both, contains a rational expression. The expression $\dfrac{\left(5 + \dfrac{3}{y}\right)}{\left(\dfrac{4}{2y-1}\right)}$ is a complex rational expression

since the numerator or denominator contains a rational expression (in this example, both do). When we simplify these expressions, we convert them into rational expressions.

MODEL PROBLEMS

1. Divide $\dfrac{x^2}{2} \div \dfrac{5}{x+1}$.

SOLUTION

Invert divisor and multiply
$$\frac{x^2}{2} \div \frac{5}{x+1}$$
Invert the divisor (second fraction) and multiply.

$$\frac{x^2}{2} \cdot \frac{x+1}{5}$$

Stated with one fraction bar
$$\frac{x^2(x+1)}{2 \cdot 5}$$
Multiply the numerators and denominators.

Perform operations
$$\frac{x^3 + x^2}{10}$$
Distribute x^2 through $(x+1)$.

2. Divide $\dfrac{12x^2 - 2x}{5} \div 2x$.

SOLUTION

Invert and multiply
$$\frac{12x^2 - 2x}{5} \div 2x$$
Invert the divisor and multiply.

$$\frac{12x^2 - 2x}{5} \cdot \frac{1}{2x}$$

Simplify
$$\frac{2x(6x-1)}{5 \cdot 2x}$$
Factor $2x$ in the numerator, and then simplify.

$$\frac{6x-1}{5}$$

Model Problems continue . . .

MODEL PROBLEMS *continued*

3. MP 7 Divide $\dfrac{4x}{x+1} \div \dfrac{2}{x+1}$.

SOLUTION

Invert divisor and multiply

$$\dfrac{4x}{x+1} \div \dfrac{2}{x+1}$$

$$\dfrac{4x}{x+1} \cdot \dfrac{x+1}{2} = \dfrac{4x(x+1)}{2(x+1)}$$

Invert the divisor and multiply.

Cancel common factors $\dfrac{2x \cdot \cancel{2(x+1)}}{\cancel{2(x+1)}} = 2x$

Cancel the common factors $x+1$ and 2.

4. Write $\dfrac{3x}{\dfrac{2}{x^2} - 1}$ as a rational expression.

SOLUTION

Restate denominator

$$\dfrac{3x}{\dfrac{2}{x^2} - 1}$$

First write the denominator as a single rational expression.

$$\dfrac{3x}{\left(\dfrac{2-x^2}{x^2}\right)}$$

Invert denominator and multiply

$3x \cdot \dfrac{x^2}{2-x^2}$

To simplify, invert and multiply.

$$\dfrac{3x^3}{2-x^2}$$

5. Simplify $\dfrac{\dfrac{3}{2x}}{\dfrac{1}{x-4}}$.

SOLUTION

Restate as division $\dfrac{3}{2x} \div \dfrac{1}{x-4}$

Rewrite the complex rational expression as a division statement; the numerator $\dfrac{3}{2x}$ is divided by the denominator, $\dfrac{1}{x-4}$.

Invert divisor and multiply

$\dfrac{3}{2x} \cdot \dfrac{x-4}{1}$

To divide the fractions, invert the divisor and multiply.

$$\dfrac{3x-12}{2x}$$

Model Problems continue . . .

6. **MP 2, 4** The *focal length* of a camera is the distance from the center of the lens to the film (or digital sensor). A typical focal length might be 50 millimeters. The focal length L of a thin camera lens is given by $L = \dfrac{1}{\dfrac{1}{p} + \dfrac{1}{q}}$ where p is the distance between a

> Calculating q will let us have an expression that states how close the lens should be to the film for a picture taken at a distance p.

photographed object and the lens, and q is the distance between the lens and the film. Write the expression for q in terms of L and p.

SOLUTION

Eliminate fractions in denominator

$$L = \frac{pq}{pq} \cdot \frac{1}{\dfrac{1}{p} + \dfrac{1}{q}}$$

To eliminate the fractions in the denominator, multiply the right side of the equation by $\dfrac{pq}{pq}$.

$$L = \frac{pq}{q + p}$$

Eliminate denominator

$$L(q + p) = \cancel{(q + p)} \cdot \frac{pq}{\cancel{(q + p)}}$$

Multiply both sides of the equation by $(q + p)$ to eliminate the denominator.

Combine like terms and solve

$$Lq + Lp = pq$$
$$Lp = pq - Lq$$
$$Lp = q(p - L)$$

Distribute L, combine like terms of q, and solve.

$$q = \frac{Lp}{p - L}$$

PRACTICE

Exercises 1–17: Simplify, if possible.

1. $\dfrac{x^2}{4} \div \dfrac{3x}{x + 5}$

2. $\dfrac{7(x + 6)}{5 - x} \div \dfrac{x + 6}{4(5 - x)}$

3. $\dfrac{5(x + 6)}{5 - x} \div \dfrac{x + 6}{2(5 - x)}$

4. $\dfrac{6x(x^2 + 6)}{x(x + 7)} \div \dfrac{(x^2 + 6)}{3x}$

5. $\dfrac{6x(x^2 + 6)}{x(x + 7)} \div \dfrac{(x^2 + 6)}{4x}$

6. $\dfrac{\left(\dfrac{2}{x + 7}\right)}{\left(\dfrac{x + 2}{9x}\right)}$

7. $\dfrac{\left(\dfrac{4}{x + 10}\right)}{\left(\dfrac{x + 4}{5x}\right)}$

8. $\dfrac{\left(\dfrac{5}{x + 6}\right)}{\left(\dfrac{7}{x} + 1\right)}$

9. $\dfrac{\left(\dfrac{4}{x + 2}\right)}{\left(\dfrac{5}{x} + 1\right)}$

10. $\dfrac{\left(\dfrac{5x + 20}{x + 3}\right)}{\left(\dfrac{x + 4}{5x^2}\right)}$

Practice Problems continue . . .

11. $\dfrac{\left(\dfrac{5x + 35}{x + 2}\right)}{\left(\dfrac{x + 7}{4x^2}\right)}$

12. MP 2 $\dfrac{\left(\dfrac{30}{x + 6}\right)}{\left(\dfrac{5x}{x^2 + 15x + 54}\right)}$

13. MP 2 $\dfrac{\left(\dfrac{30}{x + 5}\right)}{\left(\dfrac{6x}{x^2 + 12x + 35}\right)}$

14. $\dfrac{6(x + 5)}{7 - x} \div \dfrac{x + 5}{3(7 - x)}$

15. $\dfrac{6(x^2 + 4)}{x(x + 9)} \div \dfrac{x^2 + 4}{2x}$

16. $\dfrac{x}{x - y} \div \dfrac{x}{y}$

17. $\dfrac{x^2 - 64}{21} \div \dfrac{x + 8}{9}$

18. MP 3, 6 Louis divided the rational expression using the steps below:

$$\frac{x^2 - 9}{(x - 3)^2 - 36} \div \frac{x + 3}{x + 9}$$

$$\frac{(x - 3)(x + 3)}{(x - 3)(x - 3) - 36} \div \frac{x + 3}{x + 9}$$

$$\frac{x + 3}{(x - 3) - 36} \div \frac{x + 3}{x + 9}$$

$$\frac{x + 3}{x - 39} \div \frac{x + 3}{x + 9}$$

$$\frac{x + 3}{x - 39} \cdot \frac{x + 9}{x + 3}$$

$$\frac{x + 9}{x - 39}$$

a Explain his mistake.

b Show how to correctly divide these expressions.

LESSON 4.2

4.2 Adding and Subtracting Rational Expressions

Adding and Subtracting Rational Expressions with Common Denominators

When two fractions have a common denominator, such as $\dfrac{1}{7}$ and $\dfrac{3}{7}$, their sum is found by adding the numerators and keeping the same denominator. The same concept applies to rational expressions. To add rational expressions with a common denominator, add the numerators, and keep the same denominator: $\dfrac{a}{c} + \dfrac{b}{c} = \dfrac{a + b}{c}$. In other words, the numerators a and b are added, while the denominator c stays the same.

Subtracting rational expressions is also similar to subtracting numeric fractions. To subtract rational expressions with a common denominator, you subtract the numerators and keep the denominator the same: $\dfrac{a}{c} - \dfrac{b}{c} = \dfrac{a - b}{c}$. In other words, subtract b from a in the numerator, while the denominator c stays the same.

1. Add $\dfrac{3x}{x-2} + \dfrac{x+1}{x-2}$.

SOLUTION

Add numerators and keep denominator the same
$\dfrac{3x}{x-2} + \dfrac{x+1}{x-2} = \dfrac{4x+1}{x-2}$
With a common denominator, just add the numerators. The denominator stays the same, $x-2$.

2. Subtract $\dfrac{9x}{2x+6} - \dfrac{2x+1}{2x+6}$.

SOLUTION

Subtract numerators and keep denominator the same

$\dfrac{9x}{2x+6} - \dfrac{2x+1}{2x+6}$

$\dfrac{9x - (2x+1)}{2x+6}$

$\dfrac{7x-1}{2x+6}$

To subtract rational expressions with a common denominator, subtract the numerators, keeping the same denominator.

PRACTICE

Exercises 1–17: Simplify, if possible.

1. $\dfrac{x+7}{x+4} + \dfrac{x+3}{x+4}$

2. $\dfrac{x+6}{x+3} + \dfrac{x+3}{x+3}$

3. $\dfrac{x^2-7}{x^2} + \dfrac{x+4}{x^2}$

4. $\dfrac{x^2-8}{x^2} + \dfrac{x+4}{x^2}$

5. $\dfrac{5x+7}{35x} + \dfrac{7-5x}{35x}$

6. $\dfrac{5x+9}{45x} + \dfrac{9-5x}{45x}$

7. $\dfrac{3x+7}{21x} + \dfrac{7-3x}{21x}$

8. $\dfrac{5x+6}{30x} + \dfrac{6-5x}{30x}$

9. $\dfrac{7x+8}{56x} + \dfrac{8-7x}{56x}$

10. $\dfrac{2x^2+8}{x+11} - \dfrac{x^2-4}{x+11}$

11. $\dfrac{2x^2+8}{x+12} - \dfrac{x^2-4}{x+12}$

12. $\dfrac{2x^2+8}{x+11} - \dfrac{x^2-3}{x+11}$

13. $\dfrac{x^2+13x-3}{x^2} - \dfrac{3x-11}{x^2}$

14. $\dfrac{x^2+12x-4}{x^2} - \dfrac{4x-9}{x^2}$

15. $\dfrac{x^2+13x-4}{x^2} - \dfrac{6x-9}{x^2}$

16. $\dfrac{x^2+10x-4}{x^2} - \dfrac{4x-6}{x^2}$

17. $\dfrac{x^2+9x-4}{x^2} - \dfrac{5x-9}{x^2}$

Adding and Subtracting Rational Expressions with Different Denominators

When two fractions have different denominators, such as $\frac{1}{3}$ and $\frac{1}{2}$, they must be written with a common denominator before they can be added or subtracted. The same concept applies to rational expressions.

MODEL PROBLEMS

1. Add $\frac{3}{x} + \frac{1}{x-5}$.

SOLUTION

Multiply to create common denominator	$\dfrac{3}{x} = \dfrac{3}{x} \cdot \dfrac{x-5}{x-5}$ $\dfrac{3x-15}{x(x-5)}$	Multiply the first term by a fraction equal to 1 that contains the denominator of the second term.
Multiply to create common denominator	$\dfrac{1}{x-5} = \dfrac{1}{x-5} \cdot \dfrac{x}{x}$ $\dfrac{x}{x(x-5)}$	Now multiply the second term by a fraction equal to 1 that contains the denominator of the first term.
Add numerators	$\dfrac{3x-15}{x(x-5)} + \dfrac{x}{x(x-5)} = \dfrac{3x-15+x}{x(x-5)}$	Add the numerators and keep the same denominator.
Simplify	$\dfrac{3x-15+x}{x(x-5)} = \dfrac{4x-15}{x(x-5)}$	Simplify the numerator by combining like terms.

2. **MP 1, 7** Perform the operations and simplify $\dfrac{3}{x+2} + \dfrac{5x}{x+4} - \dfrac{4x^2+10}{x^2+6x+8}$.

SOLUTION

Factor denominator to identify factors	$\dfrac{3}{(x+2)} + \dfrac{5x}{(x+4)} - \dfrac{4x^2-10}{(x+2)(x+4)}$	To find a common denominator, first factor the denominator of the expression on the right. It turns out to be the product of the expressions in the other denominators.
Multiply to create common denominator	$\dfrac{3(x+4)}{(x+2)(x+4)} + \dfrac{5x(x+2)}{(x+4)(x+2)} - \dfrac{4x^2-10}{(x+2)(x+4)}$	Multiply to create a common denominator. The common denominator is $(x+2)(x+4)$.
Distribute and add	$\dfrac{3x+12+5x^2+10x-4x^2+10}{(x+2)(x+4)}$ $\dfrac{x^2+13x+22}{(x+2)(x+4)}$	Add the numerators, multiply, then combine like terms in the numerator.
Factor and simplify	$\dfrac{\cancel{(x+2)}(x+11)}{\cancel{(x+2)}(x+4)}$ $\dfrac{x+11}{x+4}$	Factor the numerator. Since there is a common factor, we can cancel it to simplify the expression.

Least Common Multiple

The **least common multiple** (LCM) of two or more numbers or algebraic expressions is a number or expression that contains as a product all the factors of all those numbers or expressions, with no extra factors. For a numeric example, the LCM of 8, 6, and 12 is 24. 24 factors into $2^3 \cdot 3$, and 8 ($= 2^3$), 6 ($= 2 \cdot 3$), and 12 ($= 2^2 \cdot 3$) are the products of some or all of these factors, with no unnecessary factors. The **least common denominator** (LCD) is the least common multiple of the denominators of two or more numeric fractions or rational expressions. The LCD is very useful for adding or subtracting rational expressions.

MODEL PROBLEMS

1. Find the LCM of the monomials $4x^4$ and $10x$.

SOLUTION

Factor each monomial	$4x^4 = 2^2 \cdot x^4$ $10x = 2 \cdot 5 \cdot x$	First factor each monomial. This includes factoring the coefficients, which are 4 and 10 here.
List each factor to its greatest power	2^2 from $4x^4$ 5 from $10x$ x^4 from $4x^4$	The factor 2 appears to the power 2 in $4x^4$. The factor 5 appears just once, in $10x$. The highest power of the variable x is 4 in $4x^4$.
Multiply	$LCM = 2^2 \cdot 5 \cdot x^4 = 20x^4$	To calculate the least common multiple, we multiply the powers we listed. The LCM is $20x^4$.

> With rational expressions, the LCM is the term with the smallest constant and the variable to the least power that is a common multiple of two or more expressions.

2. Find the LCM of the polynomials $2x - 6$ and $x^2 - 6x + 9$.

SOLUTION

Factor each polynomial	$2x - 6 = 2(x - 3)$ $x^2 - 6x + 9 = (x - 3)^2$	To find the least common multiple, first factor each polynomial.
List each factor to its greatest power	2 from $2(x - 3)$ $(x - 3)^2$ from $(x - 3)^2$	The factor 2 appears just once, in the first polynomial. The factor $x - 3$ appears once in the first polynomial, but it's squared in the second polynomial.
Multiply	$2(x - 3)^2$	To calculate the least common multiple, multiply the powers listed. The LCM is $2(x - 3)^2$.

Model Problems continue . . .

3. Subtract $\dfrac{1}{2x^3 + 2x} - \dfrac{1}{5x}$ using the LCD.

SOLUTION

Factor each denominator	$2x^3 + 2x = 2x(x^2 + 1)$ $5x = 5 \cdot x$ Factors: $2, 5, x, x^2 + 1$	To find the least common multiple, first factor each of the polynomials in the denominators. List the factors.
Multiply	$\text{LCD} = 10x(x^2 + 1)$	To calculate the least common denominator, multiply the powers listed. The LCD is $10x(x^2 + 1)$.
Multiply first fraction by fraction equivalent to 1	$\dfrac{1}{2x^3 + 2x} = \dfrac{1}{2x^3 + 2x} \cdot \dfrac{5}{5} = \dfrac{5}{10x(x^2 + 1)}$	The only factor of the least common denominator missing from the first denominator is 5. Multiply the first fraction by $\dfrac{5}{5}$.
Multiply second fraction by fraction equivalent to 1	$\dfrac{1}{5x} = \dfrac{1}{5x} \cdot \dfrac{2(x^2 + 1)}{2(x^2 + 1)} = \dfrac{2(x^2 + 1)}{10x(x^2 + 1)}$	The only factor of the LCD missing from the second denominator is $2(x^2 + 1)$. Multiply the second fraction by $\dfrac{2(x^2 + 1)}{2(x^2 + 1)}$.
Subtract with common denominator	$\dfrac{5}{10x(x^2 + 1)} - \dfrac{2(x^2 + 1)}{10x(x^2 + 1)}$	Write the rational expressions with their common denominator.
Perform operations	$\dfrac{5 - 2x^2 - 2}{10x(x^2 + 1)}$	Subtract the numerators and combine like terms.
	$\dfrac{-2x^2 + 3}{10x(x^2 + 1)}$	

PRACTICE

Exercises 1–4: Find the least common multiple.

1. $8x^4$ and $(x + 4)^8$

2. $7x$ and $49x + 147$

3. $(8x)^3$ and $64x + 640$

4. $49x$ and $16x + 112$

Exercises 5–23: Simplify, if possible.

5. $\dfrac{2x + 7}{x} + \dfrac{6x^2 + 4}{x + 4}$

6. $\dfrac{4x + 5}{x} + \dfrac{5x^2 + 4}{x + 4}$

7. $\dfrac{4x}{x} + \dfrac{x + 5}{x + 8}$

8. $\dfrac{4x}{x} + \dfrac{x + 4}{x + 6}$

9. $\dfrac{4x}{x + 3} - \dfrac{6}{x + 4}$

10. $\dfrac{6x}{x + 5} - \dfrac{7}{x + 6}$

11. $\dfrac{x - 3}{x + 8} - \dfrac{6x + 4}{x + 3}$

12. $\dfrac{x - 5}{x + 7} - \dfrac{6x + 4}{x + 5}$

Practice Problems continue . . .

13. $\dfrac{x^2 + 15x + 44}{x^2 + 7x + 12} - \dfrac{x + 8}{x^2 + 11x + 24}$

14. $\dfrac{36x + 28}{4x^2 - 64x + 252} - \dfrac{4x + 4}{x^2 - 16x + 63}$

15. $\dfrac{24x + 21}{3x^2 - 45x + 168} - \dfrac{3x + 5}{x^2 - 15x + 56}$

16. $\dfrac{x^2 + 6}{7x} - \dfrac{5x}{x^2 + 6x}$

17. $\dfrac{x^2 + 6}{6x} - \dfrac{4x}{x^2 + 5x}$

18. $\dfrac{x - 7}{17x + 68} - \dfrac{1}{x(4x + 16)}$

19. $\dfrac{x - 7}{19x + 76} - \dfrac{1}{x(4x + 16)}$

20. $\dfrac{7}{x^2 + 15x + 56} + \dfrac{8}{13x + 104}$

21. $\dfrac{9}{x^2 + 13x + 36} + \dfrac{4}{9x + 36}$

22. $\dfrac{2x^2 - 7x}{2x^2 - 13x + 21} - \dfrac{3x + 9}{x^2 - 9} + \dfrac{5}{x - 3}$

23. MP 1, 7, 8

$\dfrac{1}{1 - x} + \dfrac{1}{1 + x} + \dfrac{2}{1 + x^2} + \dfrac{4}{1 + x^4} + \dfrac{8}{1 + x^8} + \dfrac{16}{1 + x^{16}}$

24. MP 2, 3 A student says that a rational expression doesn't change if we add the same term to its numerator and its denominator. Is this a correct statement? Explain why or why not.

25. MP 2, 3 Mr. Trickmonth says the number of the month in which he was born is equal

to $\dfrac{\dfrac{1}{a + b} - \dfrac{1}{a - b}}{\dfrac{1}{a + b} + \dfrac{1}{a - b}} \div \dfrac{a}{b}$ for some a and $b \neq 0$.

Could he be correct, or is he tricking you? Explain.

26. Show that

$\dfrac{yz}{bd} + \dfrac{(y - b)(z - b)}{b(b - d)} + \dfrac{(y - d)(z - d)}{d(d - b)} = 1.$

LESSON 4.3

4.3 Rational Equations

Algebra 1 Review: Evaluating Rational Expressions and Equations

MODEL PROBLEMS

1. Evaluate $\dfrac{x^5 + 5}{x - 1}$ when $x = -2$.

SOLUTION

Substitute	$\dfrac{x^5 + 5}{x - 1}$ $\dfrac{(-2)^5 + 5}{-2 - 1}$	Substitute -2 for x in the expression.
Simplify numerator and denominator	$\dfrac{-32 + 5}{-2 - 1} = \dfrac{-27}{-3}$	In the numerator, calculate $(-2)^5$ and then subtract. In the denominator, subtract 1 from -2.
Divide	$\dfrac{-27}{-3} = 9$	With the numerator and denominator simplified, now divide.

Model Problems continue ...

2. **MP 2, 4** Amy takes 6 days to dig a hole. Beth takes 4. How long does it take them to do it together? There is a general equation for rate questions like this, as we show below. The two terms sum to 1, since they are completing one task.

$$\left(\frac{1}{a}\right)t + \left(\frac{1}{b}\right)t = 1$$

$a = A$ time alone
$b = B$ time alone
t = time together

The equation states that the amount of work done by the first worker in t units of time, plus the amount of work done by the second worker in the same time, equals 1, which means the entire task is completed. The equation can be used to solve many rate problems that ask how long it will take two to accomplish a task together.

SOLUTION

Write equation

$$\left(\frac{1}{a}\right)t + \left(\frac{1}{b}\right)t = 1$$

$$\left(\frac{1}{6}\right)t + \left(\frac{1}{4}\right)t = 1$$

The amount of work Amy does in t days, plus the amount of work Beth does in t days, equals 1, which means the entire task is completed. Substitute a = Amy's time = 6; b = Beth's time = 4; and t = time working together into the equation.

Simplify by multiplying by LCD

$$12\left(\frac{1}{6}\right)t + 12\left(\frac{1}{4}\right)t = 12 \cdot 1$$

$$2t + 3t = 12$$

Multiply all the terms in the equation by the least common denominator, 12.

Solve equation

$$t = \frac{12}{5}$$

$$2\frac{2}{5} \text{ days}$$

Solve the equation by adding like terms on the left side and then dividing by 5. The number of days to dig the hole is $2\frac{2}{5}$.

 In this activity, use the rate equation from the model problem to calculate how long it will take two beavers to eat a log together.

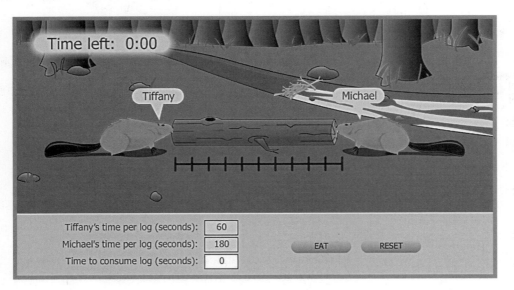

In this activity, use the rate equation from the model problem to calculate how long it would take each beaver to eat the log alone.

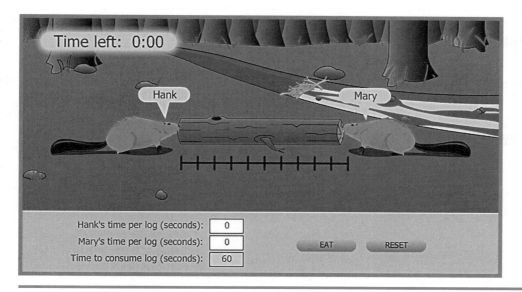

PRACTICE

1. Hero Dan can save the world in 110 years, while his teacher, Hero San needs only 70 years to do it. How soon can they save the world if they work together?

A.   180 years

B. $\dfrac{1}{180}$ year

C. $\dfrac{180}{7700}$ year

D. $\dfrac{7700}{180}$ years

2. Evaluate, to the nearest hundredth,

$\dfrac{3x^3 + 6x + 11}{x + 4}$ when $x = 4$.

3. Evaluate, to the nearest hundredth,

$\dfrac{9x^3 - 6x^2 - 2}{x + 2}$ when $x = 5$.

4. **MP 4** The equivalent (total) resistance of two resistors in parallel can be calculated

with the formula $R_E = \dfrac{1}{\dfrac{1}{R_1} + \dfrac{1}{R_2}}$. If resistors

A and *B* are in parallel and have resistances of 30 ohms and 100 ohms, respectively, what is the equivalent resistance of this circuit, to two decimal places?

5. The beavers are working together to eat a fallen log. Tiffany takes 180 seconds per log and Michael takes 130 seconds per log. How long will it take them to complete their task? Round your answer to the nearest tenth.

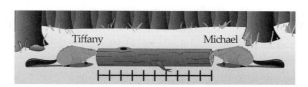

6. **MP 2, 4** Riding with the wind at her back, a cyclist takes an hour less time to cover 80 miles than without any wind. Riding with the wind increases the cyclist's speed by 2 miles per hour. What is her speed when riding with the wind?

7. Ralph takes 5 hours to clean the house, and Janice takes 6 hours to clean the house. If they work together, how long does it take them to clean the house? Express your answer to the nearest minute.

8. Jamie takes twice as long as Luke to take out the garbage, and together they take out the garbage in 26 minutes. How long would it take Jamie to take out the garbage by himself?

Practice Problems continue . . .

9. One plane travels 35 miles per hour faster than another. The faster plane can travel 2425 miles in the same amount of time that the slower one can travel 2250 miles. What is the speed of the faster plane?

10. A hiker walks north at 7 kilometers per hour, takes a 15-minute break, and walks back to her starting point at 12 kilometers per hour. The trip takes 85 minutes. How far was the trip north, to the nearest tenth of a kilometer?

11. MP 1, 2, 4 How much zinc do you need to add to 735 grams of a copper zinc alloy that contains 16% copper so that the resulting alloy contains 10% copper?

12. The Snake River flows at about 6 miles per hour. A kayaker paddles upriver a distance of 6 miles, then downriver the same distance, taking 4 hours for the entire trip. What is the speed of the kayaker in still water, to the nearest hundredth?

13. Two hikers leave their base camps at the same time and walk with constant speeds toward each other, aiming for each other's camps. When they meet on the trail, the faster hiker still needs to walk for another 4 hours to reach his new camp, while the slower hiker needs to walk for another 9 hours. Draw a diagram and find how many hours they walked on the trail until they met.

14. Sam takes 50 minutes to take out the garbage in a dormitory, and Sara takes 110 minutes to take out the garbage. If they work together, how long does it take them to take out the garbage? Round your answer to the nearest tenth.

Rational Equations

A rational equation is one that contains at least one rational expression. The equation $\frac{1}{x+4} = \frac{3}{x}$ is an example. The key to solving rational equations is the idea of clearing the denominators. To do this, we multiply both sides of the equation by the least common denominator (LCD).

MODEL PROBLEMS

1. Solve $\frac{2x-3}{x+3} = \frac{7}{2}$ by clearing denominators.

SOLUTION

Find LCD

$$LCD = 2(x + 3)$$

Find the least common denominator (LCD) of the two denominators, $x + 3$ and 2. In this case, it is just the product of the two denominators.

Multiply both sides by LCD

$$2(x + 3)\left(\frac{2x-3}{x+3}\right) = 2(x+3)\left(\frac{7}{2}\right)$$

Multiply both sides of the equation by the LCD $= 2(x + 3)$.

Cancel common factors

$$2(x+3)\left(\frac{2x-3}{x+3}\right) = 2(x+3)\left(\frac{7}{2}\right)$$

Cancel common factors on both sides of the equation.

$$2(2x - 3) = 7(x + 3)$$

Solve equation

$$4x - 6 = 7x + 21$$
$$-3x = 27$$
$$x = -9$$

Solve.

Model Problems continue . . .

2. Solve $\dfrac{3}{4 + x} + \dfrac{6}{x} = 1$ using the zero-product property.

SOLUTION

Find LCD	$LCD = x(4 + x)$	Find the least common denominator.
Multiply both sides by LCD	$x(4 + x)\dfrac{3}{4 + x} + x(4 + x)\dfrac{6}{x} = x(4 + x) \cdot 1$	Multiply both sides of the equation by the LCD = $x(4 + x)$.
Cancel common factors	$x\cancel{(4+x)}\left(\dfrac{3}{\cancel{4+x}}\right) + \cancel{x}(4 + x)\left(\dfrac{6}{\cancel{x}}\right) = x(4 + x)$	Cancel common factors.
Simplify	$3x + 24 + 6x = 4x + x^2$	Simplify.
Write equation as quadratic	$x^2 - 5x - 24 = 0$	Write the equation as a quadratic equation equal to 0.
Factor	$(x + 3)(x - 8) = 0$	Factor.
Solve	$x + 3 = 0 \text{ \textbf{\textit{or}} } x - 8 = 0$ $x = -3, 8$	Apply the zero-product property. Solve each of the resulting equations.

Extraneous Solutions

An **extraneous solution** is a solution to a derived equation that is not a solution to the original equation. We show how an extraneous solution can arise as an equation is solved in the model problems.

To eliminate extraneous solutions, you should check all solutions in the original equation. (It is always a good idea to check your work, but it's essential with rational equations to check for extraneous solutions.) If a possible solution fails to make the original equation true, it is an extraneous solution.

MODEL PROBLEMS

1. Solve $\dfrac{x^2 + 3}{x + 4} = \dfrac{19}{x + 4}$.

SOLUTION

Multiply by LCD	$x^2 + 3 = 19$	Since the two denominators are the same, the LCD is $x + 4$. Multiply both sides of the equation by $x + 4$ and cancel common factors.
Solve equation	$x^2 = 16$ $x = -4, 4$	Subtract 3 from both sides. There are two candidates for solutions to the resulting equation, -4 and 4.
Check: Substitute 4	$\dfrac{4^2 + 3}{4 + 4} \overset{?}{=} \dfrac{19}{4 + 4}$ $\dfrac{19}{8} = \dfrac{19}{8}$	Substituting $x = 4$ into the original equation results in a true statement, so 4 is a solution.
Check: Substitute -4	$\dfrac{(-4)^2 + 3}{(-4) + 4} \overset{?}{=} \dfrac{19}{(-4) + 4}$ $\dfrac{19}{0} = \dfrac{19}{0}$	Substituting $x = -4$ into the original equation results in a 0 denominator, so -4 is an extraneous solution.

Model Problems continue . . .

2. Solve $\dfrac{2}{x + 1} + 5 = \dfrac{2}{x + 1}$.

SOLUTION

Multiply both sides by LCD and solve

$$LCD = x + 1$$

$$(x + 1)\left(\dfrac{2}{x + 1} + 5\right) = \left(\dfrac{2}{x + 1}\right)(x + 1)$$

$$2 + 5x + 5 = 2$$

$$x = -1$$

Since the two denominators are the same, the LCD is just $x + 1$. Multiply both sides of the equation by $x + 1$ and solve.

Check: Substitute -1

$$\dfrac{2}{-1 + 1} + 5 \overset{?}{=} \dfrac{2}{-1 + 1}$$

$$\dfrac{2}{0} + 5 \overset{?}{=} \dfrac{2}{0}$$

Substituting $x = -1$ into the original equation results in a 0 denominator. Therefore, -1 is an extraneous solution. Since -1 was the only possible solution, the original equation has no solution.

 3. **MP 2, 3, 4, 6** Fred and Jesse both drive 300 miles. Fred drives 10 miles per hour slower and takes one hour longer to drive the 300 miles. How fast do Fred and Jesse drive?

  a Write a rational equation to describe the problem.
  b Solve the equation by finding the LCD.
  c Are there extraneous solutions to the problem? Explain.

SOLUTION

a Expressions for speeds

$$x = \text{Jesse's speed}$$
$$x - 10 = \text{Fred's speed}$$

Use x to represent Jesse's speed. Fred drives 10 miles per hour slower than Jesse, which we represent with the expression $x - 10$.

State equation

$$\text{Fred's time} = \text{Jesse's time} + 1$$

The problem states that Fred takes one hour longer to make the trip than Jesse. To make the quantities equal, add 1 to Jesse's time.

Distance equation

$$t = \dfrac{d}{s}$$

Use the distance equation: time equals distance divided by speed.

Substitute

$$\dfrac{300}{\text{Fred's speed}} = \dfrac{300}{\text{Jesse's speed}} + 1$$

$$\dfrac{300}{x - 10} = \dfrac{300}{x} + 1$$

Substitute the expressions for time. 300 divided by Fred's speed is how long it takes him to travel. Jesse's travel time is 300 divided by his speed. Then, substitute the expressions for speed.

b Find LCD

$$LCD = x(x - 10)$$

Start by finding the least common denominator.

Multiply by LCD

$$x(x - 10)\left(\dfrac{300}{x - 10}\right) = x(x - 10)\left(\dfrac{300}{x} + 1\right)$$

Multiply both sides of the equation by the least common denominator.

Simplify

$$300x = 300x - 3000 + x^2 - 10x$$

Cancel the common factors.

Model Problems continue . . .

State as quadratic	$0 = x^2 - 10x - 3000$	Combine like terms.
Solve equation	$0 = (x - 60)(x + 50)$ $x - 60 = 0 \textbf{ or } x + 50 = 0$ $x = 60, -50$	Factor the equation, and solve it. There are two solutions, but only 60 makes sense in the problem. A speed of -50 miles per hour does not.
State solution	Jesse's speed $= x = 60$ Fred's speed $= x - 10 = 50$	Jesse's speed is 60, and Fred's speed is 10 less than Jesse's. The solutions check: Jesse would take 5 hours, and Fred 6 hours, at these speeds.

c   The solution $x = -50$ does not apply to the situation. The solution of 60 is **not** an extraneous solution (it causes no division by 0).

PRACTICE

1. How many real solutions does the equation $\dfrac{x^2 + 2x + 2}{(x - 1)(x - 3)} = 0$ have?

   A. 0   C. 2

   B. 1   D. Infinitely many

2. Which of the following are the solutions to the equation $\dfrac{2 - x}{x - 1} - \dfrac{x + 2}{x + 1} = \dfrac{4}{x - 1}$?

   A. 1 and -1 only

   B. 2 and -2 only

   C. 0 and -2 only

   D. 2 only

Exercises 3–25: Solve.

3. $\dfrac{5}{2x} = \dfrac{1}{x - 3}$

4. $\dfrac{3}{x - 15} = \dfrac{6}{x + 9}$

5. $\dfrac{4}{x - 8} = \dfrac{6}{x + 12}$

6. $\dfrac{4}{x - 21} = \dfrac{7}{x + 18}$

7. $\dfrac{6}{x + 3} = \dfrac{5}{x - 5}$

8. $\dfrac{7}{x + 9} = \dfrac{4}{x - 18}$

9. $\dfrac{7}{x + 8} = \dfrac{3}{x - 32}$

10. $\dfrac{x}{x - 5} = \dfrac{3}{x + 11}$

11. $\dfrac{x}{3x - 12} = \dfrac{7}{3x + 54}$

12. $\dfrac{x}{6x - 12} = \dfrac{7}{6x + 96}$

13. $\dfrac{x}{3x - 12} = \dfrac{5}{3x + 42}$

14. $\dfrac{x}{3x - 6} = \dfrac{6}{3x + 42}$

15. $\dfrac{4x}{x + 3} + \dfrac{7}{x + 6} = 4$

16. $\dfrac{4x}{x + 4} + \dfrac{8}{x + 6} = 4$

17. $\dfrac{4x}{x + 3} + \dfrac{7}{x + 4} = 4$

18. $\dfrac{2x}{x + 6} + \dfrac{7}{x + 4} = 2$

19. $\dfrac{6x}{x - 5} + \dfrac{3}{x - 2} = 6$

20. $\dfrac{7x}{x - 5} + \dfrac{3}{x - 3} = 7$

21. $\dfrac{x^2 - 6x - 27}{x + 3} = 3$

22. $\dfrac{x^2 - 6x - 40}{x + 4} = 4$

23. $\dfrac{x^2 - 3x - 18}{x + 3} = 4$

24. $\dfrac{x^2 - 9x - 22}{x + 2} = 4$

25. $x + \dfrac{42}{x} = 13$

Practice Problems continue . . .

Practice Problems continued . . .

Exercises 26–30: Solve. Justify your reasoning.

26. $x + \dfrac{24}{x} = 11$

27. $x + \dfrac{40}{x} = 13$

28. $\dfrac{\dfrac{4}{x} + \dfrac{6}{x+4}}{\dfrac{1}{x}} = 5$

29. MP 1, 8

$$\dfrac{\left(\dfrac{1}{1+x}\right)}{1 - \dfrac{1}{1+x}} + \dfrac{\left(\dfrac{1}{1+x}\right)}{\left(\dfrac{x}{1-x}\right)} + \dfrac{\left(\dfrac{1}{1-x}\right)}{\left(\dfrac{x}{1+x}\right)} + \dfrac{3}{2x} = 0$$

30. $\dfrac{12}{x^2 + 2x} - \dfrac{3}{x^2 + 2x - 2} = 1$

31. MP 4 Your team has won 26% of its first 50 games. It then goes on a winning streak and wins the next y games in a row, which raises its winning percentage to 38%. How many games did the team play in total?

32. Sarah wants to solve the equation

$\dfrac{x+4}{x-8} - 3 = \dfrac{2x-20}{7-x}$. After converting the

left side of the equation to a fraction with the common denominator, she determined $\dfrac{2x-20}{8-x} = \dfrac{2x-20}{7-x}$. The numerators are the same. Sarah concludes the denominators should be equal as well. So $8 - x = 7 - x$, and $8 = 7$. What went wrong?

33. I think of a whole positive number. If I write "5" to the right of my number, subtract the square of my number, divide the difference by my number, and then subtract my number from the result, I get 1. What is my number?

34. MP 2, 3 Can a rational equation have more than one extraneous solution? Explain why not, or give an example of a rational equation with more than one extraneous solution.

35. For which values of y is the sum of the fractions $\dfrac{y+1}{y-7}$ and $\dfrac{14}{y+7}$ equal to their product?

36. Give an example of a rational equation with infinitely many solutions. Justify your answer.

37. MP 1, 2 For what values of m does the equation $\dfrac{m+3}{x+1} - \dfrac{5-3m}{x-2} = \dfrac{mx+3}{x^2-x-2}$ have solutions?

• Multi-Part PROBLEM Practice •

MP 3, 7 Emmett and Solomon are working on physics homework together, but both have forgotten their textbooks, so they decide to look online for the Doppler effect equation they need to complete their homework. Emmett finds $f' = \dfrac{v}{v+v_s}f$, while Solomon finds $f' = \dfrac{f}{1 + \dfrac{v_s}{v}}$.

a Show that both equations are correct, that is, that they are equivalent expressions.
b Emmett realizes that they need an equation to find v_s, not f'. Find an equation for v_s by solving one of the above equations for that variable.

4.4 Graphing Rational Functions

We show you how to graph rational functions of the form $f(x) = \dfrac{p(x)}{q(x)}$. We start

with the properties of the graph of the parent function $f(x) = \dfrac{1}{x}$. It is the parent

> Rational functions are also called **reciprocal functions**.

function of rational functions because it is the simplest rational function. Its graph helps you graph other rational functions. These graphs have asymptotes. Remember, asymptotes are lines that are approached but never reached.

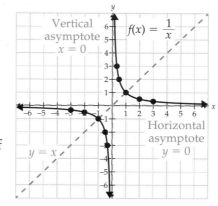

x	$f(x)$
-3	$-\dfrac{1}{3}$
-2	$-\dfrac{1}{2}$
-1	-1
$-\dfrac{1}{2}$	-2
$-\dfrac{1}{3}$	-3
0	undefined
$\dfrac{1}{3}$	3
$\dfrac{1}{2}$	2
1	1
2	$\dfrac{1}{2}$
3	$\dfrac{1}{3}$

- Domain is real numbers <u>except</u> zero

  Since division by zero is undefined, the domain of the function is all real numbers except zero.

- Range is real numbers except 0

  The range of $f(x) = \dfrac{1}{x}$ is all real numbers except zero. There is no value of x that will cause this function to equal 0.

- Asymptote at value excluded from domain

  The graph has a vertical asymptote at $x = 0$, which is the y-axis. This asymptote occurs at the domain restriction, that x cannot equal 0.

- Asymptote also at value excluded from range

  When x is positive, $\dfrac{1}{x}$ is also positive. As x gets larger, $\dfrac{1}{x}$ gets closer and closer to zero. Since $f(x) = \dfrac{1}{x}$ never equals zero, the graph has a horizontal asymptote at $y = 0$, which is the x-axis. When x gets close to 0, the absolute values of y get larger and larger.

- Two symmetric branches

  The graph of $\dfrac{1}{x}$ has two symmetric branches. One branch is in the first quadrant, and the other is in the third. The graph is symmetric about the line $y = x$. It is also symmetric about the origin, which makes it an odd function. There are two symmetric branches that approach but never reach the asymptotes.

- End behaviors

  The asymptotes define the end behaviors of the graph. As the absolute value of x increases, $f(x)$ approaches 0. And as the absolute value of x approaches 0, $|f(x)|$ becomes infinitely large.

Translating and Reflecting Rational Functions

Horizontal Translation

We show the parent function $f(x) = \dfrac{1}{x}$ in gray compared to $f(x) = \dfrac{1}{x-h}$. The function is translated (shifted) horizontally. In the example graph, $h = 3$.

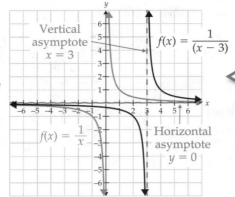

The graph of $f(x) = \dfrac{1}{x-h}$ is the graph of $f(x) = \dfrac{1}{x}$ translated horizontally to the right by positive h and to the left by negative h. It has an asymptote at $x = h$.

- Domain is all real numbers except h

  The domain of $f(x) = \dfrac{1}{x-h}$ is all real numbers except h. If $x = h$, there is division by 0. The domain of $f(x) = \dfrac{1}{x-3}$ is all real numbers except 3.

- Vertical asymptote at value excluded from domain

  The graph of $f(x) = \dfrac{1}{x-h}$ has a vertical asymptote at $x = h$. The dashed vertical line at $x = 3$ indicates that it is an asymptote of the function.

- Range is real numbers except 0

  The range of $f(x) = \dfrac{1}{x-h}$ is all real numbers except zero.

- Horizontal asymptote at value excluded from range

  The graph of $f(x) = \dfrac{1}{x-h}$ has a horizontal asymptote at $y = 0$. The dashed line on the x-axis indicates that it is an asymptote of the function.

- Graph of $\dfrac{1}{x}$ translated to right by h

  When h is positive, the graph of $f(x) = \dfrac{1}{x-h}$ is the same as the graph of $\dfrac{1}{x}$ except it is translated to the right by h. $f(x) = \dfrac{1}{x-3}$ is translated 3 units right from $\dfrac{1}{x}$. As you see, this translation locates the graph correctly relative to the vertical asymptote.

Vertical Translation

We show the parent function $f(x) = \dfrac{1}{x}$

in gray compared to $f(x) = \dfrac{1}{x} + k$. The

function is translated (shifted)
vertically. In the example graph, $k = 2$.

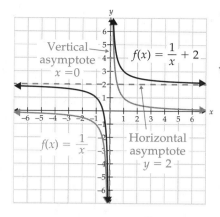

The graph of $f(x) = \dfrac{1}{x} + k$

is the graph of $f(x) = \dfrac{1}{x}$
translated up if k is positive
and down if k is negative. It
has an asymptote at $y = k$.

- Domain is all real numbers except 0

  The domain of $f(x) = \dfrac{1}{x} + k$ is all real numbers
  except 0 because when x is 0, the denominator is
  zero, and division by zero is undefined. The
  domain of $f(x) = \dfrac{1}{x} + 2$ is all real numbers except 0.

- Asymptote at value excluded from domain

  The graph of $f(x) = \dfrac{1}{x} + k$ has a vertical asymptote
  at $x = 0$. We draw a dashed line on the y-axis of our
  graph to indicate that it is an asymptote.

- Range is all real numbers except k

  The range of $f(x) = \dfrac{1}{x} + k$ is all real numbers except k.

  If $f(x) = k$, then $\dfrac{1}{x} = 0$. The range of the example

  function $f(x) = \dfrac{1}{x} + 2$ does not include 2.

- Asymptote at value excluded from range

  The graph of $f(x) = \dfrac{1}{x} + k$ has a horizontal
  asymptote at $y = k$. We draw a dashed horizontal line at
  $y = 2$ on our graph to indicate that it is an asymptote.

- Graph is the same as $\dfrac{1}{x}$ but translates up by k

  When k is positive, the graph of $f(x) = \dfrac{1}{x} + k$ is

  the same as the graph of $\dfrac{1}{x}$ except it is translated

  up by k. $f(x) = \dfrac{1}{x} + 2$ is translated 2 units up

  from $\dfrac{1}{x}$. As you can see, this translates the graph
  to the correct position relative to the horizontal
  asymptote.

Reflecting Rational Functions

We show the parent function $f(x) = \dfrac{1}{x}$ in gray compared to $f(x) = -\dfrac{1}{x}$.

Compared to the graph of the parent function, the graph of this function is reflected about the x-axis. This is because a is negative. We restate the expression to emphasize a in both functions:

$$f(x) = (a)\dfrac{1}{x} \text{ and } f(x) = (-a)\dfrac{1}{x}.$$

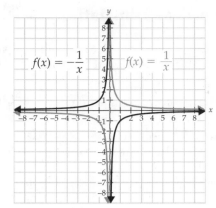

Stretching and Shrinking Rational Functions

We show the parent function $f(x) = \dfrac{1}{x}$

in gray compared to $f(x) = \dfrac{1}{2x}$. The

absolute value of a is less than 1 (in this case, $a = 0.5$), so the function is vertically compressed by half compared to the parent function.

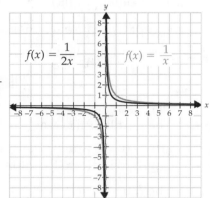

> If $0 < a < 1$, then the graph of $f(x) = \dfrac{a}{x}$ is the same as the graph of $\dfrac{1}{x}$ except it is vertically compressed by a. If $a > 1$, the graph is the function vertically stretched by a.

MODEL PROBLEMS

1. Graph $f(x) = \dfrac{2}{x}$. Identify the domain and range and asymptotes. Compare the graph to the parent

function $f(x) = \dfrac{1}{x}$.

SOLUTION

Domain and range are real numbers except 0

The domain and range of $f(x) = \dfrac{a}{x}$ are both all non-zero real numbers. $f(x)$ is undefined when $x = 0$, and the value of $f(x)$ is never zero.

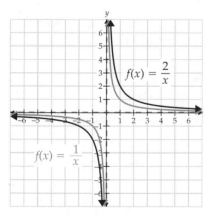

Asymptotes at $x = 0$ and $y = 0$

Similar to $\dfrac{1}{x}$, the graph of $f(x) = \dfrac{a}{x}$ has a vertical asymptote at $x = 0$ and a horizontal asymptote at $y = 0$.

Same as parent function but stretched by a

The graph of $f(x) = \dfrac{a}{x}$ is the same as the graph of $\dfrac{1}{x}$ except it is stretched vertically by a. The graph of $f(x) = \dfrac{2}{x}$ is stretched vertically by 2.

Model Problems continue . . .

2. For the reciprocal function $f(x) = \dfrac{a}{x}$, which statement is true about the graph if $a > 1$?

   A. If a increases, the horizontal asymptote moves vertically upward.

   B. If a increases, the domain and range remain the same.

   C. If a decreases, the vertical asymptote moves horizontally to the left.

   D. If a decreases, the domain and range become smaller.

SOLUTION

A. The value of a increasing stretches the graph vertically and does not change the asymptotes of $x = 0$ and $y = 0$.

B. **Correct answer.** The value of a increasing stretches the graph vertically and does not affect the domain and range of the function, which are all real numbers except 0.

C. Changing a does not move the vertical asymptote from $x = 0$.

D. Changing a does not change the domain and range of all real numbers except 0.

3. Graph $f(x) = \dfrac{1}{x + 1} - 5$. Determine the domain and asymptotes. Describe the function compared to the parent function.

SOLUTION

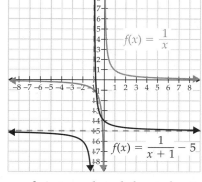

Determine domain	For this function, the denominator is zero when $x = -1$, so the domain is all real numbers except -1.
Asymptotes	The graph of this function has a vertical asymptote at $x = -1$ and a horizontal asymptote at $y = -5$.
Determine translations based on $f(x) = \dfrac{1}{x - h} + k$	Since the denominator is $x + 1$, the graph is translated to the left by 1 compared to the graph of $\dfrac{1}{x}$. To put it another way, $h = -1$.
Translate down by 5	Since the fraction has 5 subtracted from it, the graph is translated down by 5. In other words, $k = -5$. Note that the horizontal asymptote is also translated. It is $y = -5$.

4. Travis translated the graph of a reciprocal function, $g(x)$, vertically up by 2 units and graphed the new function, $h(x)$. Which could be $g(x)$?

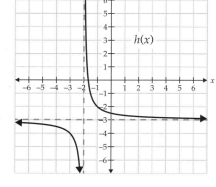

   A. $g(x) = \dfrac{1}{x} - 5$ C. $g(x) = \dfrac{1}{x + 2} - 3$

   B. $g(x) = \dfrac{1}{x - 2} - 5$ D. $g(x) = \dfrac{1}{x + 2} - 5$

SOLUTION

A. This does not have a horizontal shift as indicated in the graph.

B. The vertical asymptote of this function would be at $x = 2$, not $x = -2$.

C. This is the function of $h(x)$, not $g(x)$.

D. **Correct answer.** This function, when translated vertically 2 units, gives the graph shown.

Model Problems continue . . .

🌐 **5.** **MP 2, 4** The Doppler effect is a demonstration of relative motion. You experience the Doppler effect when a train races past you while sounding its whistle. As the train is approaching, you hear one frequency, and as it moves away, you hear a lower frequency sound. The motion of the train changes the frequency of the sound that reaches a person.

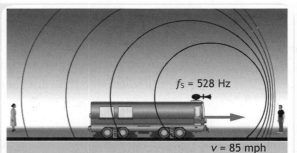

$f_s = 528$ Hz

$v = 85$ mph

We calculate this perceived frequency with the equation $f_1 = \dfrac{760 f_s}{760 - v}$. The variable f_1 represents the sound you hear, f_s is the frequency of the train's whistle when the train is stationary, and v is the velocity of the train, in miles per hour, relative to the person listening to the whistle. v is positive when the train approaches the listener and negative when it is moving away.

Frequency is the number of cycles per second. The unit for cycles per second is hertz, abbreviated Hz. A sound with a frequency of 528 Hz is about the frequency of the musical note C above middle C.

a Graph the rational function $f_1 = \dfrac{760 f_s}{760 - v}$.

b What is the perceived frequency for a sound at 528 cycles per second (Hz) when the train is approaching at 85 miles per hour?

c What happens to the perceived frequency if the velocity of the train were negative? To answer this, you can use the formula, or you may want to think about how sounds change for objects moving away from you.

SOLUTION

a

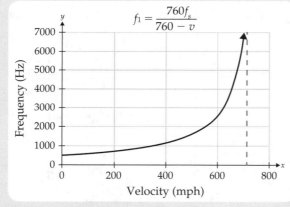

$f_1 = \dfrac{760 f_s}{760 - v}$

Graph the function. Use a very large range of velocity, from 0 to 700 miles per hour. The problem concerns the train approaching us, so we only use positive velocities.

We used a large range of data to point out that at lower velocities, the graph could be approximated by a line. It is only at speeds starting at about 400 miles per hour that the graph starts to become less linear. Its asymptote will be $v = 760$, since that value makes the denominator equal 0.

b Evaluate at 85 mph

$$f_1 = \frac{760 \cdot 528}{760 - 85}$$

$$f_1 \approx 594 \text{ cycles per second}$$

The question asks for the frequency of the train's whistle if the train was approaching you at 85 miles per hour. It would have a frequency of 594 cycles per second for the listener. The frequency 594 cycles per second is close to the musical note D. The train's motion has changed the sound you hear from about a C to a D.

c The perceived frequency will be lower than the frequency of the whistle while stationary.

Model Problems continue . . .

6. **MP 2, 4** A standard beverage can has a volume of 355 cm³. We want to determine the height and radius of a can that uses the least amount of material. From a business standpoint, the question of finding the dimensions that use the least amount of material is an important one. Using less material means spending less. Using the least material conserves resources. In the equations, V is volume, r is radius, h is height, and S is surface area: $V = \pi r^2 h$; $S = 2\pi r^2 + 2\pi rh$.

   a Use the equations to write a single equation for surface area in terms of the radius.
   b Graph that equation to find the minimum surface area required, and use that information to find the radius and height of the can.

SOLUTION

a Solve volume equation for h in terms of r

$$V = \pi r^2 h$$
$$355 = \pi r^2 h$$
$$h = \frac{355}{\pi r^2}$$

Use equations for the volume and surface area of the can. There are two variables, h and r. State the equation for surface area in terms of one variable. To do so, solve the volume equation for h in terms of r. Substitute the known value of 355 cm³ into the formula for the volume of a cylinder. Dividing both sides by πr^2 solves for h in terms of r.

Eliminate h from surface area equation

$$S = 2\pi r^2 + 2\pi rh$$
$$S = 2\pi r^2 + 2\pi r\left(\frac{355}{\pi r^2}\right)$$

Start with the equation for surface area. We have an expression for h. Substitute that into the equation.

Simplify

$$S = 2\pi r^2 + \frac{(2 \cdot 355)\pi r}{\pi r^2}$$
$$S = 2\pi r^2 + \frac{710}{r}$$

We now have surface area as a function of one variable, the radius.

b Graph function for surface area

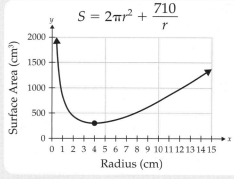

$$S = 2\pi r^2 + \frac{710}{r}$$

We use a graph of the function as a way to decide what dimensions will minimize the amount of material used. We assume the can has uniform thickness, so minimizing the surface area for the desired volume will minimize the amount of material used.

Find minimum

$$r \approx 4 \text{ cm}$$

The minimum of the graph is the least amount of material. The x-coordinate of this point is the radius of the can that uses the least amount of material.

Substitute

$$h \approx \frac{355}{\pi \cdot 4^2}$$
$$h \approx 7.1 \text{ cm}$$

Once we have an approximation for the minimum radius from the graph, we can substitute this value for r into the equation for the volume of a cylinder to solve for the height.

Solving a System of Rational Equations by Graphing

A system of equations that includes a rational expression can be solved by graphing, in the same way that simpler systems can be solved.

MODEL PROBLEM

 MP 2, 4, 5 One model rocket's velocity is modeled with the function $v(s) = \sqrt{20s}$. Another rocket's velocity is modeled with the function $v(s) = 3\left(\dfrac{1}{s+1}\right) + 8$. The variable s represents the height above Earth's surface and is never negative. The functions use meter and meters per second as their units for s and v, respectively. At what height will the two model rockets have the same velocity?

a Graph the two functions and find where they intersect, since that point represents the altitude and velocity that are the same for both rockets. Interpret the v-intercept for both graphs and the horizontal asymptote.

b Iterate to find a closer approximation to the intersection point.

SOLUTION

a
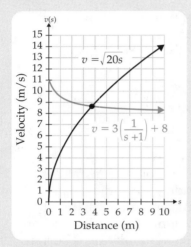

We estimate the graphs intersect at $(3.7, 8.6)$. In this situation, that means the rockets intersect at a height of 3.7 m and at a velocity of 8.6 m/s.

The velocity of the rocket modeled by the square root function has a v-intercept of 0, which means at the ground, where $s = 0$, it has 0 velocity. Its velocity would seem to increase forever.

The velocity modeled by the rational expression,

$v(s) = 3\left(\dfrac{1}{s+1}\right) + 8$, has a v-intercept of 11. This means at Earth's surface, its initial speed is 11 m/s. Its velocity will approach 8 m/s. That is the horizontal asymptote, and it equals the constant added to the rational expression.

b

s	$v = \sqrt{20s}$	$v(s) = 3\left(\dfrac{1}{s+1}\right) + 8$
3.700	8.60	8.64
3.705	8.61	8.64
3.710	8.61	8.64
3.715	8.62	8.64
3.720	8.63	8.64
3.725	8.63	8.63
3.730	8.64	8.63
3.735	8.64	8.63
3.740	8.65	8.63
3.745	8.65	8.63
3.750	8.66	8.63

We calculate the functions from 3.700 to 3.750, in increments of 0.005 meters, since that is near the intersection point we estimated from the graph. The table shows us that a closer approximation to the intersection point is $(3.725, 8.63)$.

PRACTICE

1. What is the domain of $f(x) = \dfrac{3}{x-13} - 11$?

   A. All real numbers
   B. All real numbers except 0
   C. All real numbers except 11
   D. All real numbers except -11
   E. All real numbers except 13
   F. All real numbers except -13

2. What is the domain of $f(x) = \dfrac{2}{x+25} - 28$?

   A. All real numbers
   B. All real numbers except 0
   C. All real numbers except 25
   D. All real numbers except -25
   E. All real numbers except 28
   F. All real numbers except -28

3. What is the domain of $f(x) = \dfrac{1}{x-32} + 15$?

   A. All real numbers
   B. All real numbers except 0
   C. All real numbers except 15
   D. All real numbers except -15
   E. All real numbers except 32
   F. All real numbers except -32

4. How does the graph of $f(x) = \dfrac{1}{x+12}$

   compare to the graph of $f(x) = \dfrac{1}{x}$?

   A. $f(x) = \dfrac{1}{x+12}$ is 12 units to the left

      of $f(x) = \dfrac{1}{x}$

   B. $f(x) = \dfrac{1}{x+12}$ is 12 units to the right

      of $f(x) = \dfrac{1}{x}$

   C. $f(x) = \dfrac{1}{x+12}$ is 12 units up from

      $f(x) = \dfrac{1}{x}$

   D. $f(x) = \dfrac{1}{x+12}$ is 12 units down from

      $f(x) = \dfrac{1}{x}$

5. The two branches of the parent reciprocal function $f(x) = \dfrac{1}{x}$ are symmetric about what line?

6. What is the domain of $f(x) = \dfrac{1}{x} - 8$?

7. What is the domain of $f(x) = \dfrac{1}{x-2} + 3$?

8. What are the domain and range of $f(x) = \dfrac{1}{x}$?

9. What are the domain and range of the function $f(x) = \dfrac{1}{x+2} - 10$?

10. How do the graphs of $f(x) = \dfrac{1}{x}$ and $f(x) = -\dfrac{1}{x}$ differ, and why?

11. The graph of a reciprocal function has a vertical asymptote at $x = -5$. What is the domain of this function?

Exercises 12–15: For each value of a, explain how the graph of the function $f(x) = \dfrac{a}{x}$ will differ from its parent function $f(x) = \dfrac{1}{x}$. Use terms like stretched, compressed, and reflected in your descriptions.

12. $a = 3$

13. $a = \dfrac{1}{2}$

14. $a = -1$

15. $a = -4$

16. What are the asymptotes of the graph $f(x) = \dfrac{1}{x-3}$?

17. What are the asymptotes of the graph $f(x) = \dfrac{1}{x} + 12$?

18. What are the asymptotes of the graph $f(x) = \dfrac{1}{x+6} - 4$?

19. What are the asymptotes of the graph $f(x) = \dfrac{1}{x-5} + 3$?

Practice Problems continue . . .

Exercises 20–23: Use the parent function, $f(x) = \dfrac{1}{x}$, to write expressions based on the descriptions, and then graph the expression that results.

20. An expression for the function with the graph shifted right 6 units.

21. An expression for the function with the graph shifted up 4 units.

22. An expression for the function with the graph shifted down 2 and left 7 units.

23. An expression for the function with the graph shifted up 5 and right 6 units.

Exercises 24–26: Match each graph by finding the values for h and k in $f(x) = a\left(\dfrac{1}{x - h}\right) + k$. Note that a is 1 in this case.

24.

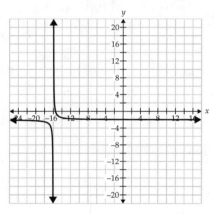

25.

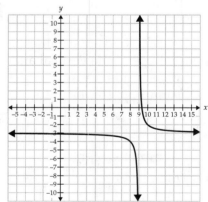

26.

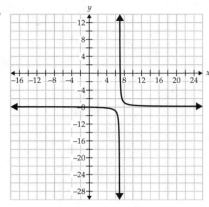

27. Write the reciprocal function that represents the graph.

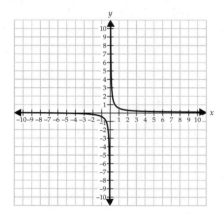

Exercises 28–30: Match the graph by finding the values for a, h, and k in $f(x) = a\left(\dfrac{1}{x - h}\right) + k$.

28. Note that a is 1 in this case.

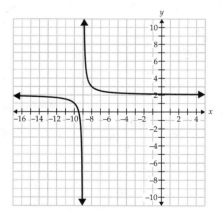

Practice Problems continue . . .

29.

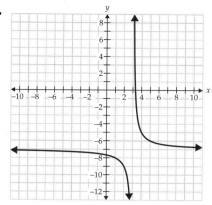

30.

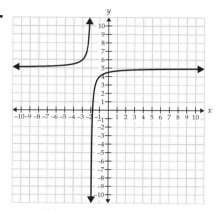

Exercises 31–34: Use the parent reciprocal function $f(x) = \dfrac{1}{x}$ to write a function equation for each problem based on the description of each graph. Then make a graph of the equation you wrote.

31. Stretches the graph by a factor of 3

32. Compresses the graph by a factor of $\dfrac{1}{3}$

33. Reflects across the x-axis and then shifts the graph down 2 units

34. Reflects across the x-axis and then shifts the graph up 1 unit and to the left 4 units

35. **MP 6** The functions $v(s) = \left(\dfrac{5}{s+4}\right) + 3$ and $v(s) = \sqrt{6s}$ model the velocity of two different projectiles, where $v(s)$ represents velocity and s represents position above the ground.

 a Graph the functions for the domain $0 \le s \le 10$.

 b Find the intersection point of the graphs of $v(s) = \left(\dfrac{5}{s+4}\right) + 3$ and $v(s) = \sqrt{6s}$. Round the coordinates to the nearest hundredth.

36. Explain how the asymptotes of a reciprocal function are related to its domain and range.

37. **MP 2** The ratio of the circumference of a circle to its area can be expressed by the formula $T = \dfrac{2\pi r}{\pi r^2}$, where T is the ratio of circumference to area, and r is the radius of the circle. Find the radius and area of a circle with a T-value of $\dfrac{1}{8}$.

38. The formula $I = \dfrac{V}{R}$, also known as Ohm's Law, is used to model the relationship between electrical current (I), voltage (V), and resistance (R) in a circuit. If the voltage is held constant at 12 volts, what will happen to the amount of electrical current when the amount of resistance is increased?

39. **MP 4** Melissa is working as a caterer at a wedding. She will be paid a flat fee of $100, plus part of a bonus of $600 that will be divided among the catering staff. Melissa's pay for the evening can be modeled by the equation $P = \dfrac{600}{C} + 100$, where P represents pay and C represents the number of catering staff who will split the bonus.

 a How much will Melissa earn if there are 8 people on the catering staff?

 b If Melissa made $125, how many people were on the catering staff?

 c Graph the function used to calculate Melissa's pay for all positive values of C. State the equations of the vertical and horizontal asymptotes.

• Multi-Part PROBLEM Practice •

MP 2, 4 Art's boat cruises at 8 miles per hour in still water. It takes him 8 hours along the river to make the 26-mile round-trip from his dock to his favorite fishing spot and back. How fast is the river's current?

a Make a table to organize the data, with entries for distance upriver and downriver and expressions for speed against the current and with the current.

b Write an equation for time, t, as a function of current speed.

c Substitute for time and solve the equation for current speed. Round your answer to the nearest tenth.

d How long does it take Art to make each one-way trip? Round your answer to the nearest tenth.

Chapter 4 Key Ideas

4.1 Multiplying and Dividing Rational Expressions

- A rational expression is one polynomial divided by another. The quotient is often stated as a fraction. For example, the rational expression $\dfrac{x^4 + 2x - 5}{4x + 7}$ represents $x^4 + 2x - 5$ divided by $4x + 7$.

- To simplify a rational expression, you may first have to factor its numerator, its denominator, or both. You then cancel any factors that are common to both the numerator and the denominator.

- The process of multiplying rational expressions is the same as multiplying numeric fractions like $\dfrac{5}{2} \cdot \dfrac{3}{4}$. You multiply the numerators, and multiply the denominators. You may need to simplify the result by canceling any common factors in the numerator and denominator.

- Division by a rational expression is equivalent to multiplication by its reciprocal.

4.2 Adding and Subtracting Rational Expressions

- When adding or subtracting rational expressions with the same denominator, you add or subtract the numerators based on the operation you are asked to do, and keep the denominator the same.

- To add or subtract rational expressions with different denominators, two steps are required: Multiply each rational expression by a fraction equal to 1 to create a common denominator, and then add or subtract.

- The least common multiple (LCM) of two polynomials contains all the factors of the polynomials, and no additional factors. You may need to factor polynomials to find their least common multiple.

- You can add or subtract rational expressions by first finding the LCM of their denominators, and using that to create a least common denominator (LCD).

- A complex rational expression like $\dfrac{\left(5 + \dfrac{3}{y}\right)}{\left(\dfrac{4}{2y - 1}\right)}$ is an expression written as a fraction where the numerator or denominator contains a rational expression. One way to simplify a complex rational expression is to invert the fraction in the denominator, and multiply it by the numerator.

- A rational expression is undefined when its denominator equals 0. You can determine when it is undefined by setting its denominator equal to 0 and solving that equation.

4.3 Rational Equations

- A rational equation, like $\dfrac{6}{2x - 3} = \dfrac{4}{x + 1}$, is an equation that contains at least one rational expression. The key to solving rational equations is the idea of clearing the denominators. To do this, you multiply both sides of the equation by the least common denominator (LCD). The desired result is to remove all terms containing the variable from the denominators. You then solve the equation as usual.

- After you solve a rational equation, it is important to check for extraneous solutions. Extraneous solutions do not hold true in the original equation. To eliminate extraneous solutions, check all solutions to the derived equation in the original equation. If a possible solution does not make the original equation true, it is an extraneous solution.

4.4 Graphing Rational Functions

- Rational functions can be graphed. Their vertical asymptotes are vertical lines, like $x = 5$, where the denominator equals 0. The graph of the rational expression approaches but never reaches a vertical asymptote. Horizontal asymptotes, such as $y = 0$, represent values that functions approach, but never reach. A rational function can be graphed using asymptotes, and by plotting points and connecting the points with curves.

1. A cube has side length s. If the side length increases by p units, what is the ratio of the surface area to volume of the new cube, in simplest form?

   A. $\dfrac{s}{s+p}$ C. $\dfrac{6}{p}$

   B. $\dfrac{s+p}{6}$ D. $\dfrac{6}{s+p}$

2. The area of a triangle is $\dfrac{2x^2 - 10x + 8}{x + 3}$, and its height is equal to $\dfrac{x - 1}{3x + 9}$. Which of the following represents the length of the base of the triangle?

   A. $\dfrac{(x-1)^2(x-4)}{6(x+3)^2}$ C. $6(x+4)$

   B. $\dfrac{3(x+4)}{x+3}$ D. $12x - 48$

3. Which function does the graph represent?

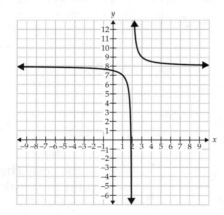

   A. $f(x) = \dfrac{1}{x-2} + 8$ C. $f(x) = \dfrac{1}{x+2} + 8$

   B. $f(x) = \dfrac{1}{x-8} + 2$ D. $f(x) = \dfrac{1}{x+2} - 8$

4. Which of the following lines is a vertical asymptote of the graph of the function?
$$f(x) = \frac{1}{x+3} - 5$$

   A. $x = 3$ C. $y = 5$

   B. $x = -3$ D. $y = -5$

Exercises 5–12: Simplify, if possible.

5. $\dfrac{40 - 8x}{x - 5}$

6. $\dfrac{48 - 8x}{x - 6}$

7. $\dfrac{x^2 + 10x + 24}{2x + 4} \cdot \dfrac{2(8 - x)}{x^2 - 4x - 32}$

8. $\dfrac{x^2 + 12x + 32}{2x + 4} \cdot \dfrac{2(9 - x)}{x^2 - 5x - 36}$

9. $\dfrac{6x^2 + 60x + 144}{x(x - 7)} \cdot \dfrac{x^2 + 4x}{x + 6} \div \dfrac{6(x + 4)}{4(7 - x)}$

10. $\dfrac{8x^2 + 88x + 192}{x(x - 5)} \cdot \dfrac{x^2 + 3x}{x + 8} \div \dfrac{8(x + 3)}{3(5 - x)}$

11. $\dfrac{x^4 - 3x}{x^2 + 8x + 3} - \dfrac{7x^2 + 10}{x^2 + 8x + 3}$

12. $\dfrac{6}{x^2 + 10x + 25} + \dfrac{x}{x^2 + 12x + 35}$

13. **MP 2, 3, 8** Show that if $\dfrac{a}{b} = \dfrac{b}{c} = \dfrac{c}{a}$, then $a = b = c$.

14. **MP 2, 6** The volume V of a cylinder is $V = \pi r^2 h$, where r is the radius of the base, and h is the height of the cylinder. If the radius of the cylinder is decreased by 25%, by what percent should its height increase so that the cylinder has the same volume V? Round your answer to the nearest tenth of a percent.

15. **MP 1, 7** "Do you want to know how many books I read this summer?" Harry asked. "It's $\left(\left(\dfrac{x}{y} - \dfrac{y}{x}\right) \div \left(\dfrac{x}{y} + \dfrac{y}{x} - 2\right)\right) \div \left(\left(1 + \dfrac{y}{x}\right)\dfrac{x}{x - y}\right)$." How many books did Harry read?

Chapter Review continues . . .

16. Perform the operations. Assume that all numerators and denominators are non-zero:

$$x \div \frac{1}{8x^2 - 20 + 8} \div \frac{x(8(x+1) - 12)}{6}$$

17. Fill in the blank cells in the table with expressions such that the sum along each row, column, and diagonal is equal to zero.

$-1 - \dfrac{b}{a}$	$2 - \dfrac{b}{a}$	
$\dfrac{3b}{a}$		

Exercises 18–22: Solve.

18. $\dfrac{1}{3x} = \dfrac{3}{5x - 8}$

19. $\dfrac{2}{x - 30} = \dfrac{7}{x + 20}$

20. $\dfrac{6}{x + 4} = \dfrac{5}{x - 9}$

21. $\dfrac{x^2 + 11x + 30}{x + 5} = 9$

22. $x + \dfrac{48}{x} = 14$

Exercises 23–24: Write the reciprocal function represented by each graph.

23.

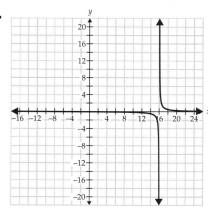

24.

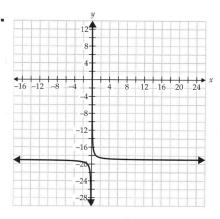

Exercises 25–27: In each problem, the asymptotes are given for a reciprocal function of the form $f(x) = \dfrac{1}{x - h} + k$. Write the equation of the function, and then graph it.

25. $x = 3, y = -5$

26. $x = -3, y = 1$

27. $x = 4, y = 0$

28. **MP 3** Explain why the output of the function $f(x) = \dfrac{1}{x} + 3$ can never be equal to 3.

29. Reciprocal functions are useful for modeling situations where a constant amount is divided by one variable to produce the other variable. Make up a situation like this, then define variables and write a reciprocal function that describes it.

30. **MP 2, 4** A group of friends are going on vacation together. They plan to rent a large house for $3000 and share the cost. They also estimate that buying food for the week will cost $150 per person.

a Write a reciprocal function to calculate the cost per person for the trip (C), based on the number of people (P) who decide to come on the vacation.

b Use your function to calculate the cost per person for 5, 8, and 10 people.

c Cassie has a budget of $400 for the trip. How many people must attend in order for her to participate?

Cumulative Review
for Chapters 1–4

1. Paula went to the grocery store and only bought 7 cans of corn, some bags of candy, and a few cartons of milk for exactly $33. It costs $1.25 for a can of corn, $2.75 for a bag of candy, and $3.50 for a carton of milk. If Paula bought a total of 15 items, how many of each did she purchase?

   A. 7 cans of corn, 3 bags of candy, and 3 cartons of milk

   B. 7 cans of corn, 4 bags of candy, and 4 cartons of milk

   C. 7 cans of corn, 5 bags of candy, and 3 cartons of milk

   D. 7 cans of corn, 6 bags of candy, and 2 cartons of milk

2. How does the graph of $f(x) = \dfrac{1}{x + 3}$ compare to the graph of $f(x) = \dfrac{1}{x}$?

   A. It is shifted up by 3.

   B. It is stretched horizontally by 3.

   C. It is shifted to the right by 3.

   D. It is shifted to the left by 3.

3. What is the line of symmetry for the graph of the function $f(x) = \dfrac{1}{x}$?

   A. $y = 0$

   B. $x = 0$

   C. $y = 1$

   D. $y = x$

Exercises 4–10: Simplify.

4. $\dfrac{4}{x^2 + 4x + 4} + \dfrac{x}{x^2 + 8x + 12}$

5. $\dfrac{6xy + 2x^2 + 10xz}{2x}$

6. $\dfrac{12x^2y + 6xy - 18xy^2}{6xy}$

7. $\dfrac{8xz^2 + 6yz^2 + 4z^2}{2z^2}$

8. $(9x^2 - 36) \div (3x + 6)$

9. $(x^4 + 17x^3 + 102x^2 + 256x + 224) \div (x + 7)$

10. $(x^4 + 20x^3 + 149x^2 + 490x + 600) \div (x + 5)$

11. Use long division to factor the polynomial $x^4 - 6x^3 - 24x^2 + 64x$. The polynomial has a factor of $x - 2$.

Exercises 12–13: Solve.

12. $\dfrac{x^2 + 10x + 25}{x + 5} = 8$

13. $\dfrac{x^2 + 9x + 18}{x + 6} = 8$

14. One solution to $x^3 - 12x^2 + 5x + 150 = 0$ is 10. List all the solutions.

15. A parabola has an equation $y = \dfrac{1}{12}x^2$. Where is its focus?

Exercises 16–18: State the other solutions to each equation.

16. $x^3 + 3x^2 - 13x - 15 = 0$; $x = -5$ is one root

17. $x^3 + 17x^2 + 59x - 77 = 0$; $x = 1$ is one root

18. $3x^3 - 27x^2 + 69x - 45 = 0$; $x = 1$ is one root

19. **MP 2** A parabola's focus is at $(0, 5)$ and its directrix is at $y = -5$. Find the y-coordinates of the points on the parabola with the x-coordinates 10 and -10.

20. How many real solutions does $-3x^2 + 12x - 12 = 0$ have?

Exercises 21–22: Find the number of real solutions for each quadratic equation.

21. $2x^2 - 5x + 13 = 0$

22. $3x^2 - 4x + 12 = 0$

Exercises 23–25: State each quadratic equation with a leading coefficient of 1 and the complex numbers as solutions.

23. $i, -i$

24. $2i, -3i$

25. $i\sqrt{2}, -i\sqrt{3}$

26. Use the graph to determine the number of real roots.

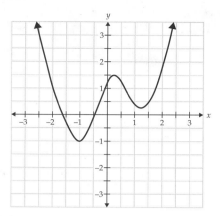

27. MP 1, 2 Find an objective function that has a maximum value at the vertex (3, 5) of the feasible region shown.

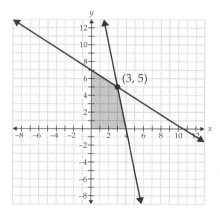

28. MP 2, 6 Write the simplified expression for the ratio of the difference of the squares of two numbers, x and y, to the sum of their cubes. Evaluate when $x = -11$ and $y = -1$.

29. MP 3, 4 The number of days that the patients with a certain illness spent at the hospital, and a particular bacterial count (in thousands) found in their blood at admission, are shown in the table.

Count (thousands)	Hospital Stay (days)
9	12
8	11
5	10
7	9
10	13
8	10
9	14
4	8
9	11
8	12

a Create a scatter plot and calculate a regression line.

b Predict the length of the hospital stay for a bacterial count of 6. Round to the nearest whole number of days.

c Predicting the length of a hospital stay for a bacterial count of 20 gives the value of about 21 days. Do you think it is a valid prediction? Explain.

30. MP 2, 7 Did you know that 2 = 1? Look at the calculations:

Pick some non–zero numbers	$m = n$
Multiply both sides by n	$nm = n^2$
Subtract m^2 from both sides	$nm - m^2 = n^2 - m^2$
Factor both sides	$m(n - m) = (n - m)(n + m)$
Divide both sides by $n - m$	$m = n + m$
Since $n = m$, we get	$m = 2m$
Divide by m	$1 = 2$

Don't believe it? Find the mistake in the calculations!

Chapter Content

Vocabulary

base

principal root

radical expression

exponent notation for roots

product rule for radicals

radicand

index

quotient rule for radicals

rationalizing the denominator

like radicals

radical equation

squaring principle

power principle

LESSON 5.1

5.1 Radical Operations

Review: Roots

Roots and powers are inverse operations because one operation "undoes" the other. This relationship provides the definition of a square root:

$$a \text{ is a square root of } b \text{ if and only if } a^2 = b.$$

In general, if $a^n = b$, then a is an nth root of b. The numbers a and b have to be real and n must be a positive integer. In the expression a^n, a is the **base** and n is the index, which represents what root is being taken of b.

MODEL PROBLEM

Find the fifth root of 32. Then write an equation in the form $a^n = b$, and identify the index.

SOLUTION

Identify 5th root	2 is the fifth root of 32 $2 \cdot 2 \cdot 2 \cdot 2 \cdot 2 = 32$ $2^5 = 32$	The number a is called an nth root of b if $a^n = b$. The number 2 is a fifth root of 32 because 2 to the fifth power is 32.	The nth root of b is a number that equals b when it is raised to the power n.
Identify index	Index is 5	The number n is called the *index* of the root. For instance, for the fifth root, the index is 5. The index must be a positive integer.	

When written as a radical $\sqrt[n]{b}$, the **radicand** is b and the **index** is n. The exponent in $a^n = b$ is also the index of the radical. If the index is odd, a negative number can have a negative root. If the index is even, the radicand must be positive to have a real value.

MODEL PROBLEM

Simplify $\sqrt[3]{-27}$. Identify the index and radicand.

SOLUTION

Identify index and radicand

-27 is the radicand
3 is the index

Simplify

-3 is the cube root of -27

$(-3)^3 = (-3) \cdot (-3) \cdot (-3) = -27$

$\sqrt[3]{-27} = -3$

-3 is the cube root of -27 since $(-3)^3$ equals -27.

> *a* is the cube root of *b* if $a^3 = b$.

The **principal root** of a number b is the positive root. To state the negative root, put a minus sign outside the radical sign. Principal roots only apply to radicals with even indices, and it is typical to state the principal root when asked for the even root of a number. If both the positive and negative roots are desired, the plus/minus sign is placed outside the radical, $\pm\sqrt{x}$.

MODEL PROBLEM

Give the principal root and the negative root of $\sqrt[4]{16}$.

SOLUTION

Principal root = positive root

$\sqrt[4]{16} = \sqrt[4]{2^4} = 2$

$2^4 = 2 \cdot 2 \cdot 2 \cdot 2 = 16$

The principal root is the positive root. For $\sqrt[4]{16}$, it is 2, since $2^4 = 16$. Another fourth root is -2, but -2 is not the principal fourth root since it is negative.

$-\sqrt[n]{b}$ = negative root

$-\sqrt[4]{16} = -2$

To find the negative root, place a minus sign outside the radical. In other words, multiply the principal root by -1.

An expression that contains one or more radical signs is called a **radical expression**. The expressions $\sqrt{7}, \sqrt{y+1}$, and $4 + \sqrt{x+2}$ are examples of radical expressions. The radical sign can act as a grouping symbol, similar to parentheses.

MODEL PROBLEM

Simplify $\sqrt[3]{2-10}$.

SOLUTION

Evaluate radicand first

$\sqrt[3]{2-10} = \sqrt[3]{-8}$

To evaluate a radical, first evaluate the radicand. Subtract and get -8.

Evaluate radical

$\sqrt[3]{2-10} = \sqrt[3]{-8} = -2$

Take the cube root. The cube root of -8 is -2.

> To evaluate a radical, first evaluate the radicand, or the expression under the radical, and then simplify the radical, if possible.

PRACTICE

1. What is the value of $\sqrt[3]{-64}$?

   A. -16 C. 4

   B. -4 D. 16

2. Which of the following represents the real square root(s) of $\sqrt{-16}$?

   A. -4 C. -4 and 4

   B. 4 D. No real roots

3. Which of the following equations has more than one real solution?

   I. $y^2 = -25$

   II. $y^3 = 64$

   III. $y^4 = 16$

   A. I only   C. III only

   B. II only   D. II and III

4. If V represents the volume of a cube, what is the area of one of the cube's faces?

   A. $\sqrt[3]{V}$ C. $\sqrt{V}$

   B. $(\sqrt[3]{V})^2$ D. V

Exercises 5–20: Evaluate.

5. $\sqrt{4}$

6. $\sqrt{81}$

7. $\sqrt{225}$

8. $\sqrt{121}$

9. $\sqrt{(-3)^2}$

10. $\sqrt{(-6)^2}$

11. $\sqrt[3]{-64}$

12. $\sqrt[3]{-125}$

13. $\sqrt[3]{-1}$

14. $\sqrt[3]{1000}$

15. $\sqrt[4]{81}$

16. $\sqrt[5]{-32}$

17. $5\sqrt{23 + 2} - 4$

18. $2\sqrt{23 + 2} - 5$

19. $6\sqrt{106 - 6} + 13$

20. $7\sqrt{87 - 6} + 13$

21. Write a definition in your own words of what it means to be the nth root of a number x.

Exercises 22–24: The surface area of a sphere is $A = 4\pi r^2$. The volume of a sphere is $V = \frac{4}{3}\pi r^3$.

22. What is the radius of a sphere whose volume is $\frac{500}{3}\pi$ cm^3?

23. **MP 2, 6** What is the volume of a sphere whose surface area is 324π cm^2?

24. What is the surface area of a sphere whose volume is $\frac{4}{3}\pi$ in^3?

Simplifying Radical Expressions

Simplifying a radical expression means writing an expression whose radicand contains no factor that has a simple root or is a fraction and has no radical expressions in the denominator. The radicand for square roots, and for other roots with even indices, must be positive.

We can use the rule $\sqrt{a^2} = |a|$ when simplifying radicals. The same simplification process can be applied to roots of any index, although for odd roots, the absolute value is not appropriate. Why is absolute value not used with odd indices? Because negative radicands simplify; for instance, $\sqrt[3]{-8} = -2$.

In the case of a square root, for example, whenever the radicand can be written as a perfect square, the radical expression simplifies to an expression without radicals. We can apply the concept of perfect squares to a real-world problem. Let's say we have a square picture that starts with sides of length x. If the area of the picture increases by a factor of 16, how much did the length of a side change? The new area is $16x^2$. The perfect square factors are $4x$, so the new length is $4x$.

MODEL PROBLEMS

1. Simplify $\sqrt{4x^6}$.

SOLUTION

Write radicand as perfect square a^2

$$\sqrt{(2 \cdot 2) \cdot (x^3 \cdot x^3)}$$
$$\sqrt{(2x^3)^2}$$

Factor the radicand, looking for pairs of identical factors. Then restate those pairs as a square.

> Since $2x^3$ is negative if x is negative, the absolute value symbol is necessary in the expression.

Identify a and apply rule $\sqrt{a^2} = |a|$

$$\sqrt{(2x^3)^2} = |2x^3|$$

The radicand is $(2x^3)^2$, so a must be $2x^3$. Apply the absolute value sign in case x is negative. The square root must be positive.

2. Simplify $\sqrt[3]{8y^{15}}$.

SOLUTION

Write radicand as perfect cube

$$\sqrt[3]{(2 \cdot 2 \cdot 2) \cdot (y^5 \cdot y^5 \cdot y^5)}$$
$$\sqrt[3]{(2y^5)^3}$$

To simplify the expression, first rewrite the expression with 3 factors of 2 and 3 factors of y^5.

> We do not need to take the absolute value of the root since nth roots with odd indices can be negative.

Apply rule

$$2y^5$$

Taking the cube root, the expression simplifies to $2y^5$.

3. Simplify $\sqrt[8]{x^{32}}$.

SOLUTION

Divide power by index

$$32 \div 8 = 4$$

To simplify the expression, divide the power of the radicand by the index.

Quotient is power

$$\sqrt[8]{x^{32}} = x^4$$

The quotient, 4, is the power. We can check the answer: $(x^4)^8 = x^{4 \cdot 8} = x^{32}$. The absolute value symbol is unnecessary since x^4 is never negative.

4. Simplify $\sqrt[5]{x^{32}}$.

Divide power by index

$$32 \div 5 = 6 \text{ remainder } 2$$
$$\sqrt[5]{(x^6)^5 x^2}$$

To simplify the expression, divide the power of the radicand by the index and rewrite the radicand.

Quotient is power outside radical

$$\sqrt[5]{x^{32}} = (x^6)\sqrt[5]{x^2}$$

The quotient, 6, is the power outside the radical. The remainder is the power inside the radical.

Product Rule for Radicals

As the name suggests, the **product rule for radicals** can be used to multiply radical expressions. The product rule for radicals states:

$$\sqrt[n]{a} \cdot \sqrt[n]{b} = \sqrt[n]{ab}, \text{ with } \sqrt[n]{a}, \sqrt[n]{b} \text{ real numbers.}$$

> The index must be the same to apply the product rule.

MODEL PROBLEMS

1. Multiply $\sqrt[7]{11y^8} \cdot \sqrt[7]{2y^2}$.

SOLUTION

Product rule applied to radicals with same index	$\sqrt[7]{11y^8 \cdot 2y^2}$ $\sqrt[7]{22y^{10}}$	Apply the product rule to any two radicals with the same index. Here, the index is 7. The product of $\sqrt[7]{11y^8}$ and $\sqrt[7]{2y^2}$ is $\sqrt[7]{22y^{10}}$.
Simplify the radical	$\sqrt[7]{22y^{10}} = \sqrt[7]{22y^7y^3}$ $y\sqrt[7]{22y^3}$	Write y^{10} as the product of $y^7 \cdot y^3$. The radical is simplified.

2. Multiply $\sqrt{x+1} \cdot \sqrt{x-1}$.

SOLUTION

Product rule applied to radicals with same index	$\sqrt{x+1} \cdot \sqrt{x-1}$ $\sqrt{(x+1)(x-1)}$ $\sqrt{x^2-1}$	Multiply the expressions under the radical sign.

3. Multiply $\sqrt[5]{3x} \cdot \sqrt[5]{2x^2}$.

SOLUTION

Product rule applied to radicals with same index	$\sqrt[5]{3x} \cdot \sqrt[5]{2x^2}$ $\sqrt[5]{3x \cdot 2x^2}$ $\sqrt[5]{6x^3}$	Multiply the expressions under the radical sign. Add the exponents to multiply the variables.

4. Simplify $\sqrt{75}$ using the product rule.

SOLUTION

Factor radicand	$\sqrt{75} = \sqrt{25 \cdot 3}$ $\sqrt{75} = \sqrt{5^2 \cdot 3}$	The radical $\sqrt{75}$ can be stated more simply because its radicand contains a perfect square factor. To simplify, state the radicand, 75, as the product of 25 and 3. Choose these factors because 25 is a perfect square.
Apply product rule	$\sqrt{5^2} \cdot \sqrt{3}$	Use the product rule to rewrite the square root as a product of two square roots.
Take square root	$5\sqrt{3}$	Take the square root of the perfect square. When simplified, $\sqrt{75}$ equals $5\sqrt{3}$.

Model Problems continue . . .

5. Simplify $\sqrt[3]{48}$ using the product rule.

SOLUTION

Factor radicand	$\sqrt[3]{48} = \sqrt[3]{8 \cdot 6} = \sqrt[3]{2^3 \cdot 6}$	The radicand, 48, is the product of 8 and 6. We choose these factors because 8 is a perfect cube, so we state it as 2^3.
Apply product rule	$\sqrt[3]{2^3} \cdot \sqrt[3]{6}$	Use the product rule to rewrite the cube root as a product of two cube roots.
Take cube root	$2\sqrt[3]{6}$	The cube root of 2^3 is 2. The radicand 6 has no perfect cube factors, so we are done. When simplified, $\sqrt[3]{48}$ equals $2\sqrt[3]{6}$.

6. Simplify $\sqrt[4]{64x^{10}}$.

SOLUTION

Factor	$\sqrt[4]{16x^8 \cdot 4x^2} = \sqrt[4]{2^4(x^2)^4 \cdot 4x^2}$	Begin by factoring out the largest perfect fourth power. In this case, it is $16x^8$.
Apply product rule	$\sqrt[4]{(2x^2)^4} \cdot \sqrt[4]{4x^2}$	Apply the product rule for radicals to write the expression as a product of two separate radicals.
Simplify radical	$(2x^2)\sqrt[4]{4x^2}$	Take the fourth root of $(2x^2)^4$, which is the principal fourth root. In this problem, it is not possible for $2x^2$ to be negative, so the absolute value signs are not necessary.

> For the remainder of the chapter, we will assume that no radicand is the square of a negative number. This means we will exclude absolute value signs from the simplified solutions.

Quotient Rule for Radicals

The **quotient rule for radicals** states:

$$\frac{\sqrt[n]{a}}{\sqrt[n]{b}} = \sqrt[n]{\frac{a}{b}} \text{ with } b \neq 0, \text{ and } \sqrt[n]{a}, \sqrt[n]{b} \text{ real numbers.}$$

> The index n has to be the same for the quotient rule to apply. Also, b cannot equal 0, to avoid division by 0.

The quotient rule can also be used to simplify radicals. A radical expression involving fractions is considered to be simplified when there is no fraction under a radical sign, and no radical in a denominator.

MODEL PROBLEMS

1. Simplify $\dfrac{\sqrt[4]{45}}{\sqrt[4]{3}}$.

SOLUTION

Quotient rule applied to radicals with same index	$\sqrt[4]{\dfrac{45}{3}} = \sqrt[4]{15}$	The quotient rule applies to radicals with the same index. Here, the index is 4. The quotient of 45 and 3 is 15. The expression cannot be simplified any further.

Model Problems continue . . .

2. Simplify $\sqrt{\dfrac{12z}{25}}$.

SOLUTION

Apply quotient rule	$\dfrac{\sqrt{12z}}{\sqrt{25}}$	By the quotient rule, $\sqrt{\dfrac{12z}{25}}$ is equal to the square root of the numerator, $\sqrt{12z}$, divided by the square root of the denominator, $\sqrt{25}$.
Apply product rule	$\dfrac{\sqrt{4}\cdot\sqrt{3z}}{\sqrt{25}}$	Apply the product rule to simplify the numerator.
Evaluate square roots	$\dfrac{2\sqrt{3z}}{5}$	Take the square roots of 4 and 25 and state the simplified expression.

3. Simplify $\dfrac{\sqrt{3x^2}}{\sqrt{12x}}$.

SOLUTION

Apply quotient rule	$\sqrt{\dfrac{3x^2}{12x}}$	To simplify, rewrite the quotient as a single radical, using the quotient rule for radicals.
Cancel common factors	$\sqrt{\dfrac{3\cdot x\cdot x}{4\cdot 3\cdot x}}=\sqrt{\dfrac{x}{4}}$	After canceling the common factors x and 3, the expression becomes $\sqrt{\dfrac{x}{4}}$.
Apply quotient rule	$\dfrac{\sqrt{x}}{\sqrt{4}}$	The expression $\sqrt{\dfrac{x}{4}}$ has a perfect square in the denominator, which means it can be simplified further.
Simplify	$\dfrac{\sqrt{x}}{2}$	Simplify the denominator. The expression is simplified.

4. Simplify $\dfrac{\sqrt[4]{5y^5}}{\sqrt[4]{16y}}$.

SOLUTION

Apply quotient rule	$\sqrt[4]{\dfrac{5y^5}{16y}}$	Rewrite the quotient as a single radical, using the quotient rule for radicals.
Cancel common factor	$\sqrt[4]{\dfrac{5y^4}{16}}$	Cancel out the common factor.
Apply quotient rule	$\dfrac{\sqrt[4]{5y^4}}{\sqrt[4]{16}}$	The quotient rule can be applied again.
Simplify	$\dfrac{y\sqrt[4]{5}}{2}$	Simplify the numerator and denominator.

PRACTICE

1. Which are equivalent to $4\sqrt{2}$? Select all that apply.

    A. $\sqrt{32}$ C. $\sqrt{2} \cdot \sqrt{8}$
    B. $2\sqrt{8}$ D. $2\sqrt{2} \cdot \sqrt{2}$

2. Which are equivalent to $10x^3\sqrt{2x}$? Select all that apply.

    A. $\sqrt{200x^7}$ C. $\sqrt{2000x^7}$
    B. $\sqrt{20x^7}$ D. $5\sqrt{2x} \cdot \sqrt{4x^6}$

3. Which is the correct simplification of $\sqrt[4]{x^{36}y^{36}}$?

    A. x^9y^9 C. x^9y^{18}
    B. $x^{18}y^9$ D. $x^{18}y^{18}$

4. Simplify $\sqrt[4]{2x^2} \cdot \sqrt[4]{16x^6}$.

    A. $2x^2\sqrt{2}$ C. $2x^2$
    B. $2x^2\sqrt[4]{2}$ D. $4x^2$

5. Donald is simplifying $\sqrt[3]{\dfrac{x}{y^5}}$. His solution steps are:

    Step 1: $\sqrt[3]{\dfrac{x}{y^5}} = \sqrt[3]{\dfrac{x}{y^5 \cdot y}}$

    Step 2: $\sqrt[3]{\dfrac{x}{y^5}} = \sqrt[3]{\dfrac{x}{y^6}}$

    Step 3: $\sqrt[3]{\dfrac{x}{y^5}} = \dfrac{\sqrt[3]{x}}{\sqrt[3]{y^6}}$

    Step 4: $\sqrt[3]{\dfrac{x}{y^5}} = \dfrac{\sqrt[3]{x}}{y^2}$

    Which is the first incorrect step?

    A. Step 1 C. Step 3
    B. Step 2 D. Step 4

6. Simplify $\dfrac{\sqrt{8x^8 + 12x^4}}{\sqrt{4x^4}}$.

    A. $\sqrt{2x^2 + 3}$ C. $\dfrac{\sqrt{2x^4 + 3}}{\sqrt{4}}$

    B. $\sqrt{2x^4 + 3}$ D. $\dfrac{\sqrt{2x^4 + 3}}{\sqrt{x}}$

Exercises 7–27: Simplify.

7. $\sqrt{208}$

8. $\sqrt{20x}$

9. $\sqrt{162x^5}$

10. $\sqrt[4]{16k^4}$

11. $\sqrt[3]{27x^9}$

12. $\sqrt[4]{81x^{16}}$

13. $\sqrt[3]{125x^{18}}$

14. $\sqrt[3]{216x^{12}}$

15. $\sqrt[5]{100{,}000x^{40}}$

16. $\sqrt{49x^8y^{16}}$

17. $\sqrt{25x^4y^8}$

18. $\sqrt{64x^{16}y^{32}}$

19. $\sqrt{49x^{14}y^{28}}$

20. $\sqrt[10]{x^{40}y^{80}}$

21. $\sqrt[8]{x^{80}y^{80}}$

22. $\sqrt{x^2 + 6x + 9}$

23. $\sqrt{x^2 + 16x + 64}$

24. $\sqrt{x^2 - 14x + 49}$

25. $\sqrt{9x^2 - 18x + 9}$

26. $\sqrt{16x^2 + 16x + 4}$

27. $\sqrt{4x^2 + 40x + 100}$

Exercises 28–37: Multiply and simplify.

28. $\sqrt{2} \cdot \sqrt{17}$

29. $\sqrt{3} \cdot \sqrt{7}$

30. $\sqrt{2} \cdot \sqrt{15}$

31. $\sqrt{18} \cdot \sqrt{2}$

32. $\sqrt{2x} \cdot \sqrt{8x}$

33. $\sqrt{6x} \cdot \sqrt{216x}$

34. $\sqrt{125x} \cdot \sqrt{5x^3}$

35. $\sqrt[3]{10} \cdot \sqrt[3]{25x^3}$

36. $\sqrt[3]{9} \cdot \sqrt[3]{12x^7}$

37. $\sqrt[3]{4} \cdot \sqrt[3]{16x^5}$

Exercises 38–48: Divide and simplify.

38. $\dfrac{\sqrt{14a^{13}}}{\sqrt{2a^5}}$

Practice Problems continue . . .

Practice Problems continued . . .

39. $\dfrac{\sqrt{81a^{13}}}{\sqrt{3a^9}}$

40. $\dfrac{\sqrt{100a^{21}}}{\sqrt{5a^7}}$

41. $\dfrac{\sqrt[3]{35}\cdot\sqrt[3]{5}}{\sqrt[3]{7}}$

42. $\dfrac{\sqrt[3]{36}\cdot\sqrt[3]{5}}{\sqrt[3]{12}}$

43. $\dfrac{\sqrt[3]{60}\cdot\sqrt[3]{7}}{\sqrt[3]{20}}$

44. $\dfrac{\sqrt[8]{36x^{15}}}{\sqrt[8]{4x^6}}$

45. $\sqrt{\dfrac{7}{36}}$

46. $\sqrt{\dfrac{7}{25}}$

47. $\dfrac{\sqrt{4x^3+2x}}{\sqrt{2x}}$

48. $\dfrac{\sqrt{16x^3+8x}}{\sqrt{8x}}$

49. MP 4 Investigators measure the lengths of skid marks to determine the speed of a car or truck. The equation $s=2\sqrt{5L}$ represents the speed of the vehicle in miles per hour as a function of the length L of skid marks in feet. Estimate the speed of a vehicle that left skid marks of 20.7 feet, to the nearest tenth.

50. MP 1 How far you can see out if the horizon is dependent on how high above the ground you are. The distance can be described by the equation $d=3.5\sqrt{h}$, where h is the height in meters above the ground and d is the distance visible in kilometers. Find out how high above the ground, to the nearest tenth of a meter, a person must be in order to see a distance of 22 kilometers.

51. MP 3 Explain what is wrong with the statement: $\sqrt{4x^2}=2x$.

Multiplying Square Root Radicals with Negative Radicands

The properties of radicals for square roots, such as the product rule and the quotient rule, require that all radicands must be 0 (unless they are in the denominator) or positive. With square roots of negative radicands, special care must be taken. To multiply square roots with negative radicands, restate the factors using i.

MODEL PROBLEM

Multiply $\sqrt{-3}\cdot\sqrt{-2}$.

SOLUTION

Write each factor in terms of i $\sqrt{-3}\cdot\sqrt{-2}$ $i\sqrt{3}\cdot i\sqrt{2}$ State each radical as an imaginary number, with $\sqrt{-3}$ equal to $i\sqrt{3}$ and $\sqrt{-2}$ equal to $i\sqrt{2}$.

Reorder factors $i^2\sqrt{3}\cdot\sqrt{2}$ Reorder the factors so that the i factors and the square root factors are next to each other.

Apply product rule for radicals $i^2\sqrt{6}$ Simplify $\sqrt{3}\cdot\sqrt{2}$ by using the product rule.

Simplify i^2 $-\sqrt{6}$ Simplify this further, since i^2 equals -1, to end up with $-\sqrt{6}$. Note that the minus sign is outside the radical.

> Note that we did not simply apply the product rule and multiply the negative radicands. We need first to express each factor as an imaginary number, and then multiply the factors.

PRACTICE

1. Which of these is equivalent to $-2\sqrt[3]{6}$? Select all that apply.

   A. $\sqrt[3]{-48}$ C. $-\sqrt[3]{4} \cdot \sqrt[3]{12}$

   B. $\sqrt[3]{-4} \cdot \sqrt[3]{-12}$ D. $\sqrt[3]{48}$

Exercises 2–22: Multiply and simplify. State your answers with i when necessary.

2. $\sqrt{-6} \cdot \sqrt{-2}$

3. $\sqrt{-5} \cdot \sqrt{-10}$

4. $\sqrt{-3} \cdot \sqrt{-20}$

5. $\sqrt{10} \cdot \sqrt{-3}$

6. $\sqrt{8} \cdot \sqrt{-9}$

7. $\sqrt{-15} \cdot \sqrt{-2}$

8. $\sqrt{-6} \cdot \sqrt{-5}$

9. $\sqrt{-1} \cdot \sqrt{-17}$

10. $\sqrt{-2} \cdot \sqrt{-13}$

11. $\sqrt{-6} \cdot \sqrt{-4}$

12. $\sqrt{-15} \cdot \sqrt{-9}$

13. $\sqrt{-1} \cdot \sqrt{-27}$

14. $\sqrt{-10} \cdot \sqrt{-5}$

15. $\sqrt{-14} \cdot \sqrt{-14}$

16. $\sqrt{-16} \cdot \sqrt{-15}$

17. $-\sqrt{-20} \cdot \sqrt{-10}$

18. $-\sqrt{-14} \cdot \sqrt{-6}$

19. $i\sqrt{-7} \cdot \sqrt{10}$

20. $i\sqrt{15} \cdot \sqrt{-15}$

21. $i\sqrt{4} \cdot \sqrt{-8}$

22. $i\sqrt{-15} \cdot \sqrt{5}$

LESSON 5.2

5.2 More Operations with Radicals

Adding and Subtracting Like Radicals

Radical expressions can be added or subtracted only when they have the same radical factor. Radical expressions with the same radical factor are called **like radicals**. For example, $\sqrt[3]{5}$ and $7\sqrt[3]{5}$ are like radicals since both include the factor $\sqrt[3]{5}$. Both the radicand and the index must be the same to be like radicals.

Combining terms with common factors requires you to combine the coefficients of the factors, as we show in the model problems.

> It is important to note that only terms with common radical factors can be combined. The sum of $\sqrt{2}$ and $\sqrt{3}$ is $\sqrt{2} + \sqrt{3}$, not $\sqrt{5}$. You **cannot** combine radicals when the radicands are not the same.

MODEL PROBLEMS

1. Add $\sqrt[3]{5} + 7\sqrt[3]{5}$.

SOLUTION

Determine if terms are like radicals	$\sqrt[3]{5} + 7\sqrt[3]{5}$	Both terms have $\sqrt[3]{5}$ as their radical factor, so these are like radicals and can be combined.
Apply distributive property	$1\sqrt[3]{5} + 7\sqrt[3]{5}$ $(1 + 7)\sqrt[3]{5}$	By the distributive property, we can state this sum as the sum of the coefficients times $\sqrt[3]{5}$.
Combine the coefficients	$8\sqrt[3]{5}$	Add the coefficients.

Model Problems continue . . .

2. Simplify $9x\sqrt{5} - 3\sqrt{20x^2}$.

SOLUTION

Simplify the radical

$$9x\sqrt{5} - 3 \cdot \sqrt{4x^2} \cdot \sqrt{5}$$
$$9x\sqrt{5} - 3 \cdot 2x \cdot \sqrt{5}$$
$$9x\sqrt{5} - 6x\sqrt{5}$$

There are no like radicals at first, but we can simplify $\sqrt{20x^2}$. Using the product rule, we restate it as $\sqrt{4x^2}$ times $\sqrt{5}$. The square root of $4x^2$ is $2x$, so now we have a factor of $2x$ for the second term.

Apply distributive property

$$(9 - 6)x\sqrt{5}$$
$$3x\sqrt{5}$$

Now that the terms have been written with a common radical factor, the distributive property can be applied. Simplify, and the result is $3x\sqrt{5}$.

PRACTICE

1. Which of these equals $6\sqrt{7}$? Select all that apply.

- A. $8\sqrt{7} - 2\sqrt{7}$
- B. $\sqrt{7} + \sqrt{28}$
- C. $4\sqrt{28} - \sqrt{28}$
- D. $\sqrt{175} + \sqrt{7}$

2. Which of these equals $4\sqrt{5}$? Select all that apply.

- A. $7\sqrt{5} - 3\sqrt{5}$
- B. $\sqrt{5} + \sqrt{60}$
- C. $4\sqrt{20} - \sqrt{20}$
- D. $\sqrt{20} + 2\sqrt{5}$

3. Which of these equals $5\sqrt{3}$? Select all that apply.

- A. $\sqrt{50} + \sqrt{3}$
- B. $3\sqrt{3} + 2\sqrt{3}$
- C. $\sqrt{45} + \sqrt{12}$
- D. $\sqrt{300} - \sqrt{48}$

Exercises 4–6: Add and simplify.

4. $5\sqrt[9]{x} + 16\sqrt[9]{x}$

5. $8\sqrt{5} + 6\sqrt{5}$

6. $19\sqrt[5]{x} + 14\sqrt[5]{x}$

Exercises 7–11: Subtract and simplify.

7. $x\sqrt[5]{3x^2} - 11\sqrt[5]{3x^7}$

8. $x\sqrt[6]{4x^2} - 11\sqrt[6]{4x^8}$

9. $14\sqrt{245} - 7\sqrt{5}$

10. $11\sqrt{45} - 3\sqrt{5}$

11. $\sqrt{27x} - 4\sqrt{3x^9}$

12. **MP 2, 8** An edge on a cube is the line segment joining two vertices. What is the sum of the lengths of the edges if each edge measures $12 + 10\sqrt{6}$ inches? Write your answer as a radical expression.

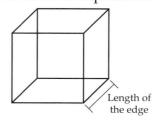

Length of the edge

13. What is the perimeter of a square with each side having length $7 + 4\sqrt[3]{5}$ centimeters? Write your answer as a radical expression.

14. Explain what is wrong with the statement $\sqrt{3} + \sqrt{2} = \sqrt{5}$.

15. Explain what is wrong with the statement $7\sqrt[3]{14} - 3\sqrt{8} = 4\sqrt{6}$.

Multiplying Monomial and Binomial Radical Expressions

The distributive property can be applied to radical expressions, as we show in the model problems.

MODEL PROBLEMS

1. Multiply the monomial radical expression by the binomial radical expression: $\sqrt[3]{11}(5 + \sqrt[3]{x^2})$

SOLUTION

Apply the distributive property

$\sqrt[3]{11} \cdot 5 + \sqrt[3]{11} \cdot \sqrt[3]{x^2}$

Apply the distributive property, multiplying each term of the binomial by $\sqrt[3]{11}$.

Multiply

$5\sqrt[3]{11} + \sqrt[3]{11x^2}$

Do the multiplications. The product of $\sqrt[3]{11}$ and 5 is $5\sqrt[3]{11}$, and by the product rule for radicals, $\sqrt[3]{11} \cdot \sqrt[3]{x^2}$ is $\sqrt[3]{11x^2}$.

2. Multiply $(5 + \sqrt{3})(11 - \sqrt{13})$ using FOIL.

SOLUTION

First $5 \cdot 11$ Start with the first term of each expression, 5 and 11, and multiply them.

> Here we multiply two radical expressions, each with two terms that cannot be combined. Use FOIL to multiply them, as we would with any two expressions that contain two terms. In general, multiplying radical expressions is the same process as multiplying polynomials.

Outer $(5)(-\sqrt{13})$ Next, multiply the two outer terms, 5 and $-\sqrt{13}$.

Inner $\sqrt{3} \cdot 11$ And multiply the inner terms, $\sqrt{3}$ and 11.

Last $(\sqrt{3})(-\sqrt{13})$ Multiply the last terms, $\sqrt{3}$ and $-\sqrt{13}$.

Simplify $55 - 5\sqrt{13} + 11\sqrt{3} - \sqrt{39}$ Simplify. Multiply constants, and state negative terms as subtraction. Simplify the radicals if possible, but in this case the answer is already simplified.

3. Multiply $(3 + 5\sqrt{7})(2 + \sqrt{7})$.

SOLUTION

Multiply using FOIL $3 \cdot 2 + 3 \cdot \sqrt{7} + 2 \cdot 5\sqrt{7} + 5\sqrt{7} \cdot \sqrt{7}$ Multiply using FOIL.

Multiply terms $6 + 3\sqrt{7} + 10\sqrt{7} + 35$ Simplify terms by multiplying.

Combine like terms $41 + 13\sqrt{7}$ Combine the like radical terms and the integers.

PRACTICE

1. Which expression will have three terms in its final simplified form?
   A. $\sqrt{m}(\sqrt{n} + \sqrt{m})$
   B. $(\sqrt{n} + \sqrt{m})(\sqrt{n} - \sqrt{m})$
   C. $(\sqrt{n} + \sqrt{m})(\sqrt{n} + \sqrt{m})$
   D. $\sqrt{m}(\sqrt{n} + \sqrt{m} + 2\sqrt{n})$

Exercises 2–14: Multiply and simplify, if possible.

2. $\sqrt{5}(\sqrt{5x} + \sqrt{10})$

3. $\sqrt{8}(\sqrt{2y} - \sqrt{6})$

4. $\sqrt{7y}(\sqrt{7} + \sqrt{3y})$

5. $(3 + 2\sqrt{5})(3 - 2\sqrt{5})$

6. $(4 + 2\sqrt{5})(4 - 2\sqrt{5})$

7. $(5 + 2\sqrt{3})(5 - 2\sqrt{3})$

8. $(\sqrt{7} - 3)(\sqrt{13} - 6)$

9. $(\sqrt{7} - 4)(\sqrt{17} - 6)$

10. $\sqrt[6]{5}(8\sqrt[6]{2} - \sqrt[6]{14x})$

11. $9(\sqrt{5} + 3) - 3(\sqrt{5} + 5)$

12. $13(\sqrt{11} + 3) - 3(\sqrt{11} + 3)$

13. $\sqrt{5}(x - \sqrt{17})$

14. $\sqrt{5}(x - \sqrt{13})$

Exercises 15–17: Add and simplify.

15. $\sqrt{9b + 27} + \sqrt{b^3 + 3b^2}$

16. $\sqrt{4x - 8} + \sqrt{x^3 - 2x^2}$

17. $\sqrt{25y + 50} - \sqrt{y^5 + 2y^4}$

18. Explain what is wrong with the statement $\sqrt{3} \cdot (\sqrt{2} + 5\sqrt{x}) = 6 + 15x$.

19. What is the area of a square with each side having length $16 + 8\sqrt[3]{2}$ inches? Give your answer in exact radical form.

Rationalizing the Denominator

Rationalizing the denominator is the process of removing a radical in the denominator of an expression. The expression $\dfrac{\sqrt{3}}{\sqrt{5}}$ is not simplified because it has a radical in its denominator. In the model problems, we show how to rationalize the denominator, starting with square roots.

> To rationalize a denominator, multiply by a fraction equal to one that has that denominator in both the numerator and denominator. You know you have multiplied by the correct fraction if the denominator simplifies to an integer.

MODEL PROBLEMS

1. Rationalize $\dfrac{\sqrt{2}}{\sqrt{7}}$.

SOLUTION

Multiply by a fraction equaling 1 containing denominator
$$\frac{\sqrt{2}}{\sqrt{7}} \cdot \frac{\sqrt{7}}{\sqrt{7}}$$

To rationalize the denominator, multiply by $\dfrac{\sqrt{7}}{\sqrt{7}}$, a fraction equal to 1 that has $\sqrt{7}$ in the denominator. (Because the fraction $\dfrac{\sqrt{7}}{\sqrt{7}}$ we multiply by is equal to 1, the value of the original expression does not change.)

Apply product rule in denominator
$$\frac{\sqrt{2} \cdot \sqrt{7}}{\sqrt{49}}$$

Apply the product rule in the denominator.

Simplify denominator
$$\frac{\sqrt{2} \cdot \sqrt{7}}{\sqrt{49}} = \frac{\sqrt{2} \cdot \sqrt{7}}{7}$$

The square root of 49 is 7. We have rationalized the denominator, since it no longer contains a radical.

Apply product rule in numerator
$$\frac{\sqrt{2} \cdot \sqrt{7}}{7} = \frac{\sqrt{14}}{7}$$

Apply the product rule in the numerator, multiplying 2 by 7 to get 14 in the radical. We have now simplified the radical expression.

Model Problems continue . . .

2. Simplify $\sqrt{\dfrac{45}{x}}$.

SOLUTION

Change fraction to quotient	$\sqrt{\dfrac{45}{x}} = \dfrac{\sqrt{45}}{\sqrt{x}}$	First, restate the radical using the quotient rule.
Rationalize denominator	$\dfrac{\sqrt{45}}{\sqrt{x}} \cdot \dfrac{\sqrt{x}}{\sqrt{x}}$	To rationalize the denominator, multiply by $\dfrac{\sqrt{x}}{\sqrt{x}}$, a fraction equal to 1 that has $\sqrt{x}$ in the denominator.
Simplify denominator	$\dfrac{\sqrt{45} \cdot \sqrt{x}}{\sqrt{x^2}} = \dfrac{\sqrt{45} \cdot \sqrt{x}}{x}$	We have rationalized the denominator, since it no longer contains a radical.
Simplify	$\dfrac{\sqrt{9} \cdot \sqrt{5} \cdot \sqrt{x}}{x} = \dfrac{3\sqrt{5x}}{x}$	Simplify $\sqrt{45}$ to get $3\sqrt{5}$ and apply the product rule in the numerator. We have now simplified the radical expression.

3. Rationalize $\dfrac{1}{\sqrt[5]{8}}$.

SOLUTION

Write radicand as power	$8 = 2^3$ $\dfrac{1}{\sqrt[5]{8}} = \dfrac{1}{\sqrt[5]{2^3}}$	The process of rationalizing a denominator with a higher index root is similar to that for a square root. Take 8, the radicand in the denominator, and write it as a power, 2^3.
Determine additional factors needed for nth power	$2^3 \cdot 2^2 = 2^5$	To take the fifth root, we need a fifth power of 2. We need 2 more factors of 2. Multiply by 2^2 to get 2^5.
Multiply by radical fraction containing additional factors	$\dfrac{1}{\sqrt[5]{2^3}} \cdot \dfrac{\sqrt[5]{2^2}}{\sqrt[5]{2^2}}$	Multiply by a fraction whose numerator and denominator are the fifth root of the additional factors (2^2) needed.
Use product rule	$\dfrac{\sqrt[5]{2^2}}{\sqrt[5]{2^5}}$	Simplify the numerator and denominator. Add the exponents to multiply.
Simplify	$\dfrac{\sqrt[5]{4}}{2}$	Simplify. In the denominator, the fifth root of 2^5 is 2. The denominator is now rationalized because it is no longer a radical.

> To rationalize a denominator that is an nth root, multiply the radicand by factors that will produce exponents that are multiples of the index n. In other words, the resulting radicand is a perfect nth power.

Summary: Simplifying Radical Expressions

Simpler is better. It is sometimes difficult to tell what is simpler. Is $\sqrt{8}$ simpler than $2\sqrt{2}$? There are three requirements that mathematicians agree on for simplified radical expressions. We state them using square roots for simplicity. Similar ideas would apply to cube roots, and so on.

1. No perfect powers in radicand.

$\sqrt{5t^3}$

The expression $\sqrt{5t^3}$ is not simplified. There is a factor of t^2 under the radical sign that is a perfect square.

$$\sqrt{5t^3} = \sqrt{t^2} \cdot \sqrt{5t} = t\sqrt{5t}$$

The product rule can be used to remove the perfect square factor. State the expression as the product of two square roots, the first of which contains a perfect square. Take the square root of t^2, which is t. That still leaves a factor $\sqrt{5t}$, but there is nothing we can do to simplify that.

2. No fractions in radicand.

$\sqrt{\dfrac{17}{9}}$

The expression $\sqrt{\dfrac{17}{9}}$ fails to be simplified because there is a fraction, $\dfrac{17}{9}$, under the radical.

$$\sqrt{\frac{17}{9}} = \frac{\sqrt{17}}{\sqrt{9}} = \frac{\sqrt{17}}{3}$$

The quotient rule can be applied to write this as a fraction of radicals. In this case, conveniently enough, the denominator is a perfect square.

3. No radicals in denominator.

$\dfrac{3t}{\sqrt{2}}$

The expression $\dfrac{3t}{\sqrt{2}}$ is not considered simplified because the denominator is a radical.

$$\frac{3t}{\sqrt{2}} = \frac{3t}{\sqrt{2}} \cdot \frac{\sqrt{2}}{\sqrt{2}} = \frac{3t\sqrt{2}}{2}$$

Rationalize $\dfrac{3t}{\sqrt{2}}$ by multiplying by the fraction $\dfrac{\sqrt{2}}{\sqrt{2}}$. This causes the denominator to be a rational number.

PRACTICE

1. **MP 5** Rationalize the denominators to determine which radical expression is not equivalent to $\dfrac{2\sqrt[3]{5x^2}}{5x^2}$.

A. $\dfrac{2\sqrt[3]{x}}{\sqrt[3]{25x^5}}$

C. $\dfrac{2\sqrt[3]{5}}{\sqrt[3]{125x^4}}$

B. $\dfrac{2\sqrt[3]{5}}{\sqrt[3]{25x^4}}$

D. $\dfrac{2}{\sqrt[3]{25x^4}}$

2. **MP 5** Rationalize the denominators to determine which radical expression is not equivalent to $\dfrac{5\sqrt[3]{4x^2}}{2x}$.

A. $\dfrac{5\sqrt[3]{x^2}}{\sqrt[3]{2x^3}}$

C. $\dfrac{5\sqrt[3]{2}}{\sqrt[3]{4x}}$

B. $\dfrac{\sqrt[3]{100x}}{2\sqrt[3]{25x^2}}$

D. $\dfrac{5\sqrt[3]{2x}}{\sqrt[3]{4}}$

Practice Problems continue . . .

3. Rationalize the denominators to determine which radical expression is not equivalent to $\dfrac{4\sqrt[3]{3x}}{3x}$.

A. $\dfrac{2\sqrt[3]{16}}{\sqrt[3]{18x^2}}$ C. $\dfrac{4\sqrt[3]{3}}{\sqrt[3]{27x^2}}$

B. $\dfrac{4}{\sqrt[3]{9x^2}}$ D. $\dfrac{4\sqrt[3]{3x}}{\sqrt[3]{9x^2}}$

Exercises 4–18: Simplify and rationalize the denominator, if necessary.

4. $\dfrac{1}{\sqrt{11}}$

5. $\dfrac{1}{\sqrt{3}}$

6. $\dfrac{\sqrt{11}}{\sqrt{3}}$

7. $\dfrac{\sqrt{11}}{\sqrt{5}}$

8. $\sqrt{\dfrac{13}{3x}}$

9. $\sqrt{\dfrac{11}{5x}}$

10. $\dfrac{\sqrt[3]{2}}{\sqrt[3]{7}}$

11. $\dfrac{\sqrt[3]{3}}{\sqrt[3]{5}}$

12. $\dfrac{\sqrt[3]{4}}{\sqrt[3]{3}}$

13. $\dfrac{8}{\sqrt[7]{x}}$

14. $\dfrac{17}{\sqrt[6]{x}}$

15. $\dfrac{\sqrt{32}}{\sqrt{21}} \cdot \dfrac{\sqrt{2}}{\sqrt{3}}$

16. $\dfrac{\sqrt{2}}{\sqrt{21}} \cdot \dfrac{\sqrt{2}}{\sqrt{3}}$

17. $2 \cdot \dfrac{\sqrt{32x^2}}{\sqrt{33}} \cdot \dfrac{\sqrt{2x^3}}{\sqrt{3}}$

18. $2 \cdot \dfrac{\sqrt{2x^2}}{\sqrt{21}} \cdot \dfrac{\sqrt{2x^3}}{\sqrt{3}}$

19. **MP 3** Frank states that another way to rationalize the denominator in $\dfrac{5}{\sqrt{3}}$ is to square both the numerator and denominator. Does Frank's method work?

• Multi-Part PROBLEM Practice •

1. **MP 2** A 30-60-90 triangle has legs with lengths of x and $\sqrt{3}x$ centimeters. Find exact expressions for
   a The perimeter of the triangle.
   b The area of the triangle.

2. **MP 7, 8** The short leg of the same triangle is increased by 1 centimeter, while the triangle remains a 30-60-90 triangle. Find exact, simplified (no parentheses) expressions for
   a The lengths of the other two sides of the triangle.
   b The perimeter of the new triangle.
   c The area of the new triangle.

5.3 Exponent Notation

Exponent Notation for Roots

The expression 4^2 is a power of 4. In this expression, 4 is the *base* and 2 is the *exponent*. **Exponent notation for roots** is the use of fractions as the exponent in expressions. When writing a root, the exponent is the reciprocal of the index:

> **To see a proof of this notation, see the table in the next section, "Derivation of Roots as Powers."**

$$x^{\frac{1}{n}} = \sqrt[n]{x}$$

The index n must be a positive integer. The nth root of x equals x to the reciprocal of n.

Expressions with fractional exponents can be simplified. Stating them as radicals can help. To evaluate roots stated as powers, you have to be careful with signs.

- When n is odd, every real number has exactly one nth root, $(a^n)^{\frac{1}{n}} = a$.

- When n is even, the principal root is the positive root, $(a^n)^{\frac{1}{n}} = |a|$.

Exponents can also be rational numbers with numerators that are not 1. These can also be written as radicals; for example, $5^{\frac{3}{4}} = \sqrt[4]{5^3}$. Use the rule:

$$x^{\frac{m}{n}} = (\sqrt[n]{x})^m = \sqrt[n]{x^m}, \text{ with } \sqrt[n]{x} \text{ a real number}$$

MODEL PROBLEMS

1. State $\sqrt[4]{81}$ with exponential notation.

SOLUTION

The exponent is the reciprocal of the index

$$\sqrt[4]{81} = 81^{\frac{1}{4}}$$

To state a root as a power, take the reciprocal of the index and use it as the exponent. Here, the index is 4, since we're taking the fourth root of 81.

2. Simplify $27^{\frac{1}{3}}$.

SOLUTION

Reciprocal of exponent is index of root

$$27^{\frac{1}{3}} = \sqrt[3]{27} = 3$$

First restate the power as a root by taking the reciprocal of the exponent and using it as the index. Here, the exponent is $\frac{1}{3}$, so the index is 3. State the expression as the cube root of 27. The cube root of 27 is 3 since 3^3 equals 27.

Model Problems continue . . .

3. State $5^{\frac{3}{4}}$ using a radical.

SOLUTION

Apply power rule to split numerator and denominator $\quad 5^{\frac{3}{4}} = (5^3)^{\frac{1}{4}}$

To state the expression as a radical expression, use the power rule for exponents. First, factor $\frac{3}{4}$ as 3 times $\frac{1}{4}$ and write the expression as a power of power.

Denominator is index and simplify $\quad (5^3)^{\frac{1}{4}} = \sqrt[4]{5^3} = \sqrt[4]{125}$

Put 5^3 under the radical sign, and take its fourth root, since the exponent of 5^3 is $\frac{1}{4}$. State it even more simply, by noting that 5^3 equals 125.

4. **MP 1, 7** Simplify $(-8)^{\frac{2}{3}}$ using two different methods.

SOLUTION

Method 1

Apply power rule to split numerator and denominator $\quad (-8)^{\frac{2}{3}} = ((-8)^2)^{\frac{1}{3}}$

Write $\frac{2}{3}$ as 2 times $\frac{1}{3}$ and state the expression as a power of power.

Denominator is index $\quad \sqrt[3]{(-8)^2}$

Put $(-8)^2$ under the radical sign, and take its third root, since the exponent of $(-8)^2$ is $\frac{1}{3}$.

Simplify $\quad \sqrt[3]{(-8)^2} = \sqrt[3]{64} = 4$

State it even more simply by squaring -8, which equals 64. The cube root of 64 is 4. The expression $(-8)^{\frac{2}{3}}$ equals 4.

Method 2

Apply power rule to split numerator and denominator $\quad (-8)^{\frac{2}{3}} = (((-2)^3)^2)^{\frac{1}{3}}$

Write -8 as $(-2)^3$, since -8 is a perfect cube.

Apply power of power rule $\quad 3 \cdot 2 \cdot \frac{1}{3} = 2$

To simplify a power of power, multiply exponents. Multiply all three exponents.

Simplify $\quad (-2)^2 = 4$

The result of multiplying the exponents was 2. Raise -2 to that power. It is the same answer as above.

> We apply the power of power rule to simplify, and then apply the exponent. This demonstrates that the rules of exponents apply to fractional exponents as well.

Model Problems continue . . .

5. Simplify $16^{\frac{3}{4}}$.

SOLUTION

Write as a power of a root $\quad 16^{\frac{3}{4}} = \left(16^{\frac{1}{4}}\right)^3 = (\sqrt[4]{16})^3 \quad$ Write the fraction as $\frac{1}{4}$ times 3. Using the rules of exponents, write the expression as the 4th root of 16, cubed. State the 4th root as a radical with an index of 4.

Take 4th root of 16 $\qquad \sqrt[4]{16} = 2 \qquad$ The 4th root of 16 is 2.

Raise 2 to the 3rd power $\qquad 2^3 = 8 \qquad$ The cube of 2 is 8.

Derivation of Roots as Powers

We show below why we can state a root as a power. We start by stating the nth root of x as some power m of x, and then show that m must be the reciprocal of n.

Derive: $\sqrt[n]{x} = x^{\frac{1}{n}}$

Solve for m	$\sqrt[n]{x} = x^m$	Assume $\sqrt[n]{x}$ equals some power of x, x^m. We want to solve for the exponent m.
Raise both sides to power n	$(\sqrt[n]{x})^n = (x^m)^n$ $x^1 = x^{mn}$	Using the power principle, raise both numbers to the nth power. We get x on the left, which we state as x^1. On the right, the exponents m and n are multiplied.
Equate exponents and solve for m	$1 = mn$ $m = \frac{1}{n}$	Since x^1 equals x^{mn}, the exponents must equal each other, since the bases are the same. Then solve for m and find that m equals the reciprocal of n.
Substitute	$\sqrt[n]{x} = x^{\frac{1}{n}}$	We showed that m equals the reciprocal of n. Substitute that back into our first equation, replacing m, and we have shown that the nth root of x equals $x^{\frac{1}{n}}$.

Rules of Exponents and Fractional Exponents

The rules of exponents also apply to expressions with fractional exponents.

> Note that all bases must be the same for the rules to apply.

Multiplying fractional powers:

Multiplying exponents with fractional powers	$2^{\frac{1}{5}} \cdot 2^{\frac{2}{5}}$	This expression is the product of two powers with the same base.
Apply product rule	$2^{\frac{1}{5}+\frac{2}{5}} = 2^{\frac{3}{5}}$	By the product of powers rule, we can write the expression with the same base, 2, and add the powers.

Dividing fractional powers:

Dividing exponents with fractional powers	$\dfrac{5^{\frac{7}{5}}}{5^{\frac{3}{4}}}$	This expression is the quotient of two powers with the same base.
Apply quotient of powers rule	$5^{\frac{7}{5}-\frac{3}{4}}$	By the quotient of powers rule, we can write the expression with the same base, 5, and the difference of the exponents as the power.
Simplify exponent	$5^{\frac{28}{20}-\frac{15}{20}} = 5^{\frac{13}{20}}$	We write the fractions in the exponent with the same denominator, 20, and then subtract.

Multiplying and Dividing Radicals with Different Indices but Same Radicand

Stating radicals with different indices in exponential form with fractional powers allows you to multiply them, if they have the same base. You can also apply other exponent rules to radicals, after writing them as powers with fractional exponents. For example, you can take a power of a radical by applying the rule that $(x^n)^m = x^{nm}$.

For instance, $(\sqrt[5]{2x})^3$ equals $(2x)^{\frac{3}{5}}$.

MODEL PROBLEMS

1. Multiply $\sqrt{5}\sqrt[3]{5}$ using fractional exponents.

SOLUTION

State radicals as powers

$\sqrt[3]{5} = 5^{\frac{1}{3}}$
$\sqrt{5} = 5^{\frac{1}{2}}$

State the radicals as powers. The exponent in each case is the reciprocal of the index of the root.

Multiply

$5^{\frac{1}{2}} \cdot 5^{\frac{1}{3}}$
$5^{\frac{1}{2}+\frac{1}{3}}$
$5^{\frac{5}{6}}$

State the multiplication using the radicals stated as powers. To multiply, add the exponents. The sum of $\dfrac{1}{2}$ and $\dfrac{1}{3}$ is $\dfrac{5}{6}$. We could state the answer as $\sqrt[6]{5^5}$ if asked to state it as a radical. We could also use a calculator to check that the product $\sqrt{5} \cdot \sqrt[3]{5}$ and the power $5^{\frac{5}{6}}$ give the same result, approximately 3.82.

Model Problems continue . . .

2. Divide $\dfrac{\sqrt[3]{7}}{\sqrt[6]{7}}$.

SOLUTION

State radicals as powers
$\dfrac{\sqrt[3]{7}}{\sqrt[6]{7}} = \dfrac{7^{\frac{1}{3}}}{7^{\frac{1}{6}}}$
Restate the division by stating the radicals as powers.

Divide
$\dfrac{7^{\frac{2}{6} - \frac{1}{6}}}{7^{\frac{1}{6}}}$
To divide powers, subtract exponents. To do the subtraction, restate $\dfrac{1}{3}$ as $\dfrac{2}{6}$ to get a common denominator, and then subtract to get $\dfrac{1}{6}$.

PRACTICE

Exercises 1–14: Simplify. Write your answers as fractions, if necessary.

1. $64^{\frac{1}{3}}$

2. $125^{\frac{1}{3}}$

3. $16^{\frac{1}{4}}$

4. $81^{\frac{5}{4}}$

5. $32^{\frac{6}{5}}$

6. $(-27)^{\frac{1}{3}}$

7. $(-32)^{\frac{3}{5}}$

8. $\left(\dfrac{1}{16}\right)^{\frac{1}{4}}$

9. $\left(-\dfrac{1}{8}\right)^{\frac{1}{3}}$

10. $\left(-\dfrac{1}{125}\right)^{\frac{2}{3}}$

11. $\left(-\dfrac{243}{32}\right)^{\frac{2}{5}}$

12. $(36x^4)^{\frac{3}{2}}$

13. $(25x^6)^{\frac{3}{2}}$

14. $(9x^2)^{\frac{3}{2}}$

Exercises 15–21: State each expression as a simplified radical expression.

15. $5^{\frac{3}{5}}$

16. $4^{\frac{3}{5}}$

17. $3^{\frac{3}{5}}$

18. $10^{\frac{3}{4}}$

19. $4^{\frac{4}{5}}$

20. $(x + 6)^{\frac{1}{5}}$

21. $(x + 3)^{\frac{2}{3}}$

Exercises 22–26: State each radical expression in exponential form.

22. $\sqrt[4]{x^3}$

23. $\sqrt[4]{x^5}$

24. $\sqrt[7]{x^4}$

25. $\sqrt[4]{x + 9}$

26. $\sqrt[5]{(y - 4)^7}$

Exercises 27–35: Multiply and simplify.

27. $7^{\frac{1}{9}} \cdot 7^{\frac{4}{9}}$

28. $10^{\frac{2}{9}} \cdot 10^{\frac{3}{4}}$

29. $\sqrt[12]{10} \cdot \sqrt[3]{10}$

30. $\sqrt[6]{11} \cdot \sqrt[4]{11}$

Practice Problems continue . . .

31. $\sqrt[7]{x} \cdot \sqrt[5]{x}$

32. $\sqrt[9]{z} \cdot \sqrt[3]{z}$

33. $\sqrt[5]{7} \cdot \sqrt[3]{7}$

34. $\sqrt[6]{2} \cdot \sqrt[4]{2}$

35. $\sqrt[6]{3} \cdot \sqrt[5]{3}$

Exercises 36–44: Divide and simplify.

36. $\dfrac{\sqrt[4]{6a^2}}{\sqrt[6]{6a^2}}$

37. $\dfrac{\sqrt[5]{5a^3}}{\sqrt[6]{5a^3}}$

38. $\dfrac{\sqrt[4]{3a^2}}{\sqrt[8]{3a^2}}$

39. $\dfrac{7^{\frac{3}{8}}}{7^{\frac{1}{12}}}$

40. $\dfrac{b^{\frac{4}{5}}}{b^{\frac{2}{3}}}$

41. $\dfrac{\sqrt[5]{11}}{\sqrt[7]{11}}$

42. $\dfrac{\sqrt[7]{12c^3}}{\sqrt[10]{12c^3}}$

43. $\dfrac{\sqrt[8]{3b^2}}{\sqrt[12]{3b^2}}$

44. $\dfrac{\sqrt[3]{28n^5}}{\sqrt[4]{28n^5}}$

Exercises 45–49: Simplify.

45. $\dfrac{y^{\frac{1}{5}}}{y^{\frac{1}{2}}} \cdot y^{\frac{2}{3}}$

46. $\dfrac{y^{\frac{1}{4}}}{y^{\frac{1}{2}}} \cdot y^{\frac{2}{5}}$

47. $\dfrac{y^{\frac{1}{3}}}{y^{\frac{1}{4}}} \cdot y^{\frac{3}{4}}$

48. $\left(y^{\frac{3}{7}} \right)^{\frac{1}{3}}$

49. $\left(d^{\frac{5}{4}} \right)^{\frac{2}{3}}$

50. **MP 7** What condition(s) must be satisfied in order for the equation $\sqrt{a^2 + b^2} = a + b$ to be true?

51. **MP 7** What condition(s) must be satisfied in order for the equation $\sqrt[4]{a^4 + b^4} = a + b$ to be true?

52. **MP 2, 8** Complete the table.

The nth Roots of a Real Number			
Real number a	Radical index n	nth root(s) of a	Examples
$a > 0$	$n > 0$ and is even		
$a < 0$	n is even		
$a = 0$	n is odd or even		
$a \neq 0$	n is odd		

Exercises 53–56: Simplify the following expressions by changing the exponent to a fraction. Write your answers in exponential notation with positive integer exponents.

53. $81^{1.75}$

54. $121^{2.5}$

55. $243^{-2.4}$

56. $256^{-1.375}$

57. Sam captures insects. In 2008, he captured $64^{\frac{1}{3}}$ jars of insects. Each jar contained $64^{\frac{1}{6}}$ insects. How many insects did Sam collect in 2008?

58. **MP 2** An equilateral triangle has sides of length x. Write a formula for the area of the equilateral triangle in terms of x.

Practice Problems continue . . .

Practice Problems continued . . .

59. What are some common mistakes that can occur when working with exponents? Give several examples.

60. MP 3 Gerald states that for any positive number x, $x^m \geq x^n$ whenever $m \geq n > 0$. Is his statement necessarily true? Explain your answer.

61. MP 3, 8 Explain how $\sqrt[3]{x^2} \cdot \sqrt{x}$ can equal $x\sqrt[6]{x}$ when there are no 6th roots in the original problem.

62. MP 3 Let m and n be positive integers and x be any positive number. To simplify the expression $x^{\frac{m}{n}}$, one can either compute by raising to the mth power first, then taking the nth root of the result, or vice versa. That is, $\left(x^m\right)^{\frac{1}{n}}$ or $\left(x^{\frac{1}{n}}\right)^m$. Compare the differences in these methods. Which method is generally easier to compute?

LESSON 5.4

5.4 Radical Equations

Squaring Principle

An equation with the variable under a radical sign, such as $\sqrt{x} + 3 = 8$, is a **radical equation**. The key to solving these equations is the **squaring principle,** which states that if an equation is true, so is the equation that results from squaring both sides.

> When solving a radical equation, if there is one radical expression, isolate it. If there are two radical expressions, put one on each side of the equation.

$$\text{If } a = b, \text{ then } a^2 = b^2.$$

If a and b are equal, then their squares are equal. The variables a and b can represent numbers or expressions. For example, if $x = 4$ then $x^2 = 4^2$. We assume that x equals 4. This means that x squared equals 4 squared. In other words, we can square both sides of an equation.

MODEL PROBLEM

Use the squaring principle to solve $13 + \sqrt{x} = 17$.

SOLUTION

Isolate radical $\sqrt{x} = 4$ Subtract 13 from both sides to isolate the radical on one side.

Square both sides $(\sqrt{x})^2 = (4)^2$ Using the squaring principle, square both sides.

Solve equation $x = 16$ The left side is the square of a square root, which simplifies to x. On the right-hand side, 4^2 equals 16. The solution is 16. We check our solution by entering 16 for x into the original equation $13 + \sqrt{x} = 17$ and doing the operations. Since $\sqrt{16} = 4$, and $13 + 4 = 17$, our solution is correct.

> To use the squaring principle to solve a radical equation, isolate the radical on one side and square both sides of the equation. Then solve the resulting equation.

Extraneous Solutions

Extraneous solutions are solutions that can be derived through a series of correct steps, but they are not solutions to the original equation. How does this come about? As an example, although every solution to $a = b$ is also a solution to $a^2 = b^2$, **not** every solution to $a^2 = b^2$ has to be a solution to $a = b$. For instance, $5^2 = (-5)^2$, but $5 \neq -5$.

> An extraneous solution is **not** a solution to the original equation. You can discover extraneous solutions by checking possible solutions in the original equation.

MODEL PROBLEMS

1. Solve $\sqrt{4x} = -6x$. Determine if there are extraneous solutions.

SOLUTION

Square both sides	$\sqrt{4x} = -6x$ $4x = 36x^2$	Use the squaring principle and square both sides of the equation.
Solve equation	$36x^2 - 4x = 0$	To solve the equation, subtract $4x$ from both sides, and write the equation with all terms on the left and 0 on the right.
Use zero-product property	$4x(9x - 1) = 0$ $x = 0 \;\textbf{\textit{or}}\; x = \dfrac{1}{9}$	Factor. The solutions to the quadratic equation are 0 and $\dfrac{1}{9}$. These are *possible* solutions to the original equation.
Check 0 in original equation	$\sqrt{4 \cdot 0} \stackrel{?}{=} (-6)(0)$ $0 = 0$	Check each of the possible solutions in the original equation $\sqrt{4x} = -6x$. Substituting 0 for x in the original equation and simplifying both sides, we have the equality $0 = 0$. This means 0 is a solution of the original equation.
Check $\dfrac{1}{9}$ in original equation	$\sqrt{4 \cdot \dfrac{1}{9}} \stackrel{?}{=} (-6) \cdot \dfrac{1}{9}$ $\dfrac{2}{3} \neq -\dfrac{2}{3}$	Substituting $\dfrac{1}{9}$ for x in the original equation and simplifying both sides, we get the equation $\dfrac{2}{3} = -\dfrac{2}{3}$, which is false. Although $\dfrac{1}{9}$ solves the quadratic equation we created by squaring both sides, it is **not** a solution of the original equation.
One solution	0 is a solution $\dfrac{1}{9}$ is extraneous	The only solution to the original equation is 0. The number $\dfrac{1}{9}$ is an extraneous solution since it is not a solution to the original equation.

Model Problems continue . . .

2. **MP 3** Two students solved the equation $-2x = \sqrt{3x}$. One student says there are two solutions, $x = 0$ and $x = \frac{3}{4}$. The other student says there is only one solution $x = 0$. Which best describes who is correct?

   A.   There are two solutions because all radical equations have two solutions.

   B.   The students solved the equation incorrectly because there should be one positive and one negative solution for a radical equation.

   C.   There is only one correct solution, $x = 0$. The other solution, $x = \frac{3}{4}$, is extraneous.

   D.   There is only one correct solution, $x = \frac{3}{4}$. The other solution, $x = 0$, is extraneous.

SOLUTION

   A.   When the solution $x = \frac{3}{4}$ is checked into the equation, the left side has a value that is negative, which cannot be equal to the positive right side.

   B.   The student is thinking that there are positive and negative roots for numbers, but this does not apply here.

   C.   **Correct answer.** Squaring both sides eliminates the negative value on the left side of the equation, but when the solution $x = \frac{3}{4}$ is checked into the original equation, the left side has a value that is negative, which cannot be equal to the positive right side.

   D.   The $x = \frac{3}{4}$ does not check into the original equation. $x = 0$ checks into the original equation.

3. Solve $\sqrt{3x - 5} - \sqrt{2x + 7} = 0$. Check for extraneous solutions.

SOLUTION

Isolate both radicals	$\sqrt{3x - 5} = \sqrt{2x + 7}$	Isolate both radicals by adding the second radical, $\sqrt{2x + 7}$, to both sides.
Square both sides	$(\sqrt{3x - 5})^2 = (\sqrt{2x + 7})^2$ $3x - 5 = 2x + 7$	Square both sides. The result of squaring is the linear equation shown.
Solve equation	$x - 5 = 7$ $x = 12$	Solve the equation by combining like terms, and so on.
Check solution in original equation	$\sqrt{3x - 5} - \sqrt{2x + 7} = 0$ $\sqrt{3(12) - 5} - \sqrt{2(12) + 7} \overset{?}{=} 0$ $\sqrt{31} - \sqrt{24 + 7} \overset{?}{=} 0$ $\sqrt{31} - \sqrt{31} \overset{?}{=} 0$ $0 = 0$	Check the possible solution, 12, in the original equation. Substitute 12 for x in the original equation and simplify the left side to get the equality $0 = 0$. Since the solution 12 makes the original equation true, it is the solution to the equation $\sqrt{3x - 5} - \sqrt{2x + 7} = 0$.

Model Problems continue . . .

4. **MP 6** Solve $x + 1 = \sqrt{2x + 5}$ for x. Check for extraneous solutions.

SOLUTION

Square both sides	$(x + 1)^2 = (\sqrt{2x + 5})^2$ $x^2 + 2x + 1 = 2x + 5$	The radical is already isolated, so square both sides. Notice from the structure of the expression that it is a quadratic.
Set equal to 0	$x^2 + 2x - 2x + 1 - 5 = 0$ $x^2 - 4 = 0$	The expression has been rearranged as a quadratic. Set one side equal to 0.
Factor	$(x + 2)(x - 2) = 0$	Factor the equation. $x^2 - 4$ is a difference of two squares, so it must be the product of the sum and difference of x and 2.
Find solutions	$x + 2 = 0$ $x = -2$ $x - 2 = 0$ $x = 2$	Since the product is equal to 0, one of the factors must be equal to 0. Solve these equations to find that x is either 2 or -2.
Check first solution: $x = 2$	$2 + 1 \stackrel{?}{=} \sqrt{2 \cdot 2 + 5}$ $3 \stackrel{?}{=} \sqrt{9}$ $3 = 3$	Check the solutions to see if either is extraneous. Plug in the first value of $x = 2$ to see if it works. It does, so $x = 2$ is a solution.
Check second solution: $x = -2$	$-2 + 1 \stackrel{?}{=} \sqrt{-2 \cdot 2 + 5}$ $-1 \stackrel{?}{=} \sqrt{1}$ $-1 \neq 1$	Check the second solution. This results in a statement which is not true, so $x = -2$ is an extraneous solution. The only solution to the original equation is 2.

Power Principle

Equations involving roots with any index can be solved in a similar manner as equations with square roots. In other words, if $a = b$, then $a^n = b^n$. To solve an equation, you can raise both sides to any power you like. The **power principle** states:

$$\text{If } a = b, \text{ then } a^n = b^n.$$

> If an equation is true, so is the equation that results from raising both sides to the same power.

If a and b are equal, then you can raise them to any power, and the equality still holds. If $\sqrt[5]{x} = 3$, for example, we can raise both sides to the fifth power: $(\sqrt[5]{x})^5 = 3^5$. If you raise both sides of an equation to an even power, you must check your solutions in the original equation to eliminate any extraneous solutions that might result. Raising the sides to an odd power does **not** introduce extraneous solutions.

MODEL PROBLEM

Solve $\sqrt[3]{x + 17} - 5 = -3$ using the power principle. Check the solution.

SOLUTION

Isolate the radical	$\sqrt[3]{x + 17} = 2$	Isolate the radical by adding 5 to both sides.
Raise both sides to the appropriate power	$(\sqrt[3]{x + 17})^3 = (2)^3$	To remove the radical, raise both sides to the third power.
Simplify	$x + 17 = 8$	Cubing a cube root results in the expression inside the radical. The cube of 2 is 8.
Solve for x	$x = -9$	Subtract 17 from both sides to get x equals -9.
Substitute -9 for x	$\sqrt[3]{-9 + 17} - 5 \overset{?}{=} -3$	Check the solution. Substitute -9 for x. The radical simplifies to the cube root of 8.
	$\sqrt[3]{8} - 5 \overset{?}{=} -3$	
Do the operations	$2 - 5 = -3$	The cube root of 8 is 2. Subtract 5 from 2, and get -3 on both sides. The solution $x = -9$ is a solution to the original equation.
	$-3 = -3$	

PRACTICE

1. Solve $\sqrt{x + 10} = 2 - x$.

   A. $x = -1$

   B. $x = 6$

   C. $x = -1$ and 6

   D. No solutions

2. **MP 2** Solve the equation $\sqrt[n]{x + m} + A$ for x. Which represents the best solution?

   A. $A^n - m$

   B. A^{n-m}

   C. $A^n + m$

   D. $(A - m)^n$

Exercises 3–35: Solve.

3. $8 = 5 + \sqrt{4x + 17}$

4. $2 = 3 - \sqrt{3x + 19}$

5. $\sqrt[3]{x} + 5 = 1$

6. $\sqrt[3]{x} - 2 = 3$

7. $4 - \sqrt[5]{3 - x} = 1$

8. $3 + \sqrt[3]{x + 2} = -1$

9. $5 - \sqrt[5]{3 - x} = 7$

10. $6 - \sqrt{5x} = 13$

11. $\sqrt{-x + 23} = x - 3$

12. $\sqrt{2x + 5} = x + 1$

13. $5 - \sqrt{6x} = 16$

14. $\sqrt{3x} + 5 = 10$

15. $\sqrt{4x} + 4 = 10$

16. $\sqrt[3]{x + 600} - 4 = 6$

17. $12 = 52 - 4\sqrt{4x - 1}$

18. $10 = 26 - 2\sqrt{5x - 1}$

19. $25 = 70 - 5\sqrt{3x - 1}$

20. $4 = 60 - 4\sqrt{2x - 1}$

21. $\dfrac{\sqrt[4]{x - 2} + 1}{4} = 1$

22. $\dfrac{\sqrt[3]{x - 5} + 1}{3} = 2$

23. $\dfrac{\sqrt[4]{x + 2} + 46}{6} = 8$

24. $\dfrac{\sqrt{x - 1} - 13}{2} = -2$

25. $\sqrt{x + 6} = \sqrt{-2x + 15}$

26. $\sqrt{4x + 1} = \sqrt{-3x + 43}$

27. $\sqrt{5x - 1} = \sqrt{4x + 9}$

28. $\sqrt{4x + 7} = \sqrt{8x - 11}$

Practice Problems continue . . .

Practice Problems continued . . .

29. $\sqrt{3x+5} = \sqrt{6x-9}$

30. $\sqrt{5x+4} = \sqrt{7x-8}$

31. $\sqrt{3x+8} = \sqrt{6x-11}$

32. $\sqrt{5x+12} - \sqrt{9x-18} = 0$

33. $\sqrt{4x+9} - \sqrt{10x-134} = 0$

34. $\sqrt{4x+9} - \sqrt{11x-100} = 0$

35. $\sqrt{5x+10} - \sqrt{9x-130} = 0$

Exercises 36–37: Solve for the real solutions of x.

36. $2x + 15 = 11\sqrt{x}$

37. **MP 2, 7** $4x^{\frac{4}{3}} = x^{\frac{2}{3}} + 18$ (Hint: Substitute $y = x^{\frac{2}{3}}$ into the equation, solve it for y, then find x.)

38. **MP 4, 6** The speed of sound in air can be calculated with the formula

$v = 331\sqrt{1 + \dfrac{T}{273}}$, where T is the

temperature in degrees Celsius and v is the speed in meters per second. On a hot 30°C day, a hiker shouts into a canyon and hears an echo 2 seconds later. How far away is the opposite side of the canyon, to the nearest hundredth of a meter?

39. Heron's formula, $A = \sqrt{s(s-a)(s-b)(s-c)}$, gives the area, A, of a triangle with side lengths of a, b, and c, and s being its semiperimeter (half its perimeter). Solve the equation for c.

40. What must be true for the following statement to be valid: "Let a and b be real numbers and n be an integer. If $a^n = b^n$, then $a = b$."

41. **MP 1, 2** The average of a number and its square root is 10. What is the number?

42. **MP 1, 2** The average of a number and its cube root is 0. What is the number?

43. If two equations have the same radical solutions, does that imply the equations are the same? Why or why not?

• Multi-Part PROBLEM Practice •

MP 3 Adam, Brian, and Carla are attempting to solve $2 = \sqrt{3x-2} - \sqrt{10-x}$.
Adam says, "This is easy. Just apply the squaring principle." He does the following:

$4 = (3x-2) - (10-x)$
$4 = 3x - 2 - 10 + x$
$4 = 4x - 12$
$16 = 4x$
$x = 4$

Brian says, "That's not right, Adam. You need to move one of the square-root terms to the other side of the equation before you square both sides."
Carla comments, "It doesn't matter whether you move one term to the other side of the equation or not. But you will have to apply the squaring principle twice in order to get the right answer."

a Who is correct?
b Explain the error(s) in the incorrect comment(s).
c If Adam is incorrect, what is the correct solution?

5.5 Radical Function Graphs

Graphing a Square Root Function

The real function $f(x) = \sqrt{x}$ is the parent function of the square root function. The domain is $x \geq 0$, since as a real function it is undefined for negative values. The range, or output, of the function must be greater than or equal to 0, or $f(x) \geq 0$, because the value of the function is the principal square root of x. The graph intercepts the axes at the origin. As x increases, $f(x)$ increases.

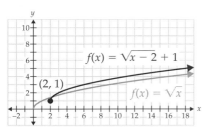

As with graphs of other functions, the graph of the parent function can be translated (shifted). For a square root function, $f(x) = \sqrt{x}$ can be translated using $\sqrt{x - h} + k$, where (h, k) shows the point where the graph has the smallest values of x and y. We show $f(x) = \sqrt{x - 2} + 1$ compared to $f(x) = \sqrt{x}$.

- Identify h and k With $f(x) = \sqrt{x - 2} + 1$, $h = 2$ and $k = 1$. The graph is translated to the right by 2 since $h = 2$, and up 1 since $k = 1$.

- Domain   The domain is $x \geq 2$ so that the function is defined. Lesser values would make the radicand negative and the function undefined.

- Range   The output of the function must be greater than or equal to 1, or $f(x) \geq 1$.

In this activity, experiment with translating square root graphs.

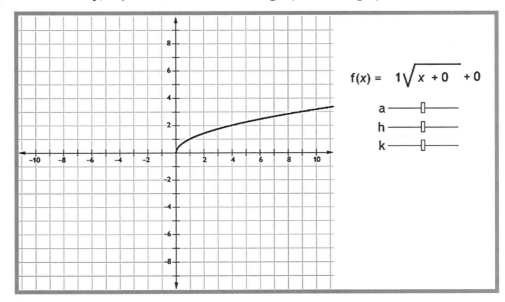

1. **MP 2, 4** The distance a person can see to the horizon, barring atmospheric conditions such as clouds, can be found with the equation $v = 1.225\sqrt{a}$, where v = miles of visibility to the horizon and a = viewing altitude, in feet, above the surface.

  a Graph the equation.

  b Determine the distance you would be able to see if you were on a ship 20 feet above the surface of the water.

  c Describe the end behavior of the function.

SOLUTION

a Graph

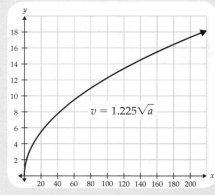

b Using the graph, at a distance of 20 feet above the surface of the water, you would be able to see 5.48 miles.

c At an altitude of 0 feet, the visibility is 0 miles. The visibility increases as the viewing altitude, in feet, above the surface increases.

2. **MP 1** Compare and contrast the graphs of $f(x) = \frac{1}{2}\sqrt{x}$, $f(x) = 2\sqrt{x}$, and $f(x) = -\sqrt{x}$.

SOLUTION

The parent function is scaled when it is multiplied by various constants. Multiplying by a constant whose absolute value is greater than 1 stretches the graph vertically. If the constant has an absolute value that is less than 1, then the graph contracts vertically. Multiplying by a negative constant reflects the graph over the x-axis. The domain is restricted to values greater than or equal to 0. The range restrictions depend on the coefficient. The range is greater than or equal to 0 if the coefficient is positive, and less than or equal to 0 if the coefficient is negative.

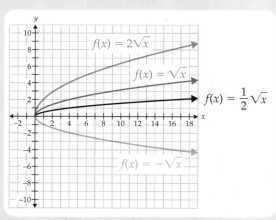

We start with $f(x) = \frac{1}{2}\sqrt{x}$. It is the same as $f(x) = \sqrt{x}$ but each output of the function is multiplied by $\frac{1}{2}$, creating a flatter curve. $f(x) = 2\sqrt{x}$ is the same as $f(x) = \sqrt{x}$ but each output of the function is multiplied by 2, creating a steeper curve. $f(x) = -\sqrt{x}$ is the same as $f(x) = \sqrt{x}$ but each output of the function is multiplied by -1, which flips the graph about the x-axis. It is symmetrical with the graph of $f(x) = \sqrt{x}$ about the x-axis.

Model Problems continue . . .

3. Compare $f(x) = \sqrt{x}$ and $f(x) = \sqrt{x - a} + b$. For what values of a and b does the graph of $f(x) = \sqrt{x - a} + b$ shift left and up from $f(x) = \sqrt{x}$?

    A. Positive a and positive b
    B. Positive a and negative b
    C. Negative a and positive b
    D. Negative a and negative b

SOLUTION

A. The graph shifts to the right and up for these values of a and b.
B. The graph shifts to the right and down for these values of a and b.
C. **Correct answer.** Negative a values create a horizontal shift to the left, and positive b values create a vertical shift up.
D. The graph shifts to the left and down for these values of a and b.

Graphing a Cube Root Function

The function $f(x) = \sqrt[3]{x}$ is the parent function of all cube root functions. Unlike the square root function, the domain is not restricted. Its domain is all real numbers since the function is defined for positive numbers, negative numbers, and 0. The graph intercepts the axes at the origin. As the absolute value of x increases, so does the absolute value of $f(x)$.

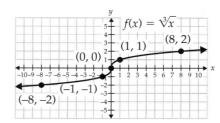

MODEL PROBLEM

Graph and compare $f(x) = \sqrt[3]{x + 3} - 2$ to the parent function $f(x) = \sqrt[3]{x}$.

SOLUTION

Identify h and k	With function $f(x) = \sqrt[3]{x + 3} - 2$, $h = -3$ and $k = -2$.
Translate left 3, down 2	The graph is shifted to the left by 3 since $h = -3$ and down 2 since $k = -2$. The domain and range of these functions are all real numbers.

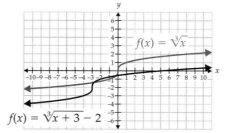

The other transformations that reflect and stretch the square root function also apply to other root functions.

PRACTICE

1. What are the domain and range of $f(x) = \sqrt{x - 9} + 4$?

   A. $x \geq 9$ and $f(x) \geq 4$

   B. $x \leq 9$ and $f(x) \geq 4$

   C. $x \geq 9$ and $f(x) \leq 4$

   D. $x \geq -9$ and $f(x) \geq -4$

2. Which of the following is the domain for the function $f(x) = \sqrt{x^2 - 9}$?

   A. $x \geq 3$

   B. $-3 \leq x \leq 3$

   C. $x \leq -3$ and $x \geq 3$

   D.   All real numbers

Exercises 3–6: Use the parent function $f(x) = \sqrt{x}$ to graph and write the function based on the description of how the parent graph is translated.

3. The graph is translated left 8 units.

4. The graph is translated down 5 units.

5. The graph is translated down 6 and right 9 units.

6. The graph is translated up 4 and left 5 units.

Exercises 7–10: Write functions that represent each graph based on the parent function $f(x) = \sqrt{x}$.

7.

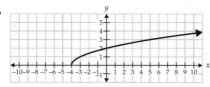

8.

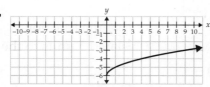

9.

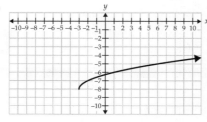

10.

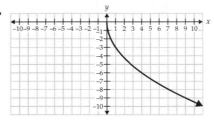

11. What are the differences between $f(x) = \sqrt{x}$ and $g(x) = -\dfrac{1}{2}\sqrt{x}$?

Exercises 12–13: State the domain and range of each function.

12. $f(x) = \sqrt{x + 3} - 2$

13. $f(x) = \sqrt{x - 12} + 4$

Exercises 14–15: Find the values of a, h, and k for each graph, which represents the function $f(x) = a\sqrt{x - h} + k$. The parent function is $f(x) = \sqrt{x}$.

14.

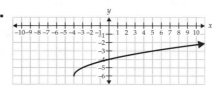

15.

Exercises 16–19: Use the graph of the parent function $f(x) = \sqrt[3]{x}$ to graph and write the function based on the description of how the parent graph is translated.

16. The graph is translated down 10 units.

17. The graph is translated right 7 units.

18. The graph is translated up 2 and left 9 units.

19. The graph is translated down 5 units and left 8 units.

Practice Problems continue . . .

Exercises 20–23: Write the expression for the function that represents each translated graph based on the parent function $f(x) = \sqrt[3]{x}$.

20.

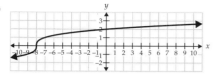

21.

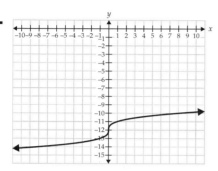

22.

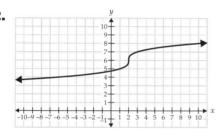

23.

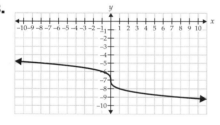

Exercises 24–25: State the domain and range of each function.

24. $f(x) = \sqrt[3]{x - 10} + 4$

25. $f(x) = \sqrt[3]{x + 1} - 11.2$

Exercises 26–27: Find the values of h and k for the graphs, which represent the function $f(x) = \sqrt[3]{x - h} + k$.

26.

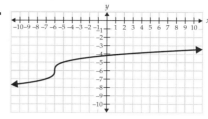

27.

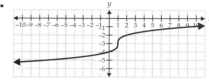

28. Write the cube root function that represents a translation from the parent function of 3 units down and 1 unit left.

29. Write the cube root function that represents, in order of application, vertical stretching by 4, reflection over the x-axis, translation of 2 units up, and translation of 3 units right.

Exercises 30–32: State the domain of each function.

30. $f(x) = \sqrt{x} + \sqrt{x - 5}$

31. $f(x) = \sqrt{x - 3} + \sqrt{x + 7}$

32. $f(x) = \sqrt{3 - 2x} + \sqrt{x + 1}$

33. **MP 2, 7** Mike states that the function $g(x) = \sqrt{2x + 5}$ is translated 5 units to the right of the function $f(x) = \sqrt{2x}$. Is this correct?

Exercises 34–36: Determine the radical function in the form $y = a\sqrt{x + b} + c$ that passes through the given points. Then graph the function.

34. **MP 1, 2** $(-3, -1)$, $(0, 0)$, and $(5, 1)$

35. **MP 1, 2** $(2, -4)$, $(5, -1)$, and $(10, 2)$

36. **MP 1, 2** $(-3, 0)$, $(2, -2)$, and $(9, -4)$

Chapter 5 Key Ideas

5.1 Radical Operations

- To multiply square roots with negative radicands, restate the factors using i.
- The quotient rule for radicals, $\dfrac{\sqrt[n]{a}}{\sqrt[n]{b}} = \sqrt[n]{\dfrac{a}{b}}$, where $b \neq 0$, allows the simplification of fractions.

  The quotient rule can also be used to simplify radicals. A radical expression involving fractions is considered to be simplified when there is no fraction under a radical sign, and no radical in the denominator.

5.2 More Operations with Radicals

- A simplified radical expression has no radical in any denominator. To rationalize a denominator, you multiply by a fraction equal to one. That fraction has an expression in its numerator and denominator that makes all the powers in the denominator multiples of the index of the radical.

5.3 Exponent Notation

- The rules of exponents apply to expressions with fractional exponents as well. The rules apply for any integer or fraction.

5.4 Radical Equations

- Although every solution to $a = b$ is also a solution to $a^2 = b^2$, not every solution to $a^2 = b^2$ has to be a solution to $a = b$. Applying the squaring principle can create extraneous solutions, which are solutions to the final equation that are not solutions to the original radical equation.
- The power principle says that if an equation is true, so is the equation that results from raising both sides to the same power.

5.5 Radical Function Graphs

- The real function $f(x) = \sqrt{x}$ is the parent function of the square root function. The domain is restricted to values 0 or greater since the function is undefined for negative values. The range consists of zero and all positive numbers.
- The cube root function $f(x) = \sqrt[3]{x}$ has a domain of all real numbers. Unlike the square root function, the domain is not restricted. The range is all real numbers as well.

CHAPTER 5 REVIEW

1. **MP 5** Karen's calculator shows part of the graph of $f(x) = \sqrt[3]{x} + 4$.

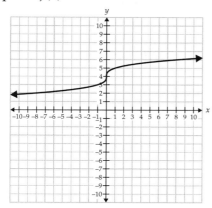

What statement is true?

A. If she scrolled to the left, where x becomes increasingly negative, she would eventually see the only x-intercept.

B. If she scrolled to the right, where x becomes increasingly positive, she would eventually see the only x-intercept.

C. If she scrolled in either direction, she would see an x-intercept.

D. No matter how far she scrolled in either direction, she would never see an x-intercept.

Exercises 2–6: Simplify.

2. $64^{\frac{2}{3}}$

3. $49^{\frac{5}{2}}$

4. $x^{\frac{1}{4}} \cdot x^{\frac{3}{2}}$

5. $\dfrac{11^{\frac{5}{7}}}{11^{\frac{2}{7}}}$

6. $(9x^4)^{\frac{3}{2}}$

Exercises 7–10: Solve.

7. $\sqrt{x} - 7 = 10$

8. $\sqrt{x} - 5 = 8$

9. $7 - \sqrt{4x} = 14$

10. $\sqrt[5]{x + 60{,}000} - 5 = 5$

Exercises 11–21: Simplify.

11. $\sqrt{700}$

12. $\sqrt{28}$

13. $\sqrt{240}$

14. $\sqrt[8]{5x} \cdot \sqrt[8]{3x^3}$

15. $\sqrt[11]{5x} \cdot \sqrt[11]{5x^2}$

16. $\sqrt[6]{4x^{16}} \cdot \sqrt[6]{16x^2}$

17. $\sqrt[3]{4x^{10}} \cdot \sqrt[3]{2x^2}$

18. $\sqrt{16x^3 - 16x^2}$

19. $\sqrt{81x^3 - 81x^2}$

20. $\dfrac{\sqrt[9]{28}}{\sqrt[9]{7}}$

21. $\dfrac{\sqrt[7]{21x^{12}}}{\sqrt[7]{7x^4}}$

Exercises 22–23: Simplify. State your answers with i when necessary.

22. $\sqrt{5} \cdot \sqrt{-3}$

23. $\sqrt{-2} \cdot \sqrt{6}$

Exercises 24–26: Simplify.

24. $8\sqrt{5} + 5\sqrt{5}$

25. $\sqrt{27x} - 7\sqrt{3x^5}$

26. $\sqrt[9]{7}(9\sqrt[9]{2} - \sqrt[9]{12x})$

27. **MP 1, 7** Find five pairs of numbers (x, y) such that $\sqrt[5]{x} = \sqrt{y}$. Find the function $y = f(x)$ that passes through the points you chose. With the help of a graphing utility, sketch a graph of the function.

28. **MP 3** Use the rules of exponents to prove $x^{-n} = \dfrac{1}{x^n}$. Hint: The proof is similar to the derivation of $\sqrt[n]{x} = x^{\frac{1}{n}}$.

29. **MP 7** What is the equivalent term for a radicand when an expression is written in exponential notation? Do all properties of radicands apply to its equivalent term?

30. **MP 2, 7** Write a quadratic equation in the form $ax^2 + bx + c = 0$ in which one of the solutions is $1 + \sqrt{3}$.

Cumulative Review
for Chapters 1–5

1. Jonathan needs to find the area of his rectangular garden. The length of his garden is $9 + 4\sqrt{3}$ and the width is $10 + 5\sqrt{3}$. What is the area of his garden?

- **A.** 235
- **B.** $100 + 135\sqrt{3}$
- **C.** $150 + 85\sqrt{3}$
- **D.** $90 + 145\sqrt{3}$

2. Find the distance between the points $(-2, 4)$ and $(-3, 8)$.

- **A.** 17
- **B.** $\sqrt{17}$
- **C.** $3\sqrt{5}$
- **D.** $\sqrt{41}$

3. **MP 8** Which of the polynomials have no remainder when divided by $(x - 3)$? Explain your answer.

- **A.** $(x - 3)(x + 2)(x - 5)$
- **B.** $x^2 + 6x + 9$
- **C.** $(x + 3)(x - 3)$
- **D.** $(x - 9)(x + 3)(x - 1)$
- **E.** $x^2 - 2x - 3$
- **F.** $x^2 - 6x + 9$

4. Saul solves the equation $(2x + 5)^2 = 6x + 15$ by letting $y = 2x + 5$. His work is shown below.

$$(y)^2 = 3(y)$$
$$y^2 - 3y = 0$$
$$y(y - 3) = 0$$

$y = 0$ and $y = 3$, so the solutions to the equation are $x = 0$ and $x = 3$.

Describe Saul's mistake in his solution. What are the actual solutions?

Exercises 5–7: Factor.

5. $4x^4 - 81y^4$

6. $x^4 + 12x^2 + 20$

7. $x^4 + 9x^2 + 18$

8. **MP 7** If $4(x + a)^2 = 48x + 144 + 4x^2$, find the value of a.

9. Consider the equations $x^2 - 36 = 0$ and $-x^2 + 36 = 0$. Show that they have the same solution set by showing they share the same factors.

10. Solve for a in terms of x and y: $64x^2 - a^2y^2 = 0$

11. Solve: $9x^2 - 64 = 0$

12. Multiply the expression by its complex conjugate and state the result: $-6 - 7i\sqrt{3}$

13. **MP 2, 3** Factor $a^2 + b^2$ using complex numbers. Do this in two different ways and show that both factorizations equal $a^2 + b^2$.

14. Factor using complex numbers: $x^4 + y^4$

Exercises 15–16: Simplify.

15. $(x^4 + 19x^3 + 95x^2 - 91x - 1176) \div (x - 3)$

16. $\dfrac{4 - 4x}{4x^2 + 44x - 48}$

Exercises 17–18: Check whether the given ordered triple (x, y, z) is a solution to the system of linear equations. Show your work.

17. $(5, 3, 1)$; $x = 5z$; $y = 3z$; $x - 2y + 4z = 3$

18. $(2, 2, -1)$; $x = y$; $-\dfrac{1}{2}x = z$; $2x + y + 6z = 2$

19. Find k such that $7x - 3$ will be a factor of $7x^3 + kx^2 - 24x + 9$.

20. **MP 7** Find the quartic polynomial with leading coefficient 2 that has the zeros shown in the graph.

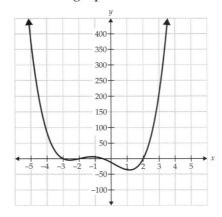

21. Determine the value of k such that the polynomial $2x^4 - kx^3 + 7x - 740$ can be divided evenly by $x + 4$.

Exercises 22–24: Solve.

22. $\dfrac{x}{x - 9} = \dfrac{5}{x + 19}$

23. $\dfrac{x}{x - 8} = \dfrac{4}{x + 16}$

24. $\dfrac{x^2 + 7x + 12}{x + 4} = 8$

25. Factor $x - y$ as the product of 2 binomials.

26. **MP 1, 5** If side A is 4 miles and B is twice as long, how fast would Becca have to ride at a constant speed if she wants to make the trip in 35 minutes? Your answer should be exact and simplified in miles per hour.

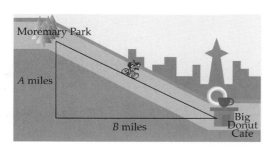

27. Write the function represented by the graph.

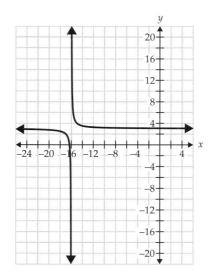

28. Write the function that, compared to the graph of $f(x) = \dfrac{1}{x}$, is reflected across the x-axis, stretched by a factor of 6, shifted up 2 units, and shifted right 4 units. Then graph the function.

29. Determine whether a linear, quadratic, or radical function would be best to model each table of data. Justify your answer.

a

x	y
2	12
4	23
6	33
8	40
10	45

b

x	y
1	1
2	3
4	7
7	14
11	23

c

x	y
1	4
2	7
3	13
5	29
7	50

30. **MP 1, 2, 3** Is it possible to write the number 1 as a sum of the fractions $\dfrac{1}{a} + \dfrac{1}{b} + \dfrac{1}{c} + \dfrac{1}{d}$, where a, b, c, and d are odd natural numbers? Explain.

Chapter 6 Exponential Functions

Chapter Content

Vocabulary

combined function   exponential decay   inverse function

composite function   exponential function   percent rate of change

constant function   exponential growth

LESSON 6.1

6.1 Exponential Function Graphs

Exponential Functions

An **exponential function** is a function with base b defined by $f(x) = b^x$, where b must be positive but not equal to 1. A function such as $f(x) = 3^x$ is an exponential function since it has a constant raised to a variable power. Exponential functions can also be generated by multiplying or adding a constant to the exponential expression, such as $f(x) = 2 \cdot 4^x$ or $f(x) = \pi^x + 5$. Exponential functions can be rewritten using the power property of exponents.

MODEL PROBLEMS

1. Write $f(x) = 2^{3x}$ with x alone as the exponent.

SOLUTION

| Power rule | $f(x) = (2^3)^x$ | Use the power rule. |
| Evaluate power | $f(x) = 8^x$ | Simplify $2^3 = 8$. |

2. Write $f(x) = 3^{-x}$ with x alone as the exponent.

SOLUTION

| Definition of negative exponents | $f(x) = \left(\dfrac{1}{3}\right)^x$ | A negative exponent is equivalent to the reciprocal of the base. |

PRACTICE

1. MP 3 Which of the following is equivalent to $y = 3 \cdot 2^{x+1}$? Justify your answer by showing the steps to get from this equation to the correct answer.

  A. $y = 6^{x+1}$ C. $y = 6 \cdot 2^x$

  B. $y = 6^x$ D. $y = 6 \cdot 2^{x+1}$

Exercises 2–7: Evaluate.

2. $f(x) = 10^{2x}$ for $x = -2$

3. $f(x) = 5^{-2x}$ for $x = -2$

4. $f(x) = 2^{-3x}$ for $x = 3$

5. $f(x) = 4^x$ for $x = 3$

Practice Problems continue . . .

Practice Problems continued . . .

6. $f(x) = 2^x$ for $x = 5$

7. $g(x) = 8^x$ for $x = \dfrac{1}{3}$

Exercises 8–20: Simplify.

8. $3^{\sqrt{2}} \cdot 3^{\sqrt{2}}$

9. $\sqrt{7}^{\sqrt{5}} \cdot \sqrt{7}^{-\sqrt{5}}$

10. $2^{\sqrt{4}} \cdot 2^{\sqrt{5}}$

11. $\dfrac{5^{2\sqrt{3}}}{5^{\sqrt{3}}}$

12. $\dfrac{8^{\sqrt{3}+1}}{8^{\sqrt{3}-1}}$

13. $(5^{\sqrt{3}})^2$

14. $(2^{\sqrt{5}})^3$

15. $(7^{\sqrt{2}})^{\sqrt{2}}$

16. $(61^{\sqrt{5}})^{\sqrt{3}}$

17. $(4^{\pi})^3$

18. $(4^{-\pi})^{-2}$

19. $\sqrt{5^{2\pi}}$

20. $\sqrt[4]{3^{12\pi}}$

21. **MP 2, 6** Which number is greater, $2^{1.41}$ or $(0.25)^{-\frac{\sqrt{2}}{2}}$? Explain.

Exponential Function Graphs

Exponential Growth

We show a graph of an exponential function with base > 1. The graph shows **exponential growth**.

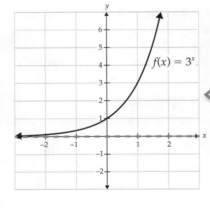

> The basic properties of the graph of an exponential function depend on whether the base is greater than 1, or between 0 and 1.

- Graph rises to the right of the origin.

  The graph becomes very steep as x becomes larger positive values. Its end behavior is that the graph becomes ever steeper and the y-values ever greater.

- x-axis is horizontal asymptote to left of origin.

  On this side of the origin, the end behavior of the graph is that it becomes a very small positive value. The expression 3^x can become very small. For instance, when $x = -10$, it equals $\dfrac{1}{3^{10}}$, which is approximately equal to 0.0000169, and it would be even smaller for $x = -100$. The graph will approach 0 (the x-axis) but never reach this value. The line $y = 0$ is called a *horizontal asymptote*, which is a horizontal line that a curve approaches but never reaches.

The graph to the right is of the world population over the last 2000 years. It can be closely approximated by the graph of an exponential function. The fact that some natural phenomena can be modeled as exponential functions is one reason for the interest in these functions.

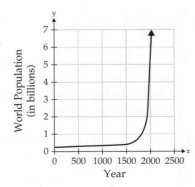

Exponential Decay

We show a graph of an exponential function with base < 1. The graph shows **exponential decay**.

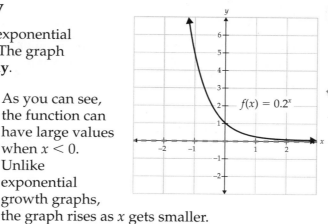

- Graph rises to left of origin.

As you can see, the function can have large values when $x < 0$. Unlike exponential growth graphs, the graph rises as x gets smaller.

> Graphs of exponential functions follow a particular pattern. On one side of the y-axis, they become very steep. On the other side, they asymptotically approach the x-axis.

- x-axis is horizontal asymptote to right of origin.

As x gets larger, the graph approaches the horizontal axis but never reaches it. The horizontal axis is an asymptote. We show why this is the case using $x = 4$ as our example. $f(4) = 0.2^4$, which is 0.0016, a small number. If x were larger, $f(x)$ would be even smaller.

MODEL PROBLEMS

1. **MP 3, 6** **a** Graph $g(x) = 4^x$.

b The graph of $g(x) = 4^x$ is a smooth curve without gaps, or what mathematicians call *continuous*. Explain whether the function is defined for all rational and irrational numbers.

SOLUTION

a Create x-y table

x	$g(x)$
-2	$\dfrac{1}{16}$
-1	$\dfrac{1}{4}$
0	1
1	4
2	16

Evaluate the function $g(x) = 4^x$ for some values of x. Start with $x = -2$. Raise 4 to the power of -2, which equals $\dfrac{1}{16}$. Place those values in an x-y table. Repeat for $x = -1, 0, 1,$ and 2.

Graph

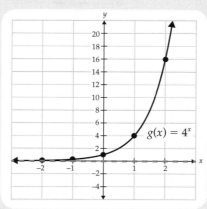

Graph the points. Connect the points with a curve.

Model Problems continue . . .

b Since each real number can be found on the *x*-axis of the graph (a number line), the function must be defined for real numbers, both rational and irrational, since that is the definition of real numbers. This means the graph must be defined for values such as $\sqrt{2}$ or $\sqrt{11.435}$, since both are real numbers. The table in part **a** shows how the function is defined for rational numbers.

We begin demonstrating this concept by evaluating $g(x) = 4^x$ for $x = \sqrt{2}$. Substituting $\sqrt{2}$ into the function, we get $g(\sqrt{2}) = 4^{\sqrt{2}}$. In order to locate the point on the graph, we approximate $\sqrt{2} \approx 1.4$. Raising 4 to the 1.4 power, we get 7.00, as we approximate the output to the nearest hundredth. If we approximate the square root as 1.41, we get approximately 7.10. Using rational exponents, we could plot points more and more finely, until we get as close as we like to $\sqrt{2}$. The values of the function will get closer and closer to $4^{\sqrt{2}}$, and we create a continuous curve.

2. **MP 5** Solve the system of equations graphically: $y = 0.5^x - 13$ and $y = -3x + 22$. Identify the types of functions.

SOLUTION

Use a graphing calculator to graph the two equations. Any intersection point is the solution to the system. We can read both the *x*- and *y*-values from the screen. The solutions to $y = 0.5^x - 13$ and $y = -3x + 22$ are $x \approx -5.70$ and $y \approx 39.11$, and $x \approx 11.67$ and $y \approx -13$, respectively.

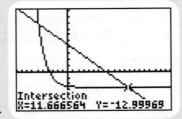

One function is linear, since the slope is constant. The other function is exponential decay, since it has a number less than 1 raised to the *x* power.

Translating Exponential Function Graphs

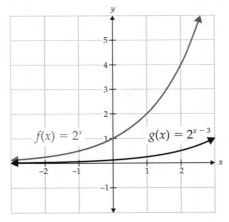

We graph the function $g(x) = 2^{x-3}$ on the right. It has the same graph as the exponential function $f(x) = 2^x$, but is translated (shifted) to the right 3 units, since 3 is subtracted from the function's input. The two functions are related, since $g(x) = f(x - 3)$. This means the graph of $g(x)$ is the graph of $f(x)$ translated to the right 3 units.

 In this activity, translate an exponential function.

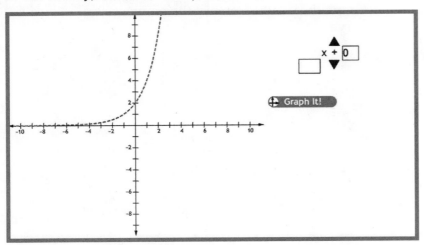

MP 7 For the exponential function $f(x) = 2^x + m$, which set of values for m **all** make the horizontal asymptote of the function shift up vertically?

A. $m = \{-2, 0, 2\}$
B. $m = \{-3, -2, -1, 0, 1, 2, 3\}$
C. $m = \{0, 1, 2, 3\}$
D. $m = \{1, 2, 3\}$

SOLUTION

A. Only $m = 2$ makes the function shift up vertically.
B. Only $m = 1, 2,$ and 3 make the function shift up vertically.
C. $m = 0$ does not move the function at all.
D. **Correct answer.** The values $m = 1, 2,$ and 3 all shift the graph of the function 1, 2, and 3 units vertically.

Rate of Change in Exponential Functions

Radioactive decay can be modeled by an exponential decay function. Radioactive decay is when one substance decays to become another substance. For instance, Substance A decays into Substance B with a half-life of 1 minute. If there is 1 gram of Substance A to start with, after 1 minute there are 0.50 grams, after 2 minutes there are 0.25 grams, and so on. Each 1 minute, half of Substance A decays to become Substance B. The function for half-life is $f(x) = 0.5^x$.

Minutes	Grams Remaining	Average Rate of Change	Percent Rate of Change
0	1	–	–
1	0.5	−0.5	−50%
2	0.25	−0.25	−50%
3	0.125	−0.125	−50%

Average rate of change: $\dfrac{\text{change in } y\text{-values}}{\text{change in } x\text{-values}}$

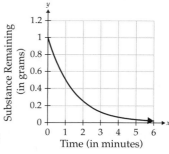

In a linear relationship, the slope is used to measure the rate of change, but in nonlinear functions, we must find the average rate of change. To find the average rate of change, find the slope of the line between two intervals.

Between $(1, 0.5)$ and $(2, 0.25)$ the rate of change is $\dfrac{0.25 - 0.5}{2 - 1} = -0.25$.

The average rate of change column shows the amount the original substance is reduced. The absolute value of the average rate of change decreases over time, as the amount of the remaining original substance falls. For instance, $|-0.5| > |-0.25| > |-0.125|$, and so on.

Percent rate of change: $\dfrac{\text{final} - \text{initial}}{\text{initial}}$

As the time interval increases by one minute, the amount of material remaining will be multiplied by 0.5; there will always be 50% less material from minute to minute. This is shown in the **percent rate of change** column, with the negative sign showing the change is a reduction. The percent rate of change is constant at -50%. The percent rate of change between the first and second minutes is $\dfrac{0.25 - 0.5}{0.5} = -0.5 = -50\%$. You might also observe something: The percent rate of change for an interval of one equals the base minus 1, expressed as a percent. For this exponential decay function the base is 0.5, so $0.5 - 1 = -0.5$, or the percent rate of change.

> Notice that for exponential functions, the amount of change in the function over each regular interval of input is different. However, the percent change between regular intervals is the same.

We consider an exponential growth model. We model the balance of a bank account earning interest. Let's consider a bank that is kind enough to pay 5% interest a year, when we initially deposit $2500. We model our balance as $P(1 + r)^t$, with P representing the initial deposit, r representing the interest rate, and t representing the time in years.

Year	Amount in Account	Average Rate of Change	Percent Rate of Change
0	$2500	–	–
1	$2625	$125	5%
2	$2756	$131	5%
3	$2894	$138	5%

Average rate of change: $\dfrac{\text{change in } y\text{-values}}{\text{change in } x\text{-values}}$

Again, with nonlinear relationships we find the average rate of change between two intervals. Over the first year, the average rate of change is $\dfrac{2625 - 2500}{1 - 0} = 125$.

Percent rate of change: $\dfrac{\text{final} - \text{initial}}{\text{initial}}$

We compute the percent change over the first year, $\dfrac{2625 - 2500}{2500} = 5\%$. It is 5%, the interest rate. The percent change for the function is always 5%. The percent change is again the base minus 1. In this case, the base of the function is $(1 + r)$, with r being 0.05. The base is 1.05. The percent change is $1.05 - 1 = 5\%$. The percent change does not depend on P, the starting amount, but only on the percent added to 1 in the parentheses in this expression.

> In exponential decay functions, the percent rate of change is negative. In exponential growth functions, the percent rate of change is positive.

MODEL PROBLEM

MP 6, 8 Show that the percent change in an exponential function is always the same for the same change in x. For example, if a change in x of 1 causes the function to increase by 20%, that will be true no matter what the values of x are: The change might be from $x = 2$ to $x = 3$, or it might be from $x = 3000$ to $x = 3001$. In both cases the exponential function will change by 20%. The change in x does not have to be 1. It might be 5, for instance, or -2. But whatever it is, for an exponential function of x, the same change in x brings about the same percent change in the function.

SOLUTION

Function	$f(x) = b^x$	Start with an exponential function, a base b to the x power.
Percent change	$\text{percent change} = \dfrac{\text{final} - \text{initial}}{\text{initial}}$	Use the definition for percent rate of change. The difference of the final and initial output values is divided by the initial value.
Substitute	$\text{percent change} = \dfrac{b^{x+c} - b^x}{b^x}$	The final value is found by substituting $x + c$ for x. The initial value is b^x.
Simplify	$\text{percent change} = \dfrac{b^{x+c}}{b^x} - \dfrac{b^x}{b^x}$	Separate into two fractions.
	$\text{percent change} = b^{x+c-x} - b^{x-x}$	Then we apply a law of exponents, subtracting exponents to divide.
	$\text{percent change} = b^c - b^0$	Simplify.
	$\text{percent change} = b^c - 1$	We have shown that the percent change equals one less than the base to the c. As claimed, this result does not depend on the value of x. It depends only on the value of c, the change in x.

PRACTICE

1. Which of the following best describes the graph of $f(x) = 4^{-x}$?

   A. It increases on the right, and it approaches but never reaches the horizontal axis to the left of the origin.

   B. It increases on the right, and it approaches but never reaches the horizontal axis to the right of the origin.

   C. It increases on the left, and it approaches but never reaches the horizontal axis to the left of the origin.

   D. It increases on the left, and it approaches but never reaches the horizontal axis to the right of the origin.

2. Which of the following best describes the graph of $f(x) = \left(\dfrac{1}{5}\right)^{-x}$?

   A. It increases on the right, and it approaches but never reaches the horizontal axis to the left of the origin.

   B. It increases on the right, and it approaches but never reaches the horizontal axis to the right of the origin.

   C. It increases on the left, and it approaches but never reaches the horizontal axis to the left of the origin.

   D. It increases on the left, and it approaches but never reaches the horizontal axis to the right of the origin.

3. Which of the following best describes the graph of $f(x) = \left(\dfrac{25}{17}\right)^{x}$?

   A. It increases on the right, and it approaches but never reaches the horizontal axis to the left of the origin.

   B. It increases on the right, and it approaches but never reaches the horizontal axis to the right of the origin.

   C. It increases on the left, and it approaches but never reaches the horizontal axis to the left of the origin.

   D. It increases on the left, and it approaches but never reaches the horizontal axis to the right of the origin.

4. Which statement concerning the graph of the exponential function $y = 5^x$ is true?

   A. The graph never intersects the graph of $y = 2^x$.

   B. The graph passes through the point $(0, 1)$.

   C. For $x < 0$, the graph can dip below the x-axis.

   D. As x increases, the graph gets closer to the x-axis.

5. Brad sketches the graph of an exponential function $f(x)$.

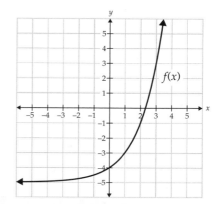

Which exponential function could generate a graph of this form?

   A. $f(x) = 2^x$ C. $f(x) = 2^x - 5$

   B. $f(x) = 2^x + 5$ D. $f(x) = 5 \cdot 2^x$

6. Leonard states that $y = 1^x + 4$ is an exponential function on a math test. He gets the question wrong. Which reason explains why the base of an exponential function cannot be equal to 1?

   A. The graph of the equation is a point.

   B. The graph of the equation is a line.

   C. For increasing values of x, the value of the function decreases.

   D. For negative values of x, the value of the function increases.

Exercises 7–12: Graph each function.

7. $f(x) = 2^x$

8. $f(x) = 2^{x+3}$

9. $g(x) = 0.5^x$

10. $g(x) = 0.5^{x-2}$

Practice Problems continue . . .

Practice Problems continued . . .

11. $y = 5^{-x} - 2$

12. $y = \left(\dfrac{1}{2}\right)^{-x} + 1$

13. If $(0.34)^a < (0.34)^b$, which is greater, a or b? Explain.

14. If $\left(\dfrac{3}{4}\right)^a < \left(\dfrac{3}{4}\right)^b$, which is greater, a or b? Explain.

Exercises 15–19: Use the structure of the expression to determine how the graph of $g(x)$ is shifted compared to the graph of $f(x)$.

15. $g(x) = 10^{x-3}; f(x) = 10^x$

16. $g(x) = \left(\dfrac{2}{3}\right)^{x+7}; f(x) = \left(\dfrac{2}{3}\right)^x$

17. $g(x) = 0.4^{2+x}; f(x) = 0.4^x$

18. $g(x) = a^{-5+x}; f(x) = a^x$

19. $g(x) = a^{b+x}; f(x) = a^x$; assume b is positive.

20. **MP 7** Given the function, $f(x) = 2^x$, what is the percent of change over intervals of 1 unit?

21. Given the function, $g(x) = 0.6^x$, what is the percent of change over intervals of 1 unit?

22. Write both an exponential function and a translated version of the same function, and describe the differences between the graphs of the two functions.

23. **MP 2, 3** Explain why a function having a plus sign like $g(x) = 3^{x+2}$ results in a left-horizontal shift and a minus sign like $h(x) = 3^{x-2}$ results in a right-horizontal shift of the function $f(x) = 3^x$.

24. **MP 2** Rewrite the function $g(x) = \left(\dfrac{5}{2}\right)^{3-x}$ as an exponential function of the form a^{x+b}. Hint: b might be negative.

25. Lisa claims that for any positive value of a, the function $f(x) = a^x$ will always have a curvy shape either increasing upward or leveling to a horizontal asymptote on the x-axis. Is her reasoning flawed? If so, what positive value(s) of a contradict her claim?

LESSON 6.2

6.2 Modeling with Exponential Functions

Spreadsheet and Graphing Calculator: Modeling Exponential Functions

Rapid growth may be modeled with an exponential equation of the form $y = ab^x$. For example, the table shows the rapid increase of Web hosts (computers that run Web sites) from 1969 to 2004.

Years Since Dec. 1969	Web Hosts
0.00	4
4.50	62
10.01	188
14.84	1024
19.59	130,000
24.60	3,212,000
29.60	56,218,000
34.61	285,139,107

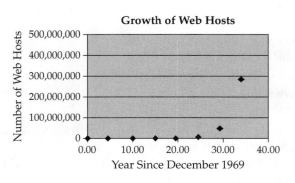

We use an *exponential regression* to model this data, where y represents the number of Web hosts and x represents the number of years since December 1969, the first date in the table.

Spreadsheet

In a spreadsheet, start by entering the data and creating a scatter plot. Make sure the chart is selected, and then choose **Add Trendline** from the **Chart** menu. To do an exponential regression, choose the **Exponential** option under **Trend/Regression type**. You can add the model equation and the coefficient of determination r^2 using the **Options** tab. The equation in the spreadsheet has the form $y = ae^{cx}$, where e is the mathematical constant whose value is approximately 2.71828, and a and c are constants that are adjusted to get a good fit to the data.

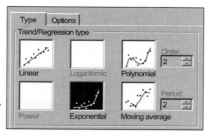

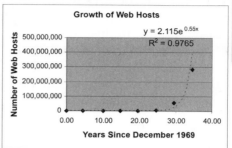

> e is an irrational constant used in many exponential models. It is equal to approximately 2.71828. We will discuss it in more detail in the next chapter.

Graphing Calculator

With a graphing calculator, start by entering the data and creating a scatter plot. Then, choose exponential regression. To do this, press STAT and then scroll right to the **CALC** menu. Scroll down to **0:ExpReg** and press ENTER to set up the **ExpReg** command. Then enter the parameters and do the regression as for linear regression. The calculator displays the results as shown to the right. This is an equation of the form $y = ab^x$.

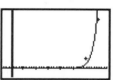

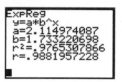

Although the spreadsheet and calculator use different exponential equations to model the data, it can be shown that the equations are equivalent. From the values of a and b given by the calculator, the equation is $y = (2.115)(1.7332^x)$. This equation can be rewritten as $y = 2.115e^{0.55x}$, which is the equation given by the spreadsheet. (You can use the product of powers rule to see that the two expressions are equivalent.) The models are equivalent, even though the equations are different in form. The value of $r^2 = 0.9765$ indicates a good fit.

MODEL PROBLEMS

1. **MP 2, 4, 5** Imagine we have a population of animals that grows by 3% per year. We release 200 of these animals into a wilderness preserve. How many years would it take for the population to grow to 500 animals?

SOLUTION

We can model the population with the function $P(t) = 200(1.03)^t$. To answer our question, we will need to solve the equation $200(1.03)^t = 500$. Use a graphing calculator to graph the two functions on either side of the equation. From the screen, we see that x is approximately 31, so the population will reach 500 animals 31 years after they are released in the preserve.

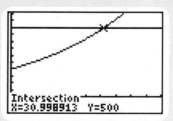

Model Problems continue . . .

2. **MP 5** You see a table showing the temperature of a cup of coffee over time. According to Newton's law of cooling, the falling temperature is an exponential function of time. The general form of this function is $y = ae^{cx} + T_0$, where T_0 is the temperature surrounding the cooling object, x is the elapsed time, a is the difference between the object's initial temperature and the lower surrounding temperature, and y is the temperature of the object after elapsed time x. In this example, the surrounding temperature is 0°F, which simplifies the function. The falling temperature means that for $y = ae^{cx}$, the constant c is negative. Equivalently, for the form of exponential function $y = ab^x$, the base b is between 0 and 1.

Time (minutes)	Temperature (°Fahrenheit)
0	190.6
5	161.4
10	134.3
15	114.4
20	93.4
25	80.9

Use a spreadsheet to find an exponential function that models this set of data, and the corresponding value of r^2.

SOLUTION

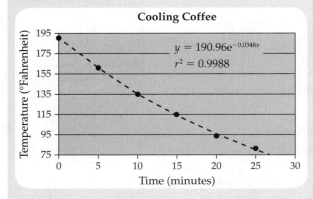

Cooling Coffee

$y = 190.96e^{-0.0348x}$

$r^2 = 0.9988$

This spreadsheet function is in the form $y = ae^{cx}$. It is equivalent to the function $y = (190.96)(0.9658^x)$, which is what you should find with a graphing calculator.

 3. **MP 2, 4** For interest compounded annually, $f(t)$ is equal to P, the initial deposit, times 1 plus the interest rate r raised to the exponent t. The variable t represents the number of years. $10,000 is the initial deposit in a bank account. The interest is compounded annually at a rate of 10%.

a Write and calculate the function for every five years for 25 years.

b Create a graph of the amount of money in the account for the first 25 years, with time on the horizontal axis and the amount on the vertical axis.

c Use the graph to determine which five-year interval had the largest amount of growth between years 0 to 25.

SOLUTION

a Evaluate the function for every 5 years

$f(t) = P(1 + r)^t$

$f(5) = 10{,}000(1 + 0.10)^5 = 16{,}105$

$f(10) = 10{,}000(1 + 0.10)^{10} = 25{,}937$

$f(15) = 10{,}000(1 + 0.10)^{15} = 41{,}772$

$f(20) = 10{,}000(1 + 0.10)^{20} = 67{,}275$

$f(25) = 10{,}000(1 + 0.10)^{25} = 108{,}347$

The function is $f(t) = P(1 + r)^t$. Calculate the amount of money for every fifth year, up to year 25, as the problem asked. Round the results to the nearest dollar.

Model Problems continue . . .

b

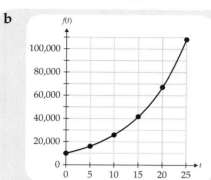

t	f(t)
0	10,000
5	16,105
10	25,937
15	41,772
20	67,275
25	108,347

> Note that the graph has the form typical of an exponential function with a base greater than 1.

c From the graph, we can tell that the growth is getting exponentially larger. The slope between years 20–25 is much steeper than the growth between years 0–5.

 4. **MP 2, 4** The formula that follows calculates interest when the interest is compounded n times a year. For interest compounded monthly, use the formula $f(t) = P\left(1 + \dfrac{r}{n}\right)^{nt}$. This formula calculates how much

> When the money is compounded monthly, that means it is compounded 12 times a year.

money there will be if P dollars are deposited for t years with an interest rate of r that is compounded n times per year. *Compounding* means that interest is being paid on an amount that includes interest already paid.

For instance, if $100 is deposited and the interest rate is an annual rate of 12% and it is compounded monthly, then the monthly rate is 1% (because 12% divided by 12 months). The deposit would earn $1 dollar the first month (because $100 · 1%), and the balance would be $101. The interest the second month would be $1.01 (because $101 · 1%), and the new balance would be $102.01. In other words, the interest is being calculated each month and added to the amount in the bank, resulting in a larger amount than if just 12% interest was calculated on $100.

$10,000 is deposited in a bank account. The interest is compounded monthly with an annual interest rate of 10%. How much money will be in the account after 25 years? Assume no money is withdrawn (removed) from the account.

SOLUTION

Substitute and evaluate

$$f(t) = P\left(1 + \frac{r}{n}\right)^{nt}$$

$$f(25) = 10,000\left(1 + \frac{0.10}{12}\right)^{(12 \cdot 25)}$$

$$f(25) = 120,569.45$$

Substitute $P = 10,000$ for the starting number, $r = 0.10$ for the rate of interest, and $n = 12$, since it compounds monthly. The money is in the account for 25 years. You would have $120,569.45 in the account after 25 years. Note: The amount of money is about $12,000 more than if the interest was compounded annually.

Model Problems continue . . .

5. **MP 2, 4, 7** Suppose the annual interest rate at a bank is 4%. We can write the function $f(t) = 1.04^t$ to describe this. How can we calculate the equivalent monthly rate?

SOLUTION

From annual to monthly	$f(t) = 1.04^t$	Approximate *monthly* rate for interest that is 4% a year.
Write monthly function	$f(m) = (1.04)^{\frac{m}{12}}$	Write the function in terms of months, m.
Use property of exponents	$f(m) = \left(1.04^{\frac{1}{12}}\right)^m$	Use a property of exponents: $a^{bc} = \left(a^b\right)^c$.
Evaluate	$1.04^{\frac{1}{12}} \approx 1.00327$	Approximate 1.04 to the $\frac{1}{12}$ power.
Calculate percent change	$1.00327 - 1 = 0.00327$ Monthly interest rate $\approx 0.327\%$	The base, 1.00327, minus 1 equals the monthly fractional change. It is about 0.00327, which we state as 0.327%. One way to approximate the monthly rate is to divide 4% by 12 months, which yields 0.325%. Our approach here gives a more accurate result.

6. **MP 2, 4** Dioxin was part of Agent Orange, an herbicide that the United States military sprayed over Vietnam during the conflict there. The herbicide was intended to destroy vegetation. Dioxin was an unintended component of Agent Orange, and it turned out to have significant negative effects on the human body. Although Agent Orange decays rapidly, the half-life of dioxin when it is buried in locations such as river sediment can be 100 years. By half-life, we mean that after every period, there will be half as much of the original material left. The data table to the right illustrates this idea.

Original amount	128 g
After 100 years	64 g
After 200 years	32 g
After 300 years	16 g
After 400 years	8 g

a Create a graph of the function.

b Determine an expression for the function and check your solution.

SOLUTION

a
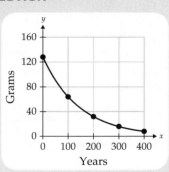

Model Problems continue . . .

b Formula $\qquad\qquad f(x) = a\left(\dfrac{1}{2}\right)^x$

Substitute $\qquad\qquad f(3) = 128\left(\dfrac{1}{2}\right)^3$

Apply exponent $\qquad f(3) = 128\left(\dfrac{1}{8}\right)$

Multiply $\qquad\qquad f(3) = 16$ g

We can model this with an exponential function: $f(x) = a\left(\dfrac{1}{2}\right)^x$ where a is the initial amount, and x is the number of intervals (in this case, centuries). Note that because x is the number of intervals, when evaluating this function, 300 years is 3 intervals. We can confirm this solution by calculating how much dioxin would be present after 300 years, if the original amount were 128 grams.

7. **MP 2, 4** After each successive round of dilution, there is 40% less salt in a solution. You are given four functions as options to model the situation: $f(x) = 0.4^x$, $g(x) = 0.6^x$, $h(x) = 1 - 0.4x$, and $b(x) = 0.6x^2$.

a Identify the types of functions being used to model the situation.

b Graph the amount of salt after successive rounds of dilution using each function.

c Determine which function correctly models the situation.

d Identify where the quadratic and exponential expressions intersect. Identify the y-intercepts of each function and which expression has the greatest absolute value as x increases.

SOLUTION

a $f(x) = 0.4^x$ and $g(x) = 0.6^x$ are exponential decay functions. $h(x) = 1 - 0.4x$ is a linear function. $b(x) = 0.6x^2$ is a quadratic function.

b

Number of Dilutions	$f(x) = 0.4^x$	$g(x) = 0.6^x$	$h(x) = 1 - 0.4x$	$b(x) = 0.6x^2$
0	1.00	1.00	1	0
1	0.40	0.60	0.6	0.60
2	0.16	0.36	0.2	2.40
3	0.06	0.22	-0.2	5.40
4	0.03	0.13	-0.6	9.60

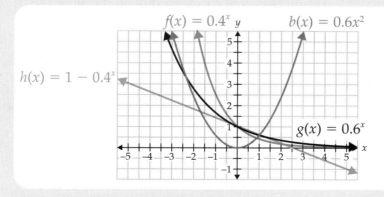

Although the expressions might be considered to be stepwise functions, graph them with curves or lines so you can better see their properties.

Model Problems continue . . .

c You were asked to model a process where in each step, there was 40% less of a substance, salt. That is the same as saying that 60% of the material remains. There are two ways to answer the question about which function models a process where 60% remains each time. One is to simply recognize that an exponential function's base minus 1 equals the percent change for each interval. Since $0.6 - 1 = 0.40 = -40\%$, 0.6^x is the right choice. Another way to choose the right expression is the table. The 0.6^x function goes 1.00, 0.60, 0.36, and so on. Each succeeding value is 60% of the prior value.

d The exponential functions intersect at $(0, 1)$. For the next pair, 0.6^x and $0.6x^2$ have the same values at $(1, 0.6)$. For the final pair, 0.4^x and $0.6x^2$ have the same values at about $(0.9, 0.5)$.

The y-intercepts for the exponential functions are 1. A quadratic of this form has a y-intercept of 0. Zero to any power is 0. The linear equation has a y-intercept of 1.

It is clear from the pattern of the graphs that the quadratic function will have the largest absolute value as x increases.

8. **MP 2, 4, 7** Radioactive iodine, I-131, is used to treat thyroid disease. Its half-life is 8 days, which means after 8 days, the amount of I-131 remaining is half the original amount. After 16 days, only one-quarter of the original amount is left, after 24 days, one-eighth is left, and so on.

a Write $f(x) = \left(\dfrac{1}{2}\right)^{\frac{x}{8}}$ with only x as the exponent.

b Graph the equation from part **a**.

c Describe the end behavior of the function.

SOLUTION

a Power rule $\qquad f(x) = \left(\left(\dfrac{1}{2}\right)^{\frac{1}{8}}\right)^{x}$ $\qquad$ Use the property of exponents $x^{ab} = (x^a)^b$.

Evaluate power $\qquad f(x) \approx 0.917^x$ $\qquad$ Approximate $\left(\dfrac{1}{2}\right)^{\frac{1}{8}}$.

b

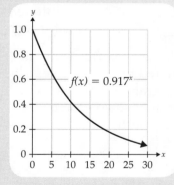

x	$f(x)$
0	1.00
5	0.65
10	0.42
15	0.27
20	0.18
25	0.11
30	0.07

With the exponent now solely x, we graph the expression. Its domain is 0 and positive numbers, since time cannot be negative. The graph of radioactive decay shows the typical form of a graph of an exponential function with a base less than 1. In model problem 6, we discussed an exponential decay expression. The interval was 100 years, and we wrote the expression using "intervals"—centuries—as the input. In model problem 8, we rewrite the expression so that we can use the actual input—days—instead of an interval. This function's value is the proportion of radioactive material left in a sample of radioactive iodine I-131 at a given point in time. The variable x represents the number of days that have passed.

c End behavior $\qquad$ The base of the function is less than 1, which means the amount of iodine falls rapidly at first and then approaches 0.

PRACTICE

1. The number of bacteria, N, present in an agar culture dish is growing exponentially with time, t, as shown in the table. Which of the following equations correctly models the data for the number of bacteria N present at time t?

t	N
0	1000
10	2000
20	4000
30	8000

A. $N = 1000 + 2^{10t}$

B. $N = 1000 \cdot 2^{\frac{t}{10}}$

C. $N = 2000^{\frac{t}{10}}$

D. $N = 2000 \cdot 2^{\frac{t}{10}}$

2. $200 is deposited in a bank account. The interest is compounded annually at a rate of 6%. How much money is in the account after 5 years, to the nearest dollar?

3. A fruit fly population doubles every hour. If the population starts at 6, how many will there be after 4 hours?

4. You have 10 grams of beryllium–11, which has a half-life of about 14 seconds. After 3.5 minutes, how many grams would you have? Use scientific notation to express your answer.

5. **MP 2, 7** A population of bacteria can be described with the function $N(t) = N_0 10^{0.02t}$ where N_0 is the initial number of bacteria and t is the time in minutes. How long does it take this population of bacteria to double, to the nearest tenth of a minute?

6. A sociologist models the spread of rumors with the function $N(t) = N_0 10^{0.08t}$, where N_0 is the initial number of people who know the rumor and t is the time in hours. How long does it take the number of people who know the rumor to double, to the nearest tenth of an hour?

7. Lucky you: You won $1,000,000 at a bingo tournament. Smart you: You save all the money, earning 7% interest a year, compounded annually. How much money will you have after 20 years, to the nearest cent?

8. Write an exponential function that describes the area of the green part of a rectangle. The area of an entire rectangle is 1. The rectangles are numbered 1, 2, 3, … as you move from left to right.

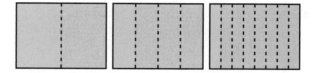

9. How many years must you wait for your money to double in a savings account if the annual interest rate is 10%? Use iteration to answer the question. State the first year in which the money is at least double the original amount.

10. As you move away from Earth's surface, atmospheric pressure decreases approximately exponentially as altitude increases. It decreases about 12% for each 1000 meters of increased altitude. The air pressure at Earth's surface is about 100,000 pascals. What is it at 10,000 meters above Earth's surface?

11. a Moore's law states that the number of transistors in a microprocessor doubles every two years. A microprocessor in 1971 had 2300 transistors. How many transistors would the law predict for a microprocessor in 1989?

    b How many transistors would the law predict for a microprocessor introduced in 2000, based on 2300 transistors in 1971?

Practice Problems continue . . .

12. The recycling rate for aluminum cans is about 51%. About 100 billion new cans are produced in a year. For sake of discussion, assume the world ran out of aluminum and was forced to exist solely on recycled cans, starting with a batch of 100 billion new cans. How many of those cans would be available, assuming a 51% recycling rate each year, after 25 years?

13. The amount of a radioactive material remaining in a 1-kilogram sample of material is given by the formula $r(t) = 0.95^t$ where t represents time in minutes. After one minute, what percentage of the sample is no longer radioactive?

14. Derek invested $500 in a Certificate of Deposit (CD), and after a year the CD was worth $517.50. What percent interest was being paid on the CD if the interest is compounded annually?

15. A car that was originally worth $20,000 depreciates, or loses value, at a rate of 10% per year.

   a Write a function to represent the value of the car, v, after t years.

   b What is the value of the car after 10 years, to the nearest thousand dollars?

   c Determine the percent decrease in the value of the car over a 10-year period.

16. MP 1, 2, 4 The fraction of incident light reaching a certain depth in water decreases exponentially with depth. If a water layer 3 meters deep absorbs half of the incoming light, what fraction of the incoming light will reach a depth of 30 meters? Hint: Compare this problem to the half-life of radioactive elements.

17. After the first year of use, a new car loses 15% of its initial value each year. Write an exponential function that describes the value $P(t)$ of a car with an initial value of $15,000, after t years.

18. MP 2, 4 A cup of tea at an initial temperature of 75.4°C is placed in a room at a constant temperature of 20°C. The temperature of the tea is measured every 5 minutes, and the results are recorded in the table. A model for the tea temperature is created based on the data: $T = 20 + 55.36 \cdot 2.78^{-0.037t}$, where t is measured in minutes.

t	T
0	75.4
5	65.8
10	57.9
15	51.4
20	46.0
25	41.5
30	37.8

   a According to the model, what will be the tea temperature in 1 hour? Round your answer to the nearest degree Celsius.

   b What is the significance of the "20" term in the equation of the temperature model?

19. MP 2, 3 After simplifying an equation you get $\left(\dfrac{2}{3}\right)^a = 2$. What should you conclude about the sign of the number a?

20. The percent change in the value of an exponential function over a period of one year is 10%. What will the percent change for the function be over the next year?

21. The percent change in the value of a stock over a 5-year period was 16%. If the value of the stock can be modeled by an exponential function, will the percent change be 16% over a 2-year period? Explain your reasoning.

22. The effective annual interest rate on a bond is 5%. Calculate the monthly interest rate, to the nearest tenth of a percent.

23. The effective monthly interest rate on a bond is 0.6%. What is the annual interest rate of the bond, to the nearest tenth of a percent?

Practice Problems continue . . .

24. The annual interest rate paid on a bond is 10%. What is the effective quarterly rate, to the nearest tenth of a percent?

25. Write a function to express the value of a bond after t years, with interest compounded annually, whose effective quarterly rate is 1.8%.

26. The exponential decay function $k(t) = 0.7^t$ is used to determine what portion of a drug remains in a person's system after t hours. Rewrite the expression, giving the amount of the drug remaining as a function of the number of minutes, and express the base of the function to the thousandths place.

27. MP 2, 6 Rewrite the exponential decay function $r(t) = 0.6^t$, where t represents time in months, as an equivalent function where t represents time in weeks. Assume there are 4 weeks in one month, and round the base of the new function to the hundredths place.

28. The exponential function $p(t) = 0.99^t$ represents the part of the original population of a town that remains after t months. Write a new function to calculate the remaining population if time is measured in years. Round the base of the new function to the nearest thousandths place.

29. For a chemistry experiment, a student is diluting a solution of alcohol with water. After each successive dilution, 10% less alcohol remains in the solution than before.

  a Using x and y, write a function to model the portion of alcohol that remains after x dilutions.

  b Graph the function you wrote in part **a**.

  c After how many dilutions is the solution less than 50% alcohol, if the student began with pure alcohol?

  d The student performs 10 dilutions. What percent alcohol is the resulting solution?

30. In an archeological excavation, a fragment of a burned log is found in an ancient fire pit. By measuring the amount of carbon-14 and the other isotopes in the log, an archeologist determines the amount of carbon-14 is 0.034 times the original amount. The half-life of carbon-14 is 5730 years. How old is the log, to the nearest 1000 years?

• Multi-Part PROBLEM Practice •

MP 4 You have $8000 to put in a savings account that earns 5% interest. Leaving the money untouched, find the total amount, to the nearest dollar, you will have after 20 years if the interest is compounded

a Annually?

b Quarterly (4 times a year)?

c Monthly?

d Daily? (Use 365.25 days in a year.)

6.3 Combining Functions

A **combined function** results from adding, subtracting, multiplying, and/or dividing two or more functions.

Adding $\qquad\qquad (f + g)(x) = f(x) + g(x)$

Subtracting $\qquad\quad (f - g)(x) = f(x) - g(x)$

Multiplying $\qquad\quad (f \cdot g)(x) = f(x) \cdot g(x)$

Dividing $\qquad\qquad \left(\dfrac{f}{g}\right)(x) = \dfrac{f(x)}{g(x)}$

The domain of the combined function is the set of x-values common to both functions. Sometimes, numbers that are in the domain of both functions are not in the domain of the combined function. For example, because division by 0 is undefined, $\left(\dfrac{f}{g}\right)(x)$ is undefined when $g(x) = 0$.

MODEL PROBLEMS

1. Add $(f + g)(x)$ when $f(x) = x + 1$ and $g(x) = 2x - 3$ and determine the domain.

SOLUTION

Add the expressions

$(f + g)(x) = f(x) + g(x)$
$(f + g)(x) = (x + 1) + (2x - 3)$
$(f + g)(x) = 3x - 2$

Add the expressions that define the two functions f and g to find an expression that represents the combined function $f + g$. Substitute in for $f(x)$ and $g(x)$ the expressions that define the two functions: $x + 1$ and $2x - 3$. When you add the expressions, you get $3x - 2$ as a result. This expression defines the function $f + g$.

Domain $\qquad$ All real numbers

The domain of the function is all real numbers, since that is true for each function.

2. Divide $\left(\dfrac{f}{g}\right)(x)$ when $f(x) = x^3$ and $g(x) = x^2$ and determine the domain.

SOLUTION

Divide the expressions

$\left(\dfrac{f}{g}\right)(x) = \dfrac{f(x)}{g(x)}$

$\left(\dfrac{f}{g}\right)(x) = \dfrac{x^3}{x^2}$

$\left(\dfrac{f}{g}\right)(x) = x$

Substitute in the expressions and then divide.

Domain $\qquad$ Real numbers except 0

If $x = 0$, then $g(x) = 0$, and $\left(\dfrac{f}{g}\right)(x)$ is undefined since it requires dividing by 0. The domain of this function is all real numbers except 0 because we need to restrict the function for when $g(x)$, the divisor, equals 0. *Model Problems continue . . .*

3. Multiply $(f \cdot g)(x)$ when $f(x) = 2\sqrt{x}$ and $g(x) = \sqrt{x}$ and determine the domain.

SOLUTION

Multiply $(f \cdot g)(x) = f(x) \cdot g(x)$ Multiply the expressions.

$(f \cdot g)(x) = 2\sqrt{x} \cdot \sqrt{x}$

$(f \cdot g)(x) = 2x$

Domain   0 and positive numbers   The domain of $(f \cdot g)(x)$ excludes negative numbers, since negative numbers are excluded from the domain of $f(x)$ and $g(x)$. The domain reflects the fact that $f(x)$ is only real when x is 0 or positive.

4. **MP 2, 4** In a video game, you start with 20 points. You have 60 seconds to grab the 10 cherries in the game. You get 8 points for each cherry you grab, but lose 2 points for each cherry that is still there when the 60 seconds expire. Write a function describing the points.

SOLUTION

Constant function $S(c) = 20$ You always start with 20 points. Write a constant function. It is always equal to 20.

> The function we create is a combination of other functions. It will include a constant function and some composition. When a function always has the same output for any input, it is called a **constant function**.

Score for cherries grabbed $G(c) = 8c$ You get 8 points for each cherry you grab.

Number not grabbed $10 - c$ There are 10 cherries. If you grab c cherries, this means that you did not grab $10 - c$ cherries.

Score for cherries not grabbed $N(c) = -2(10 - c)$ You lose 2 points for every ungrabbed cherry. Multiply -2 by the number you failed to grab, which is $10 - c$ cherries.

Combine functions $p(c) = $ total points function   Combine the three functions. The combined function confirms the description. You start with 20 points, gain 8 points for each cherry you grab, but lose 2 points for each cherry you fail to grab.

$p(c) = S(c) + G(c) + N(c)$

$p(c) = 20 + 8c - 2(10 - c)$

$p(c) = 10c$

Evaluating a Combined Function

We want to evaluate a combined function for a particular value. We show two ways to do so, starting with combining the functions' expressions before evaluating.

MODEL PROBLEMS

1. What is $(f - g)(5)$ when $f(x) = 3x + 7$ and $g(x) = x - 2$?

SOLUTION

Subtract the expressions	$(f - g)(x) = f(x) - g(x)$ $(f - g)(x) = 3x + 7 - (x - 2)$ $(f - g)(x) = 2x + 9$	To evaluate the function $f - g$ for $x = 5$, we could first combine the functions to find an expression for $f - g$. Subtract the functions that define the expressions.
Substitute and evaluate	$(f - g)(5) = 2(5) + 9$ $(f - g)(x) = 19$	Now substitute 5 into the combined expression and evaluate it.

2. What is $(f - g)(5)$ when $f(x) = 3x + 7$ and $g(x) = x - 2$?

SOLUTION

Definition of $f - g$	$(f - g)(x) = f(x) - g(x)$	The functions $f(x)$ and $g(x)$ shown here have the same domain, the set of all real numbers. We want to find $(f - g)(5)$. Use the definition of the function $f - g$, which says to subtract the outputs of f and g.
Substitute 5 and evaluate each function	$f(5) = 3 \cdot 5 + 7 = 22$ $g(5) = 5 - 2 = 3$	We want to subtract $g(5)$ from $f(5)$. First calculate the values of $f(5)$ and $g(5)$.
Subtract outputs	$(f - g)(5) = f(5) - g(5)$ $(f - g)(5) = 22 - 3$ $(f - g)(5) = 19$	Evaluate $f - g$ for the input 5 by subtracting the outputs $g(5)$ from $f(5)$. The result is 19.

PRACTICE

Exercises 1–5: What is $(f + g)(x)$?

1. $f(x) = -3x; g(x) = 5x + 4$

2. $f(x) = -5x; g(x) = 7x + 5$

3. $f(x) = 2x + 1; g(x) = 3x - 2$

4. $f(x) = -9x; g(x) = 7x + 2$

5. $f(x) = -3x; g(x) = 5x + 8$

Exercises 6–9: What is $(q - r)(y)$?

6. $q(y) = 8y - 9; r(y) = 6y + 8$

7. $q(y) = 10y - 8; r(y) = 7y + 9$

8. $q(y) = 9y - 8; r(y) = 4y + 4$

9. $q(y) = 3y - 5; r(y) = 8y + 7$

Exercises 10–13: What is $(g \cdot h)(z)$?

10. $g(z) = 4z + 3; h(z) = 9z$

11. $g(z) = 7z + 8; h(z) = 8z$

12. $g(z) = 8z + 1; h(z) = 9z$

13. $g(z) = 7z + 3; h(z) = 8z$

Exercises 14–17: What is $\left(\dfrac{g}{h}\right)(x)$?

14. $g(x) = 12x; h(x) = 4$

15. $g(x) = 28x; h(x) = 4$

16. $g(x) = 16x; h(x) = 2$

17. $g(x) = 54x; h(x) = 9$

Practice Problems continue . . .

18. What is $(f + g)(-2)$ if $f(x) = 2x$ and $g(x) = 9x - 4$?

19. What is $(f + g)(-3)$ if $f(x) = 8x$ and $g(x) = 4x - 9$?

20. **MP 6** What is $(g - h)(3)$ if $g(y) = 2y + 5$ and $h(y) = 10y - 6$?

21. What is $(f \cdot g)(5)$ if $f(z) = 4z - 9$ and $g(z) = 4z$?

22. What is $(f \cdot g)(3)$ if $f(z) = 9z - 4$ and $g(z) = 5z$?

23. What is $\left(\dfrac{x}{y}\right)(-5)$ if $x(z) = 42z - 120$ and $y(z) = 6z$?

24. What is $\left(\dfrac{x}{y}\right)(-4)$ if $x(z) = 70z - 280$ and $y(z) = 10z$?

25. Carolina receives an allowance that is tied to completing her chores during the week. She starts off with an allowance of $20. She has five chores to complete during the week, and for each chore she completes, she receives $3. However, for each chore that is not done by the end of the week, she loses $4 from her allowance.

    a Write an expression describing Carolina's allowance as a function of the number of chores, C, that she completes during the week.

    b If Carolina completes 4 chores, what is her allowance?

26. **MP 2, 7** Is $f(a + b) = f(a) + f(b)$? Give a proof or provide a counterexample.

LESSON 6.4

6.4 Inverse and Composite Functions

Inverse Functions

An **inverse function** is one that reverses the action of a function, returning the original input value from the original output value. To explain an inverse function, we use the example of a coded message. To encode your message, to make it hard for others to read, you convert letters into numbers, as shown in the diagram. The arrows show which number is assigned to each letter. The function uses a rule that takes the position of the letter in the alphabet ($A = 1$, $B = 2$, ...) and adds 9 to it. To decode the message, to read it, your friend Alan looks at the number and also uses the table to calculate the letter.

A	B	C	D	E	F
10	11	12	13	14	15

f: encipher

D   13

f^{-1}: decipher

> An inverse function reverses the action of a function, returning the original input value.

In the language of mathematics, he applies an inverse function to read your message, a function that reverses the effect of another function. The output of the function is the original input. For instance, if you input B and got 11, he then reads the 11 and outputs B, which was your original input.

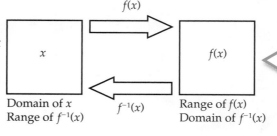

Domain of x
Range of $f^{-1}(x)$

$f^{-1}(x)$

$f(x)$

Range of $f(x)$
Domain of $f^{-1}(x)$

> We will be discussing the inverse functions of exponential functions in the next chapter.

The inverse of f is written as f^{-1}. This is read as "f inverse." It does **not** represent the exponent -1.

What is the inverse of $f(x) = x + 2$?

SOLUTION

Replace $f(x)$ with y	$y = x + 2$	Start by replacing the function notation with y.
Swap x and y	$x = y + 2$	Swap x and y in the equation. This is the step that "reverses" the function.
Solve for y	$y + 2 = x$ $y = x - 2$	Solve for y. Our first step is just to switch the sides of the equation around, so y is on the left. It makes it easier to see what we are doing. Subtract 2 from both sides to isolate y.
State as inverse function	$f^{-1}(x) = x - 2$	The resulting expression is the inverse function.

> To find an expression for the inverse function of $f(x)$, replace $f(x)$ with y, swap the x- and y-variables in the equation, and solve for y. The resulting expression will be the expression for $f^{-1}(x)$.

 In this activity, decode the first message. It was encoded using the function $f(x) = x + 2$.

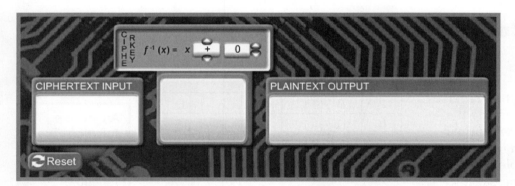

 In this activity, decode the second message. It was encoded using the function $f(x) = 4x - 3$.

The Graph of a Function and Its Inverse

We show the graphs of $f(x) = 2x$, and its inverse, $f^{-1}(x) = \dfrac{1}{2}x$, to the right. The two graphs are symmetrical about the line $y = x$. They are reflections about this line.

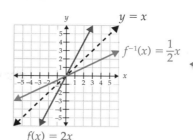

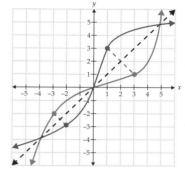

The graph of a function and its inverse are symmetrical about the line $y = x$.

Another way to state the symmetry is to say that for every point on the graph of a function, you can find a point on the graph of its inverse function that is the same distance from the line $y = x$.

We show another graph of a function and its inverse. You can see that for every point on a function's graph, we can find a point on the graph of its inverse that is the same distance from the line $y = x$.

MODEL PROBLEMS

1. **MP 2, 4** The function $f(x) = \dfrac{9}{5}x + 32$ converts a temperature from Celsius (C) to Fahrenheit (F). For instance, we can convert 10°C to Fahrenheit: $f(10) = \dfrac{9}{5}(10) + 32 = 50°F$. What is the inverse of $f(x) = \dfrac{9}{5}x + 32$?

SOLUTION

Replace $f(x)$ with y

$f(x) = \dfrac{9}{5}x + 32$

Start by replacing the function notation with y.

$y = \dfrac{9}{5}x + 32$

Swap x and y

$x = \dfrac{9}{5}y + 32$

Swap x and y in the equation. This is the step that reverses the function.

Solve for y

$\dfrac{9}{5}y + 32 = x$

$\dfrac{9}{5}y = x - 32$

$y = \dfrac{5}{9}(x - 32)$

Solve for y. Our first step is just to switch the sides of the equation around, so y is on the left. It makes it easier to see what we are doing. Subtract 32 from both sides, and then multiply by $\dfrac{5}{9}$.

State as inverse function

$f^{-1}(x) = \dfrac{5}{9}(x - 32)$

The resulting expression is the inverse function. Above, we said that 10°C was 50°F. Let's check our inverse function: $f^{-1}(x) = \dfrac{5}{9}(x - 32)$. Substituting 50 for x, we get

$f^{-1}(50) = \dfrac{5}{9}(50 - 32)$, which equals 10.

Model Problems continue . . .

2. **MP 2, 4** The distance a car travels equals the product of its rate of fuel consumption (its gas mileage) and the number of gallons of gas it uses. The car we are considering gets 30 miles per gallon. What is the inverse of this function?

SOLUTION

Write function	$d(x) = 30x$	We represent the number of gallons the car uses with x, so the distance it travels can be written as $d(x) = 30x$.
Replace $d(x)$ with y	$y = 30x$	Start by replacing the function notation with y.
Swap x and y	$x = 30y$	Swap x and y in the equation.
Solve for y	$y = \dfrac{x}{30}$	Solve for y.
State as inverse function	$d^{-1}(x) = \dfrac{x}{30}$	The resulting expression is the inverse function. In this function, x represents the number of miles the car was driven. The inverse function allows us to calculate how many gallons of gas we would need for a trip of x miles. For instance, we would need 10 gallons for a 300-mile trip.

Optional: When Does a Function Have an Inverse Function?

> A one-to-one function pairs exactly one input with each output. A one-to-one function has an inverse. A function that is not one-to-one does not have an inverse function.

Not every function has an inverse. Every function pairs exactly one output to each input. To have an inverse function, the function must also pair **exactly one input** to each distinct output. To put it another way, no output can be the result of two or more inputs. If say $f(3) = 9$ and $f(-3) = 9$, then the function will **not** have an inverse function, since two different inputs, 3 and -3, have the same output, 9.

A function that matches each output with one input is called a *one-to-one function*. The domain of the original function is the same as the range of the inverse function. A function is one-to-one if for every x and y in its domain, $f(x) = f(y)$ if and only if $x = y$.

Has inverse function	$f(x) = x + 3$ If $f(x) = 5$, $x = 2$ One-to-one	The only input x with an output of 5 is 2. No other value of x when added to 3 equals 5. Since this is true for every output of this function, $f(x) = x + 3$ is one-to-one.
Does not have inverse function	$f(x) = x^2$ If $f(x) = 9$, $x = 3$ **or** $x = -3$ Not one-to-one	The function $f(x) = x^2$ is not one-to-one. The inputs 3 and -3 are both paired with the output 9, so there is more than one input for a given output.

Another way to tell if a function has an inverse is to apply the *horizontal line test* to the graph of the function. If there is a horizontal line that intersects the graph of the function at more than one point, the function has no inverse. Why? If a horizontal line intersects the function at two or more points, then the same *y*-value, which is the output, comes from two or more *x*-values, which are the inputs. This

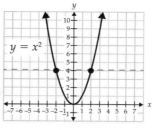

If a horizontal line intersects the graph of a function more than once, the function has no inverse.

means that it is not a one-to-one function. Because the line intersects the graph twice, this function has no inverse.

PRACTICE

1. Which of these functions is the inverse of $y = 5x + 2$?

A. $y = -3x - 6$ C. $y = -5x + 2$

B. $y = \dfrac{x - 2}{5}$ D. $y = -2x + 5$

2. Which of these functions is the inverse of *a*?

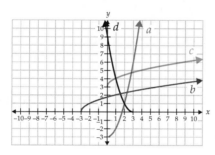

A. *a* C. *c*
B. *b* D. *d*

3. A student starts with the function shown in the graph below. The student translates this function vertically down 3 units and then calculates the inverse. What is the inverse of the new function?

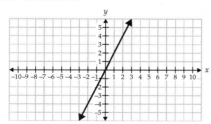

A. $f^{-1}(x) = 2x - 3$

B. $f^{-1}(x) = \dfrac{x}{2} + 3$

C. $f^{-1}(x) = \dfrac{x + 3}{2}$

D. $f^{-1}(x) = -2x + 3$

Exercises 4–20: Find the inverse of each function.

4. $f(x) = 3x - 5$

5. $f(x) = 4x + 1$

6. $g(x) = \dfrac{x - 4}{7}$

7. $g(x) = \dfrac{x + 3}{10}$

8. $f(x) = 5x - 9$

9. $g(x) = \dfrac{x - 1}{8}$

10. $f(x) = x + 31$

11. $f(x) = x + 18$

12. $f(x) = -32x$

13. $f(x) = -5x$

14. $f(x) = 4x + 7$

15. $f(x) = 5x + 8$

16. $g(x) = x - 3$

17. $g(x) = x - 9$

18. $f(z) = 9z$

19. $f(z) = 8z$

20. $h(y) = -8y + 112$

Composite Functions

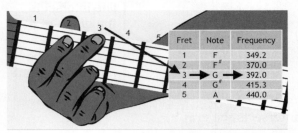

Fret	Note	Frequency
1	F	349.2
2	F#	370.0
3	G	392.0
4	G#	415.3
5	A	440.0

A **composite function** is the result of one function being applied to the results of another function. The composite function is written $f(g(x))$. This is stated as "f of g of x." We use playing a guitar as our example of a composite function. The frequency of the note is stated in cycles per second, with a unit called *hertz*.

> A composite function is made up of two functions, taking the output of the first function as input to the second.

One function
• Fret to note

The inputs to the first function are fret positions, which are the numbers of the white regions between the black lines on the neck. The outputs are musical notes. If a player strums at position 3, for example, the guitar plays the note G.

Second function
• Note to frequency

The second function takes a note as input, and its output is the frequency of the note. For example, G has a frequency of 392 hertz.

Composite function
• Fret to frequency

The composite function takes the fret position as input and states its frequency as output. This composite function goes directly from fret position to frequency.

There are two ways we can evaluate a composition for an input. One way is to use the expression for the composition. Another way is to evaluate the innermost function first. It is like working with parentheses because we work from the inside out.

MODEL PROBLEMS

1. a Write the composite of f with g when $f(x) = x + 1$ and $g(x) = 2x$.
  b Evaluate at $x = 3$ by using the expression for the composition.
  c Evaluate at $x = 3$ by evaluating the innermost function first.

SOLUTION

> The inner function is $g(x)$ and the outer function is $f(x)$.

a Composite function $f(g(x))$

$f(g(x)) = g(x) + 1$

To write an expression for the composite function $f(g(x))$, replace x in the expression for $f(x)$ with $g(x)$.

Replace $g(x)$ with its expression

$f(g(x)) = 2x + 1$

Replace $g(x)$ with its expression, $2x$. The result is an expression for $f(g(x)) = 2x + 1$.

b Substitute and evaluate

$f(g(3)) = 2x + 1$

$f(g(3)) = 2(3) + 1 = 7$

c Evaluate inner function first

$g(3) = 2 \cdot 3$

$g(3) = 6$

To evaluate a composite function, find the value of the innermost function first. To find $f(g(3))$, start by finding $g(3)$. It equals 6.

Evaluate outer function using output of inner function

$f(g(3)) = f(6)$

$f(6) = x + 1$

$f(6) = 6 + 1$

Now replace the inner function with the value calculated in the previous step. Since $g(3)$ equals 6, $f(g(3))$ equals $f(6)$.

Evaluate composite

$f(g(3)) = 7$

Evaluate $f(g(3))$ by finding $f(6)$, which is 7.

Model Problems continue . . .

2. A tree's trunk grows 2 centimeters wider each year, and its height increases by 4 centimeters each year. Its mass density is 510 kilograms per cubic meter. If the tree starts out 10 meters tall with a 0.8 meters diameter, write a function describing its mass as a function of the year.

SOLUTION

We will write functions to describe the tree's various dimensions and take advantage of the formula for the volume of a cylinder, $V = \pi r^2 h$. Its mass will be the product of its density and volume. This application lets us compose functions three levels deep. We are composing $M(V(h(t), r(t)))$. The height and radius are functions of time, and the volume is a function of the height and radius. In turn, the mass is a function of the volume.

Mass	$M(V(h(t), r(t)))$	The mass is a function of the volume, which in turn is a function of the height and radius, which are functions of the time.
Volume	$V(h, r) = \pi r^2 h$ $V(t) = \pi(r(t))^2 \cdot h(t)$	Use the definition of volume. Write a function for the volume as a function of time.
Height	$h(t) = 10 + 0.04t$	Write the expression for the tree's height from the problem. It increases by 4 cm every year, but we need consistent units, so we convert centimeters to meters and get 0.04 m.
Radius	$r(t) = 0.4 + 0.01t$	Write a function for the radius of the tree. We convert the diameter to a radius: 0.8 m diameter = 0.4 m radius. If the diameter increases by 2.0 cm, its radius increases by half that.
Substitute expressions	$V(t) = \pi(0.4 + 0.01t)^2 \cdot (10 + 0.04t)$	Substitute the expressions.
Mass	$M(V(t)) = 510 \cdot V(t)$	The mass of the tree is a function of its volume.
Substitute	$M(t) = 510\pi(0.4 + 0.01t)^2 \cdot (10 + 0.04t)$	Substitute the expression for the volume.

Optional: Domain Restrictions of Composite Functions

Determining the domain restrictions of a composite function is a two-step process. First, determine any restrictions on the domain of the inner function. Any restrictions on the inner function's domain are restrictions on the composite function. Second, add any restrictions to the composite function expression to the restrictions of the inner function. This combination of restrictions is the domain restrictions of the composite function.

> The domain restrictions of a composite function include any restrictions on the expression that result from the composition and any restrictions on the inner function.

For instance, the $g(f(x)) = \sqrt{4 - x^2}$ when $f(x) = x^2 + 1$ and $g(x) = \sqrt{5 - x}$. The inner function, $f(x)$, has the domain of all real numbers. However, the domain of the composite function is limited to $-2 \le x \le 2$ because that is the domain of the composite function expression, $\sqrt{4 - x^2}$. If the absolute value of x is greater than 2, then the expression has a negative radicand, and the output is not a real number.

Determine the domain of:

a $f(g(x))$ when $f(x) = \dfrac{1}{x}$ and $g(x) = \dfrac{1}{x+1}$

b $g(f(x))$ when $f(x) = \dfrac{1}{x}$ and $g(x) = \dfrac{1}{x+1}$

c $f(f(x))$ when $f(x) = \dfrac{1}{x}$ and $g(x) = \dfrac{1}{x+1}$

SOLUTION

a $f(g(x))$ $f(g(x)) = \dfrac{1}{\left(\dfrac{1}{x+1}\right)} = x+1$

State the composite function $f(g(x))$.

Substitute $\dfrac{1}{x+1}$ for x in the expression $\dfrac{1}{x}$ and simplify.

Domain   Inner function $g(x)$ undefined for -1
Domain is all real numbers except -1

State the domain restrictions. x cannot equal -1 because it causes the innermost function, $g(x)$, to be undefined. Even though the composite expression, $x+1$, has the domain of all real numbers, the domain of the composite function must include any restrictions on the inner function $g(x)$. Therefore, the domain of the composite function is all real numbers except -1.

b $g(f(x))$ $g(f(x)) = \dfrac{1}{\dfrac{1}{x} + 1}$

State the composite function $g(f(x))$. Substitute the expression for $f(x)$ into the $g(x)$ function. The composite function is undefined for -1 because that value causes the denominator of the composite expression to equal 0.

Domain $g(f(x))$ is undefined for -1
Inner function $f(x)$ undefined for 0
Domain is all real numbers except -1 and 0

Another domain restriction is $x \neq 0$ since $f(x)$ is not defined for $x = 0$. The domain restrictions are all real numbers except -1 and 0.

c $f(f(x))$ $f(f(x)) = \dfrac{1}{\left(\dfrac{1}{x}\right)} = x$

State the composite function $f(f(x))$.

Domain   Inner function $f(x)$ undefined for 0
Domain is all real numbers except 0

This composite function has the domain of all real numbers except 0, since $f(x)$ is undefined for 0.

PRACTICE

1. `MP 6` If $f(x) = 3x - 4$ and $g(x) = x^3$, what is the positive difference between $f(g(2))$ and $g(f(2))$?

   A. 8   C. 20

   B. 12   D. 28

2. `MP 1, 2` Which of the following statements are true?

   I. $(f - g)(x) = -(g - f)(x)$ for all x.

   II. If f and g are functions such that $f^{-1}(x) = g^{-1}(x)$ for all x, then $f(x) = g(x)$.

   III. If $f(g(x)) = x$, then $g(f(x)) = x$ for all x.

   A. I only   C. I and II

   B. II only   D. I, II, and III

3. What is $f(g(4))$ if $f(x) = 3x - 1$ and $g(x) = -4x + 11$?

4. What is $f(g(-5))$ if $f(x) = -2x - 5$ and $g(x) = 6x + 20$?

5. What is $f(g(7))$ if $f(x) = 4x + 14$ and $g(x) = -9x + 60$?

6. What is $g(f(5))$ if $f(x) = x^2 - 16$ and $g(x) = 3x - 7$?

7. What is $g(f(6))$ if $f(x) = x^2 - 31$ and $g(x) = -5x + 17$?

8. What is $g(f(7))$ if $f(x) = x^2 - 40$ and $g(x) = -2x + 8$?

9. What is $g(h(x))$ if $g(x) = 4x - 6$ and $h(x) = -5x + 2$?

10. What is $f(g(x))$ if $f(x) = -3x - 19$ and $g(x) = -8x + 20$?

11. What is $z(y(x))$ if $z(x) = 2x + 15$ and $y(x) = -4x - 9$?

12. What is $f(g(2))$ if $f(x) = -2x + 6$ and $g(x) = 8x$?

13. What is $f(g(3))$ if $f(x) = -2x + 14$ and $g(x) = 4x$?

14. What is $g(f(3))$ if $f(x) = -6x + 14$ and $g(x) = 8x$?

15. What is $g(f(-2))$ if $f(x) = -10x + 20$ and $g(x) = 10x$?

16. Write an expression for $g(h(x))$ given $g(x) = 5x$ and $h(x) = 4x - 14$.

17. Write an expression for $g(h(x))$ given $g(x) = 2x$ and $h(x) = 8x - 13$.

18. Write an expression for $h(g(x))$ given $g(x) = 8x$ and $h(x) = 3x - 15$.

19. Write an expression for $h(g(x))$ given $g(x) = 6x$ and $h(x) = 2x - 2$.

20. $f(x) = 275x - 535$. What is $f(f^{-1}(-4050))$?

21. $f(x) = 255x - 510$. What is $f(f^{-1}(-2700))$?

22. `MP 4, 6` A barrel cactus grows in the shape of a cylinder. The cactus is currently 0.2 meters in diameter and 1.2 meters high. It grows 10 centimeters higher and 6 centimeters wider each year. Its mass density is 700 kilograms per cubic meter.

   a Write a function to represent the volume of the barrel cactus in cubic meters as a function of time.

   b What is the mass of the cactus, to the nearest whole kilogram, after 5 years?

• Multi-Part PROBLEM Practice •

`MP 3` Consider the function $y = 2x^2$ with the domain restricted to $x \geq 0$.

a Find the inverse.

b Is the inverse a function? Explain.

c Algebraically, show that the function you found for part **a** is an inverse. In other words, show that $f(f^{-1}(x)) = x$.

Chapter 6 Key Ideas

6.1 Exponential Function Graphs

- An exponential function has a constant raised to a variable power, $f(x) = b^x$. The base b must be positive but cannot equal 1.
- To graph an exponential function, you can plot points and draw a curve through them. Exponential functions can be translated up or down, left or right.
- The basic properties of the graph of an exponential function depend on whether the base is greater than 1, or between 0 and 1.

6.2 Modeling with Exponential Functions

- Exponential functions can be restated using properties of exponents in order to solve for different variables.
- For exponential models, use exponential regression to determine if the model is a good fit.

6.3 Combining Functions

- A combined function is the result of adding, subtracting, multiplying, or dividing two or more functions.

6.4 Inverse and Composite Functions

- An inverse function reverses the action of a function, returning the original input value from the original output value. The inverse of f is written as f^{-1}.
- Not every function has an inverse. Every function pairs exactly one output, an element of the range, to each input, or element of the domain. To have an inverse function, the function must also pair exactly one input to each output. Such a function is called a *one-to-one function*.
- You can find an expression for an inverse function by replacing $f(x)$ with y. You then switch the x- and y-variables, and solve for y. The expression equal to y defines the inverse function.
- The graphs of a function and its inverse are symmetrical about the line $y = x$. By symmetrical, we mean the graph of one is the reflection of the other across the line.
- A composite function is made up of two functions. The composite function takes the output of one function and uses it as the input of the other function. For any value of x, the composite function $f(g(x))$ takes the output of g, $g(x)$, and uses that as the input to f. To put it another way, you evaluate the inner function first.

CHAPTER 6 REVIEW

1. How does the graph of $9^x + 7$ compare to the graph of the parent function 9^x?

   A. It is shifted to the left 7 units from the parent function.

   B. It is shifted up 7 units from the parent function.

   C. It is shifted down 7 units from the parent function.

   D. It is shifted to the right 7 units from the parent function.

2. **MP 4, 6** Ainsley opened a certificate of deposit account with an initial deposit of $1,800. At the end of Year 1, she had $1,872 in the account. At the end of Year 2, she had $1,946.88 in the account. At the end of Year 3, she had approximately $2,024.76 in the account. Which of the following best represents the interest rate she secured?

   A. 0.02%   C. 0.04%

   B. 0.03%   D. 0.05%

Chapter Review continues . . .

3. A species of bacteria doubles three times every 8 hours. If there are only 3 to start with, how many are there after a day?

    A. 24   C. 768

    B. 192   D. 1536

Exercises 4–7: Evaluate the following functions.

4. $f(x) = 4^x$ for $x = 3$

5. $f(x) = \left(\dfrac{1}{6}\right)^x$ for $x = 3$

6. $g(x) = 8^x$ for $x = \dfrac{1}{3}$

7. $g(x) = 6^x$ for $x = -2$

8. Simplify: $7^{\sqrt{5}} \cdot 7^{\sqrt{3}}$

9. Which number is greater, $3^{\sqrt{3}}$ or $3^{\sqrt[3]{2}}$? Explain.

10. Chelsea was given a loan by the bank and purchased a house for half a million dollars. She put a down payment of 20% on the house, but forgot to make her monthly payments for the next five years. Her annual interest rate, which is compounded monthly, is 4.9%. How much will she owe the bank in 5 years, to the nearest dollar?

11. Scientists counted only 15 bacteria five years ago in a petri dish experiment and observed that the bacterial population quadrupled every three years. What will be the bacterial population four years from now?

12. [MP 3, 4] Broker Bob notices that inflation has caused the median salary to increase by approximately 2% each year. Based on his observations, he says that if you earn P dollars today, you'll be earning $P \cdot (0.02)^{20}$ in 20 years. Is his formula correct? If not, modify it so it represents the expected median salary amount earned in t years based on a 2% inflation rate.

13. Amanda's annual interest rate is represented by the function, $f(t) = 1.05^t$. What is the quarterly interest rate, to the nearest tenth of a percent?

14. [MP 4, 5] Carbon-14 has a half-life of 5730 years. Given a full sample of carbon-14, what percentage of its original amount is left after a millennium?

15. [MP 4, 5, 6] Magnesium-27 has a half-life of about 9.5 minutes. At 3:45 P.M., only a sixteenth of magnesium-27 was left from its original amount. What time was magnesium-27 in its original state?

16. If a principal P is invested at an annual interest rate r, compounded n times per year, in t years it will grow to an amount A given by $A = P\left(1 + \dfrac{r}{n}\right)^{nt}$.

  a A check deposit of \$10,000 is accumulating an annual interest rate of 3.6%, compounded quarterly. How much is the check deposit worth if it is left to accrue interest for two decades? Round your answer to the nearest dollar.

  b Suppose that \$2500 is invested at an interest rate of 4.5%, compounded monthly. How much is the investment worth at the end of 8 years? Round your answer to the nearest dollar.

  c Banks A and B offer an annual interest rate of 6%. However, Bank A compounds monthly and Bank B compounds annually. Which bank offers a better plan?

17. Find the inverse: $h(y) = -5y + 5$

Exercises 18–20: What is $(f + g)(x)$? Simplify your answer.

18. $f(x) = 5x - 9; g(x) = -2x + 1$

19. $f(x) = -11x - 3; g(x) = 4x + 5$

20. $f(x) = -3x - 5; g(x) = 2x + 17$

Exercises 21–22: What is $(f \cdot g)(x)$?

21. $f(x) = x - 7; g(x) = x + 5$

22. $f(x) = x + 9; g(x) = x + 4$

23. What is $(f - g)(4)$ if $f(x) = 8x - 9$ and $g(x) = 3x - 2$?

24. What is $\left(\dfrac{f}{g}\right)(3)$ if $f(x) = x + 2$ and $g(x) = 7x - 11$?

25. [MP 4, 7] A rocket is launched straight up into the air from the ground with a starting velocity of 50 m/s. (Hint: Position = initial position + initial velocity · time − $4.9t^2$, with position in meters and time in seconds.)

  a What is the height of the rocket after 3 s, in meters?

  b Write an expression to model the height of a ball that is thrown directly upward from a starting height of 1 m with an initial velocity of 7 m/s. Use the variable t to represent time.

Cumulative Review
for Chapters 1–6

1. Which of the following could be the coordinates of an x-intercept of the graph of a function?

    A. $(-1, 2)$
    B. $(0, -1)$
    C. $(5, 0)$
    D. $(2, 5)$

2. The solutions to $-x^2 - 4x - 5 = 0$ are

    A. $i, -i$
    B. $-2 - i, -2 + i$
    C. $-4 + 2i, 4 - 2i$
    D. $-2 + 2i, -2 - 2i$

3. What are the conditions for adding or subtracting radical terms?

    I. The index of the radical must be the same.

    II. The radicand must be the same.

    III. The coefficient in front of the radical must be the same.

    A. I only
    B. II only
    C. I and II
    D. II and III

4. How does the graph of $14^{x-6} + 3$ compare to the graph of the parent function 14^x?

    A. It is shifted to the left 6 units and up 3 units from the parent function.
    B. It is shifted to the left 6 units and down 3 units from the parent function.
    C. It is shifted to the right 6 units and up 3 units from the parent function.
    D. It is shifted to the right 6 units and down 3 units from the parent function.

5. The bank offers a 3.8% interest rate for a savings account, compounded annually. How much money could be expected in the savings account in 10 years if $100 is deposited today?

    A. $128.48
    B. $145.20
    C. $192.75
    D. $239.09

Exercises 6–7: Factor.

6. $x^4 + 13x^2 + 42$

7. $x^3 + 4x^2 - 45x$

8. **MP 2, 3** Show that the quadratic equation $ax^2 + bx + c = 0$, $(a \neq 0)$ has two different negative solutions if $a \cdot c > 0, a \cdot b > 0$, and $b^2 - 4ac > 0$.

9. $(x + 3)$ times $(x - 7)$ equals $x^2 - 4x - 21$. What are the x-intercepts of the function $f(x) = x^2 - 4x - 21$? State only the x-coordinate of the x-intercept(s).

10. Find the x-intercepts of the graph of $f(x) = x^2 + 7x + 12$. State only the x-coordinate of the x-intercept(s).

11. If $x + 1$ is a factor of $x^{101} + kx + 7$, what is the value of k?

Exercises 12–13: Determine whether the expressions are factors of the polynomial function.

12. Expression $x - 2$; $f(x) = 6x^3 - 7x^2 + 8x - 9$

13. Expression $x + 5$; $f(x) = x^3 + 5x^2 + 4x + 15$

14. For the expression $-x^3 - 3x^2 + 4$, if $x + 2$ is a factor, what is $P(-2)$?

15. Is $(5, 4, -2)$ a solution to the following system of equations? Show your work.
$-2z = y; y - 1 = x; 2y - 3x + 2z = -6$

16. Simplify: $\dfrac{5 - 4x}{4x^2 + 27x - 40}$

17. Solve: $\dfrac{x}{x - 4} = \dfrac{5}{x + 14}$

18. a Complete the table. Write the quotients as integers with a remainder, if necessary. The first one is completed.

Problem	Quotient	Does the quotient have a remainder?
i. $142 \div 5$	28 R2	Yes
ii. $142 \div 3$		
iii. $142 \div 71$		
iv. $142 \div 2$		
v. $142 \div 6$		

b What can you say about the remainder when the divisor is a factor of the dividend? What can you say about the remainder when the divisor is not a factor?

19. If $x - 5$ is a factor of $x^3 - 3x^2 - 13x + 15$, what does that imply about the remainder in the quotient of $\dfrac{x^3 - 3x^2 - 13x + 15}{x - 5}$?

20. **MP 2** Sam divides $ax^2 + bx + c$ by $x - f$ and finds that the remainder is 0. What does that say about $x - f$ in relation to $ax^2 + bx + c$?

Exercises 21–22: Write the reciprocal function that is represented by each graph.

21.

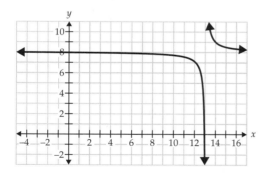

22. **MP 2**

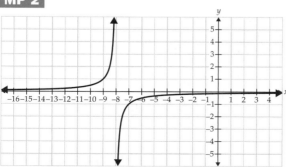

Exercises 23–27: Simplify.

23. $25^{\frac{3}{2}}$

24. $125^{\frac{2}{3}}$

25. $a^{\frac{3}{4}} \cdot a^{\frac{1}{6}}$

26. $\dfrac{5^{\frac{3}{4}}}{5^{\frac{1}{4}}}$

27. $\sqrt[15]{x^{17}y^{14}}$

28. What is $(f - g)(x)$ if $f(x) = 6x - 1$ and $g(x) = x + 8$? Simplify your answer.

29. **MP 1, 2, 7** The function $g(x) = 4^{x-3} + 2$ can be obtained by shifting the function $f(x) = 4^x$ to the right 3 units and up 2 units. Each point on $f(x)$ is shifted 3 units right and 2 units up, which is a total distance of $\sqrt{3^2 + 2^2} = \sqrt{13} \approx 3.6$ units (using the Pythagorean theorem). Find an exponential function with a total distance shift of 5 units from the function a^x for each function below.

a $f(x) = a^{x+b}$

b $g(x) = a^x + c$

c $h(x) = a^{x+b} + c$

Chapter 7

Logarithmic Functions

Chapter Content

Vocabulary

argument	e	power rule for logarithms
base	logarithmic function	product rule for logarithms
change-of-base formula	natural base exponential function	quotient rule for logarithms
common logarithm	natural logarithm	

LESSON 7.1

7.1 Logarithms

Logarithmic Functions

A **logarithmic function** is the inverse of an exponential function. If $b^y = x$, then $\log_b x = y$. With $\log_b x$, b represents the **base**, and x is the **argument** of the logarithm. The logarithm is the power y that base b is raised to so that it equals x. Both b and x must be greater than 0, and b cannot equal 1.

Example:

$\log_2 8 = ?$ The expression is read as "the base 2 logarithm of 8."

Power of 2 that results in 8   The expression $\log_2 8$ means the power to which 2 must be raised to equals 8.

$\log_2 8 = 3$
$\quad 2^3 = 8$ The base 2 logarithm of 8 is 3, since 2 to the third power is 8.

We show some examples of how logarithms and exponents are related:

Exponential Equation	Logarithmic Equation
$4^2 = 16$	$\log_4 16 = 2$
$2^3 = 8$	$\log_2 8 = 3$
$5^3 = 125$	$\log_5 125 = 3$
$10^4 = 10,000$	$\log_{10} 10,000 = 4$
$b^y = x$	$\log_b x = y$

You can see how the exponent on the left **equals** the value of the logarithm on the right. In the first row of the table, the exponent is 2 and the value of the logarithm is also 2. You can also see that the bases are the **same** on both sides of each row. For instance, in the first row the base is 4 for both the exponential expression and the logarithm.

Finally, you can see that the value of the exponential expression **equals** the argument of the logarithmic function. In the first row, the value of the first exponential expression is 16, and 16 is the argument of the first logarithm, and so on.

In this activity, move tiles from a logarithmic function to create an equivalent exponential equation, and vice versa.

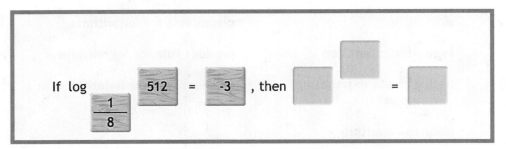

If log $\boxed{\dfrac{1}{8}}$ $\boxed{512}$ = $\boxed{-3}$, then $\boxed{}$ = $\boxed{}$

 In this activity, restate exponential equations as logarithmic functions.

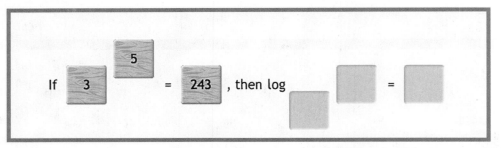

If $\boxed{3}^{\boxed{5}}$ = $\boxed{243}$, then log $\boxed{}\boxed{}$ = $\boxed{}$

In this activity, you get a mix of transformations from logarithmic function to exponential equation, and vice versa.

If $\boxed{45}^{\boxed{2}}$ = $\boxed{2025}$, then log $\boxed{}\boxed{}$ = $\boxed{}$

MODEL PROBLEMS

Exercises 1–4: Evaluate.

SOLUTION

1. $\log_7 49$ $\log_7 49 = 2$ The logarithm equals 2, since $7^2 = 49$.

2. $\log_{10} 1000$ $\log_{10} 1000 = 3$ The logarithm equals 3, since $10^3 = 1000$.

3. $\log_2 \dfrac{1}{32}$ $\log_2 \dfrac{1}{32} = -5$ The logarithm equals -5, since $2^{-5} = \dfrac{1}{32}$.

4. $\log_{\frac{1}{2}} \dfrac{1}{16}$ $\log_{\frac{1}{2}} \dfrac{1}{16} = 4$ The logarithm equals 4, since $\left(\dfrac{1}{2}\right)^4 = \dfrac{1}{16}$.

Common Logarithms

A **common logarithm** is a logarithm with base 10. A logarithm written as $\log 5$ is a common logarithm; it is equivalent to $\log_{10} 5$. In other words, if the base is not stated, it is assumed to be 10, and it is a common logarithm. Many calculators calculate common logarithms when the "log" key is pressed.

MODEL PROBLEM

Calculate the common logarithm of $\log 1000 = x$.

SOLUTION

Restate as exponential equation	$10^x = 1000$	Use the definition of logarithms. If $\log 1000 = x$ then $10^x = 1000$.
Write 1000 as power of 10	$10^x = 10^3$	Write 1000 as 10^3 so the same base appears on both sides of the equation.
Solve	$x = 3$	The exponents can be set equal to each other because the bases are the same. The solution is $x = 3$. The common logarithm of 1000 is 3.

> We show how to calculate the common logarithm of 1000 using the relationship of logarithmic and exponential equations. An expression like $\log 1000$ has no base stated. It is a common logarithm and its base is 10. For example, $\log 1000$ is equivalent to $\log_{10} 1000$.

Solving Logarithmic Equations

Since $y = \log_b x$ is equivalent to $b^y = x$, we can convert a logarithmic equation to an equivalent exponential equation to solve it.

MODEL PROBLEMS

1. Solve $\log_x 8 = 3$ for the base of the logarithm.

SOLUTION

Convert to exponential equation	$x^3 = 8$	Restate the equation as an exponential equation. The equations $\log_x 8 = 3$ and $x^3 = 8$ are equivalent.
Solve	$x = \sqrt[3]{8}$ $x = 2$	Take the cube root of both sides of the equation. The cube root of 8 is 2, or to put it another way, $2^3 = 8$. This means $x = 2$. This is the solution to the equation.

2. Solve $\log_5 x = 2$ for x.

SOLUTION

Convert to exponential equation	$5^2 = x$	Restate the logarithmic equation as an exponential equation. The equations $\log_5 x = 2$ and $5^2 = x$ are equivalent.
Solve	$x = 25$	Simplify 5^2 to solve the equation. The solution is $x = 25$.

Model Problems continue . . .

3. Solve $\log_4 x = -3$.

SOLUTION

Convert to exponential equation $4^{-3} = x$ Restate the logarithmic equation as the equivalent exponential equation $4^{-3} = x$.

Solve $x = \dfrac{1}{64}$ Since $4^{-3} = \dfrac{1}{64}$, $x = \dfrac{1}{64}$.

4. Solve $\log_4 \dfrac{126 + x}{x} = 3$.

SOLUTION

Convert to exponential equation $4^3 = \dfrac{126 + x}{x}$ Restate the logarithmic equation as an equivalent exponential equation.

Solve $64 = \dfrac{126 + x}{x}$ Solve the equation and find that $x = 2$.

$$64x = 126 + x$$
$$63x = 126$$
$$x = 2$$

5. Which equations have a solution between 0 and 1? Select all that apply.

   A. $\log_3 x = -2$

   B. $\log_{16} x = \dfrac{1}{2}$

   C. $\log_x \left(\dfrac{1}{9}\right) = 2$

   D. $\log_{\frac{1}{3}} x = -2$

SOLUTION

A. **Correct answer.** The answer is $3^{-2} = \dfrac{1}{9}$.

B. The answer is $16^{\frac{1}{2}} = 4$.

C. **Correct answer.** First write as an exponential equation, $x^2 = \dfrac{1}{9}$. Then take the square root and disregard the extraneous negative answer because the base of a logarithm must be positive. The answer is $\dfrac{1}{3}$.

D. The answer is $\left(\dfrac{1}{3}\right)^{-2} = 9$.

PRACTICE

1. If $\log_{10} x = -2$, then $x =$

   A. $\sqrt{\dfrac{1}{10}}$ C. $\dfrac{1}{100}$

   B. -100 D. $(-2) \cdot 10$

Exercises 2–10: Restate each logarithmic equation as an exponential equation.

2. $\log_3 2187 = 7$

3. $\log_5 0.04 = -2$

4. $\log_2 128 = 7$

5. $\log_4 64 = 3$

6. $\log_5 625 = 4$

7. $\log_2 6 = x$

8. $\log_3 729 = 6$

9. $\log_8 512 = 3$

10. $\log_{10} 0.01 = -2$

Exercises 11–20: Restate each exponential equation as a logarithmic equation.

11. $3^2 = 9$

12. $6^3 = 216$

13. $3^6 = 729$

14. $5^2 = 25$

15. $17^x = 4913$

16. $3^{0.234} = y$

17. $x^y = z$

18. $4^{-5} = \dfrac{1}{1024}$

19. $16^{\frac{1}{4}} = 2$

20. $a^{-c} = b$

Exercises 21–35: Evaluate.

21. $\log_2 16$

22. $\log_3 27$

23. $\log_6 1$

24. $\log_8 1$

25. $\log 10^{25}$

26. $\log 10^{17}$

27. $\log_5 25$

28. $\log_{\frac{1}{2}} \dfrac{1}{8}$

29. $\log_{32} 2$

30. $\log_{\frac{1}{4}} \dfrac{1}{16}$

31. $\log_{\sqrt{4}} 4$

32. $\log_2 0.5$

33. $\log_3 3\sqrt{3}$

34. $\log_5 \sqrt[4]{25}$

35. $\log_2 \sqrt[3]{\dfrac{1}{4}}$

Exercises 36–49: Solve.

36. $\log 10{,}000 = x$

37. $\log 100 = x$

38. $\log 100{,}000 = x$

39. $\log_7 x = 2$

40. $\log_x 81 = 4$

41. $\log_9 x = \dfrac{1}{2}$

42. $\log_4 x = 3$

43. $\log_{\frac{1}{27}} x = -\dfrac{1}{3}$

44. $\log_x 5 = 1$

45. $\log_2 x = -1$

46. $\log_x 8 = 3$

47. $\log_3 x = -2$

48. $\log x = 2.453$

49. $\log x = 2$

Exercises 50–51: State the answer to the nearest hundredth. Use a calculator or a spreadsheet.

50. If $\log x = 0.396$, what is x?

51. If $\log x = 4.500$, what is x?

52. MP 2, 3 Why can't there be a logarithm of a negative number?

7.2 Logarithmic Function Graphs

The graph is a typical logarithmic function. As x approaches 0, $f(x)$ becomes increasingly negative. As x becomes larger, the graph "flattens out." The vertical axis is the vertical asymptote for the logarithmic function. The graph of the logarithmic function does not extend to the left of the y-axis because logarithms are not defined for 0 or for negative numbers.

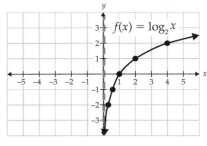

x	$f(x)$
$\frac{1}{4}$	-2
$\frac{1}{2}$	-1
1	0
2	1
4	2

An exponential function and the appropriate logarithmic function are inverses of each other. Two functions that are inverses have graphs that are mirror images of each other and are symmetric about the line $y = x$. Since the exponential function $f(x) = 2^x$ and the logarithmic function $f^{-1}(x) = \log_2 x$ are inverses, their graphs are symmetric about $y = x$.

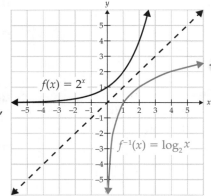

> Just as with other inverse functions, the graphs of a function and its inverse are symmetric about the line $y = x$.

MODEL PROBLEMS

1. Solve the system of equations, $y = \log_4 x$ and $y = 2^x - 15$, by graphing.

SOLUTION

Create table and graph

x	$\log_4 x$	$2^x - 15$
1	0	-13
2	0.50	-11
3	0.79	-7
4	1	1
5	1.16	17

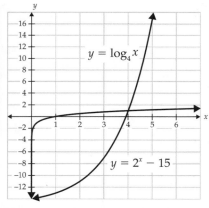

Solution: (4, 1)   A solution to the system is where the graphs intersect. In this example, the graphs intersect twice. We can use x-y tables to get a sense of the number of solutions. A solution in the table is a row where the two functions have the same value of y for a given x. A logarithmic function is undefined for 0 and negative inputs, so there cannot be an intersection for values less than or equal to 0. Using the x-y table, we know one solution to this system of equations is (4, 1). The other solution is where $y = 2^x - 15$ crosses $y = \log_4 x$, very close to the y-axis. If you iterate a solution, you will find it between 10^{-8} and 10^{-9}.

Model Problems continue . . .

2. **MP 1, 5, 6** a Solve $y = (\log_{10} x) + 2$ and $y = 1.2^x$ to find approximate solutions.

    b Continue to iterate to find a more precise solution for the greater value of x.

SOLUTION

a Create table
and graph

x	$(\log_{10} x) + 2$	1.2^x
1	2	1.2
2	2.30	1.44
3	2.48	1.73
4	2.60	2.07
5	2.70	2.49
6	2.78	2.99
7	2.85	3.58

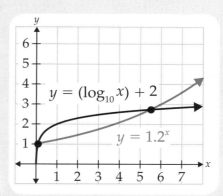

Two solutions Approximately (0.1, 1.1)

              Approximately (5.5, 2.7)

Use the graph to find approximate solutions. One seems to be about (0.1, 1.1). The other seems to be about (5.5, 2.7).

b

x	$(\log_{10} x) + 2$	1.2^x
5.45	2.74	2.70
5.475	2.74	2.71
5.5	2.74	2.73
5.525	2.74	2.74
5.55	2.74	2.75
5.575	2.75	2.76
5.6	2.75	2.78
5.625	2.75	2.79

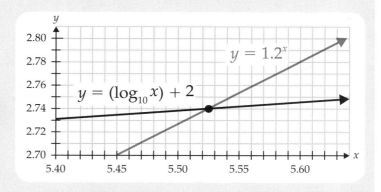

Iterate values between 5.45 and 5.625

We estimate that the solution for the greater value of x was about 5.5. Using a spreadsheet, generate values for x, starting with 5.45, and adding 0.025 to create each additional value.

Approximately (5.525, 2.74)

Using the graph, we can approximate the solution as (5.525, 2.74). We could also state that the x-value of the solution is between 5.525 and 5.55, and the y-value is between 2.74 and 2.75.

We could continue to iterate: We could start with 5.525 and add even smaller increments, such as 0.01, to calculate an even more precise solution.

Translating Logarithmic Function Graphs

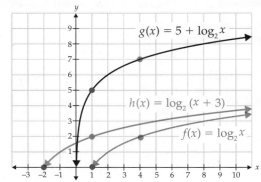

As with other functions, the graph of a logarithmic function can be transformed. As our parent function, we choose $f(x) = \log_2 x$. Two outputs for specific values of x of the parent function will make comparing our transformations easy. When the input of the function is 1, then the output is 0. This is represented by the gray point. (Remember, $x^0 = 1$, so $\log_x 1 = 0$.) Another point we can use is (4, 2). This is represented by the green point. (Remember, $x^2 = x$, so $\log_x x = 2$.)

Translate up or down by adding or subtracting a constant to the function's output. For example, $g(x) = 5 + \log_2 x$ has a positive constant of 5 added to the function, which translates the graph up. The points (1, 0) and (4, 2) have been translated and are (1, 5) and (4, 7).

Translate left or right by adding or subtracting from the input of the function. For example, $h(x) = \log_2 (x + 3)$ has 3 added to the input of the function. As expected, the graph is translated horizontally; it is shifted to the left 3.

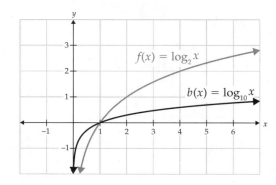

The choice of the base determines the precise shape of the parent graph. For example, compare $f(x) = \log_2 x$ to $b(x) = \log_{10} x$. As the base becomes greater, the graph is less steeply curved than the parent function.

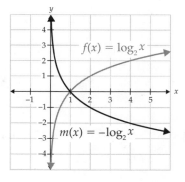

We can note that other transformations are true for logarithms as for other functions. For example, the graph of $m(x) = -\log_2 x$ is a reflection over the x-axis of the graph of the parent function $f(x) = \log_2 x$. Multiplying the parent function by a -1 creates a reflection. If the base is less than 1, then the graph of the function will also have the characteristics of a negative log function graph. For example, the graphs of $-\log_2 x$ and $\log_{0.5} x$ are identical.

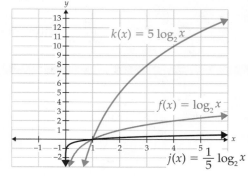

If the coefficient of the function is greater than 1, such as $k(x) = 5 \log_2 x$, the function vertically stretches compared to the parent function. If the coefficient of the function is less than 1 but greater than 0, such as $j(x) = \frac{1}{5} \log_2 x$, the function vertically shrinks compared to the parent function.

Using the parent function $f(x) = \log_4 x$, graph $g(x) = 5 + \log_4 (x - 3)$.

SOLUTION

Create table

$f(x) = \log_4 x$	(x, y)	$(1, 0)$	$(4, 1)$	$(16, 2)$
$g(x) = 5 + \log_4 (x - 3)$	$(x + 3, y + 5)$	$(4, 5)$	$(7, 6)$	$(19, 7)$

Create a table of values that satisfies the parent function, $f(x)$, and the new function, $g(x)$. Using properties of logarithms you can identify simple points for the graph of $f(x)$, $(1, 0)$ and $(4, 1)$, and the corresponding translated points, $(4, 5)$ and $(7, 6)$. You also know that $4^2 = 16$, so $(16, 2)$ is a point on the $f(x)$ graph, with corresponding translated point $(19, 7)$.

Compare functions

The new function $g(x) = 5 + \log_4 (x - 3)$ has the same shape as the parent function. It's simply translated. The $(x - 3)$ part of the function indicates that the graph of the function moves 3 units to the right. The constant of 5 moves the function 5 units vertically.

Consider domain

Before plotting the points on a graph, the domain of the translated function must be considered. $(x - 3)$ can only be a positive value. Setting $x - 3 > 0$ and solving finds that $x > 3$. If $x > 3$, then the graph of $g(x)$ approaches the vertical line $x = 3$.

Graph

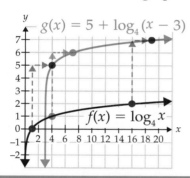

Plot the points $(4, 5)$, $(7, 6)$, and $(19, 7)$ and sketch a logarithmic curve approaching the vertical line $x = 3$. Both the translated function and the parent function are shown on the graph. Note the translation is shown by the arrows.

PRACTICE

1. Which is true about the graph of $y = \log_5 (x - 2)$? Choose all that apply.

A. The graph is 2 units left of $y = \log_5 x$.
B. The graph is 2 units right of $y = \log_5 x$.
C. The graph is 5 units left of $y = \log_2 x$.
D. The graph is 2 units down from $y = \log_5 x$.
E. The graph has the same shape as $y = \log_5 x$.
F. The graph is a steeper curve than $y = \log_5 x$.

Exercises 2–5: Graph.

2. $f(x) = \log_3 x$

3. $f(x) = \log_{1.5} x$

4. $f(x) = \log_4 x$ and $g(x) = 4^x$

5. $f(x) = \log_{0.5} x$ and $g(x) = 0.5^x$

6. Describe the difference between the graphs of $y = \log x$ and $y = 5 + \log x$ using a translation.

7. Describe the difference between $y = \log_2 x$ and $y = \log_2 (x + 5)$ using a translation.

8. Describe the translations that change the graph of $y = \log_3 x$ into the graph of $y = \log_3 (x + 1) - 9$.

9. Describe the translations that change the graph of $y = 2 \log_6 x$ into the graph of $y = 2 \log_6 (x - 3) + 2$.

10. How are the graphs of $y = \log_7 x$ and $y = \log_7 (x + 10) - 4$ similar?

Practice Problems continue . . .

Exercises 11–13: The graph of the parent function, $y = \log x$, is shown below. Graph each given function. Describe the transformations necessary to return from each given function to the parent function.

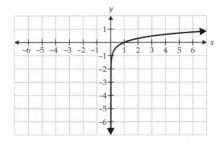

11. $f(x) = 4 + \log (x + 3)$

12. $f(x) = -\log x$

13. $f(x) = 4 - \log (x + 3)$

14. Give three integer coordinate points that are on the graph of $f(x) = 2 \log_4 (x - 3)$. Then sketch the graph.

15. Use the given values of x to find points that are on the graph of $y = \log_2 x$. Then translate the points to find integer coordinates of points on the graph of $y = \log_2 (x + 6) - 1$. Two points have been completed for you, as well as x-values for $y = \log_2 x$.

Points on $y = \log_2 x$	Points on $y = \log_2 (x + 6) - 1$
(1, 0)	
(2,	
(4,	(−2, 1)
(8,	
(16,	
(32,	

16. Based on the number of times their graphs intersect, how many solutions exist to the system of equations consisting of $y = 5 + \log x$ and $y = 2^x$?

17. How many solutions exist for the systems of equations $y = 4 + \log x$ and $y = |x - 5|$?

18. State the coordinate points that are solutions to the system $y = 4 + \log x$ and $y = |x - 5|$.

19. The graphs of the functions $y = 5 \log x$ and $y = (x - 3)^2$ intersect between $4.5 < x < 5$. Use iteration to find the x-coordinate of their point of intersection, to the nearest hundredth.

20. **MP 3, 7** Explain how the graph of $y = \log_3 x$ could be obtained from the graph of the function $y = 3^x$.

21. The graph shown below describes an exponential function. If it is reflected across the line $y = x$, what function is described by the resulting graph?

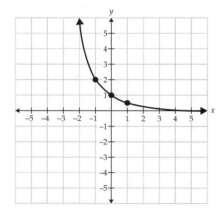

Exercises 22–24: For which values of x is each statement true? Explain your reasoning.

22. $\log_{11} x < \log_{11} 2x$

23. $\log_{0.25} x > \log_{0.25} \dfrac{x}{2}$

24. $\log_x 5 < \log_x 6$

25. Can the point (125, 5) belong to the graph of $f(x) = \log_5 x$? Explain.

26. Marvin starts with the graph of $y = \log (x + 8) + 3$ and wants to draw the graph of $y = \log x$. Describe the two translations Marvin can perform on the graph of $y = \log (x + 8) + 3$ to create the graph of $y = \log (x)$.

27. Describe the differences and similarities between $f(x) = 5 \log_7 x$ and $g(x) = \log_7 x$.

28. **MP 3** Shaya graphed the function $y = \log (x - 3) + 3$ by translating the graph of $y = \log x$. She moved the parent function left 3 units and up 3 units to find her new graph of $y = \log (x - 3) + 3$. Is Shaya correct? If so, sketch the graph. If not, explain why and sketch the correct graph.

Practice Problems continue . . .

29. MP 6 Consider the table of values for the function $y = \log_3 (x)$. In order to graph $y = \log_3 (x) + 4$, a student made the second table of values. Will the second table correctly graph the new function? Explain.

$$y = \log_3 (x)$$

x	y
1	0
3	1
9	2
27	3

$$y = \log_3 (x) + 4$$

x	y
5	4
7	5
13	6
31	7

30. Consider the graphs of $f(x) = 17 \log x$ and $g(x) = -17 \log x$. Tara says that the graph $f(x)$ is the graph of $g(x)$ shifted 17 units vertically. Is Tara correct? Explain.

31. MP 8 Describe the transformations required to graph each function. For example, what is needed to transform y_1 to y_2, y_2 to y_3, etc.?

$y_1 = \log x$
$y_2 = 3 \log x$
$y_3 = -3 \log x$
$y_4 = -3 \log (x + 4)$
$y_5 = -3 \log (x + 4) - 1$

32. MP 2, 7 When $a > 1$ and $N > 1$, which expression is greater, $\log_a N$ or $\log_a \dfrac{1}{N}$?

When $a < 1$ and $N > 1$? Justify your answer.

LESSON 7.3

7.3 Natural Logarithms and e

A **natural logarithm** has a base of **e**. The number e is an *irrational constant*, which is a number that repeats without a pattern, like π. The first digits of e are 2.718281828459. Some important equations in science, mathematics, and economics are stated using logarithmic or exponential functions with a base of e.

A logarithm with base e, such as $\log_e 7$, is called a *natural logarithm*. A natural logarithm is written as "ln," as in "ln 7." This is equivalent to $\log_e 7$. Some calculators have a key labeled "ln" that calculates the natural logarithm. If you evaluate ln 7, you will see that the first digits of ln 7 are 1.9459.

> The rules of logarithms apply to logarithms with base e.

The constant e can be calculated using the function below:

We evaluate and compare the values when $n = 1$ and $n = 10{,}000$. When $n = 1$, the value of the function equals 2.

When we increase the value of n to a large number like 10,000, the result is close to e; the first three digits to the right of the decimal are the same as e. If we used an even larger number, like 10 million, we would get even closer. As n gets larger (and approaches infinity), the value of the function becomes closer and closer to e.

Evaluate function for $n = 1$	$f(n) = \left(1 + \dfrac{1}{n}\right)^n$ $f(1) = \left(1 + \dfrac{1}{1}\right)^1$ $f(1) = 2$
Evaluate function for $n = 10{,}000$	$f(10{,}000) = \left(1 + \dfrac{1}{10{,}000}\right)^{10{,}000}$ $f(10{,}000) = 1.0001^{10{,}000}$ $f(10{,}000) = 2.718145936$

MODEL PROBLEMS

1. Restate $\log_2 x = 5$ and $\ln x = 5$ as exponential equations.

SOLUTION

$\log_2 x = 5 \qquad x = 2^5 \qquad$ If $\log_2 x = 5$, then $x = 2^5$. (This is just a reminder of the general definition of logarithms before you practice with natural logarithms.)

$\ln x = 5 \qquad x = e^5 \qquad$ If $\ln x = 5$, then $x = e^5$.

2. Restate $4^x = 9$ and $e^x = 9$ as logarithmic equations.

SOLUTION

$4^x = 9 \qquad \log_4 9 = x \qquad$ If $4^x = 9$, then $\log_4 9 = x$.

$e^x = 9 \qquad \ln 9 = x \qquad$ If $e^x = 9$, then $\ln 9 = x$.

3. Solve $\ln y = 9$ for y.

SOLUTION

$\ln y = 9 \qquad\qquad y = e^9 \qquad$ If $\ln y = 9$, then $y = e^9$.

> We can never get exact solutions for y, because e is an irrational number.

4. Solve $\ln \dfrac{1}{y} = 5$ for y.

SOLUTION

$\ln \dfrac{1}{y} = 5 \qquad \dfrac{1}{y} = e^5$

$\qquad\qquad\qquad y = \dfrac{1}{e^5} = e^{-5} \qquad$ Write the natural logarithm in exponential form. If $\ln \dfrac{1}{y} = 5$, then $\dfrac{1}{y} = e^5$. Then solve for y.

---

2. **MP 2, 4** The interest on savings at a bank can be calculated by stating that the interest is compounded at certain regular intervals, such as 12 times a year (once a month). But there is also *continuously compounded interest*, in which banks, in essence, compound the interest every moment. With this type of interest, you can use the formula $f(t) = Pe^{rt}$. This formula calculates how much money there will be if P dollars are deposited for t years with an annual interest rate of r.

> Like other positive numbers, the number e can be raised to a power and graphed. A function of form $f(x) = ae^{rx}$, is called a **natural base exponential function**.

$10,000 is deposited in a bank account with an annual interest rate of 10%. The interest is compounded continuously. How much money will there be in the account after 25 years? Assume no money is withdrawn (removed) from the account. Compare to compounding interest yearly and monthly after 25 years.

SOLUTION

Substitute and evaluate

$f(t) = Pe^{rt}$

$f(25) = (10,000)(e^{(0.10)(25)})$

$f(25) = \$121,824.94$

Substitute 10,000 for the original deposit, 0.10 for the 10 percent interest, and 25 for number of years. After 25 years, there will be $121,824.94 in the bank account.

Model Problems continue . . .

Compare to compounding the interest yearly and monthly	$f(25) = (10,000)(1 + 0.10)^{25}$ $f(25) = \$108,347.06$ $f(25) = (10,000)\left(1 + \dfrac{0.10}{12}\right)^{(12 \cdot 25)}$ $f(25) = \$120,569.45$	If the interest were compounded just once a year, then our calculations show about \$13,500 less interest would be earned. On the other hand, if the interest were compounded once a month, the difference would only be about \$1250.

PRACTICE

1. The graph below is most likely to be the graph of which function?

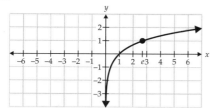

   A. $y = e^x$ C. $y = e^{2x}$

   B. $y = e^{-x}$ D. $y = \ln x$

2. What is the x-intercept of the function $y = \ln (2x + 1) - \ln (x + 2)$?

   A. -2 C. 1

   B. -1 D.   The function doesn't have an x-intercept.

Exercises 3–7: Evaluate.

3. $\ln e$

4. $\ln e^2$

5. $\ln \dfrac{1}{e}$

6. $\ln \dfrac{1}{\sqrt{e}}$

7. $\ln \dfrac{1}{\sqrt[3]{e}}$

Exercises 8–10: Restate the following as exponential equations.

8. $\ln x = 17$

9. $\ln z = 4.5$

10. $\ln z = 0.5$

Exercises 11–13: Restate each equation as a logarithmic equation.

11. $e^6 = k$

12. $e^3 = a$

13. $e^b = 7$

14. Graph the function $y = e^x$ and the line $y = x + 1$ on the same coordinate grid.

15. Graph the function $y = \ln x$ and the line $y = x - 1$ on the same coordinate grid.

16. a Fill in the table for given values of x.

x	1	3	5	10	50	100	1000
e^x							
x^{10}							
$\ln x$							

   b Which function increases fastest for small values of x? for large values of x?

   c Which function shows the slowest growth?

17. If you deposited \$2000, withdrew no money, and earned a 3% continuously compounded annual interest for 10 years, how much money would you have in the account? You made no other deposits.

18. If you deposited \$5000, withdrew no money, and earned a 2% continuously compounded annual interest for 1 year, how much money would you have in the account?

19. If you deposited \$1000, withdrew no money, and earned a 2.5% continuously compounded annual interest for 2 years and 6 months, how much money would you have in the account?

20. Recall that the function $h(x)$ is called *even* if $h(x) = h(-x)$, and *odd* if $h(-x) = -h(x)$. If $f(x) = \dfrac{e^x - e^{-x}}{2}$ and $g(x) = \dfrac{e^x + e^{-x}}{2}$, is each of the functions $f(x)$ and $g(x)$ even or odd? Explain.

7.4 Laws of Logarithms

Logarithmic Identities

The identities $\log_b b^x = x$ and $b^{\log_b x} = x$ are useful to know when working with logarithms. These identities follow from the fact that the exponential and logarithmic functions are inverses.

MODEL PROBLEMS

1. Evaluate $\log_{10} 10^5$.

SOLUTION

Evaluate $\log_{10} 10^5 = 5$ Following the identity, $\log_{10} 10^5$ equals 5.

2. Evaluate $3^{\log_3 7}$.

SOLUTION

Evaluate $3^{\log_3 7} = 7$ Raising 3 to the power $\log_3 7$ results in 7, the argument of the logarithm.

3. Evaluate $\log_7 1$.

SOLUTION

Evaluate $\log_7 1 = 0$ For example, $\log_7 1 = 0$, because $7^0 = 1$.

> The base b logarithm of 1 is 0: $\log_b 1 = 0$. Why? Because any base other than zero raised to the power 0 equals 1.

4. Evaluate $\log_4 4$.

SOLUTION

Evaluate $\log_4 4 = 1$ For example, $\log_4 4 = 1$ because $4^1 = 4$.

> The base b logarithm of b is 1: $\log_b b = 1$. This is because any number raised to the power 1 equals itself.

Logarithmic Equations

The equation $\log_b x = \log_b y$ is true if and only if $x = y$. As long as x and y are positive, these are equivalent equations.

MODEL PROBLEMS

1. Solve $\log_5 2x = \log_5 10$.

SOLUTION

$\log_b x = \log_b y$ and $x = y$ are equivalent	$2x = 10$	Since the bases of the logarithms are equal, we can write the equation shown on the left.
Solve	$x = 5$	Solve the equation.

2. Solve $\log_3 (x^2 - 3) = \log_3 2x$.

SOLUTION

$\log_b x = \log_b y$ and $x = y$ are equivalent	$x^2 - 3 = 2x$	Since the bases are the same, we can set the arguments of the logarithms equal to each other.
Solve	$x^2 - 2x - 3 = 0$ $(x - 3)(x + 1) = 0$ $x = 3 \; \textbf{or} \; x = -1$	Solve the resulting quadratic equation. There are two solutions, 3 and -1.
Check solutions in original equation	$\log_3 (3^2 - 3) \stackrel{?}{=} \log_3 (2 \cdot 3)$ $\log_3 6 = \log_3 6$	Check the potential solutions in the original equation. For $x = 3$, the equation is true, with $\log_3 6$ on each side.
	$\log_3 ((-1)^2 - 3) \stackrel{?}{=} \log_3 2(-1)$ $\log_3 -2 \stackrel{?}{=} \log_3 -2$	For $x = -1$, the tentative equation has $\log_3 -2$ on each side. Since the logarithm of a negative number is not defined, the equation cannot be confirmed so -1 is not a solution to the original equation.
State solution	$x = 3$	State the solution to the original equation, which is $x = 3$.

> When solving an equation involving logarithms, check potential solutions to make sure the logarithms are defined. We want to make sure we know which solutions are extraneous.

3. Solve $\log_5 (x - 2) = 3$.

SOLUTION

Write the equation in its exponential form	$5^3 = x - 2$	Since 5 is the base of the logarithm, then 5 is the base of the exponential equation.
Solve the equation	$125 = x - 2$ $x = 127$	Solve the equation to find that $x = 127$.
Check the solution	$\log_5 (127 - 2) = 3$ $\log_5 (125) = 3$	Check the solution in the original equation to see that $x = 127$ is not extraneous.

PRACTICE

1. Which statement(s) about logarithms is incorrect?

   A. $\log_c c$ is equal to 1.
   B. $\log_m 1$ is equal to 1.
   C. The solution to $\log_k 1 = 0$ is any positive number.
   D. In the equation $\log_w x = 1$, $w = x$.

2. **MP 2, 7** If $\log_2 (\sqrt{b^4}) = 2a$ then

   A. $b^2 = 2^a$
   B. $2^a = b$
   C. $b^2 = 2a$
   D. $2a = b$

Exercises 3–17: Evaluate.

3. $7^{\log_7 5}$

4. $8^{\log_8 2}$

5. $5^{\log_5 7}$

6. $15^{\log_{15} 25}$

7. $6^{\log_6 456}$

8. $x^{\log_x \sqrt{2}}$

9. $\log_2 \sqrt[3]{2}$

10. $\log_2 2\sqrt{2}$

11. $\log_5 5^3$

12. $\log_{12} 12^4$

13. $\log_z z^8$

14. $\log_2 32^n$

15. $\log_{11} 1$

16. $\log 100$

17. $\log 0.01$

18. If $\log_b x = 3$, what is $\log_b \dfrac{1}{x}$?

19. If $\log_b x = 3$, what is $\log_{\frac{1}{b}} x$?

Exercises 20–31: Solve.

20. $\log_x 1024 = 5$

21. $\log_x 1296 = 4$

22. $\log_4 x = 1.5$

23. $\log_{27} x = \dfrac{2}{3}$

24. $\log_7 (2x + 3) = 2$

25. $\log_2 (5x - 14) = 4$

26. $\log_2 (x^2 + 2x) = \log_2 (x + 2)$

27. $\log_8 (1 - x^2) = \log_8 (x^2 + x)$

28. $\log_5 (x^2 - 7x + 37) = 2$

29. $\log_a \left(64 \sqrt[4]{2^{x^2 - 12x}} \right) = 0$

30. $4^{\left(\frac{1}{\log_{125} x} \right)} = \dfrac{1}{64}$

31. $\log_{10} \sqrt{75 + 5\sqrt{x + 1}} = 1$

32. **MP 1, 5** Solve $4 - \log_{17} x = 3\sqrt{\log_{17} x}$; Hint: Let $\sqrt{\log_{17} x} = t$, then solve a quadratic equation for t.

33. **MP 2, 3** Martha says that a logarithmic equation can have only one extraneous solution. Is this a correct statement? Explain. Hint: Consider that extraneous solutions can occur because logarithms are only defined for positive arguments.

34. Solve the inequality $\ln (2x - 3) < 1$. Leave your answer in terms of e.

Logarithms of Products

The **product rule for logarithms** states that the logarithm of a product of numbers equals the sum of the logarithms of the factors. To state this as an equation:

$$\log_b MN = \log_b M + \log_b N$$

M, N, and b must be greater than 0, and b cannot equal 1.

> The product rule can let you calculate the sum of two logarithms. The logarithms must have the same base.

MODEL PROBLEMS

1. a Calculate the value of $\log_2 (4 \cdot 8)$ using the product rule for logarithms.

b Check by evaluating the logarithm of the product directly and comparing the results.

SOLUTION

a Apply product rule for logarithms

$\log_2 (4 \cdot 8) = \log_2 4 + \log_2 8$

The product rule says to add the logarithms of the two numbers that are being multiplied in the argument.

Evaluate

$\log_2 (4 \cdot 8) = 2 + 3$

$\log_2 (4 \cdot 8) = 5$

Evaluate the logarithms. The first equals 2 since $2^2 = 4$, and the second equals 3, since $2^3 = 8$.

b Check

$\log_2 (4 \cdot 8) = ?$

Whether we use the rule or multiply first, we should get the same results. We check this conclusion.

Multiply

$\log_2 (4 \cdot 8)$

$\log_2 32$

Now, multiply first. The product of 4 and 8 is 32.

Evaluate logarithm

$\log_2 32 = 5$

Since $2^5 = 32$, $\log_2 32 = 5$. This agrees with the result we got using the product rule.

2. Use the product rule to evaluate $\log_6 4 + \log_6 9$.

SOLUTION

Apply product rule for logarithms

$\log_6 4 + \log_6 9$

$\log_6 (4 \cdot 9)$

If two logarithms with the same base are added, their arguments can be multiplied.

$\log_6 36$

Multiply, and get the base 6 logarithm of 36. Using the product rule results in a number that is a power of 6.

Evaluate logarithm

$\log_6 36 = 2$

Since $6^2 = 36$, $\log_6 36 = 2$.

Logarithms of Quotients

The **quotient rule for logarithms** states that the logarithm of the quotient of two numbers equals the difference of the logarithms of those numbers. To state it as an equation:

$$\log_b \frac{M}{N} = \log_b M - \log_b N$$

M, N, and b must be greater than 0, and b cannot equal 1.

MODEL PROBLEMS

1. a Calculate the base 3 logarithm of the quotient of 81 and 3 using the quotient rule for logarithms.
   b Check by evaluating the logarithm of the quotient directly and comparing the results.

SOLUTION

a Apply quotient rule for logarithms

$$\log_3 \frac{81}{3} = \log_3 81 - \log_3 3$$

The quotient rule says that to calculate the logarithm of the quotient, we subtract.

Evaluate logs

$$\log_3 \frac{81}{3} = 4 - 1$$

$$\log_3 \frac{81}{3} = 3$$

The first logarithm equals 4 since $3^4 = 81$, and the second equals 1, since $3^1 = 1$.

b Check

$$\log_3 \frac{81}{3} = ?$$

Whether we use the rule or divide first, we should get the same results. We check this.

Divide

$$\log_3 \frac{81}{3}$$

$$\log_3 27$$

We divide first: 81 divided by 3 equals 27.

Evaluate logarithm

$$\log_3 27 = 3$$

Since $3^3 = 27$, $\log_3 27 = 3$. This agrees with the result we got using the quotient rule.

2. Use the quotient rule to evaluate $\log_3 72 - \log_3 8$.

SOLUTION

Apply quotient rule for logarithms

$$\log_3 72 - \log_3 8 = \log_3 \frac{72}{8}$$

If two logarithms with the same base are subtracted, their arguments can be divided.

Divide

$$\log_3 9$$

Now divide and get the base 3 logarithm of 9. Using the quotient rule results in a number that is a power of 3.

Evaluate logarithm

$$\log_3 9 = 2$$

Since $3^2 = 9$, $\log_3 9 = 2$.

Logarithms of Powers

Another tool in evaluating logarithms is the **power rule for logarithms**. It states that the logarithm of a power of M can be calculated as the product of the exponent and the logarithm of M. To state it as an equation:

$$\log_b M^p = p \cdot \log_b M$$

M and b must be greater than 0, and b cannot equal 1.

> To evaluate the logarithm of a number M raised to a power, you can multiply the logarithm of M by the exponent.

MODEL PROBLEM

Use the power rule for logarithms to calculate $\log_2 8^{16}$.

SOLUTION

Apply power rule for logarithms

$\log_2 8^{16}$

$16 \cdot \log_2 8$

The power rule says to take the exponent and multiply it by the logarithm of its base. The exponent is 16, so multiply that by $\log_2 8$.

Evaluate the logarithm and multiply

$16 \cdot 2^3$

$16 \cdot 3 = 48$

Since 2^3 equals 8, $\log_2 8$ equals 3. Multiply 16 by 3 to get 48, so $\log_2 8^{16} = 48$.

Change-of-Base Formula

The **change-of-base formula** allows you to write a logarithm with one base as a logarithmic expression with a different base. The logarithm of the "old" base is in the denominator, and the logarithm of the argument is in the numerator. Use the change-of-base formula when you do not know how to calculate a log directly. You can change the base of logarithms using the following formula:

$$\log_a x = \frac{\log_b x}{\log_b a}$$

MODEL PROBLEMS

1. a Restate $\log_{16} 32$ using only base 2 logarithms and the change-of-base formula.

b Use the change of base from part **a** to evaluate $\log_{16} 32$.

SOLUTION

a Change-of-base formula

$\log_a x = \frac{\log_b x}{\log_b a}$

We want to restate the $\log_{16} 32$ as an expression using only base 2 logarithms. To do so, we will need to use the change-of-base formula. Restate the logarithm base a of x as a quotient of logarithms with base b.

Restate logarithm using change-of-base formula

$\log_{16} 32 = \frac{\log_2 32}{\log_2 16}$

To answer the question, apply the formula. Identify that $a = 16$, $b = 2$, and $x = 32$, then substitute the values into the formula. The result is an equivalent expression that uses only base 2 logarithms.

Model Problems continue . . .

b Evaluate each logarithm

$$\frac{\log_2 32}{\log_2 16} = \frac{5}{4}$$

The two base 2 logarithms can be evaluated. Since $2^5 = 32$, $\log_2 32 = 5$. And since $2^4 = 16$, $\log_2 16 = 4$. Using the change-of-base formula, $\log_{16} 32 = \frac{5}{4}$.

Check solution

$$16^{\frac{5}{4}} \stackrel{?}{=} 32$$

$$\left(\sqrt[4]{16}\right)^5 \stackrel{?}{=} 32$$

$$2^5 \stackrel{?}{=} 32$$

$$32 = 32$$

To check the answer, we can use the definition of logarithms. The power $16^{\frac{5}{4}}$ (with the original base 16) should equal 32. Evaluate the fractional exponent. It equals the fourth root of 16 to the fifth power. Evaluate the radical. The fourth root of 16 is 2, and 2^5 equals 32. Our evaluation checks.

2. **MP 5, 7** Use the change-of-base formula and a calculator to evaluate $\log_7 12$.

SOLUTION

Apply formula

$$\log_7 12 = \frac{\log_{10} 12}{\log_{10} 7}$$

We change the base to 10, because many calculators can evaluate with this base.

> Using the change-of-base formula to change the base to 10 is helpful since many calculators only evaluate the common (base 10) log. This is useful when a decimal approximation is needed.

Use calculator

$$\log_7 12 \approx \frac{1.08}{0.845} \approx 1.28$$

We use a calculator to find that $\log_{10} 12 \approx 1.08$ and $\log_{10} 7 \approx 0.845$. We then divide.

Summary of Logarithm Rules

The rules for logarithms work for any base. This includes e, so the rules apply for natural logarithms too.

Product rule	$\log_b MN = \log_b M + \log_b N$
Quotient rule	$\log_b \dfrac{M}{N} = \log_b M - \log_b N$
Power rule	$\log_b M^p = p \cdot \log_b M$
Change-of-base formula	$\log_a x = \dfrac{\log_b x}{\log_b a}$

PRACTICE

1. $\log_{12} 72 + \log_{12} 2 =$

A. 2

B. 144

C. $\log_{12} 36$

D. $\log_{12} 74$

2. $\log_3 27^5 =$

A. 8

B. $\dfrac{3}{5}$

C. 35

D. 15

Practice Problems continue . . .

3. Donald is simplifying the expression

$$y = \frac{\log_3 81}{\log_3 27}:$$

Step 1: $y = \log_3 81 - \log_3 27$
Step 2: $y = \log_3 81 - 3$
Step 3: $y = 4 - 3$
Step 4: $y = 1$

Which is the first incorrect step in his work?

A. Step 1   C. Step 3
B. Step 2   D. Step 4

Exercises 4–5: State as a sum of logarithms. There may be more than one correct answer.

4. $\log_2 15$

5. $\log_7 56$

Exercises 6–10: State as a single logarithm.

6. $\log_4 11 + \log_4 2$

7. $\log_2 5 + \log_2 4$

8. $\log_b 4 + \log_b 5$

9. $\log_b 3 + \log_b 6$

10. $\log_5 m + \log_5 n$

Exercises 11–14: State as a difference of logarithms.

11. $\log_4 \dfrac{9}{5}$

12. $\log_3 \dfrac{8}{7}$

13. $\log_b \dfrac{17}{3}$

14. $\log_4 \dfrac{1}{12}$

Exercises 15–18: State as a single logarithm.

15. $\log_2 5 - \log_2 7$

16. $\log_5 2 - \log_5 13$

17. $\log_5 40 - \log_5 4$

18. $\log_{16} 3 - \log_{16} 2$

Exercises 19–20: Express as a single logarithm with an integer argument.

19. $\log_7 4 + \log_7 6 - \log_7 8$

20. $\log_5 15 - \log_5 3 + \log_5 4$

21. Express $\log_2 y^4$ in terms of $\log_2 y$.

22. Express $\log_3 x^3$ in terms of $\log_3 x$.

Exercises 23–26: State the logs without a power.

23. $\log_b y^5$

24. $\log_4 6^5$

25. $\log_7 8^9$

26. $\log_5 p^9$

Exercises 27–32: Evaluate. Round to three decimal places, if needed.

27. $\log_3 8$

28. $\log_7 4$

29. $\log_8 4 + \log_8 16$

30. $\log_2 2 + \log_2 16$

31. $\log_5 500 - \log_5 4$

32. $\log_2 1 - \log_2 8$

Exercises 33–36: State as a single natural logarithm.

33. $\ln 5 + \ln 3$

34. $\ln 18 - \ln 12$

35. $2 \ln x - 2 + \ln 3$

36. $4 \ln y + \ln 7 - 1$

37. MP 1, 2 A logarithm in base 3 of a product of two consecutive numbers is one more than the logarithm of 10 in base 3. Find the smaller of the numbers.

38. MP 1, 7 A right triangle has legs a and b, and its hypotenuse is c. Show that $\log_a (c - b) + \log_a (c + b) = 2$.

39. Show that $\dfrac{\log_a b}{\log_{ax} b} = 1 + \log_a x$.

40. MP 2, 8 Show that

$$\frac{1}{\log_a b} + \frac{1}{\log_{a^2} b} + \frac{1}{\log_{a^3} b} + \frac{1}{\log_{a^4} b} = 10 \log_b a.$$

41. Simplify the expression: $a^{\frac{\log_b (\log_b a)}{\log_b a}}$

42. If $\log_6 2 = a$ and $\log_6 5 = b$, find $\log_3 5$.

43. Solve: $x^{\frac{1}{\log_5 x}} = 5^{x^4}$ (Hint: Use change-of-base formula. If there are no solutions, state this.)

44. Solve: $x^{(\log_{10} x) - 2} = 1000$ (Hint: Take $\log_x$ of both sides and use change-of-base formula. If there are no solutions, state this.)

45. MP 3, 7 Which is greater: $\log_{\frac{1}{3}} 2$ or $\log_3 \dfrac{1}{2}$? Justify your answer.

Solving Exponential Equations

Exponential equations can be solved by taking the logarithms of both sides of the equation to create an equivalent equation. You can take the logarithm of both sides using any base.

MODEL PROBLEMS

1. Solve $3^x = 20$ using logarithms.

SOLUTION

Take logarithm base 10 of both sides	$\log_{10} 3^x = \log_{10} 20$	Take the logarithm of both sides. We are using common logarithms with base 10.
Power rule	$x \log_{10} 3 = \log_{10} 20$	Use the power rule to restate the logarithm on the left without any exponent.
Solve for x	$x = \dfrac{\log_{10} 20}{\log_{10} 3}$	Solve for x.
Evaluate	$x \approx \dfrac{1.3010}{0.4771} \approx 2.7268$	Evaluate the common logarithms using a calculator and state the answer to the nearest ten-thousandth.

2. Solve $3^{2x-2} = 81$.

SOLUTION

Take logarithm base 3 of both sides	$\log_3 3^{2x-2} = \log_3 81$	Take the logarithm base 3 of both sides.
Use logarithmic identity, evaluate	$2x - 2 = 4$	Use the logarithmic identity $\log_b b^x = x$ on the left and evaluate the logarithm on the right.
Solve for x	$2x = 6$ $x = 3$	Solve for x.

> There is another way to solve model problem 2. The equations $b^x = b^y$ and $x = y$ are equivalent equations. All values for x and y that make the one equation true also make the other one true.

3. Solve $3^{2x-2} = 81$ using the identity $b^x = b^y$ and $x = y$ are equivalent.

SOLUTION

Restate right side with exponent	$3^{2x-2} = 3^4$	Restate the right side of the equation as a power of 3.
$b^x = b^y$ and $x = y$ are equivalent	$2x - 2 = 4$	State the equation as an equivalent equation without exponents.
Solve for x	$x = 3$	Solve for x.

PRACTICE

Exercises 1–15: Solve. If there is no solution, say so.

1. $a^{2x+2} = a^2$

2. $a^{3x+3} = a^3$

3. $a^{5x+5} = a^5$

4. $a^{x-2} = a^{2x-6}$

5. $2^{2x+2} = 4^{3x-1}$

6. $4^{4x+4} = 16^{5x-1}$

7. $2^{3x+3} = 4^{4x-1}$

8. $9^{x+1} = 27^{x-2}$

9. $2^{7x-16} = 32$

10. $3^{-4x+19} = 27$

11. $6^x = 19$

12. MP 1, 2 $e^{2x^3} = 8$

13. $3 = e^{x-4}$

14. $5^{(2^x)} = 625$

15. $3^{(9^x)} = 27$

LESSON 7.5

7.5 Modeling with Logarithms

Spreadsheet and Graphing Calculator: Modeling Logarithmic Functions

The sound level provides a scale that relates how humans perceive sound to a physical measure of its power. *Sound intensity* is a measure of how much power a sound transmits. An intensity of approximately 10^{-12} W/m^2 (watts per square meter) is the minimum perceptible by the human ear, and is represented by I_0. The *sound level* is logarithmically related to the intensity, and is measured in units called *decibels* (dB). The equation relating sound intensity and sound level is $\beta = (10 \text{ dB}) \log \frac{I}{I_0}$,

Intensity	Sound Level
0.1	110
1	120
2	123.01
3	124.77
10	130
20	133.01

where β (beta), in decibels, is the sound level and I is the sound intensity. We use a *logarithmic regression* to model this data, where y represents the sound level and x represents the intensity.

Spreadsheet

In a spreadsheet, start by entering the data and creating a scatter plot. Make sure the chart is selected, and then choose **Add Trendline** from the **Chart** menu. To do a logarithmic regression, choose the **Logarithmic** option under **Trend/Regression type**. You can add the model equation and the coefficient of determination r^2 using the **Options** tab. The equation in the spreadsheet has the form $y = a + b \ln x$.

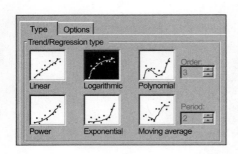

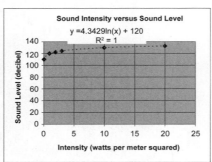

Logarithmic regressions produce an equation of the form $y = a + b \ln x$. In a subsequent model problem you will see this equation written in another equivalent form using "log" instead of "ln."

Graphing Calculator

With a graphing calculator, start by entering the data and creating a scatter plot. Then, choose logarithmic regression. To do this, press [STAT] and then scroll right to the **CALC** menu. Scroll down to **9:LnReg** and press [ENTER] to set up the **LnReg** command. Then enter the parameters and do the regression as for linear regression. The calculator displays the results as shown. This is an equation of the form $y = a + b \ln x$.

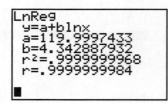

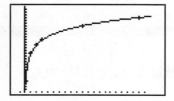

MODEL PROBLEMS

1. **MP 2, 4** When an amount of money P is invested in an account that pays interest at rate r, compounded annually, the accumulated amount in the account after t years is given by the function $A(t) = P(1 + r)^t$. If $5000 is invested in an account paying 8% interest compounded annually, how many years will it take for the account to be worth $100,000?

   a   Set up the problem.
   b   Solve the equation from part **a**.

SOLUTION

a   Choose variable $t =$ number of years   We are asked for the number of years it takes for the amount in the account to reach $100,000. We represent this time with t.

    Substitute $A(t) = P(1 + r)^t$ State the function, and substitute the stated values. Next, we will solve the equation.

$$100,000 = 5000(1 + 0.08)^t$$

Model Problems continue . . .

b Add inside parentheses $100,000 = 5000(1.08)^t$ Solve the equation stated in part **a**. We start by adding 1 and 0.08.

Divide by 5000 $20 = 1.08^t$ Divide both sides of the equation by 5000.

Take common logarithm of both sides
$$\log 20 = \log 1.08^t$$
$$\log 20 = t \cdot \log 1.08$$
Take the common logarithm of both sides. Then use the power rule.

Solve
$$t = \frac{\log 20}{\log 1.08}$$

$$t \approx \frac{1.3010}{0.0334}$$

$$t \approx 38.9 \text{ years}$$

Solve for t. Use a calculator to evaluate the logarithms and find that $t = 38.9$ years. If you invested \$5000 at 8% interest compounded annually at age 21 and paid no taxes or other withdrawals, by the time you are 60 you would have \$100,000.

 2. **MP 2, 4** The value of an exponential function of time will always double in the same amount of time. For example, if bacteria double from 10 to 20 bacteria in the first 5 minutes, they will double from 20 to 40 in the next 5 minutes, and double again from 40 to 80 in the next 5 minutes, and so on.

A colony of bacteria can show exponential growth under ideal conditions. The equation for the number of bacteria in a colony after t minutes is given by the function $N(t) = N_0 10^{0.015t}$, where N_0 is the initial number of bacteria. How long will it take the number of bacteria to double?

SOLUTION

Write equation $N(t) = N_0 10^{0.015t}$ Write the equation that represents the number of bacteria.

Substitute
$$2N_0 = N_0 10^{0.015t}$$
$$2 = 10^{0.015t}$$
We want to know how long it takes for N_0 bacteria to double. Substitute $2N_0$ into the equation and divide by N_0.

Take common logarithm
$$\log 2 = \log 10^{0.015t}$$
$$\log 2 = 0.015t$$
Take the common logarithm of both sides, and then use an identity to simplify the right side.

Solve
$$t = \frac{\log 2}{0.015}$$

$$t \approx \frac{0.3010}{0.015}$$

$$t \approx 20.07 \text{ minutes}$$

Solve for t, evaluate the logarithm of 2 and divide the answer by 0.015. It takes approximately 20.01 minutes for the bacteria to double. The colony of bacteria doubles in size about every 20 minutes, ignoring real-world limits like food or space. At this rate, if you started with 2 bacteria, you would have more than 250,000 after about 6 hours.

Model Problems continue . . .

3. **MP 2, 4** The equation relating sound intensity and sound level is $\beta = (10\ dB) \log \dfrac{I}{I_0}$,

where β (beta), in decibels, is the sound level and I is the sound intensity. What is the intensity when the level of the sound is 75 dB?

a Set up the problem.

b Solve the equation from part **a**.

SOLUTION

a Substitute

$$\beta = (10\ dB) \log \frac{I}{I_0}$$

$$75 = (10) \log \frac{I}{10^{-12}}$$

Enter the values $\beta = 75$ dB and $I_0 = 1 \times 10^{-12}$ W/m^2 into the equation relating sound level and sound intensity.

b Quotient rule for logarithms

$$75 = 10\,[\log I - \log\,(10^{-12})]$$

On the right side of the equation is the logarithm of a quotient. Use the quotient rule to rewrite this as a difference.

Logarithmic identity

$$75 = 10\,[\log I - (-12)]$$

The common logarithm of 10^{-12} is -12.

Solve for $\log I$

$$75 = 10 \log I + 120$$

$$-45 = 10 \log I$$

$$-4.5 = \log I$$

Distribute, subtract a constant, and divide.

Convert to exponential equation and evaluate

$$10^{-4.5} = I$$

$$I \approx 3.16 \times 10^{-5}\ \text{W/m}^2$$

Convert the logarithmic equation to an exponential one. This solves the equation for I. Using a calculator, we find the intensity is about 3.16×10^{-5} watts per square meter.

Model Problems continue . . .

4. **MP 2, 4** In 2014, a deadly outbreak of the Ebola virus appeared in West Africa. The data in the table gives the number of total cases during four different months in the country of Liberia. The data was taken from www.cdc.gov.

Month, x	April	July	October	December
Number of Cases, y	13	329	6535	8018

a Plot the 4 data points on a graph, labeling the scale and axes. Let $x = 4$ represent the month of April.

b Find and interpret the rate of change between April and July. Compare that to the rate of change between October and December. Round to the nearest whole number.

c Suppose the Ebola virus later surfaces in Asia and the growth of the virus is modeled by the function $y = 10 \log (x + 1)$, where x is the number of months after January 2014 and y is the total number of cases. Sketch this function, labeling the scale and axes.

d Compare the actual growth of the Ebola virus in Liberia and the fictional outbreak in Asia.

SOLUTION

a Graph

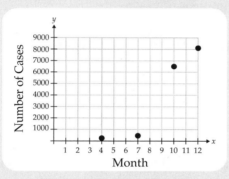

The x-axis represents the number of months after January 2014, where each mark represents 1 month. The y-axis represents the number of cases of Ebola reported in Liberia, where each mark represents 1000 cases.

b Find the rate of change from April to July

$$\frac{329 - 13}{7 - 4} = 105$$

The ratio of the change in the number of cases to the number of elapsed months gives the rate of change. From April to July, the rate of change was 105 cases per month.

Find the rate of change from October to December

$$\frac{8018 - 6535}{12 - 10} = 742$$

From October to December, the rate of change was 742 cases per month. This shows that as the year progressed, the rate of change of cases of Ebola increased dramatically.

Model Problems continue . . .

c Create table

x	1	2	10	20
y	3.01	4.77	10.41	13.22

The x-axis is the months past January 2014 and the y-axis is the total number of cases. Using the function, a table of values can be created by substituting numbers in for x in the logarithm function.

Graph

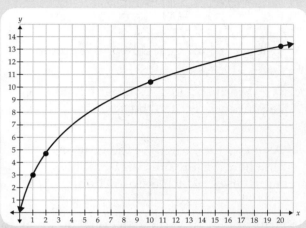

Plot the points and sketch the curve. The y-axis shows the number of cases, with each mark representing one case.

d Based on the data in the table for Liberia, the growth of the virus appears to fit an exponential growth model showing that the virus is growing very quickly. In contrast, the Asia outbreak following the logarithmic model is growing much more slowly, as seen above in the graph and the table of values.

PRACTICE

1. If you invest $150 at 7% interest compounded annually, in how many years will you have $400? Give your answer to the nearest tenth of a year.

2. If you invest $4000 at 9% interest compounded annually, in how many years will you have $20,000? Give your answer to the nearest tenth of a year.

Exercises 3–4: The formula relating sound intensity and sound level is $\beta = (10 \text{ dB}) \log \frac{I}{I_0}$, where β in decibels is the sound level, I is the sound intensity, and I_0 is approximately 10^{-12} W/m². Calculate the sound intensity in decibels.

3. Two people whispering: $I = 10^{-8}$ W/m²

4. A jet: $I = 10^4$ W/m²

5. **MP 1, 4, 6** A species is disappearing at the rate of 8% a year. To the nearest hundredth of a year, how long until only 10% of the species remains?

6. **MP 1, 4, 6** A radioactive substance decays from 1000 grams to 15.625 grams in 12 hours. What is its half-life, to the nearest minute?

7. **MP 1, 2, 4** The pH factor measures the hydrogen ion concentration in a solution and varies between 0 and 14. Values of pH in the range of 0 to 7 correspond to acidic substances, such as stomach acid, while values greater than 7 correspond to alkaline substances. Pure water has a pH of 7, which is considered neutral. If x is the effective concentration of hydrogen ions, in moles per liter, then pH $= -\log_{10} x$. The pH of human blood is about 7.4. What is the hydrogen ion concentration in human blood? You may leave your answer in exponential form.

8. **MP 2, 4, 6** The population $P(t)$ of Logarithmville is described by the equation $P(t) = 500,000e^{kt}$, where t is the time measured in years. The time $t = 0$ represents the year 2010. The population of the town in 1990 was 270,000. Use the value of k to estimate the population for the year 2020, to the nearest 10,000 people.

Practice Problems continue . . .

Practice Problems continued . . .

9. A cup of water at an initial temperature of 76°C is placed in a room at a constant temperature of 20°C. As the water cools, its temperature is described by the equation $T = 20 + 56e^{-0.037t}$, where t is the time elapsed in minutes.

  a What is the temperature of the water one half-hour after the cup was placed in the room, to the nearest degree Celsius?

  b How many minutes will it take for the water to cool off to 25°C?

10. The rule of 70 states that if you want to determine how long it will take a quantity to double, divide 70 by the interest rate expressed as an integer. Calculate how long it will take $1000 to double at a 4% interest rate using the rule. Then calculate the actual interest earned during that time if the interest is continuously compounded.

  a By how many dollars does the actual interest differ from simply doubling over this period of time?

  b Use the rules of logarithms to derive the rule of 70.

11. **MP 2, 4, 6** The speed, v, of an object moving in a resisting substance (such as water or air), when the resistance is proportional to the speed, is given by the equation $v = v_0e^{-kt}$, where v_0 is the initial speed, t is the elapsed time, in seconds, and k, in inverse seconds, is a constant that depends on the resistance of the substance and the mass of the object. v and v_0 are in meters per second.

  a A boat has an initial speed of 1.5 meters per second. In 4 seconds, its speed is 1 meter per second. Use the formula for the speed to find k, and then find the speed of the boat after 15 seconds.

  b When will the boat's speed be 1 centimeter per second? Round your answer to the nearest second.

• Multi-Part PROBLEM Practice •

MP 2, 4 Jared is tuning his piano (keyboard depicted), and his tuner reads the following frequencies for the white notes, starting with A:

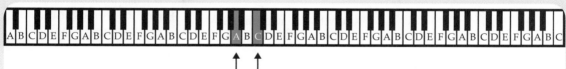

220 Hz

middle C

a Create a scatter plot of the data.

b Find an exponential regression equation to fit the data.

c Use your equation to find the notes with the following frequencies:
  (i)   1046.50 Hz
  (ii) 30.87 Hz

Note	Note # *	Frequency (Hz)
A	0	220
B	2	247
C	3	262
D	5	295
E	7	330
F	8	350
G	10	390
A	12	440

* Every key on the piano is numbered, with A below middle C arbitrarily given position zero.

7.6 More Logarithmic Operations

Breaking Up and Combining Logarithmic Expressions

We apply the rules of logarithms to logarithmic expressions with variables. We can use the rules of logarithms to combine logarithms and write them as sums and differences.

MODEL PROBLEMS

1. Express $\log_b \dfrac{x^4}{y^2 z}$ in terms of logarithms of each variable.

SOLUTION

Use quotient rule $\log_b \dfrac{x^4}{y^2 z}$

$\log_b x^4 - \log_b y^2 z$

Restate the logarithm in terms of $\log_b x$, $\log_b y$, and $\log_b z$. Use the quotient rule to restate the logarithm of the quotient as the difference of logarithms.

Use product rule $\log_b x^4 - (\log_b y^2 + \log_b z)$
$\log_b x^4 - \log_b y^2 - \log_b z$

Use the product rule to split up the variables in the logarithm on the right. Then distribute the minus sign.

Use power rule $4 \log_b x - 2 \log_b y - \log_b z$ Use the power rule to remove the exponents.

2. Express $\log_b \sqrt[3]{\dfrac{5}{z^2}}$ in terms of logarithms of each variable.

SOLUTION

Write root as exponent $\log_b \left(\dfrac{5}{z^2} \right)^{\frac{1}{3}}$

Rewrite the radical as a fractional exponent.

> We use the fact that a root can be written with a fractional exponent to rewrite the logarithmic expression.

Use power rule $\dfrac{1}{3} \log_b \left(\dfrac{5}{z^2} \right)$ Use the power rule to remove the exponent.

Use quotient rule $\dfrac{1}{3} (\log_b 5 - \log_b z^2)$ Use the quotient rule.

Use power rule $\dfrac{1}{3} (\log_b 5 - 2 \log_b z)$ And use the power rule once more to remove the exponent from z.

3. State $2 \log_b x - 4 \log_b z$ as a single logarithm.

SOLUTION

Use power rule $\log_b x^2 - \log_b z^4$ Use the power rule to remove the coefficients of the logarithms.

Use quotient rule $\log_b \dfrac{x^2}{z^4}$

The logarithms have the same base b and no coefficients. Use the quotient rule to rewrite the subtraction of logarithms as the logarithm of a quotient.

Model Problems continue . . .

4. State $\log_b \dfrac{4}{\sqrt{x}} + \log_b 2\sqrt{x}$ as a single logarithm.

SOLUTION

| Use product rule | $\log_b \dfrac{4 \cdot 2\sqrt{x}}{\sqrt{x}}$ | The logarithms have the same base b and no coefficients. Use the product rule to rewrite the addition of logarithms as the logarithm of a product. |
| Simplify | $\log_b 8$ | Simplify the argument of the logarithm. |

5. Evaluate $\log_b 6$, $\log_b \dfrac{2}{3}$, $\log_b \dfrac{3}{2}$, $\log_b 8$, and $\log_b 5$ using $\log_b 2 = 0.43$ and $\log_b 3 = 0.68$.

SOLUTION

$\log_b 6$	$\log_b (2 \cdot 3)$ $\log_b 2 + \log_b 3$ $0.43 + 0.68 = 1.11$	Use the product rule, since 2 times 3 equals 6. This means we add the logarithms.
$\log_b \dfrac{2}{3}$	$\log_b 2 - \log_b 3$ $0.43 - 0.68 = -0.25$	Apply the quotient rule and subtract.
$\log_b \dfrac{3}{2}$	$\log_b 3 - \log_b 2$ $0.68 - 0.43 = 0.25$	Apply the quotient rule and subtract.
$\log_b 8$	$\log_b 2^3$ $3 \cdot \log_b 2$ $3(0.43) = 1.29$	Restate 8 as a power of 2, and then apply the power rule. Evaluate, multiplying the stated value of $\log_b 2$ by 3.
$\log_b 5$	$\log_b 5 \ne \log_b 2 + \log_b 3$	The logarithm rules cannot be used to calculate $\log_b 5$ from the values given. The product rule does not apply because 5 is the sum of 2 and 3, not the product.

Derivations of the Rules of Logarithms

We derive the rules for logarithms here. The product, quotient, and power rules for logarithms are proved using the corresponding rules for exponents.

Prove the product rule: $\log_b MN = \log_b M + \log_b N$

> The product rule is derived from the product of powers rule.

Use variables m and n for $\log_b M$, $\log_b N$	$m = \log_b M$; $n = \log_b N$	Use the variables m and n to represent $\log_b M$ and $\log_b N$.
Convert to exponential equations	$M = b^m$; $N = b^n$	Write the equations for m and n in exponential form.
Multiply M and N	$MN = b^m b^n = b^{m+n}$	Multiply M and N and use the product of powers rule to write the product as b^{m+n}.
Convert to logarithmic form and replace m and n	$\log_b MN = m + n$ $\log_b MN = \log_b M + \log_b N$	Convert to logarithmic form. Replace m and n with $\log_b M$ and $\log_b N$. This proves the product rule for logarithms.

Prove the quotient rule: $\log_b \dfrac{M}{N} = \log_b M - \log_b N$		The quotient rule for logarithms is derived from the quotient of powers rule.

Use variables m and n for $\log_b M$, $\log_b N$	$m = \log_b M$; $n = \log_b N$	Use the variables m and n to represent $\log_b M$ and $\log_b N$.
Convert to exponential equations	$M = b^m$; $N = b^n$	Write the equations for m and n in exponential form.
Divide M by N	$\dfrac{M}{N} = \dfrac{b^m}{b^n} = b^{m-n}$	Divide M by N and use the quotient of powers rule to write the quotient as b^{m-n}.
Convert to logarithmic form and replace m and n	$\log_b \dfrac{M}{N} = m - n$ $\log_b \dfrac{M}{N} = \log_b M - \log_b N$	Convert to logarithmic form. Replace m and n with $\log_b M$ and $\log_b N$. This proves the quotient rule for logarithms.

Prove the power rule: $\log_b M^p = p \cdot \log_b M$		The power rule for logarithms is proved using the power of powers rule, $(x^m)^n = x^{mn}$.

Use variable m for $\log_b M$	$m = \log_b M$	Use the variable m to represent $\log_b M$.
Convert to exponential equation	$M = b^m$	Write the equation in exponential form.
Raise to power p	$M^p = (b^m)^p = b^{pm}$	Raise both sides of the equation to the power p. Use the power of powers rule to write the power on the right side as b^{pm}.
Convert to logarithmic form and replace m	$\log_b M^p = \log_b b^{pm}$ $\log_b M^p = pm$ $\log_b M^p = p \cdot \log_b M$	Convert to logarithmic form. Then replace m with $\log_b M$. This proves the power rule for logarithms.

Prove the change-of-base formula: $\log_a x = \dfrac{\log_b x}{\log_b a}$		We use the power rule for logarithms to prove the change-of-base formula.

Use variable d for $\log_a x$	$d = \log_a x$	Use the variable d to represent $\log_a x$.
Convert to exponential equation	$x = a^d$	Write the equation in exponential form.
Take logarithm base b of both sides	$\log_b x = \log_b a^d$	Take the logarithm base b of both sides of the equation.
Apply the power rule	$\log_b x = d \cdot \log_b a$	Apply the power rule on the right side.
Solve for d and replace	$d = \dfrac{\log_b x}{\log_b a}$ $\log_a x = \dfrac{\log_b x}{\log_b a}$	Solve the equation for d and replace it with the expression it represents. This proves the change-of-base formula.

PRACTICE

Exercises 1–4: State in terms of logarithms of x, y, and z.

1. $\log_b (2x^3y^2z^{21})$

2. $\log_a 5\left(\dfrac{x}{y}\right)^z$

3. $\log_4 (7^3x^6y^8z^5)$

4. $\log_5 \left(x \cdot 6^7 \left(\dfrac{y}{4}\right)^3 9^2\right)$

Exercises 5–12: State as a single logarithm.

5. $\dfrac{1}{2} \log_b x^4 - 6 \log_b \sqrt{y}$

6. $3 \log_b x + 2 \log_b y^5 - \dfrac{1}{2} \log_b z$

7. $3 \log_b x - \dfrac{1}{2} \log_b x + 2 \log_b z$

8. $\log_b \dfrac{5}{\sqrt{x}} - \log_b \sqrt{5x}$

9. $\log_r 15 - 6 \log_r x + y \log_r (16 + w)$

10. $\log_5 \dfrac{\sqrt{4}}{2} + y \log_5 x + \log_5 \dfrac{6}{\sqrt{4}}$

11. **MP 2** $c \log_a b - d \log_a \dfrac{e}{f} + h \log_a g$

12. $2 \log_3 \sqrt{45} + 2 \log_3 \sqrt{6} - \log_3 27$

13. Express $\log_{10} \dfrac{\sqrt[3]{y}}{4x^2}$ in terms of $\log_{10} x$, $\log_{10} y$, and $\log_{10} 4$.

14. Express $\log_3 \dfrac{5a^3}{\sqrt{x}}$ in terms of $\log_3 x$, $\log_3 a$, and $\log_3 5$.

Exercises 15–18: $\log_4 5 \approx 1.161$, $\log_4 12 \approx 1.792$, and $\log_4 6 \approx 1.292$. Use these approximate values to evaluate each logarithm.

15. $\log_4 60$

16. $\log_4 2.4$

17. $\log_4 25$

18. $\log_4 2$

19. **MP 6, 7** To the nearest hundredth, $\log_b 42 = 2.09$, $\log_b 2 = 0.39$, and $\log_b 3 = 0.61$. What is $\log_b 7$, to the nearest hundredth?

20. **MP 6, 7** To the nearest hundredth, $\log_b 2 = 0.39$ and $\log_b 3 = 0.61$. What is $\log_b 72$, to the nearest hundredth?

21. **MP 6, 7** To the nearest thousandth, $\log_b 6 = 0.921$ and $\log_b 3 = 0.565$. What is $\log_b 54$, to the nearest hundredth?

• Multi-Part PROBLEM Practice •

MP 2, 4 Earthquake magnitude is measured by seismographs on the Richter scale using $R = \log \dfrac{I}{I_0}$, where I is the intensity of the earthquake being measured, and I_0 is the intensity of the weakest measureable quake (the "threshold quake").

a An earthquake has an intensity of 3.5×10^8 times I_0. What is its measure on the Richter scale, to the nearest tenth?

b An earthquake occurs with an intensity 6000 times that of the threshold quake. What magnitude will it measure on the Richter scale? Round your answer to the nearest hundredth.

c How many times more intense is an earthquake measuring magnitude 8.2 on the Richter scale than one that measures 6.8? Round your answer to the nearest hundredth.

d An earthquake measures magnitude 7.5 on the Richter scale. What is the magnitude of an aftershock with half the intensity of the original? Round your answer to the nearest tenth.

e The deadly San Francisco earthquake of 1906 is approximated at 8.25 on the Richter scale. What was its intensity in terms of I_0? Write your answer in scientific notation with 2 significant digits.

f The magnitude of the 2011 Japan earthquake was 8.9 on the Richter scale. The San Francisco Bay Area earthquake of 1989 was 100 times less intense. What was the magnitude of the San Francisco earthquake on the Richter scale?

Chapter 7 Key Ideas

7.1 Logarithms

- Logarithmic and exponential functions are inverse functions. To state the relationship using an equation: $y = \log_b x$ if and only if $b^y = x$.
- Logarithms with base 10 are called *common logarithms*. These are written with the usual logarithm notation, but without the base; for instance, log 5.

7.2 Logarithmic Function Graphs

- The graph of a logarithmic function and the graph of its inverse exponential equation are symmetric with respect to the line $y = x$.

7.3 Natural Logarithms and e

- A logarithm with base e is called a *natural logarithm*. The number e is an irrational constant. Its first digits are 2.718281828459. A natural logarithm is written as "ln," as in "ln x." This is equivalent to $\log_e x$. The rules you have learned about logarithms apply to natural logarithms.
- The function $f(n) = \left(1 + \dfrac{1}{n}\right)^n$ as n approaches infinity can be used to calculate the value of e.

7.4 Laws of Logarithms

- Some useful logarithmic identities include $\log_b b^x = x$, $b^{\log_b x} = x$, $\log_b 1 = 0$, and $\log_b b = 1$.
- $\log_b x = \log_b y$ and $x = y$ are equivalent equations. We can use this relationship to solve equations.
- The product rule states that $\log_b MN = \log_b M + \log_b N$.
- The quotient rule states that $\log_b \dfrac{M}{N} = \log_b M - \log_b N$.
- The power rule states that $\log_b M^p = p \cdot \log_b M$. To evaluate the logarithm of a number M raised to a power, you can multiply the logarithm of M by the exponent.
- Change the base of logarithms using the formula $\log_a x = \dfrac{\log_b x}{\log_b a}$.

7.5 Modeling with Logarithms

- Logarithmic functions can be used to model situations.
- For logarithmic functions, use logarithmic regression to determine if the model is a good fit.

7.6 More Logarithmic Operations

- The product, quotient, and power rules for logarithms can be proved using the corresponding rules for exponents.

CHAPTER 7 REVIEW

1. Which of the following pairs of functions are inverses?

   A. x^3 and $\log_3 x$
   B. 100^x and x^{100}
   C. 2^x and $\sqrt{x}$
   D. 3^x and $\log_3 x$

Exercises 2–5: Restate each equation as an exponential equation.

2. $\log_x m = k$

3. $\log_5 y = x$

4. $\log_7 7 = 1$

5. $\log_{0.5} 0.0625 = 4$

Exercises 6–8: Restate each equation as a logarithmic equation.

6. $2^1 = 2$

7. $5^{16.89} = x$

8. $3^5 = 243$

Exercises 9–16: Evaluate or simplify.

9. $\log_5 25$

10. $\log 10^4$

11. $\log 10^{-5}$

12. $\log 10^x$

13. $\log 10^{-2x}$

14. $\ln \sqrt[7]{e}$

15. $9^{\log_9 3}$

16. $\log_2 \sqrt[3]{8}$

Exercises 17–23: Solve.

17. $\log_x 729 = 6$

18. $\log_2 x = 7$

19. $\log_{64} (6x - 10) = \dfrac{1}{2}$

20. $\log_5 (x^2 - 3) = \log_5 (-2x)$

21. $e^{2x+1} = 12$

22. $\log (\log 10^x) = 2$

23. $\log 10 + \dfrac{1}{3} \log (375 + 5^{\sqrt{2x}}) = 2$

Exercises 24–25: Use the properties of powers and logarithms to simplify the expressions.

24. **MP 1, 8** $\log_a \sqrt{b\sqrt{b\sqrt{b}}}$

25. $2\left(\log_a \sqrt{b} - \dfrac{1}{4} \log_a \sqrt{c} + \log_a \sqrt{d} \right)$

26. **MP 1, 6** Given that log 2 = 0.3010 and log 3 = 0.4771, find log 75 without using the log function on a calculator. Give your answer to the nearest thousandth.

27. **MP 2, 7** The logarithm in base 5 of a number is equal to the common logarithm of one-tenth this number. Find the number to the nearest ten thousandth.

28. **MP 4** If you invest $2000 at 4% interest compounded annually, in how many years will you have $5000? Give your answer to the nearest tenth of a year.

29. **MP 4** The pH factor measures the hydrogen ion concentration in a solution and varies between 0 and 14. Values of pH in the range of 0 to 7 correspond to acidic substances, such as stomach acid, while values greater than 7 correspond to alkaline substances. Pure water has a pH of 7, which is considered neutral. If x is the effective concentration of hydrogen ions, in moles per liter, then pH $= -\log_{10} x$. The concentration of hydrogen ions in milk is $10^{-6.6}$. What is the pH factor of milk?

1. Which of the following equations could be part of a system that has the solution $(2, 5, -4)$?

A. $-a + 3b + 2c = 10$

B. $2a + 5b - 4c = 0$

C. $3a - b - 2c = -7$

D. $-4a + 2b - c = 6$

2. **MP 1, 2, 7** When can the exponential function $y = a^{bx}$ be restated as an exponential function in the form $y = c^x$?

A. If the product of a and b is a negative number.

B. If a raised to the b power is equal to 1.

C. If a raised to the b power is a positive number.

D. If the product of a and b has a variable term.

3. Which is the inverse of $f(x) = px - qx + r$?

A. $f^{-1}(x) = -px + qx - r$

B. $f^{-1}(x) = \dfrac{x - r}{p - q}$

C. $f^{-1}(x) = \dfrac{x - r}{pq}$

D. $f^{-1}(x) = py - qy + r$

4. Given the equation $y = 2^x + 4$, which line would create a system of equations that has *no solutions*?

A. $x = -4$

B. $y = 6$

C. $x = 100{,}000$

D. $y = 4$

5. Find the value of the discriminant of $3x^2 - 3x + 6 = 0$.

6. Find a quadratic function of the form $y = ax^2 + bx + c$ that passes through the points $(-2, 5)$, $(2, 1)$, and $(1, -4)$.

7. **MP 2, 7** Determine the value of k such that the polynomial $x^3 + kx^2 - 3x + 6$ can be divided evenly by $x - 2$.

8. In the expression $\dfrac{AB(-C)}{(-A)(-B)C}$, each capital letter represents a binomial in the form $(x - a)$. Simplify the expression.

9. **MP 2, 7** Use the fact that $\dfrac{9}{5} = 1 + \dfrac{4}{5}$ to write $\dfrac{x + 9}{x + 5}$ in a similar structure.

Exercises 10–11: Simplify.

10. $\left(\dfrac{x^2 - 9}{x - 3} \div \dfrac{5x - 15}{x^2 - 9x + 18} \right) \cdot \left(\dfrac{15}{x^2 - 6x} \right)$

11. $\left(\dfrac{x^2 - 9}{x - 6} \div \dfrac{3x - 9}{x^2 - 12x + 36} \right) \cdot \left(\dfrac{9}{x^2 - 6x} \right)$

12. Solve: $\dfrac{2}{3x} = \dfrac{1}{x + 4}$

13. Write the reciprocal function that best represents the graph.

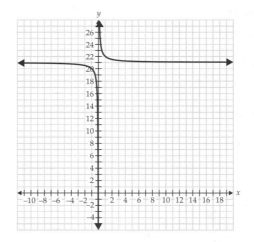

Exercises 14–17: Simplify.

14. $\dfrac{s^{\frac{1}{6}}}{s^{\frac{1}{8}}} \cdot s^{\frac{3}{4}}$

15. $(4x^4)^{\frac{1}{2}}$

16. $\sqrt{52} \cdot \sqrt{2x}$

17. $\sqrt{x^2 - 24x + 144}$

18. **MP 2, 3** Explain why using exponents is almost always better than using radicals.

19. Write a cubic equation in the form $ax^3 + bx^2 + cx + d = 0$ in which one of the solutions is $3 + \sqrt{4}$.

Exercises 20–21: Solve.

20. $25^{4x} = \dfrac{1}{125}$

21. $(0.5)^{x^2 - 20x + 72.5} = \dfrac{8}{\sqrt{2}}$

22. What is $\left(\dfrac{f}{g}\right)(-2)$ if $f(x) = 3x - 6$ and $g(x) = -5x - 2$?

23. Express as a difference of logarithms: $\log_9 \dfrac{4}{3}$

24. **MP 1, 6** Given that $\log 2 = 0.3010$, find $\log 125$ without using the log function on a calculator. Give your answer to the nearest thousandth.

Exercises 25–27: Let $f(x) = \dfrac{e^x - e^{-x}}{2}$ and $g(x) = \dfrac{e^x + e^{-x}}{2}$.

25. **MP 2, 7** Show that
$$f(x) \cdot f(y) = \frac{g(x+y) - g(x-y)}{2}.$$

26. **MP 2, 7** Show that
$$f(x) \cdot g(y) = \frac{f(x+y) + f(x-y)}{2}.$$

27. **MP 2, 7** Show that $f^2(x) - g^2(x) = -1$.

28. Write $3 \ln p - 4 + \ln 2$ as a single natural logarithm of a rational expression.

Exercises 29–30: Graph the functions.

29. $y = \log_2 (x^2 - 9) - \log_2 (x + 3)$

30. $y = \log_2 \dfrac{1}{x^3} + \log_2 x^2$

Chapter 8   Sequences and Series

Chapter Content

Vocabulary

arithmetic sequence	explicit formula	partial sum of an arithmetic series
arithmetic series	factorial notation	recursive formula
binomial coefficient	finite sequence	sequence
binomial expansion	general term	series
binomial theorem	geometric sequence	sigma notation
common difference	geometric series	summand
common ratio	infinite sequence	summation sign
converge	partial sum of a geometric series	term

LESSON 8.1

8.1 Arithmetic Sequences

You likely have bumped into sequences in your study of mathematics. A **sequence** is an ordered list of numbers. A number in a sequence is called a **term**.

- Sequence notation

$$1, 2, 4, 8, 16$$

We use the sequence 1, 2, 4, 8, 16 to discuss sequence notation, the mathematical vocabulary of sequences.

- Subscript indicates index

$a_1 = $ 1st term $= 1$
$a_2 = $ 2nd term $= 2$
$a_3 = $ 3rd term $= 4$

A sequence can be represented with a variable, like a. A subscripted number is used to indicate the place of a term in the sequence, called its *index*. The first term is a_1, which is 1 in this sequence. The second term is a_2, which is 2 in this sequence. The third term is a_3, which equals 4 in this sequence. This notation continues for other terms in the sequence.

- a_n is the general term and stands for any term

$a_n = $ general term

The term a_n is the **general term**, or nth term, in a sequence. This means it can stand for any term.

- If $n = 5$

$a_n = a_5 = 16$

The variable n can be replaced with an integer. In the sequence 1, 2, 4, 8, 16, if $n = 5$, then $a_5 = 16$.

A **finite sequence** like 2, 4, 6, 8, 10 comes to an end. An **infinite sequence** continues forever. An infinite sequence can be stated as 2, 4, 16, 64, … where the three dots indicate the sequence continues forever.

Recursive Formula for Arithmetic Sequences

In an **arithmetic sequence**, each term equals the sum of the preceding term and a constant called the **common difference**. The common difference is positive if the sequence is increasing, and negative if the sequence is decreasing. For instance, 2, 5, 8, 11, 14 is an arithmetic sequence. It starts with 2, and each term that follows is the result of adding the constant 3 to the prior term. The common difference for this sequence is 3. To form other terms in the sequence, we add 3 again and again. The sum of 5 and 3 is 8, the sum of 8 and 3 is 11, and the pattern continues.

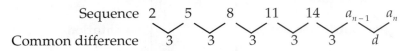

We state the definition of an arithmetic sequence as a formula:

> $a_n = a_{n-1} + d$
> d = common difference
> a_n = general term
> a_{n-1} = term before a_n
> The formula states that a_n equals the previous term a_{n-1} plus a constant, the common difference d.

The formula for the general term a_n in an arithmetic sequence is a **recursive formula**. A recursive formula shows how to calculate a_n based on the value of a_{n-1}, the previous term.

MODEL PROBLEMS

1. The sixth term of an arithmetic sequence is 11 and the common difference is -2. What is the seventh term?

SOLUTION

Definition of arithmetic sequence	$a_n = a_{n-1} + d$	Start with the formula that defines an arithmetic sequence.
Substitute	$a_7 = a_6 + d$	The question asks for a_7, the seventh term, and we are told the sixth term and d. Substitute, replacing the subscripts with the indices stated in the problem.
Substitute terms	$a_7 = 11 + (-2)$	Substitute again, replacing a_6 with 11 since we are told 11 is the sixth term. Replace d with the stated common difference, -2.
Evaluate	$a_7 = 9$	Add to get the seventh term, 9.

2. What is the common difference for the arithmetic sequence 10, 7, 4, 1, -2, ... ?

SOLUTION

Common difference	$a_n = a_{n-1} + d$ $d = a_n - a_{n-1}$	Rearrange the recursive formula for the common difference d. The common difference is calculated by subtracting any term from the term that follows it.
Subtract first term from second	$d = a_2 - a_1$	Subtract the first term, a_1, from the second term, a_2.
Substitute	$d = 7 - 10$	Substitute, replacing the variables with the values of the terms.
Subtract	$d = -3$	Subtract. The common difference is -3.

Model Problems continue . . .

3. If the first four terms of an arithmetic sequence are 13, 9, 5, and 1, what is a_6?

SOLUTION

Calculate common difference	$d = a_2 - a_1$ $d = 9 - 13$ $d = -4$	To calculate d, subtract the first term, 13, from the second term, 9. The common difference is -4.
Definition of arithmetic sequence	$a_n = a_{n-1} + d$	Use the formula that defines an arithmetic sequence.
To calculate a_6, first calculate a_5	$a_5 = a_4 + d$ $a_5 = 1 + (-4)$ $a_5 = -3$	We are asked for a_6, which is calculated by adding d to a_5. We can first calculate a_5, since we know a_4 and have calculated d, the common difference.
Add d to calculate a_6	$a_6 = a_5 + d$ $a_6 = -3 + (-4)$ $a_6 = -7$	Now that we know a_5, we can calculate a_6.

Explicit Formula for the General Term

Although you could calculate any term in an arithmetic sequence by starting with the first term and repeatedly adding the common difference, this would be a lot of work if you needed to find the 100th term or the 1000th term. There is a way to calculate a term directly. To provide an informal derivation, we calculate the first four terms of an arithmetic sequence to find a pattern.

First term	a_1	The first term of an arithmetic sequence is a_1.
Second term	$a_2 = a_1 + d$	The second term is the sum of the first term a_1 and the common difference d.
Third term	$a_3 = a_2 + d$ $a_3 = (a_1 + d) + d$ $a_3 = a_1 + 2d$	The third term is the sum of a_2 and d. We can write a_2 as the sum $a_1 + d$. Rewrite this as $a_1 + 2d$.
Fourth term	$a_4 = a_3 + d$ $a_4 = (a_1 + 2d) + d$ $a_4 = a_1 + 3d$	Follow the same process for the fourth term. Take the expression for the third term, and add another d.

Use the pattern above to write a formula for a_n, the general term.

$$a_n = a_1 + (n - 1)d$$
d = common difference
a_n = general (nth) term
n = index of general term
The nth term, a_n, equals the first term, a_1, plus $n - 1$ times d. For instance, as shown above, $a_4 = a_1 + 3d$. In this case, the index n is 4, which means $n - 1$ is 3.

Because you can find the value of any term, this formula is called an **explicit formula**.

1. a An arithmetic sequence starts with 3 and 5 is added to create the next term. Write an expression for a_n.

   b Use the expression to calculate the eighth term.

SOLUTION

a Formula for a_n $a_n = a_1 + (n - 1)d$ This is the formula for the nth term of an arithmetic sequence. It equals the first term, a_1, plus $n - 1$ times the common difference d.

   Substitute values to write expression for a_n $a_n = 3 + 5(n - 1)$ To write an expression for a_n, substitute the values for a_1 and d. The first term of the sequence is 3. The common difference is 5. Write the 5 in front of the parentheses for ease of reading.

b Substitute $a_n = 3 + 5(n - 1)$ We are asked for the eighth term, so n is 8.
   $a_8 = 3 + 5(8 - 1)$

   Evaluate $a_8 = 3 + 5 \cdot 7$ Evaluate the expression to find that the eighth term is 38.
   $a_8 = 38$

2. An arithmetic sequence starts 4, 9, 14, 19. What is the ninth term?

SOLUTION

Determine values for a_1 and n $a_1 = 4$ The first term is 4. We are asked for the ninth term, so n is 9.
   $n = 9$

Calculate common difference d $d = 9 - 4$ Subtract the first term from the second term to calculate the common difference d, which is 5.
   $d = 5$

Formula for a_n $a_n = a_1 + (n - 1)d$ Use the formula for a_n.

Substitute $a_9 = 4 + (9 - 1)5$ Substitute for a_1, n, and d.

Evaluate $a_9 = 4 + 8 \cdot 5$ Evaluate the expression. The ninth term in the sequence is 44.
   $a_9 = 44$

3. The fifth, sixth, and seventh terms in an arithmetic sequence are 20, 21.5, and 23. What is the first term?

SOLUTION

Determine values for n and a_n $n = 5$ We are told the fifth term, so we choose 5 for n.
   $a_5 = 20$

Calculate common difference d $d = a_6 - a_5$ Subtract the fifth term in the sequence from the sixth to calculate the common difference, 1.5.
   $d = 21.5 - 20$
   $d = 1.5$

Formula for a_n $a_n = a_1 + (n - 1)d$ Use the formula for a_n.

Substitute $20 = a_1 + (5 - 1)(1.5)$ Substitute the values for a_n, n, and d.

Solve for a_1 $20 = a_1 + 6$ Solve the equation for a_1, which is 14.
   $a_1 = 14$

Model Problems continue . . .

4. The first two terms of an arithmetic sequence are 26 and 23. A later term is 2. What is the index of the term 2 in the sequence?

SOLUTION

Determine values for a_n and a_1	$a_n = 2$ $a_1 = 26$	To use the formula for the general term a_n, we need values for the nth term a_n, the first term a_1, and the common difference d. The nth term is 2 and the first term is 26.
Calculate common difference d	$d = 23 - 26$ $d = -3$	Subtract the first term from the second to calculate the common difference, -3.
Formula for a_n	$a_n = a_1 + (n-1)d$	Use the formula for a_n.
Substitute	$2 = 26 + (n-1)(-3)$	Substitute the values for a_n, a_1, and d.
Solve for n	$-24 = (n-1)(-3)$ $8 = n - 1$ $n = 9$	Solve the equation for n, which equals 9. The number 2 is the ninth term in the sequence.

5. Calculate a_8 from $a_5 = 41$ and $a_{11} = 17$ in an arithmetic sequence.

SOLUTION

Write equation for a_5	$a_n = a_1 + (n-1)d$ $41 = a_1 + (5-1)d$ $41 = a_1 + 4d$	We do not know a_1 or d, but can write two equations with a_1 and d from the terms given. This gives two equations in two unknowns.
Write equation for a_{11}	$a_n = a_1 + (n-1)d$ $17 = a_1 + (11-1)d$ $17 = a_1 + 10d$	Use the formula for a_n to write an equation for a_{11}.
Solve the system of equations	$41 = a_1 + 4d$ $-(17 = a_1 + 10d)$ $\overline{24 = 4d - 10d}$ $d = -4$	Subtract the second equation from the first. The a_1 terms cancel out when we subtract. Solve the equation for d, which is -4.
Solve first equation for a_1	$41 = a_1 + 4(-4)$ $a_1 = 57$	Substitute -4 for d in the first equation and solve for a_1, which is 57.
Formula for a_n	$a_n = a_1 + (n-1)d$	To calculate a_8, use the formula for a_n, now that you know the first term of the sequence.
Determine value for n	$n = 8$	We are asked for a_8, so n is 8.
Substitute	$a_8 = 57 + (8-1)(-4)$	Substitute the values for a_1, n, and d.
Evaluate	$a_8 = 29$	Evaluate the right side of the equation to calculate a_8, which is 29.

Model Problems continue . . .

6. MP 2, 4 In its first year, the annual "Bulldog Night" sports fundraiser started with 135 people attending. Each year, a dozen more people attend. Use the formula for an arithmetic sequence to determine the first year in which at least 200 people attend.

SOLUTION

Equation	$a_n = a_1 + (n-1)d$	Start with the equation for an arithmetic sequence.
Substitute	$200 = 135 + (n-1)12$	Substitute 200 for a_n since that is the number of people after n years. Start with 135 people so that is a_1 and the common difference d is 12, the number of additional people attending each year.
Solve equation	$200 = 135 + 12n - 12$ $77 = 12n$ $n \approx 6.4 \rightarrow$ Year 7	Distribute, combine like terms, and divide by 12. The solution to the equation is about 6.4. Since the event is annual and the question asks for at least 200 people, we must round up to 7 years.

7. MP 2, 4 Justin has $40,000 in his bank account on June 1. On July 1, his parents give him his $10,000 monthly allowance and continue to do so every month. In how many months can he buy his sports car ($70,000), or if he decides to really save, when can he buy his yacht ($110,000)? Use a graph to answer the question.

SOLUTION

Write equation   Savings = $40,000 + 10,000n$ Justin starts with $40,000 and adds $10,000 each month.

Create table

Month	Savings
n	$40,000 + 10,000n$
0	40,000
1	50,000
2	60,000
3	70,000
4	80,000
5	90,000
6	100,000
7	110,000

We start with the $n = 0$ for the first term. Note that in this problem, the first term of the sequence starts with $n = 0$. For an application problem, it sometimes makes more sense for the initial value, in this case the investment amount, to occur at the "0th" time interval. So we are actually using a modified form of the formula, $a_n = a_0 + nd$.

Graph

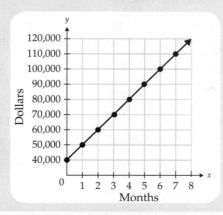

> Looking at the graph, you may have noticed that points are on a line. The slope of the line is the *common difference*.

Justin can buy a car after 3 months or a yacht after 7 months.

We show one of two similar activities below. In these activities, you help a frog locate his (mathematically oriented) flies using your knowledge of arithmetic sequences.

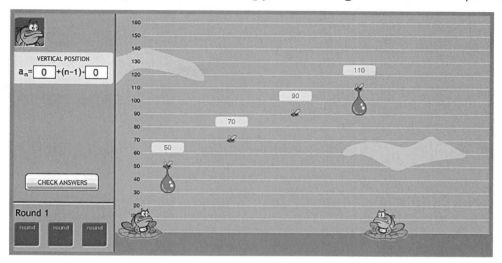

 We show one of three similar activities below. In these activities, enter values for the formulas for the odd rows of the pattern as well as the even rows.

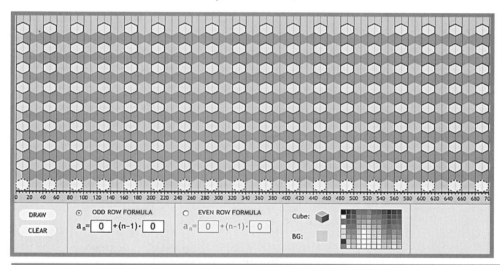

PRACTICE

1. Which of these are arithmetic sequences? Select all that apply.

    A. 13, 6, −1, −8, ...

    B. 2, 6, 12, 20, ...

    C. −13, −10, −7, −4, ...

    D. −8, −1, 6, 13, ...

2. Which of these are arithmetic sequences? Select all that apply.

    A. 0, 3, 8, 15, ...

    B. 1, 3, 9, 27, ...

    C. 7, 13, 19, 25, ...

    D. 27, 9, 3, 1, ...

3. Which of these are arithmetic sequences? Select all that apply.

    A. −12, −22, −32, −42, ...

    B. −12, −4, 4, 12, ...

    C. 2, 2, 0, 20, −4, ...

    D. −12, −22, 4, −42, ...

4. **MP 2, 7** A sequence is given by the formula, $a_n = k + s(n − 1)$. What are the first three terms?

    A. $k + 3s, k + 4s, k + 5s$

    B. $k, k + 1, k + 2$

    C. $k, ks, 2ks$

    D. $k, k + s, k + 2s$

Practice Problems continue . . .

5. Which of the following represents the formula for the given sequence 3, 8, 13, 18, 23, … ?

 A. $a_n = a_{n-1} - 5$, where $a_1 = 3$
 B. $a_n = a_{n-1} + 5$, where $a_1 = 3$
 C. $a_n = 2a_{n-1} + 2$, where $a_1 = 1$
 D. $a_n = 5a_{n-1}$, where $a_1 = 1$

6. Which of the following is true about an arithmetic sequence?

 A. There is a common difference between adjacent terms.
 B. There is a common ratio between adjacent terms.
 C. The sequence always increases.
 D. The sequence always decreases.

7. Given the sequence 10, 14, 18, 22, … , what is a_{16}?

 A. 60   C. 70
 B. 66   D. 74

8. **MP 7** Which of the sequences represents the given graph?

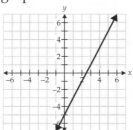

 A. $a_n = -5 + 2(n-1)$
 B. $a_n = -3 + 2(n-1)$
 C. $a_n = -2 + 5(n-1)$
 D. $a_n = 2 - 5(n-1)$

9. What is the largest term in the infinite arithmetic sequence $-3, -7, -10, …$?

10. What is the smallest term in the infinite arithmetic sequence 10, 12, 14, … ?

11. In the sequence 3, 5, 7, 9, what does a_1 equal?

Exercises 12–15: Each sequence can be described by the equation $a_n = a_{n-1} + 4$.

12. The fourth term of a sequence is 11. Find the fifth term.

13. The ninth term of a sequence is 81. Find the tenth term.

14. The thirteenth term of a sequence is −9. Find the fourteenth term.

15. The second term of a sequence is −4. Find the third term.

Exercises 16–18: Calculate the term.

16. The term after the number 2 when the common difference is 5.

17. The term after the number 9 when the common difference is −1.

18. The term after the number −1 when the common difference is −5.

Exercises 19–21: Calculate the common difference for each arithmetic sequence.

19. 0, 2, 4, 6, 8

20. 12, 15, 18, 21

21. 11, 8, 5, 2

Exercises 22–26: Calculate the next term in each arithmetic sequence.

22. 5, 7, 9, 11, …

23. 101, 105, 109, 113, …

24. −5, −7, −9, −11, …

25. 8.4, 10.5, 12.6, 14.7, …

26. −6.4, −9.6, −12.8, −16, …

Exercises 27–28: Calculate the requested term in each arithmetic sequence.

27. A sequence starts 10, 13, 16. What is the fifth term in the sequence?

28. A sequence starts −2, 5, 12. What is the fifth term?

Exercises 29–32: The equation for the general term of a sequence is $a_n = 5 + 4(n-1)$. Calculate the requested term in the sequence.

29. The third term

30. The first term

31. a_7

32. a_{11}

Practice Problems continue . . .

Exercises 33–39: State the equation for the general term for the given arithmetic sequence.

33. 4, 9, 14, 19, …

34. 1, 10, 19, 28, …

35. 14, 21, 28, 35, …

36. −2, −7, −12, −17, …

37. 28, 26, 24, 22, …

38. $c, c + a, c + 2a, c + 3a, …$

39. $11, 11 − k, 11 − 2k, 11 − 3k, …$

Exercises 40–53: Calculate the requested term for each arithmetic sequence.

40. A sequence starts 5, 7, 9, 11. What is the 17th term in the sequence?

41. A sequence starts 4, 7, 10, 13. What is the 13th term in the sequence?

42. For the sequence 11, 15, 19, 23, … , what is a_9?

43. For the sequence 1, 9, 17, 25, … , what is a_{21}?

44. A sequence starts 2, −1, −4, −7. What is the 25th term?

45. A sequence starts −4, −9, −14, −19. What is the 8th term?

46. For the sequence 0.5, 3, 5.5, 8, … , what is a_{14}?

47. For the sequence 2, −2.5, −7 −11.5, … , what is a_9?

48. A sequence starts $\frac{3}{4}, \frac{13}{4}, \frac{23}{4}, \frac{33}{4}$. What is the 10th term in this sequence?

49. A sequence starts $\frac{5}{2}, \frac{7}{4}, 1, \frac{1}{4}$. What is the 11th term in this sequence?

50. The eighth, ninth, and tenth terms in an arithmetic sequence are 55, 61, and 67. What is the first term?

51. The twelfth, thirteenth, and fourteenth terms in an arithmetic sequence are −23.5, −26.5, and −29.5. What is the first term?

52. The first two terms of an arithmetic sequence are 9.4 and 10.7. A later term is 25. What is the index of that term in the sequence?

53. The first two terms of an arithmetic sequence are 19.1 and 16.8. A later term is 3. What is the index of that term in the sequence?

Exercises 54–56: State the expression for the general term of the sequence.

54. The fourth term of an arithmetic sequence is 18 and the common difference is 5.

55. The fifth term of an arithmetic sequence is 35 and the seventh term is 27.

56. The ninth term of an arithmetic sequence is 26 and the eleventh term is 33.

57. What would be the slope of a line that passes through a graph defined by the arithmetic sequence $a_n = 4 + 3(n − 1)$?

58. Determine the formula for the sequence of the given graph.

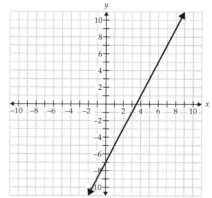

59. Sketch the graph of $a_n = \frac{4}{3}(n − 1)$.

60. **MP 1, 8** You open a savings account by depositing $10. The next month, and every month that follows, you deposit $2 more than the previous month.

   a In the month that begins the third year, how much will you be depositing?

   b Write the equation for calculating the amount you deposit in any month.

61. **MP 1, 8** Liz agrees to loan her younger brother some money each month. She gives him $150 in April. Each month thereafter, she decreases the loan amount by $12.

   a How much will she loan her brother in December?

   b Write the equation for calculating the amount Liz loans in any month.

Practice Problems continue . . .

Practice Problems continued . . .

62. **MP 2, 3, 7** Connor states that the linear graph below can be modeled by the arithmetic sequence that starts with 4 and has a common difference of $\frac{1}{2}$, as given by the formula $a_n = 4 + \frac{1}{2}(n - 1)$. Simplify Connor's formula to the slope-intercept form and graph it. Was Connor correct? Why or why not?

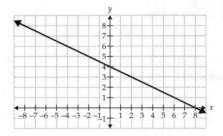

63. Describe what it means for a sequence to be an arithmetic sequence.

64. Does order matter in a sequence? Why or why not?

65. **MP 3, 8** If $a_1, a_2, a_3, \ldots$ and $b_1, b_2, b_3, \ldots$ are both arithmetic sequences, is $a_1 + b_1, a_2 + b_2, a_3 + b_3, \ldots$ an arithmetic sequence? Explain.

66. Prove that if two distinct terms are equal in an arithmetic sequence, then the sequence must be constant. (A sequence is constant when all terms are equal.)

67. A sequence can be defined by a function $a_n = f(n)$. That is, the nth term of the sequence can be determined by a function that depends only on n. How else can one define a sequence? Use this to define the arithmetic sequence $a_n = a_1 + d(n - 1)$.

LESSON 8.2

8.2 Optional: Arithmetic Series

When the terms of an arithmetic sequence are added together, the resulting expression is an **arithmetic series**. For instance, adding the terms of a finite arithmetic sequence 4, 6, 8, 10, 12 creates a *finite arithmetic series* $4 + 6 + 8 + 10 + 12$. If an arithmetic sequence is infinite, such as 3, 6, 9, 12, ... , the result is an *infinite arithmetic series*, $3 + 6 + 9 + 12 + \ldots$.

> A **series** is composed of the sum of the terms of a sequence.

MODEL PROBLEM

Write the arithmetic series for the arithmetic sequence 2, 4, 6, 8.

SOLUTION

Arithmetic series: terms in sequence, added $\qquad 2 + 4 + 6 + 8 \qquad$ To write the series, insert + signs between the terms. This is called *writing the series in expanded form*.

Sigma Notation

A series can be written using **sigma notation**. The Greek letter Σ (sigma) indicates a sum, and is called the **summation sign**. This notation uses an expression for the nth term of the sequence, called the **summand**.

$$\sum_{n=1}^{4} 2n$$

$n = 1, 2, 3, 4$

In sigma notation, an expression for the general term in the series is used. For this example of an arithmetic series, $2n$ represents the nth term, so the summand is $2n$.

The variable n is called the *index of the summation*, and it must be an integer. Each term in the series is calculated from a value of n.

The range of the index n starts with the value below Σ and ends with the value above. For this summation, n starts at 1 and ends at 4 so n has the values 1, 2, 3, and 4.

We show how to expand a series written in sigma notation:

Start with the value of n below Σ	$\displaystyle\sum_{n=1}^{4} 2n$ $\displaystyle\sum_{n=1}^{4} 2n = 2 \cdot 1 + \dots$	To expand the series, we start with the value of n below Σ, which is 1. Replace n in the expression with 1 and write the first term of the series.
Increase n by 1, and add term	$\displaystyle\sum_{n=1}^{4} 2n = 2 \cdot 1 + 2 \cdot 2 + \dots$	The next term is always created by increasing n by 1 and substituting that value in the expression. Do this to create the second term and add the result to the first term.
Repeat until n equals value above Σ	$\displaystyle\sum_{n=1}^{4} 2n = 2 \cdot 1 + 2 \cdot 2 + 2 \cdot 3 + 2 \cdot 4$	Repeat the process, increasing n by 1, to get 3, and substituting that. This creates the third term, which is added to the expression. Keep increasing n by 1 until it equals 4, the value above Σ, adding the terms as we go.
Simplify	$\displaystyle\sum_{n=1}^{4} 2n = 2 + 4 + 6 + 8$	Simplify the series by doing the multiplication for each term.

MODEL PROBLEM

Write the infinite arithmetic series $1 + 3 + 5 + \dots$ using sigma notation.

SOLUTION

Use formula for a_n	$a_n = a_1 + (n - 1)d$ $a_n = 1 + (n - 1)(2)$	To write a series using sigma notation, we need an expression for the nth term. Use the formula for a_n, the nth term of an arithmetic sequence, substituting 1 for a_1 and 2 for d.
Simplify	$a_n = 2n - 1$	The resulting expression simplifies to $2n - 1$.
Write summation, using ∞	$\displaystyle\sum_{n=1}^{\infty} (2n - 1)$	Write the summation, using the expression for the general term as the summand. There are an infinite number of terms, so the summation is written with the infinity symbol above Σ. This indicates the series continues forever.

> In sigma notation, an infinite series is written with the infinity symbol ∞ above Σ.

Partial Sum of an Infinite Arithmetic Series

The sum of the first n terms of an infinite series is represented by S_n and is called a **partial sum of an arithmetic series**. For example, for the arithmetic series $3 + 5 + 7 + 9 + \ldots$, the partial sum $S_2 = 8$, represents the sum of the first two terms. This is found by adding the first two terms 3 and 5.

A partial sum can always be calculated by adding the terms, but the formula for the partial sum can be useful for large sums:

$$S_n = \frac{n}{2}(a_1 + a_n)$$

S_n = partial sum of an arithmetic series

n = number of terms being added

a_1 = first term

a_n = nth term

> Here is a way to remember the formula for the partial sum of an arithmetic series: It is the average of the first and last terms, $\dfrac{a_1 + a_n}{2}$, multiplied by the number of terms, n.

Derivation of Formula for Arithmetic Series

The formula for S_n for the sum of the first n terms of an arithmetic series is derived below. We pair the first and last terms in the series, the second and next-to-last ones, and so on.

Derive: $S_n = \frac{n}{2}(a_1 + a_n)$		
$S_n = \sum\limits_{i=1}^{n} a_i$	$S_n = a_1 + a_2 + a_3 + \ldots + a_{n-2} + a_{n-1} + a_n$	Start with the expression for an arithmetic series with n terms, from a_1 to a_n.
Each term d greater	$S_n = a_1 + (a_1 + d) + (a_1 + 2d) + \ldots + (a_n - 2d) + (a_n - d) + a_n$	Each term in the series is d greater than the previous term. This means the first three terms are a_1, $a_1 + d$, and $a_1 + 2d$. The last term is a_n. The term before it is $a_n - d$, and the term before that is $a_n - 2d$.
Commutative property	$S_n = a_n + (a_n - d) + (a_n - 2d) + \ldots + (a_1 + 2d) + (a_1 + d) + a_1$	Using the commutative property, write the same sum in reverse order, from a_n to a_1.
Add equations	$\begin{aligned} S_n = \quad a_1 \quad + (a_1 + d) + \ldots + (a_n - d) + \quad a_n \\ S_n = \quad a_n \quad + (a_n - d) + \ldots + (a_1 + d) + \quad a_1 \\ \hline 2S_n = (a_1 + a_n) + (a_1 + a_n) + \ldots + (a_1 + a_n) + (a_1 + a_n) \end{aligned}$	Add these two equations, which results in $2S_n$ on the left. On the right side, add each pair of terms. Each pair adds up to $a_1 + a_n$.
n terms of $(a_1 + a_n)$	$2S_n = n(a_1 + a_n)$	On the right, there are n terms of $a_1 + a_n$, so we write the sum as $n(a_1 + a_n)$.
Divide by 2	$S_n = \frac{n}{2}(a_1 + a_n)$	Divide by 2 to derive the formula.

1. Calculate S_4 for the series $3 + 7 + 11 + 15 + \ldots$.

SOLUTION

Formula for S_n	$S_n = \dfrac{n}{2}(a_1 + a_n)$	Start with the formula for the partial sum of the first n terms of an arithmetic series.
Substitute	$S_4 = \dfrac{4}{2}(3 + 15)$	We are asked to calculate the sum S_4. The number of terms is 4, the first term is 3, and the fourth term is 15. Replace the variables with their values.
Evaluate	$S_4 = 2(18) = 36$	Evaluate the expression. S_4 equals 36. The answer can be checked by adding the first four terms of the series. The sum of $3 + 7 + 11 + 15$ equals 36.

2. For the arithmetic series $3 + 10 + 17 + \ldots$,

   a Find the value of the ninth term.

   b Use the formula for S_n to calculate S_9, the sum of the first nine terms in the series.

SOLUTION

a	Calculate common difference d	$d = a_2 - a_1$ $d = 10 - 3$ $d = 7$	First, calculate the common difference, d. Subtract the first term from the second term. The common difference is 7.
	Formula for a_n	$a_n = a_1 + (n - 1)d$	Use the formula for a_n.
	Substitute	$a_9 = 3 + (9 - 1)(7)$	We want to calculate the ninth term, which means $n = 9$. Substitute these values, $n = 9$, $a_1 = 3$, and $d = 7$.
	Evaluate	$a_9 = 59$	Evaluate the expression and find that a_9 is 59.
b	Formula for S_n	$S_n = \dfrac{n}{2}(a_1 + a_n)$	Use the formula for S_n.
	Substitute and evaluate	$S_9 = \dfrac{9}{2}(3 + 59)$ $S_9 = 279$	Replace the variables with their values and evaluate the expression. The sum of the first nine terms is 279.

Model Problems continue . . .

3. Find S_5 for the arithmetic series $\sum\limits_{n=1}^{\infty} (11 - 2(n - 1))$.

SOLUTION

Calculate a_1 and a_5	$a_n = 11 - 2(n - 1)$	We need to find the sum of the first 5 terms. To use the formula for S_n, we need a_1 and a_5. The expression in the summation, $11 - 2(n - 1)$, is an expression for the general term a_n.
$n = 1$	$a_1 = 11 - 2(1 - 1)$ $a_1 = 11$	To calculate a_1, replace n with 1 in the summand, the expression for the general term of the series. Evaluate the expression to find that $a_1 = 11$.
$n = 5$	$a_5 = 11 - 2(5 - 1)$ $a_5 = 3$	Then replace n with 5 to calculate a_5, which is 3.
Substitute and evaluate	$S_n = \dfrac{n}{2}(a_1 + a_n)$ $S_5 = \dfrac{5}{2}(11 + 3)$ $S_5 = 35$	Replace the variables with their values and evaluate the expression. The sum of the five terms is 35. The expanded form of the first five terms of the series is $11 + 9 + 7 + 5 + 3$. If you do the addition, you can confirm the answer by checking that the sum equals 35.

4. Find S_p for $\sum\limits_{n=1}^{\infty} 2 + \dfrac{1}{2}(n - 1)$. Write your answer in simplest form.

A. $2 + \dfrac{1}{2}p$

B. $\dfrac{3}{2} + \dfrac{1}{2}p$

C. $\dfrac{7}{4}p + \dfrac{1}{4}p^2$

D. $4p + p^2$

SOLUTION

A. This is not p times the average of the first and pth terms.

B. This is the pth term, not the sum of the first p terms.

C. **Correct answer.** To use the sum formula, we first calculate the first and last terms. When we substitute in $n = 1$, we get $a_1 = 2$. To calculate the last term, we substitute $n = p$, and $a_p = 2 + \dfrac{1}{2}(p - 1) = \dfrac{3}{2} + \dfrac{1}{2}p$. Then using the formula for the sum of the first n terms

$$S_n = \dfrac{n}{2}(a_1 + a_n), \quad S_p = \dfrac{p}{2}\left(2 + \left(\dfrac{3}{2} + \dfrac{1}{2}p\right)\right) = \dfrac{7}{4}p + \dfrac{1}{4}p^2.$$

D. This is not p times the average of the first and pth terms.

Model Problems continue . . .

5. MP 2 A pile of logs has 13 on the bottom row, 12 on the row immediately above, 11 on the next row above, and so on. There are 6 rows of logs. What is the total number of logs in the log pile?

a Calculate the number of logs in the sixth row. Use the fact that the number of logs in consecutive rows forms an arithmetic sequence and use the number of logs in the bottom row as the first term in the sequence.

b Use the formula for S_n to find the total number of logs in the pile.

SOLUTION

a Number of logs in rows is arithmetic sequence

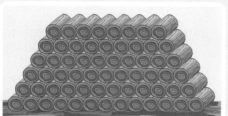

The number of logs in each row forms an arithmetic sequence. Each row has one fewer log than the row below it.

Use formula for a_n

$a_n = a_1 + (n-1)d$
$a_6 = 13 + (6-1)(-1)$

Use the formula for the general term of an arithmetic sequence. Substitute 13 for a_1 since there are 13 logs in the first row, and 6 for n, since there are 6 rows. The common difference is -1.

Evaluate

$a_6 = 13 + (5)(-1)$
$a_6 = 8$

Evaluate the expression on the right, and see that there are 8 logs in the sixth row.

b Substitute and evaluate

$S_n = \dfrac{n}{2}(a_1 + a_n)$

$S_6 = \dfrac{6}{2}(13 + 8)$

$S_6 = 63$

Use the formula for the sum of an arithmetic series. Replace the variables with their values. Evaluate the expression. There are 63 logs in the 6 rows.

Arithmetic Series in History

A famous story about the German mathematician Karl Friedrich Gauss says that when he was a young student and the teacher presented his class with the problem, "Add up the integers from 1 to 100," he quickly wrote down 5050.

What was his insight? He paired numbers that summed to 101, and calculated that there were 50 pairs of them. In the diagram to the right, the integers are arranged to show the pattern Gauss is said to have used. Each integer is paired with another integer to sum to 101. The first term, 1, is paired with the last term, 100, the second term, 2, with the next to last term, 99, and so on. The 50th pair is 50 and 51. This means there are 50 pairs of terms, each of which sums to 101. The sum of the integers from 1 to 100 equals the product of the number of pairs of added terms, 50, times the sum of each pair, 101. The product of 50 and 101 is 5050.

$$\left.\begin{array}{l} 1 + 100 = 101 \\ 2 + 99 = 101 \\ 3 + 98 = 101 \\ \sim \\ 50 + 51 = 101 \end{array}\right\} 50 \text{ pairs}$$

$S_n = \dfrac{n}{2}(a_1 + a_n)$

Gauss's insight agrees with the formula for S_n, the sum of the terms in a series. There are half as many pairs of terms as the original number of terms. We divide the number of terms n by 2. Each pair of terms has the same sum. We use the sum of a_1, the first term, and a_n, the last term. The product of $\dfrac{n}{2}$ and $a_1 + a_n$ is the sum of the series.

PRACTICE

1. What is the sum of the first 12 terms of the sequence $a_n = 3n + 2$?

   A. 142   C. 258
   B. 210   D. 322

2. Evaluate $\sum_{n=2}^{6} (2n - 1)$.

   A. 28   C. 33
   B. 30   D. 35

3. Keisha opened a savings account in January with a deposit of $500. She plans to increase each monthly deposit by $100. How much money will she have saved by the end of the year?

   A. $10,400   C. $12,600
   B. $11,100   D. $13,100

Exercises 4–6: Write the series corresponding to each sequence.

4. 2, 4, 6, 8

5. −3, 0, 3, 6

6. −12, −4, 4, 12

Exercises 7–12: Write the series in expanded form.

7. $\sum_{n=1}^{4} (6n + 2)$

8. $\sum_{n=1}^{6} (-7n)$

9. $\sum_{n=1}^{3} (n + 1)$

10. $\sum_{n=1}^{5} 2n$

11. $\sum_{n=1}^{4} (5n + 3)$

12. $\sum_{n=1}^{3} (3n - 6)$

Exercises 13–15: Evaluate the sum.

13. $\sum_{n=1}^{3} (n - 2)$

14. $\sum_{n=1}^{4} 3n$

15. $\sum_{n=1}^{6} (4n + 1)$

Exercises 16–18: Write each arithmetic series using sigma notation.

16. $-45 + (-31) + (-17) + (-3) + \ldots$

17. $98 + 74 + 50 + 26 + 2 + \ldots$

18. $10 + 23 + 36 + 49 + \ldots$

19. What is S_{10} for the arithmetic series $-25 + (-11) + 3 + 17 + \ldots$?

20. What is S_8 for the arithmetic series $13 + 6 + (-1) + (-8) + \ldots$?

21. What is S_{11} for the arithmetic series $-13 + (-10) + (-7) + (-4) + \ldots$?

22. For the arithmetic series $\sum_{n=1}^{\infty} (-3n + 80)$, what is S_{50}?

23. For the arithmetic series $\sum_{n=1}^{\infty} (15n - 40)$, what is S_{20}?

24. For the arithmetic series $\sum_{n=1}^{\infty} (-8n + 43)$, what is S_{15}?

25. What is the sum of the first 30 terms of an arithmetic series if the series begins $5 + 6 + 7 + \ldots$?

26. What is the sum of the first 25 terms of an arithmetic series if the series begins $3 + 5 + 7 + 9 + \ldots$?

27. Theaters often expand with distance from the stage. How many seats are there in 6 rows, if the first row has four seats, and each additional row has two more seats?

28. a Use the diagram below to make a sketch for the arithmetic sequence $a_n = -1 + 2n$ for at least the first 5 terms.

a_1 a_2

   b Determine the 12th term of the sequence.

Practice Problems continue . . .

Practice Problems continued . . .

29. You save $10 on the first day of the month, $20 on the second, $30 on the third, and so on. In a month that has 30 days, how much do you save?

30. **MP 1, 4** You inherit a piggy bank containing $2.50. On the first day of the month, you deposit a dime, and each day of that month you deposit a nickel more than the previous day. At the end of a 30-day month, how much money is in the piggy bank? You do not take any money out.

31. To save for a bicycle, you make a plan to save $10 the first day, $20 the second day, $30 the third day, and so on. If the racing bicycle you want to buy costs $2760, on what day can you afford the bicycle?

32. A stack of logs starts with 13 logs in a row on the bottom, and each row has one fewer log than the row below it. The stack continues until there is one log on top. How many logs are in the stack?

33. **MP 2, 3** Alisa claims that if a_n defines a term in an arithmetic sequence, then the sequence S_n of partial sums defined by a_n is also arithmetic. Is her claim correct? Why or why not?

34. What are the difference(s) between a sequence and a series?

35. **MP 1, 2, 8** Derive a formula for the partial sum from the kth term to the nth term where $k < n$ for an arithmetic sequence a_n.

36. **MP 2, 3** Can the sequence of partial sums of an arithmetic sequence a_n contain both positive and negative terms? Explain.

Exercises 37–40: Find the infinite arithmetic sequence a_n that generates the infinite series S_n given.

37. $S_n = -4, -8, -12, -16, -20, \ldots, -4n, \ldots$

38. $S_n = 1, 3, 6, 10, 15, \ldots, \frac{n}{2}(1 + n), \ldots$

39. $S_n = 1, 4, 9, 16, 25, \ldots, n^2, \ldots$

40. $S_n = 1, 0, -3, -8, -15, \ldots, 1 - (n-1)^2, \ldots$

41. Find the value of $\sum_{j=1}^{6} \left(\sum_{k=1}^{j} k \right)$.

42. **MP 2, 3** The arithmetic sequence $a_1, a_2, a_3, \ldots$ has the common difference d. Prove that the sum of the first n terms of the series $a_1 + a_2 + a_3 + \ldots$ is given by the formula $S_n = \frac{n}{2}[2a_1 + (n-1)d]$.

• Multi-Part PROBLEM Practice •

MP 5, 7 Armand starts the year off slowly in math class, but makes regular progress on his test scores. His first 6 scores, in order, are 48, 50, 52, 54, 56, and 58.

a Find an expression for an arithmetic sequence that best represents this data.

b If Armand's test scores continue to improve following this sequence, what will he score on his 15th test?

c The class will take 20 tests over the course of the year. Again, assuming this sequence holds, what will be Armand's total for his test scores?

d What will be his average test score?

8.2 Optional: Arithmetic Series **349**

8.3 Geometric Sequences

Recursive Formula for Geometric Sequences

In a **geometric sequence**, each term equals the product of the preceding term and a constant called the **common ratio**. For instance, 3, 12, 48, 192 is a geometric sequence. It starts with 3, and each term that follows is formed by multiplying the prior term by 4, which is the common ratio for this sequence.

As with an arithmetic sequence, the terms of a geometric sequence are often referred to using the notation a_1, a_2, a_3, and so on, with a_n representing the general term.

$$\text{Sequence} \quad 3 \quad\quad 12 \quad\quad 48 \quad\quad 192 \quad\quad a_{n-1} \quad a_n$$
$$\text{Common ratio} \quad 4 \quad\quad 4 \quad\quad 4 \quad\quad 4 \quad\quad r$$

You can perhaps see how the common ratio gets its name. It is the ratio of a term to the term that precedes it. For instance, in the sequence 3, 12, 48, 192, $\frac{12}{3} = 4$, $\frac{48}{12} = 4$, $\frac{192}{48} = 4$, etc. The ratio is common (the same) for every pair of terms.

We state the definition of a geometric sequence as a formula for calculating any term in the sequence from the previous term:

$$a_n = a_{n-1} \cdot r$$
$$r = \text{common ratio}$$
$$a_n = \text{general term}$$
$$a_{n-1} = \text{term before } a_n$$

The formula states that a_n equals the previous term a_{n-1} times the common ratio r.

> A geometric sequence starts with an initial term. Each term that follows is the product of the prior term and a constant, r, called the *common ratio*.

MODEL PROBLEMS

1. The second term of a geometric sequence equals 16, and the common ratio is 2. What is the third term?

SOLUTION

Definition of geometric sequence	$a_n = a_{n-1} \cdot r$	Start with the formula that defines a geometric sequence.
Substitute	$a_3 = 16 \cdot 2$	We were asked to calculate the third term when the second term equals 16, and the common ratio is 2. Replace the variables with these values.
Evaluate	$a_3 = 32$	Multiply to get 32, which is the third term.

Model Problems continue . . .

2. What is the common ratio for the geometric sequence 10, 2, 0.4?

SOLUTION

Common ratio $\quad r = \dfrac{a_n}{a_{n-1}}$ $\qquad$ The common ratio r can be calculated by dividing a term, such as a_n, by the term before it, a_{n-1}.

Divide second term $\quad r = \dfrac{a_2}{a_1}$ $\qquad$ For instance, to calculate r we could divide the second term, a_2, by first
by the first, a_1.

Substitute $\quad r = \dfrac{2}{10}$ $\qquad$ Substitute, replacing the variables with the values of the terms.

Evaluate $\quad r = \dfrac{1}{5} = 0.2$ $\qquad$ Divide. The common ratio is 0.2.

Explicit Formula for the General Term

The explicit formula for the general term of a geometric sequence can be derived in a similar way to the explicit formula for the general term of an arithmetic sequence.

First term	a_1	The first term of an arithmetic sequence is a_1.
Second term	$a_2 = a_1 \cdot r$	The second term is the product of the first term a_1 and the common ratio r.
Third term	$a_3 = a_2 \cdot r$ $a_3 = (a_1 \cdot r) \cdot r$ $a_3 = a_1 \cdot r^2$	The third term is the product of a_2 and r. We can write a_2 as the product of $a_1 \cdot r$. Rewrite this as $a_1 \cdot r^2$.
Fourth term	$a_4 = a_3 \cdot r$ $a_4 = (a_1 \cdot r^2) \cdot r$ $a_4 = a_1 \cdot r^3$	Follow the same process for the fourth term. Take the expression for the third term, and multiply by another r.

Use the pattern above to write a formula for a_n, the general term.

$$a_n = a_1 r^{n-1}$$
r = common ratio
a_n = general (nth) term
n = index of general term
The nth term, a_n, equals the first term, a_1, multiplied by the common ratio, r, to the $n-1$ power.

MODEL PROBLEMS

1. What is the fourth term in a geometric sequence where the common ratio is -2, and the first term is 3?

SOLUTION

Formula for a_n	$a_n = a_1 r^{n-1}$	Any term in a geometric sequence can be calculated directly with this formula. To calculate the nth term, multiply the first term a_1 by the common ratio r raised to the power $n-1$.
Substitute	$a_4 = 3(-2)^{4-1}$	The question asked for the fourth term, with the common ratio equal to -2, and the first term being 3. Replace the variables with the values stated in the problem.
Evaluate	$a_4 = 3(-2)^3$ $a_4 = 3(-8)$ $a_4 = -24$	Evaluate the expression. The fourth term is -24.

2. A geometric sequence starts with 2, 6, 18. What is the fifth term?

SOLUTION

Calculate common ratio r	$r = \dfrac{a_n}{a_{n-1}}$	Use the formula for the common ratio.
Divide second term by first	$r = \dfrac{6}{2}$ $r = 3$	Divide the second term by the first to calculate the common ratio, which is 3.
Formula for a_n	$a_n = a_1 r^{n-1}$	Use the formula for the general term of a geometric sequence.
Substitute	$a_5 = 2 \cdot 3^{5-1}$	The first term, a_1, is 2 and we found the common ratio, r. We are asked for the fifth term, so $n = 5$. Substitute these values into the formula.
Evaluate	$a_5 = 2 \cdot 81$ $a_5 = 162$	Evaluate the expression. The fifth term is 162. Check the solution. Since $a_3 = 18$ and the common ratio is 3, $a_4 = 54$ and $a_5 = 162$.

3. The first three terms in a geometric sequence are $8b$, $32b^2$, and $128b^3$. What is a_6?

SOLUTION

Calculate common ratio r	$r = \dfrac{a_n}{a_{n-1}}$ $r = \dfrac{32b^2}{8b}$ $r = 4b$	Divide the second term by the first and get the common ratio, $4b$.
Formula for a_n	$a_n = a_1 r^{n-1}$	Use the explicit formula for a term in a geometric sequence.
Substitute and simplify	$a_6 = 8b(4b)^{6-1}$ $a_6 = (8b)4^5 b^5$ $a_6 = 8192\, b^6$	Substitute the values for a_1, r, and n and simplify the expression. The sixth term is $8192\, b^6$.

> The terms in a geometric sequence can contain variables. We can use the same formulas to find the common ratio and particular terms, as we do here.

Model Problems continue . . .

4. In a geometric sequence, $a_6 = 48$ and $a_7 = 24$. What is a_1?

SOLUTION

Calculate common ratio r

$$r = \frac{a_7}{a_6}$$

$$r = \frac{24}{48}$$

$$r = \frac{1}{2}$$

First, we calculate r from the two terms we are given, a_6 and a_7. The common ratio is $\frac{1}{2}$.

Substitute

$$a_n = a_1 r^{n-1}$$

$$48 = a_1\left(\frac{1}{2}\right)^{6-1}$$

Use the formula for the general term in a geometric sequence. Substitute the values for a_6, r, and n and simplify.

Solve for a_1

$$48 = \frac{a_1}{32}$$

$$a_1 = 1536$$

Solve the equation for a_1. The first term is 1536.

5. Write an equation for the general term of the geometric sequence 2, −6, 18, ...

SOLUTION

Calculate common ratio r

$$r = \frac{a_2}{a_1}$$

$$r = \frac{-6}{2}$$

$$r = -3$$

First, calculate r from the first two terms. The common ratio is −3.

> Multiplying a number by a negative number changes its sign. If the common ratio for a geometric sequence is negative, the terms alternate in sign.

Substitute

$$a_n = a_1 r^{n-1}$$
$$a_n = a_1 r^{n-1}$$
$$a_n = 2(-3)^{n-1}$$

To write the equation for the general term in this sequence, use the formula for a_n. Substitute the values for a_1 and r.

6. **MP 2, 4** You enlarge a photograph to make the linear dimensions 25% larger over and over again. The photograph started at 8 inches wide. Write an equation to represent the width after each increase and use it to calculate the width after it has been enlarged five times.

> Increasing a photograph's size by 25% means each photograph is 125% the size of the previous photograph. We restate 125% as 1.25. If we enlarge the photograph five times, we have the sixth image of the photograph.

SOLUTION

Substitute

$$a_n = a_1 r^{n-1}$$
$$\text{width} = (8)(1.25^{n-1})$$

The photograph starts with an 8-inch width, so $a_1 = 8$. Each time we increase it we must multiply by 125%, which is 1.25. The common ratio is 1.25.

$$\text{width} = (8)(1.25^{6-1})$$

Set n equal to 6. Why? If we enlarge it five times, it is our sixth photograph. The original photograph is $n = 1$, the first enlargement is $n = 2$, and so on. The fifth enlargement is the sixth photograph.

Evaluate

$$\text{width} = (8)(1.25^5)$$
$$\text{width} \approx 24.4 \text{ inches}$$

Evaluate. The final width after five enlargements is about 24.4 inches.

Model Problems continue . . .

7. **MP 2, 4** You have 4 pet amoebas. They each undergo mitosis once an hour, which means each amoeba splits into 2 amoebas. None perish. After 24 hours, how many pet amoebas do you have?

    a Determine a formula for how many amoebas there are after t hours and graph the first 8 hours.

    b Solve the formula for 24 hours and discuss some real-life limitations to the model.

SOLUTION

a Determine a_1 and r

$a_1 = 4$
$r = 2$

The initial number of amoebas is 4. Every hour each amoeba splits into two, so the total number of amoebas doubles. The common ratio between each hour is 2, since the number increases to 200% of the previous number.

Write formula for geometric sequence

$a_n = a_1 r^{n-1}$
$a_n = 4 \cdot 2^{n-1}$
$A_t = 4 \cdot 2^t$

Substitute the initial term and the common ratio into the equation for geometric sequences. For the initial term when $n = 1$ the number of hours equals 0, and for the second term when $n = 2$ the number of hours equals 1. Because the number of hours t is always 1 fewer than n, substitute t into the equation for $n - 1$. Use A_t for the number of amoebas after each hour.

Plot points and graph

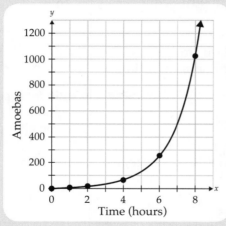

Evaluate the formula for several points from $t = 0$ to $t = 8$, and plot them on a graph. The number of amoebas increases exponentially.

> If the common ratio is greater than 1, then the geometric sequence can be described as exponential growth. If the common ratio is less than 1, but greater than 0, the geometric sequence can be described as exponential decay.

b Find the number of amoebas when $t = 24$

$A_t = 4 \cdot 2^t$
$A_{24} = 4 \cdot 2^{24}$
$A_{24} = 4 \cdot 16{,}777{,}216$
$A_{24} = 67{,}108{,}864$

Substitute the value of 24 for t, and multiply. There are 67,108,864 amoebas after 1 day.

The number of amoebas goes from just 4 to more than 67 million over the course of one day, doubling each hour. Left at this exponential rate, there would be more than one quadrillion at the end of the next day. This seems unrealistic, since in real life there would be external factors in their environment to limit such growth. It is highly unlikely that no amoebas would perish during the 24 hours.

We show one of two similar activities below. In these activities, you help a frog locate his (mathematically oriented) flies using your knowledge of geometric sequences.

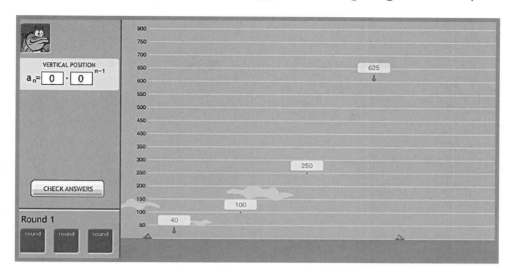

What Type of Sequence?

In the following model problems, the sequences are either arithmetic or geometric. The first step is to determine the type of sequence by finding if there is a common difference or a common ratio.

MODEL PROBLEMS

1. Given the sequence 54, 36, 24, 16, ... ,

    a   Determine if the sequence is arithmetic or geometric.

    b   Find the sixth term of the sequence.

SOLUTION

a   Calculate differences

$$a_n - a_{n-1} = d$$
$$36 - 54 = -18$$
$$24 - 36 = -12$$

If the sequence is arithmetic, then the difference between any two consecutive terms will be the same. Subtract the first two terms, and get a difference of -18. Then subtract the second term from the third to get -12.

Arithmetic?   Sequence is **not** arithmetic

The differences between the pairs of terms are not the same. There is no common difference. This means the sequence is not arithmetic.

Calculate ratios

$$r = \frac{a_n}{a_{n-1}}$$

$$\frac{36}{54} = \frac{2}{3}$$

$$\frac{24}{36} = \frac{2}{3}$$

$$\frac{16}{24} = \frac{2}{3}$$

If the series is geometric, then the ratio between any two consecutive terms will be the same. We calculate the ratios of each pair of terms, dividing each term by the term before it.

Geometric?   Sequence is geometric

Since there is a common ratio of $\frac{2}{3}$, the sequence is geometric.

Model Problems continue . . .

b Substitute $\quad a_n = a_1 r^{n-1}$

$$a_6 = (54)\left(\frac{2}{3}\right)^{6-1}$$

Calculate the sixth term in the sequence by using the formula for the nth term of a geometric sequence. Substitute $r = \frac{2}{3}$, $a_1 = 54$, and $n = 6$ since we are looking for the sixth term.

Evaluate $\quad a_6 = (54)\left(\frac{2}{3}\right)^5$

Evaluate. Start by simplifying the exponent.

Factor $\quad a_6 = \dfrac{54 \cdot 2^5}{3^5} = \dfrac{(2 \cdot 3^3) \cdot 2^5}{3^5}$

Write the expression as a single fraction. We want to cancel common factors, so state 54 as $2 \cdot 3^3$, which is 2 times 27.

Simplify $\quad a_6 = \dfrac{2^6}{3^2} = \dfrac{64}{9}$

Now cancel common factors, and get $\dfrac{2^6}{3^2}$.

The sixth term is $\dfrac{64}{9}$.

2. Calculate the ninth term of the sequence $12x^2$, $16x^2$, $20x^2$, $24x^2$, ...

SOLUTION

Calculate differences

$$a_n - a_{n-1} = d$$
$$16x^2 - 12x^2 = 4x^2$$
$$20x^2 - 16x^2 = 4x^2$$
$$24x^2 - 20x^2 = 4x^2$$

To calculate the ninth term of the sequence, first determine if the sequence is arithmetic or geometric. Calculate the differences for the three pairs of terms.

Arithmetic? $\quad$ Sequence is arithmetic

Since all of the differences are the same, $4x^2$, the sequence is arithmetic.

Formula for a_n in arithmetic sequence $\quad a_n = a_1 + (n-1)d$

Calculate the ninth term in the sequence by using the formula for the nth term of an arithmetic sequence.

Substitute $\quad a_9 = 12x^2 + (9-1)4x^2$

Substitute $n = 9$, $d = 4x^2$, and $a_1 = 12x^2$ and evaluate.

Evaluate $\quad a_9 = 44x^2$

The ninth term is $44x^2$.

 In this activity, use your knowledge of arithmetic and geometric sequences to locate the flies.

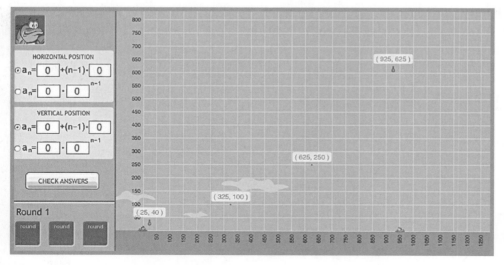

We show one of two similar activities below. In these activities, you are asked to state formulas for both the horizontal and vertical locations of the shape in order to create art.

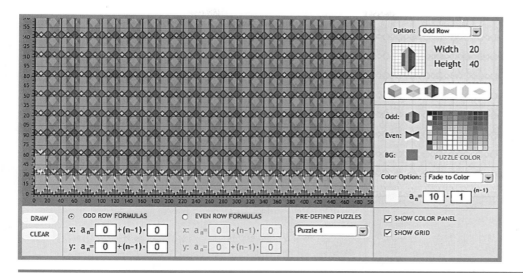

PRACTICE

1. Which of the following represents the formula for the given sequence
   $a_n = 3, 9, 27, 81, 243, \ldots$?

   A. $a_n = 3n$ C. $a_n = 3^n$

   B. $a_n = n^3$ D. $a_n = 9^{n-1}$

2. If the fourth term is $\dfrac{2}{5}$ and the sixth term is $\dfrac{18}{5}$ in a geometric sequence, what is the only possible value of the fifth term?

   A. 9

   B. 3

   C. $\dfrac{9}{5}$

   D. There is not enough information to determine the only possible value of the fifth term.

3. **MP 1, 7** The sequence $a_1, a_2, a_3, \ldots$ is a geometric sequence with common ratio r, and $b_1, b_2, b_3, \ldots$ is a geometric sequence with common ratio q. If $a_1 + b_1, a_2 + b_2, a_3 + b_3, \ldots$ is also a geometric sequence, what must be true of r and q?

   A. r is equal to q.

   B. r and q are reciprocal.

   C. r and q are opposites.

   D. r and q can be any non-zero numbers.

4. Which of the following could represent the geometric sequence $a_n = 7\left(\dfrac{3}{4}\right)^{n-1}$?

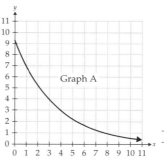

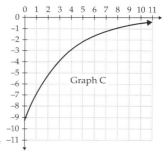

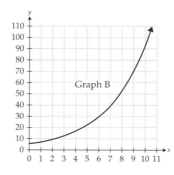

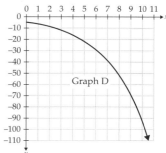

   A. Graph A   C. Graph C

   B. Graph B   D. Graph D

Practice Problems continue . . .

5. Anna analyzes the first three terms of a sequence: $mn + p, kmn + kp, k^2mn + k^2p$. She says the sequence is arithmetic because the terms increase by k each time. Which statement best describes Anna's analysis?

   A. Anna is correct because the common difference is k.

   B. Anna is correct because the terms increase by a power of k.

   C. Anna is incorrect because the sequence is geometric with a common ratio k.

   D. Anna is incorrect because the sequence is geometric with a common ratio of $kmn + p$.

6. The graph of a sequence is shown below. Which most likely is true about the sequence?

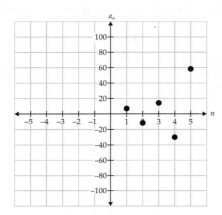

   A. The sequence is arithmetic with a common difference of -2.

   B. The sequence is geometric with a common ratio of 2.

   C. The sequence is geometric with a common ratio of -2.

   D. The sequence is arithmetic with a common difference of 2.

7. What is the greatest term in the infinite geometric sequence $-1, \dfrac{1}{2}, -\dfrac{1}{4}, \dfrac{1}{8}, \ldots$?

8. What is the smallest term in the infinite geometric sequence $6, -2, \dfrac{2}{3}, -\dfrac{2}{9}, \ldots$?

Exercises 9–10: Find the requested term.

  9. The term after 6 when the common ratio is 5.

10. The term after 2 when the common ratio is -3.

Exercises 11–18: Calculate the common ratio.

11. 5, 25, 125, 625, …

12. 3, 6, 12, 24, 48, …

13. $-2, 6, -18, 54, \ldots$

14. $96, -48, 24, -12, 6, \ldots$

15. $\sqrt{2}, 2, 2\sqrt{2}, 4$

16. $5\sqrt{2}, 5\sqrt{6}, 15\sqrt{2}$

17. 2.25, 3.375, 5.0625

18. 3, -2.25, 1.6875

Exercises 19–22: State the next term in the geometric sequence.

19. 3, 6, 12, …

20. 4, 20, 100, …

21. 4, 6, 9, …

22. 12, -6, 3, …

Exercises 23–26: The equation for the general term of a sequence is $a_n = 5(-3)^{n-1}$. Calculate the requested term in the sequence.

23. The first term

24. The third term

25. a_4

26. a_7

Exercises 27–35: Calculate the requested term in the geometric sequence.

27. A sequence starts 2, 6, 18. What is the seventh term in the sequence?

28. A sequence starts 10, 30, 90. What is the eighth term?

29. In the infinite sequence 16, 24, 36, … , what is a_6?

30. A sequence starts 32, 24, 18. What is a_5?

31. What is the eighth term in the infinite sequence 1000, -100, 10, -1, … ?

32. A sequence starts 625, -125, 25, -5. What is the sixth term?

33. A sequence starts 5, -5, 5, -5. What is the 398th term?

34. A sequence starts $ab^2, 2a^3b^3, 4a^5b^4$. What is the fifth term?

Practice Problems continue . . .

35. A sequence starts $1296y^5z^2$, $648y^4z^5$, $324y^3z^8$. What is the sixth term?

Exercises 36–39: State each term in the form $a_1 r^{n-1}$, such as $3 \cdot 5^{17}$.

36. A sequence starts 2, 8, 32, 128. What is the 11th term in the sequence?

37. A sequence starts 125, 25, 5, 1. What is the 13th term in the sequence?

38. A sequence starts 5, −15, 45, −135. What is a_9?

39. A sequence starts $1, -\dfrac{1}{2}, \dfrac{1}{4}, -\dfrac{1}{8}$. What is a_{21}?

Exercises 40–45: State the expression for the general term for the given geometric sequence.

40. 3, 12, 48, 192, …

41. 2, 10, 50, 250, …

42. 16, 12, 9, 6.75, …

43. 32, −8, 2, −0.5, …

44. $\pi, \pi^2, \pi^3, \dots$

45. $3ab^2, 27a^3b^3, 243a^5b^4, \dots$

46. **MP 4, 6**

    a Write an expression to represent the area of a photograph being enlarged n times, as shown below, with the original considered as the first step in the process.

    3.9
    3
    5   6.5

    b What will the area of the photograph be after the fourth time it has been enlarged?

Exercises 47–51: Determine whether the sequence is arithmetic, geometric, or neither. If the sequence is arithmetic or geometric, calculate its common difference or ratio, respectively.

47. 5, 9, 13, 17, …

48. 4, 12, 36, 108, …

49. $2a, 2a^3, 2a^5, 2a^7, \dots$

50. $3 + a, 6 + a^2, 9 + a^3, 12 + a^4, \dots$

51. $1 + \sqrt{2}, 3 + 2\sqrt{2}, 5 + 3\sqrt{2}, \dots$

Exercises 52–59: Determine whether the sequence is arithmetic or geometric. Then calculate the sixth term.

52. 7, 4, 1, …

53. 6, 12, 24, …

54. −128, 96, −72, …

55. −4, −1, 2, …

56. 80, −40, 20, −10, …

57. 4, −1, −6, −11, …

58. 16, 8, 0, −8, …

59. 10, 30, 90, 270, …

MP 1, 2 Exercises 60–61: Determine the formula for the sequence of the given graph.

60.

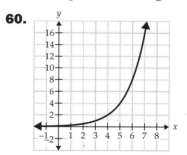

61.

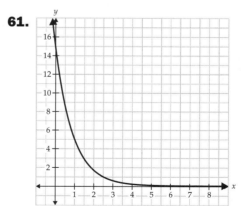

62. Sketch the graph of $a_n = -\dfrac{1}{4}\left(\dfrac{3}{2}\right)^{n-1}$.

63. You are chewing a piece of gum. Every minute, it loses 10% of its flavor. After six minutes, how much flavor is left? State your answer as a percent, and round the percent to the nearest whole percent.

Practice Problems continue . . .

64. If you make an initial investment cf $1,000,000, a llama will pay you 10% interest on your total amount of money at the end of each year. You keep the interest, and the animal pays you the interest based on your total amount of money (the interest compounds annually). After five years, how much money will you have?

65. Native Americans sold Manhattan to the Dutch in 1626 for beads and trinkets that have been said to be worth $24. Let's say these Native Americans took this money, put it in the bank at an annual interest rate of 5%. Their descendants decide to withdraw the money in 2026, earning 400 years of interest. To the nearest dollar, how much money will they have? The interest is compounded annually. Note: An estimate of Manhattan's value in 2006 is on the order of $100 billion, based on tax assessments.

66. You won the lottery. Congratulations! You receive a check for $1,000,000, put it in the bank, and keep it there for 10 years until you retire. Let's say you deposit the check in a bank account that pays 5% interest annually. The interest is compounded annually. How much money will you have after the 10 years, to the nearest dollar?

67. A deposit of $7000 is made in an account that earns 3.5% interest compounded quarterly. The balance in the account after n quarters is given by $A_n = 7000\left(1 + \dfrac{0.035}{4}\right)^n$ where $n \geq 1$. Find the balance after 10 years.

68. You put $2500 in the bank. The bank pays a 6% annual interest compounded monthly. How much money do you have after 18 months, to the nearest dollar? (Hint: Divide 6% by 12 to get the monthly rate.)

69. You drop a ball from 5 meters above the ground. Each time it bounces, it reaches 40% of its previous peak height. After it hits the ground the third time, how high will it bounce?

70. A baby kangaroo is learning to jump. Her first jump one day is 0.3 meters, and each jump is 10% higher. How high is her fourth jump? Round your answer to the nearest hundredth of a meter.

71. **MP 3** Lani claims that a geometric sequence must have terms that are all positive like $a_n = 2^n$ or terms of alternating signs like $a_n = (-2)^n$. Is her claim necessarily true? Explain.

72. **MP 3** Mack states that a nonzero sequence must either be arithmetic, geometric, or neither and can never satisfy both arithmetic and geometric properties. Is his statement true?

73. In a geometric sequence a_n with common ratio $r \neq 0$ where the second term is 3, does the number 0 occur in the sequence? Why or why not?

74. Prove that if a geometric sequence a_n contains a term that is 0 and the common ratio is not 0, then $a_k = 0$ for all k.

75. Why is it necessary to exclude $r = 0$ as the common ratio in our definition of a geometric sequence?

76. Research an application of the geometric sequence and explain your findings.

77. The midpoints of the sides of a square are connected to form an inscribed square, and a square is inscribed in it the same way. This process continues. The areas of the squares form a geometric sequence. What is the common ratio?

78. The chromatic musical scale contains 13 notes: all of the notes on a piano (both the white and black keys) from one note to the note an octave higher. The frequencies of the notes form a geometric sequence. The 13th frequency is twice the first frequency. What is the common ratio of the sequence?

79. The product of the 2nd and 5th term in a geometric sequence is 288. If the 6th term is 96, what is the first term in the sequence?

80. **MP 3, 7** If $a_n = a_1, a_2, a_3, \ldots$ and $b_n = b_1, b_2, b_3, \ldots$ are geometric sequences, prove that $a_n \cdot b_n = a_1 \cdot b_1, a_2 \cdot b_2, a_3 \cdot b_3, \ldots$ is a geometric sequence.

81. If $a_n = a_1, a_2, a_3, \ldots$ and $b_n = b_1, b_2, b_3, \ldots$ are geometric sequences and $b_k \neq 0$ for all positive integers k, prove that $\dfrac{a_n}{b_n} = \dfrac{a_1}{b_1}, \dfrac{a_2}{b_2}, \dfrac{a_3}{b_3}, \ldots$ is a geometric sequence.

8.4 Geometric Series

Geometric Series and Partial Sums

Adding the terms of a geometric sequence creates a **geometric series**. The series $4 + 8 + 16$ is a *finite geometric series*, and $2 + 6 + 18 + \ldots$ is an *infinite geometric series*.

As with an arithmetic series, S_n is the sum of the first n terms of a series. For instance, with the series $4 + 8 + 16 + 32$, S_2 represents the sum of the first two terms. Adding 4 and 8 gives that S_2 is 12. S_n is a **partial sum of a geometric series**, the result of adding a finite number of terms, starting with the first term in the series. The formula for a partial sum is shown below.

$$S_n = \frac{a_1(1 - r^n)}{1 - r}$$

S_n = partial sum of geometric series
n = number of terms
a_1 = first term
r = common ratio, where $r \neq 1$

Derivation of Formula for Geometric Series

We derive the formula for S_n for a geometric series below.

Derive: $S_n = \dfrac{a_1(1 - r^n)}{1 - r}$

S_n = sum from a_1 to a_n	$S_n = a_1 + a_2 + \ldots + a_n$	We start with the expression for a geometric series with n terms, from a_1 to a_n.
Each term is r times previous	$S_n = a_1 + a_1r + a_1r^2 + \ldots + a_1r^{n-1}$	Each term is r times the previous term, so the second term is a_1r and the last term is a_1r^{n-1}.
Multiply by r	$rS_n = a_1r + a_1r^2 + \ldots + a_1r^{n-1} + a_1r^n$	Multiply each side of the equation by r.
Subtract equations	$\begin{aligned} S_n &= a_1 + a_1r + a_1r^2 + \ldots + a_1r^{n-1} \\ -(rS_n &= \quad\ a_1r + a_1r^2 + \ldots + a_1r^{n-1} + a_1r^n) \\ \hline S_n - rS_n &= a_1 + 0 + 0 + \ldots + 0 \quad - a_1r^n \end{aligned}$	Subtract the second equation from the first one, lining up like terms vertically. Many like terms cancel when we subtract.
Factor and divide	$(1 - r)S_n = a_1 - a_1r^n$ $S_n = \dfrac{a_1 - a_1r^n}{1 - r}$	On the left, factor out S_n to write the left side as $(1 - r)S_n$. Divide both sides of the equation by $1 - r$.
Factor out a_1	$S_n = \dfrac{a_1(1 - r^n)}{1 - r}$	Factor out the common factor a_1 in the numerator to get the formula for S_n.

1. What is the sum of the first six terms of a geometric series that starts with 5, and has a common ratio of 4?

SOLUTION

Formula for S_n	$S_n = \dfrac{a_1(1 - r^n)}{1 - r}$	Use the formula for calculating the partial sum of the first n terms of a geometric series.
Substitute	$S_6 = \dfrac{5(1 - 4^6)}{1 - 4}$	Replace the variables with the values stated in the problem. The series starts with 5, so $a_1 = 5$. The common ratio is 4, so replace r with 4. Calculate the sum of the first six terms, so $n = 6$.
Evaluate	$S_6 = \dfrac{5(1 - 4096)}{-3}$ $S_6 = 6825$	Evaluate the expression. The sum of the first six terms is 6825.

2. A geometric series begins $a_1 + 12 + 18 + \ldots$,

    a Calculate the common ratio.

    b What is the sum of the first five terms?

SOLUTION

a Calculate common ratio	$r = \dfrac{a_n}{a_{n-1}}$ $r = \dfrac{18}{12} = 1.5$	First, determine the common ratio. We are given the second and third terms, so divide the third term by the second term and calculate that $r = 1.5$.
Calculate first term	$a_1 = \dfrac{a_2}{r}$ $a_1 = \dfrac{12}{1.5}$ $a_1 = 8$	We determine the first term a_1 by dividing the second term, a_2, by the common ratio, r. The first term is 8.
b Formula for S_n	$S_n = \dfrac{a_1(1 - r^n)}{1 - r}$	Start with the formula for a partial sum.
Substitute	$S_5 = \dfrac{8(1 - 1.5^5)}{1 - 1.5}$	We found $a_1 = 8$ and $r = 1.5$, and we substitute those values. Substitute 5 for n, since we are asked to calculate the sum of the first five terms.
Evaluate	$S_5 = 105.5$	We used a calculator to evaluate the expression, first raising 1.5 to the fifth power. The answer is 105.5.

Model Problems continue . . .

3. Evaluate $\sum_{n=1}^{4} 5(-2)^{n-1}$.

SOLUTION

Evaluate with sigma notation	$\sum_{n=1}^{4} 5(-2)^{n-1}$	This geometric series is described by using sigma notation, and has four terms, since it starts with $n = 1$, and ends with $n = 4$. To use the formula for S_n, we need a_1, n, and r.
General term of geometric series	$a_n = a_1 \cdot r^{n-1}$	The summand describes the general term of a geometric series. We can identify a_1 and r directly from this expression. By matching terms in the sigma notation with the variables in the formula for the general term, we find $a_1 = 5$ and $r = -2$.
Formula for S_n	$S_n = \dfrac{a_1(1 - r^n)}{1 - r}$ $S_4 = \dfrac{5(1 - (-2)^4)}{1 - (-2)}$	Use the formula for the sum of a series. Replace the variables with their values. Since the summation was from $n = 1$ to 4, the number of terms equals 4.
Evaluate	$S_4 = \dfrac{5(1 - 16)}{3}$ $S_4 = -25$	Evaluate the expression. The sum of the four terms is -25. Check the answer by expanding the series as $5 - 10 + 20 - 40$. Evaluating the sum, we get -25, which confirms our answer.

 4. **MP 2, 4** A ball is dropped from 4 feet. When it bounces, it rises to 60% of the height from which it was dropped. After 7 bounces, as the ball just touches the ground, how far vertically has it traveled?

a Calculate how far the ball travels for all the "up" bounces.

b Calculate the total vertical distance traveled.

4 feet

SOLUTION

a

"Up" distances are a geometric sequence	$r = 0.6$	The "up" distances form a geometric sequence, since each bounce is 60% of the height of the previous bounce. Write this as a common ratio of 0.6.
Determine a_1	$a_1 = (0.6)(4) = 2.4$	The ball was dropped from 4 ft, so on its first bounce up it travels 2.4 ft.
Formula for S_n	$S_n = \dfrac{a_1(1 - r^n)}{1 - r}$ $S_7 = \dfrac{2.4(1 - 0.6^7)}{1 - 0.6}$ $S_7 = 5.83$ ft	Use the formula for the partial sum of a geometric series. The ball makes seven bounces, so $n = 7$. Enter the values and calculate that the ball travels 5.83 ft on the upward bounces.

b

Total distance	distance = first drop + twice "up" distance distance = 4 + 2(5.83) distance = 15.66 ft	The total vertical distance traveled is the sum of the first drop, the rises after all the bounces, and the falls following all the rises. After each bounce, the ball rises and falls the same distance. So, we multiply its total upward distance of 5.83 ft by 2 and add the initial fall of 4 ft. The ball travels a total distance of 15.66 ft.

Infinite Geometric Series

An *infinite geometric series* is an expression for the sum of the terms in an infinite geometric sequence. The sequence $1, \frac{1}{2}, \frac{1}{4}, \frac{1}{8}, \frac{1}{16}, \ldots$ goes on forever. Each term equals the prior term times a common ratio of $\frac{1}{2}$. The infinite series for this sequence is $1 + \frac{1}{2} + \frac{1}{4} + \ldots$. The first five partial sums of this series are $S_1 = 1$, $S_2 = 1.5$, $S_3 = 1.75$, $S_4 = 1.875$, and $S_5 = 1.9375$. Note that the increase from one partial sum to the next is getting smaller. The second partial sum is 0.5 larger than the first, but the third is just 0.25 larger than the second partial sum. The difference between S_5 and S_4 is only 0.625. It appears that the partial sums are getting larger, but approaching a value around 2.

Not all geometric series have a finite sum. The common ratio r must be greater than -1 and less than 1, or $|r| < 1$, for the series to **converge** to a finite sum. When the sum of an infinite series converges, it can be calculated with the formula:

$$S = \frac{a_1}{1 - r}$$

S = sum of infinite series

a_1 = first term

r = common ratio, where $|r| < 1$

In a converging geometric series, as n gets larger and larger, the values of S_n converge to a limit. We evaluate several partial sums for the following series, expressed in sigma notation to show how a geometric series converges:

$S_n = \sum_{i=1}^{n} (0.5)^{i-1}$	$S_1 = 1$ $S_2 = 1.5$ $S_3 = 1.75$ $S_4 = 1.875$ $S_5 = 1.9375$ $S_6 = 1.96875$ $S_7 = 1.984375$ $S_8 = 1.9921875$ $S_9 = 1.99609375$ $S_{10} = 1.998046875$ ... $S_{100} = 1.9999999999999999999999999999984$	We show the first 10 partial sums. The partial sums are getting closer and closer to 2. We skip a few partial sums and calculate the 100th partial sum. You can see it is very close to 2. The partial sums of this infinite series continue to approach the number 2 as the number of terms increases. We say the series *converges*.

Another way to show that the partial sums approach 2 is with a graph. We graph the partial sums of the first 10 terms. The partial sums get closer and closer to 2. The graph of the partial sums rises toward a horizontal asymptote of $y = S = 2$.

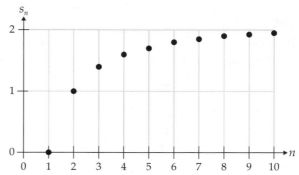

Derivation of Formula for Infinite Geometric Series

Paragraph Proof

To show that the formula for the sum of an infinite series is true, we start with the formula for the partial sum of the first n terms of a geometric sequence, $S_n = a_1 \left(\dfrac{1 - r^n}{1 - r} \right)$. When $|r| < 1$, raising r to a large positive exponent results in a number that is close to 0. For instance, think about $\left(\dfrac{1}{3} \right)^{2000}$, which is the same as $\dfrac{1}{3^{2000}}$. This is a very small positive number, very close to 0. As n gets very large, r^n gets very close to 0 and the numerator of the fraction in $a_1 \left(\dfrac{1 - r^n}{1 - r} \right)$ gets close to 1. Since r^n essentially becomes 0 when n is very large, the formula becomes $a_1 \left(\dfrac{1 - 0}{1 - r} \right)$, which equals $\dfrac{a_1}{1 - r}$.

> Why must $|r|$ be less than 1 for the formula to apply? Consider the infinite series $1 + 3 + 9 + 27 + 81 + 243 + \dots$, where r is 3. The partial sums become increasingly large. Since the partial sums do not approach a particular value, this infinite series does not have a sum.

MODEL PROBLEMS

1. Calculate the sum of the infinite geometric series with the first term 9, and common ratio $\dfrac{1}{3}$.

SOLUTION

Substitute
$$S = \frac{a_1}{1 - r}$$
$$S = \frac{9}{1 - \dfrac{1}{3}}$$

Substitute the values stated in the problem. The first term of the series, a_1, is 9 and r is $\dfrac{1}{3}$. Because r is between -1 and 1, the series converges to a finite sum.

Evaluate
$$S = \frac{9}{\left(\dfrac{2}{3} \right)} = 9 \cdot \frac{3}{2}$$
$$S = 13.5$$

Subtract in the denominator first, and then invert and multiply. The sum is 13.5.

2. Calculate the sum of the infinite series $3 - 1.5 + 0.75 + \dots$.

SOLUTION

Common ratio
$$r = \frac{-1.5}{3} = -\frac{1}{2}$$

Calculate the common ratio r by dividing the second term by the first to get $-\dfrac{1}{2}$. Since $\left| -\dfrac{1}{2} \right| < 1$, the infinite geometric series has a sum.

Substitute
$$S = \frac{a_1}{1 - r}$$
$$S = \frac{3}{1 - \left(-\dfrac{1}{2} \right)}$$

The problem states the first term is 3, and we calculated that r equals $-\dfrac{1}{2}$. Substitute those values into the formula.

Evaluate
$$S = \frac{3}{\left(\dfrac{3}{2} \right)} = 3 \cdot \frac{2}{3}$$
$$S = 2$$

Evaluate the expression, which requires dividing by a fraction. The sum is 2.

Model Problems continue . . .

3. a Calculate the sum of the infinite series: $n + (-2mn) + 4m^2n + (-8m^3n) + \dots$.
Which expression best represents the sum?

A. $\dfrac{n}{3}$ C. $\dfrac{n}{1 - 2m}$

B. $\dfrac{1 + 2m}{n}$ D. $\dfrac{n}{1 + 2m}$

b In part **a**, what restrictions must be placed on m in order for this infinite series to have a sum? Explain.

SOLUTION

a A. This is the sum of the infinite series with a first term n and common ratio -2. But since an infinite series with a ratio of 2 does not have a finite sum, the formula cannot be used.

B. This is the reciprocal of the formula for the sum of the infinite series.

C. The denominator of the formula is $1 - r$ and since $r = -2m$, the denominator should be $1 - (-2m) = 1 + 2m$.

D. **Correct answer.** The first term is n and the common ratio is $-2m$. Using the formula for the sum of the infinite geometric series, $S = \dfrac{n}{1-(-2m)} = \dfrac{n}{1 + 2m}$.

b The absolute value of the common ratio, $-2m$, must be less than 1, so $-\dfrac{1}{2} < m < \dfrac{1}{2}$. Another restriction is $m \neq 0$; otherwise the series is not infinite, consisting only of its first term, n.

 4. **MP 2, 4** A *fractal* is a geometric shape that can be split into parts, each of which is a reduced-size copy of the whole. The triangles in the diagram to the right are examples. Fractals often can be defined with a simple, recursive formula. The *Sierpinski triangle* is a fractal created using equilateral triangles. The process of creating it involves removing smaller triangles from larger ones.

a Find a rule for a_n, the number of triangles removed by the nth iteration, and determine the total number of triangles removed by the 12th iteration.

b Find the remaining area of the triangle after the nth stage, and calculate the remaining area after the eighth iteration.

SOLUTION

a Determine common ratio — At each iteration one triangle is removed from each black triangle, leaving three smaller black triangles behind. The number of triangles removed by each iteration equals the number of remaining black triangles before the iteration. The sequence of numbers of triangles removed by each iteration (or remaining before the iteration) is a geometric sequence with initial term 1 and a common ratio of 3.

Substitute values into formula for geometric sequence
$$a_n = a_1 r^{n-1}$$
$$a_n = (1)(3^{n-1})$$
$$a_n = 3^{n-1}$$
To find the expression for the nth term of the sequence, substitute the common ratio and the initial term into the formula for geometric sequences and simplify.

Substitute values into formula for partial sum
$$S_n = \dfrac{a_1(1 - r^n)}{1 - r}$$
$$S_n = \dfrac{1(1 - 3^n)}{1 - 3}$$
$$S_n = \dfrac{1 - 3^n}{-2}$$
Find an expression for the total number of triangles removed after the 12th iteration by substituting the common ratio and initial term into the formula for S_n.

Model Problems continue . . .

Calculate S_{12} $S_{12} = \dfrac{1 - 3^{12}}{-2}$ To calculate the total number of triangles removed after the 12th iteration, substitute 12 for n into the formula for S_n.

$S_{12} = \dfrac{1 - 531,441}{-2}$

$S_{12} = 265,720$

b Calculate area after n iterations

Take the initial area to be 1 unit. After the first iteration, $\dfrac{3}{4}$ of that area remains. After the second iteration, $\dfrac{3}{4}$ of the remaining area remains, and so on. We see that the sequence of remaining areas is a geometric sequence with common ratio $\dfrac{3}{4}$ and initial term 1.

Substitute values into formula for geometric sequence

$a_n = a_1 r^{n-1}$

$a_n = (1)\left(\dfrac{3}{4}\right)^{n-1}$

$a_n = \left(\dfrac{3}{4}\right)^{n-1}$

Substitute the common ratio and the initial term into the formula for geometric sequences and simplify.

Calculate a_8

$a_8 = \left(\dfrac{3}{4}\right)^{8-1}$

$a_8 = \dfrac{3^7}{4^7}$

$a_8 \approx 0.1335$

To find the remaining area of the original triangle after the eighth iteration, substitute 8 for n into a_n and calculate. Since the original area was 1, the remaining area a_8 is approximately 0.1335.

5. **MP 7** Every rational number can be written as a decimal that either terminates or has a repeating pattern of digits. For example, $\dfrac{3}{8} = 0.375$ terminates, and $\dfrac{41}{33} = 1.\overline{24}$ does not terminate. The bar over 24 indicates those digits repeat forever. One way to consider a repeating decimal is as an infinite series. Use this approach to write $0.\overline{345}$ as a ratio of integers.

SOLUTION

Write as infinite series

$0.\overline{345} = 0.345 + 0.000345 + 0.000000345 + \ldots$

$r = \dfrac{1}{1000}$

Each term of the series is $\dfrac{1}{1000}$ of the previous term, so this is a geometric series with the common ratio $\dfrac{1}{1000}$. For instance, the second term, 0.000345 is the product of the first term 0.345 and $\dfrac{1}{1000}$.

Substitute

$S = \dfrac{a_1}{1 - r}$

$S = \dfrac{0.345}{1 - \dfrac{1}{1000}} = \dfrac{0.345}{\dfrac{999}{1000}}$

Since $|r| < 1$, the infinite series has a sum S and we can use the formula to calculate it. Replace the variables a_1 and r with their values and subtract.

Simplify

$S = \dfrac{345}{999} = \dfrac{115}{333}$

If you divide 115 by 333 on a calculator, you will see that it equals $0.\overline{345}$.

PRACTICE

1. Which of the following best represents the sum of the first 20 terms for the infinite series $200 + 100 + 50 + \ldots$?

   A. 375   C. 400

   B. 395   D. 425

2. Given the infinite series: $-2 + 1 - \dfrac{1}{2} + \ldots$, which of the following represents the sum?

   A. -4 C. $-\dfrac{5}{4}$

   B. $-\dfrac{4}{3}$ D. -1

3. If an infinite geometric series is convergent, then which of the following must be true?

   A. The common ratio $|r| < 1$.

   B. The terms in the series must be of alternating signs.

   C. The sequence of partial sums must be decreasing.

   D. None of the above.

Exercises 4–7: Find the partial sum as indicated.

4. The first five terms of a geometric sequence that starts with 3 and has a common ratio of 2.

5. The first seven terms of a geometric sequence that starts with 2 and has a common ratio of 3.

6. The first seven terms of a geometric sequence that starts with 2 and has a common ratio of -4.

7. The first nine terms of a geometric sequence that starts with -3 and has a common ratio of -2.

Exercises 8–11: Write the series in expanded form.

8. $\displaystyle\sum_{n=1}^{4} 5(2)^{n-1}$

9. $\displaystyle\sum_{n=1}^{4} 3(4)^{n-1}$

10. $\displaystyle\sum_{n=1}^{3} -2(-3)^{n-1}$

11. $\displaystyle\sum_{n=1}^{3} -3(-2)^{n-1}$

12. Find the sum of the first six terms of the geometric series that starts $243 + 81 + 27 + \ldots$.

13. Find the sum of the first eight terms of the geometric series that starts $2 + (-6) + 18 + \ldots$.

Exercises 14–15: Calculate the sum.

14. $\displaystyle\sum_{n=1}^{5} 72\left(\dfrac{1}{2}\right)^{n-1}$

15. $\displaystyle\sum_{n=1}^{6} -25(-0.4)^{n-1}$

16. Use the diagram to answer the following questions.

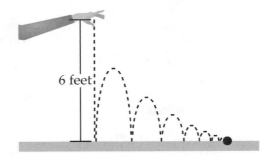

6 feet

   a After six bounces, with the ball rising $\dfrac{2}{3}$ of its prior height each time, how far has the ball traveled vertically?

   b After seven bounces, with the ball rising 60% of its prior height each time, how far has the ball traveled vertically?

Exercises 17–20: If the infinite geometric series converges, calculate its sum. If the infinite geometric series does not converge, state so.

17. $4 + \dfrac{4}{3} + \dfrac{4}{9} + \dfrac{4}{27} + \ldots$

18. $18 + 9 + \dfrac{9}{2} + \dfrac{9}{4} + \ldots$

19. $25 + 5 + 1 + \dfrac{1}{5} + \ldots$

20. $\dfrac{1}{6} - \dfrac{1}{2} + \dfrac{3}{2} - \dfrac{9}{2} + \ldots$

Practice Problems continue . . .

Exercises 21–23: Rewrite the repeating decimal as the ratio of two integers in simplest form.

21. $0.\overline{72}$

22. $0.\overline{189}$

23. $0.0\overline{411}$

24. As the number of iterations of the Sierpinski triangle goes to infinity, what value does the area approach?

25. **MP 7, 8** The diagram below is known as the famous Koch snowflake fractal, which is created using the following steps:

  (i) Start with an equilateral triangle.

  (ii) Divide each side into thirds.

  (iii) For each side, create a new equilateral triangle, pointing outward from the original, whose base is the middle third of the side.

  (iv) Remove the base of the newly created triangle.

  (v) Repeat steps (ii)–(iv) as many times are you want.

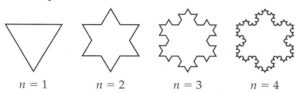

$n = 1$ $n = 2$ $n = 3$ $n = 4$

If the side of the original equilateral triangle is 5 inches and the pattern continues forever, what is the perimeter of the 10th Koch snowflake?

Exercises 26–28: For each problem, complete the table and plot the points (n, S_n) on the coordinate system. Then use the infinite series formula to find the value of the infinite series.

Index n	1	2	3	4	5	6	7
Sequence a_n							
Partial sums S_n							

26. $a_n = (3)\left(\dfrac{1}{2}\right)^{n-1}$

27. $a_n = (4)\left(\dfrac{2}{3}\right)^{n-1}$

28. $a_n = (5)\left(-\dfrac{1}{2}\right)^{n-1}$

29. **MP 2, 4** A fuse is cut into 5 parts forming a geometric sequence. If the shortest length is 6 centimeters and the longest length is 96 centimeters, what is the total length of the fuse?

30. A pile driver drives a steel column into the earth. On its first drive, the column moves 2 meters into the earth. On its second drive, it moves a further 1.8 meters. Assume its movement is a geometric sequence and calculate how far the column has been driven into the earth after five drives. Round your answer to the nearest tenth.

31. You decide to trace back your ancestors. You count your two parents as the first generation back, and their four parents as the second generation back, and so on. If you go back seven generations, how many total ancestors would you have traced back?

32. A phone tree is a way to contact a large number of people, perhaps to say a school is closed because it lost electricity. The tree starts with one person calling five people (which is round one), and each of those people calling five more people (round two), and so on. If 3500 people have to be called, how many rounds are required? In the last round, a caller might call fewer than five people.

33. A ball is attached to the end of a swinging rod in a damped pendulum system. If its initial swing makes an arc 15 inches long and each successive swing travels only 95% of its preceding swing, what is the total distance traveled by the ball? Assume the pendulum in this damped system is allowed to swing forever.

34. A ball is dropped from 12 meters and after each bounce it rises 20% of the height from which it falls. If the ball is allowed to bounce forever, what is the total vertical distance the ball travels?

35. **MP 3** June calculated the infinite series

$$2 - 3 + \frac{9}{2} - \frac{27}{4} + \ldots \text{ by applying the}$$

formula $S = \dfrac{a_1}{1 - r} = \dfrac{2}{1 - \left(-\dfrac{3}{2}\right)} = \dfrac{4}{5}.$

She concludes the sum is $\dfrac{4}{5}$. Is she correct?

Practice Problems continue . . .

36. What does it mean for a series to converge? What do you call a series that isn't convergent?

37. If an infinite sequence converges to a number, does it necessarily imply its corresponding infinite series converges? Why or why not?

38. `MP 3, 8` Prove that if an infinite geometric sequence approaches 0, its corresponding infinite series converges.

39. `MP 3, 8` Explain how we can use infinite series to show that all numbers containing repeated digits after the decimal are rational numbers.

40. A convergent infinite geometric series starts with 6, and the sum is $\frac{9}{2}$. What is the sum of the first five terms?

41. Assume $|x| < 1$. Write an expression for the sum of the infinite series $1 + 2x + 3x^2 + 4x^3 + \dots$. (Hint: Consider $S - xS$.)

42. Develop your own fractal defined by using geometric sequences. Then use its corresponding infinite series to determine the area or perimeter of your fractal. If neither infinite series converges, find a formula for calculating its nth iteration.

• Multi-Part PROBLEM Practice •

`MP 2, 4` You are allowed to use a 4-by-6-inch note card on your physics test, but the amount of notes you write take up a much larger space. By the time you finish writing your notes, you have filled an 8-by-12-inch piece of paper. You can use the photocopier to shrink your notes, but the copier will only reduce the area to 86% of the original. Note that your card and paper are similar rectangles and the photocopy of any figure is a similar figure.

a Write an equation for the general term of the geometric sequence that represents the area on the nth reduction.

b On what reduction (which value of n) will your copy be small enough to fit on the 4-by-6-inch card?

c Discuss how close you are to an actual 4-by-6-inch card.

d How much paper, in total area, will you have used for your images? Round your answer to the nearest whole number. Hint: Find the partial sum of the series for the requisite number of terms.

LESSON 8.5

8.5 Binomial Theorem

Binomial Expansion

We expand the binomial $a + b$ for the powers from 0 to 4 below. The sum of terms for each binomial is a binomial expansion. There are patterns evident in these expansions involving the exponents and the coefficients. We will start with the pattern in exponents and then describe the pattern in cofficients.

Exponents

$(a + b)^0 = 1$
$(a + b)^1 = a + b$
$(a + b)^2 = a^2 + 2ab + b^2$
$(a + b)^3 = a^3 + 3a^2b + 3ab^2 + b^3$
$(a + b)^4 = a^4 + 4a^3b + 6a^2b^2 + 4ab^3 + b^4$

A **binomial expansion** is created by raising a binomial like $a + b$ to a power.

- Sum of exponents for a term of $(a + b)^n$ equals n

In each term, the sum of the exponents of a and b equals n, the power to which the binomial is raised. In the bottom row, that power is 4, so the sum of the exponents must equal 4. For instance, the third term of $(a + b)^4$ is $6a^2b^2$. The exponents of both a and b in this term are 2, and $2 + 2 = 4$.

- Exponents of a start with n, go to 0

The exponents of a start with n, the power the binomial is raised to, and decrease by 1 with each term. For $(a + b)^4$, the exponents of a start with 4, which means the expansion starts with a^4. The exponents of a decrease by 1 from one term to the next. This means the factor of a in the second term is a^3. In the third term, the factor of a is a^2, and a^1, which is just a, appears in the fourth term. The pattern continues until the exponent equals 0, which is to say a^0 appears in the last term. Since $a^0 = 1$, the last term just has b as its variable.

> The sum of the exponents of any term of $(a + b)^n$ is n. The exponents of a decrease by 1 with each term while the exponents of b increase by 1.

- Exponents of b start with 0, go to n

The exponents of b start with 0 (so there is no b in the first term, just a^4). The exponents of b then increase by 1 each term and stop at n, which is 4 in this expansion. The last term is b^4. The binomial expansion of $(a + b)^n$ is written as a polynomial in descending order of the power of a. Because the exponents of a (or b) in the terms of $(a + b)^n$ include all of the integers from 0 to n, the expansion of $(a + b)^n$ has $n + 1$ terms, one more than the power n.

Coefficients

> In each binomial expansion, the coefficients are symmetric as they increase toward the middle and then decrease.

$$(a + b)^0 = 1$$
$$(a + b)^1 = 1a + 1b$$
$$(a + b)^2 = 1a^2 + 2ab + 1b^2$$
$$(a + b)^3 = 1a^3 + 3a^2b + 3ab^2 + 1b^3$$
$$(a + b)^4 = 1a^4 + 4a^3b + 6a^2b^2 + 4ab^3 + 1b^4$$

- Start at 1

The coefficients in each expansion start with 1. For example, in the expansion of $(a + b)^4$, the coefficient of a^4 is 1. We show coefficients of 1 here so the pattern is easier to see.

- Increase

The coefficients then increase from left to right. For $(a + b)^4$, the coefficients increase from 1 to 4 to 6.

- Decrease back to 1 in reverse pattern

The coefficients then decrease back to 1, in the reverse order of their increase. The entire pattern of coefficients for $(a + b)^4$ is 1, 4, 6, 4, 1.

We can determine the coefficients for a binomial expansion using a pattern called *Pascal's triangle*. This is named for Blaise Pascal, the French mathematician, philosopher, and religious scholar. (Other scholars also "discovered" or studied the triangle. For instance, in China it is called the *Yanghui triangle*, after the Chinese mathematician who studied it about 500 years before Pascal.) Pascal's triangle starts with 1 on its left and right edges. Each of the other numbers is the sum of the two numbers directly above it.

$(a + b)^0$
$(a + b)^1$
$(a + b)^2$
$(a + b)^3$
$(a + b)^4$
$(a + b)^5$

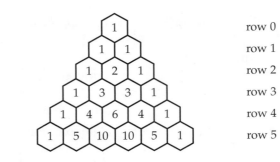

row 0
row 1
row 2
row 3
row 4
row 5

The numbers in a row of Pascal's triangle are the same as the coefficients of the terms in each binomial expansion $(a + b)^n$ shown previously. The coefficients for $(a + b)^n$ are found in row n of the triangle. The top row is row 0.

We use Pascal's triangle to expand $(a + b)^5$. Row 5 of Pascal's triangle gives us the coefficients for the binomial expansion of $(a + b)^5$. We use the pattern of exponents to write the terms of the series. The exponents of a go from 5 down to 0 and the exponents of b go from 0 up to 5. The final expanded form of $(a + b)^5$ is $a^5 + 5a^4b + 10a^3b^2 + 10a^2b^3 + 5ab^4 + b^5$.

MODEL PROBLEMS

1. Expand $(a + b)^7$. The seventh row of Pascal's triangle is 1 7 21 35 35 21 7 1.

SOLUTION

Sum of exponents is 7

$\_a^7 + \_a^6b^1 + \_a^5b^2 + \_a^4b^3 + \_a^3b^4 + \_a^2b^5 + \_a^1b^6 + \_b^7$

The problem asks you to use the seventh row of Pascal's triangle to expand $(a + b)^7$. The sum of the exponents in each term is 7. Ignore the coefficients of the terms for now.

Coefficients correspond to row 7 of Pascal's triangle

$a^7 + 7a^6b + 21a^5b^2 + 35a^4b^3 + 35a^3b^4 + 21a^2b^5 + 7ab^6 + b^7$

Fill in the coefficients for all of the terms. The coefficients correspond to the numbers in the seventh row of Pascal's triangle.

2. The seventh row of Pascal's triangle is 1 7 21 35 35 21 7 1. What is the eighth row?

SOLUTION

Outside edges are all 1

The problem asks you to use the seventh row of Pascal's triangle to find the eighth. Fill in the first and last numbers in the row. The outside edges of Pascal's triangle are all 1.

Second number is sum of two above

Find the second number in the eighth row. It is the sum of the two numbers above it in Pascal's triangle, so it is the sum of the first and second numbers in the seventh row. *Model Problems continue . . .*

Each other
number is sum
of two above

Each of the remaining numbers in the row
is the sum of the two numbers directly
above it. The third number in the eighth
row is the sum of the second and third
numbers in the seventh row, and so on.

3. Write the first three terms of the expansion of $(2x - 1)^5$.

SOLUTION

Coefficients 1 5 10	We use Pascal's triangle to write the first three terms of this binomial expansion. This requires handling the coefficients carefully. Start by writing the first three terms of the expansion of $(a + b)^5$. Write the coefficients from the appropriate row of Pascal's triangle.
Exponents $1a^5 + 5a^4b + 10a^3b^2$	Enter the variables a and b with the appropriate exponents and write the expression as a sum.
Substitute $2x$ for a and -1 for b $(2x)^5 + 5(2x)^4(-1) + 10(2x)^3(-1)^2$	The expression we were asked to raise to the 5th power was $2x - 1$, so substitute $2x$ for a and -1 for b.
Simplify $32x^5 - 80x^4 + 80x^3$	Simplify the resulting expression to write the three terms.

4. The first three terms in the expansion of $(a + b)^{19}$ are $a^{19} + 19a^{18}b + 171a^{17}b^2$. Write the last three terms.

SOLUTION

Coefficients 171 19 1	The coefficients of the last three terms in the expansion of $(a + b)^{19}$ are the same as the coefficients of the first three terms, but in reverse order. They are 171, 19, and 1.
Exponents $171a^2b^{17} + 19ab^{18} + b^{19}$	For the last three terms, the exponents of a and b are symmetrical. The exponent of a becomes the exponent of b, and vice versa. Do the same with the term that starts with 19. $19a^{18}b$ is one of the first three terms, so $19ab^{18}$ must be one of the last three. And since a^{19} is the first term, b^{19} must be the last. Remember that a^{19} is equivalent to $a^{19}b^0$. Write the expression as a sum.

Factorial Notation

Factorial notation is an efficient way to write products of integers. To calculate the factorial of integer n, denoted $n!$, start with n, and multiply n by all the positive integers that are less than n, $n! = n \cdot (n-1) \cdot (n-2) \cdot \ldots !$ until the final factor equals 1. For instance, $3! = 3 \cdot 2 \cdot 1 = 6$.

> The factorial of 0 is defined as 1 so $0! = 1$.

MODEL PROBLEMS

1. Compute $7!$

SOLUTION

$7! = 7 \cdot 6 \cdot 5 \cdot 4 \cdot 3 \cdot 2 \cdot 1$
$7! = 5040$

2. Compute $\dfrac{5!}{3!}$

SOLUTION

Cancel factorials $\quad \dfrac{5!}{3!} = \dfrac{5 \cdot 4 \cdot 3!}{3!} = \dfrac{5 \cdot 4 \cdot \cancel{3!}}{\cancel{3!}} = 20$

There is a shortcut for dividing $5!$ by $3!$. Instead of expanding the numerator all the way, stop when we reach 3, and state it as $5 \cdot 4 \cdot 3!$. Cancel the $3!$ factor, which leaves the product of 5 and 4, which is 20.

> Formulas involving factorials often involve division of factorials. In model problem 2, we show a shortcut for dividing factorials.

Binomial Coefficients

The coefficients of the terms in the expansion of $(a + b)^n$ are called **binomial coefficients**. The formula in the box can be used to calculate the coefficients of a binomial expansion. The variable n represents the exponent in the binomial expansion and k gives the $k + 1$ term in the expansion. For example, if $n = 5$ and $k = 3$, the formula finds the coefficient for the fourth term in the expansion of $(a + b)^5$. The binomial coefficient for n and k is written using parentheses as you see, with n above k and no fraction bar between them. This is read as "n choose k." It is defined using factorials.

$$\binom{n}{k} = \frac{n!}{k!(n-k)!}$$

$\binom{n}{k}$ = binomial coefficients

There is a connection between binomial coefficients and Pascal's triangle. Using the binomial coefficient formula, any number in Pascal's triangle can be calculated directly:

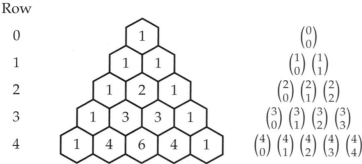

Row
0
1
2
3
4

The binomial coefficient $\binom{n}{k}$ is the number at position $k + 1$ in row n of Pascal's triangle. The diagram shows the first four rows of Pascal's triangle, including row 0, on the left, and the corresponding binomial coefficients on the right.

MODEL PROBLEMS

1. What is $\binom{12}{9}$?

SOLUTION

Substitute and evaluate

$$\binom{n}{k} = \frac{n!}{k!(n-k)!}$$

$$\binom{12}{9} = \frac{12!}{9!(12-9)!}$$

$$\binom{12}{9} = \frac{12 \cdot 11 \cdot 10 \cdot 9!}{9! \, 3!} = \frac{1320}{6}$$

$$\binom{12}{9} = 220$$

We calculate the binomial coefficient for 12 choose 9 by entering those values into the formula. Because 12! is the product of all the integers from 12 to 1, write it as $12 \cdot 11 \cdot 10 \cdot 9!$ and cancel to simplify. The binomial coefficient is 220.

2. What is the fourth number in row 4 of Pascal's triangle?

SOLUTION

Number in row n, at position $k + 1$

$$\binom{n}{k} = \frac{n!}{k!(n-k)!}$$

We start with the formula for finding the binomial coefficients.

For row 4, position 4

$$\binom{4}{3} = \frac{4!}{3!(4-3)!}$$

The number at position 4 in row 4 of Pascal's triangle is the binomial coefficient of the fourth term in the expansion of $(a + b)^4$.

Factor and simplify

$$\binom{4}{3} = \frac{4 \cdot 3!}{3! \cdot 1!} = 4$$

Factor the numerator to cancel 3!. The binomial coefficient is 4, which is the number shown at position 4 in row 4 of Pascal's triangle.

Model Problems continue . . .

MODEL PROBLEMS *continued*

3. What is $\binom{n}{0}$?

SOLUTION

The first number in any row of Pascal's triangle is 1. This means $\binom{n}{0}$ should be 1. We check this, using the fact that $0! = 1$. $\binom{n}{0} = \frac{n!}{0!(n-0)!} = \frac{n!}{1 \cdot n!} = 1$, so any binomial coefficient with $k = 0$ is 1.

4. What is $\binom{39}{8}$?

SOLUTION

Substitute $\binom{n}{k} = \frac{n!}{k!(n-k)!}$ — Substitute the values for n and k.

$$\binom{39}{8} = \frac{39!}{8!(39-8)!}$$

Evaluate $\binom{39}{8} = \frac{39!}{8!\,31!}$ — Factor the numerator to cancel 31!. Calculate the binomial coefficient to be 61,523,748.

$$\binom{39}{8} = \frac{39 \cdot 38 \cdot 37 \cdot 36 \cdot 35 \cdot 34 \cdot 33 \cdot 32 \cdot \cancel{31!}}{8! \cdot \cancel{31!}}$$

$$\binom{39}{8} = 61{,}523{,}748$$

5. What is the seventh number in row 18 of Pascal's triangle?

SOLUTION

Substitute $\binom{n}{k} = \frac{n!}{k!(n-k)!}$ — To calculate the seventh number in row 18, substitute 18 for n and 6 for k.

$$\binom{18}{6} = \frac{18!}{6!(18-6)!}$$

Evaluate $\binom{18}{6} = \frac{18!}{6!12!}$ — Factor the numerator to cancel 12!. Calculate the binomial coefficient to be 18,564.

$$\binom{18}{6} = \frac{18 \cdot 17 \cdot 16 \cdot 15 \cdot 14 \cdot 13 \cdot \cancel{12!}}{6! \cdot \cancel{12!}}$$

$$\binom{18}{6} = 18{,}564$$

Binomial Theorem

The formula below can be used to calculate any term in a binomial expansion, and it is part of the *binomial theorem*:

$$\binom{n}{k} a^{n-k} b^k$$

The coefficients of these terms appear in Pascal's triangle. In row n the numbers run from $\binom{n}{0}$ to $\binom{n}{n}$. As k takes values from 0 to n, the exponent of a starts at n and decreases in steps of 1 until it reaches 0, while the exponent of b follows the opposite of that pattern.

The formula for the sum of all these terms—with n fixed and k running from 0 to n—is called the **binomial theorem**. Note that the summation index k indeed runs from 0 to n in the formula.

$$(a + b)^n = \sum_{k=0}^{n} \binom{n}{k} a^{n-k} b^k$$

MODEL PROBLEMS

1. What is the term that contains b^3 in $(a + b)^5$?

SOLUTION

Formula for term with b^k in $(a + b)^n$	$\binom{n}{k} a^{n-k} b^k$	Use the formula for calculating any term in a binomial expansion of $(a + b)^n$. We want the term that contains b^k.
Substitute values	$\binom{5}{3} a^{5-3} b^3$	Substitute the values. We want the term for b^3 in $(a + b)^5$, so $n = 5$ and $k = 3$.
Do the operations	$\binom{5}{3} a^{5-3} b^3 = \dfrac{5!}{3!(5-3)!} a^2 b^3$	Use the formula for the binomial coefficient and subtract to simplify the exponent of a.
Simplify	$\binom{5}{3} a^{5-3} b^3 = \dfrac{5 \cdot 4 \cdot 3!}{3!\, 2!} a^2 b^3$	Factor the numerator to cancel 3! and simplify the expression. The term is $10a^2b^3$.
	$\binom{5}{3} a^{5-3} b^3 = 10\, a^2 b^3$	

2. What term contains y^7 in $(3x - y)^9$?

SOLUTION

Term with b^7 in $(a + b)^9$	$\binom{9}{7} a^{9-7} b^7$ $36a^2 b^7$	The first step is to use the formula to calculate the term with b^7 in $(a + b)^9$.
Substitute	$36(3x)^2(-y)^7$ $-36(9x^2)y^7$ $-324x^2y^7$	In the original binomial, the first term is $3x$ and the second term is $-y$. Replace a and b with these expressions, and simplify the result. The term is $-324x^2y^7$.

Model Problems continue . . .

3. Expand $(a + b)^5$.

SOLUTION

$(a + b)^n = \sum_{k=0}^{n} \binom{n}{k} a^{n-k} b^k$

$(a + b)^5 = \binom{5}{0} a^5 b^0 + \binom{5}{1} a^4 b^1 + \binom{5}{2} a^3 b^2 + \binom{5}{3} a^2 b^3 + \binom{5}{4} ab^4 + \binom{5}{5} a^0 b^5$

$(a + b)^5 = \binom{5}{0} a^5 + \binom{5}{1} a^4 b + \binom{5}{2} a^3 b^2 + \binom{5}{3} a^2 b^3 + \binom{5}{4} ab^4 + \binom{5}{5} b^5$

The binomial theorem with $n = 5$ and values of k from 0 to 5 gives us the six terms in the expansion for $(a + b)^5$. The power of a starts at 5, and decreases by 1 with each term. The power of b starts at 0, and increases by 1 with each term.

Evaluate binomial coefficients

$\binom{5}{0} = \frac{5!}{0!5!} = \frac{5!}{5!} = 1$ $\binom{5}{3} = \frac{5!}{3!2!} = \frac{5 \cdot 4}{2 \cdot 1} = 10$

$\binom{5}{1} = \frac{5!}{1!4!} = \frac{5}{1} = 5$ $\binom{5}{4} = \frac{5!}{4!1!} = \frac{5}{1} = 5$

$\binom{5}{2} = \frac{5!}{2!3!} = \frac{5 \cdot 4}{2 \cdot 1} = 10$ $\binom{5}{5} = \frac{5!}{5!0!} = \frac{5}{5} = 1$

Evaluate the binomial coefficients.

Write expansion

$a^5 + 5a^4 b + 10a^3 b^2 + 10a^2 b^3 + 5ab^4 + b^5$

Substitute the coefficients to complete the expansion.

4. Expand $(2x + \sqrt{3})^4$.

SOLUTION

$(a + b)^n = \sum_{k=0}^{n} \binom{n}{k} a^{n-k} b^k$

$(a + b)^4 = \binom{4}{0} a^4 + \binom{4}{1} a^3 b + \binom{4}{2} a^2 b^2 + \binom{4}{3} ab^3 + \binom{4}{4} b^4$

The binomial theorem with $n = 4$ and values of k from 0 to 4 gives us the terms in the expansion for $(a + b)^4$.

Evaluate binomial coefficients

$\binom{4}{0} = \frac{4!}{0!4!} = \frac{4!}{4!} = 1$ $\binom{4}{3} = \frac{4!}{3!1!} = \frac{4}{1} = 4$

$\binom{4}{1} = \frac{4!}{1!3!} = \frac{4}{1} = 4$ $\binom{4}{4} = \frac{4!}{4!0!} = \frac{4}{4} = 1$

$\binom{4}{2} = \frac{4!}{2!2!} = \frac{4 \cdot 3}{2 \cdot 1} = 6$

Evaluate the binomial coefficients.

Write expansion

$a^4 + 4a^3 b + 6a^2 b^2 + 4ab^3 + b^4$

Write the binomial coefficients.

Substitute

$(2x + \sqrt{3})^4 = (2x)^4 + 4(2x)^3 (\sqrt{3}) + 6(2x)^2 (\sqrt{3})^2 + 4(2x)(\sqrt{3})^3 + (\sqrt{3})^4$

Replace a and b with $2x$ and $\sqrt{3}$.

Simplify

$(2x + \sqrt{3})^4 = 16x^4 + 32\sqrt{3}x^3 + 72x^2 + 24\sqrt{3}x + 9$

Simplify.

PRACTICE

1. Which of the following is the third term in the binomial expansion of $(\sqrt{2x} - y)^4$?

   A. $-4\sqrt{2x}y^3$ C. $24x^2y^2$

   B. $12xy^2$ D. $-32x^3y$

2. How many terms are in the binomial expansion $(7a + b)^{2k-1}$?

   A. $2k - 2$ C. $2k$

   B. $2k - 1$ D. $2k + 1$

3. Find the binomial coefficient represented by $\begin{pmatrix} 2m - p \\ 0 \end{pmatrix}$ and describe its location in Pascal's triangle.

   A. $\begin{pmatrix} 2m - p \\ 0 \end{pmatrix} = 2m - p$. It is the first number in the 0th row of Pascal's triangle.

   B. $\begin{pmatrix} 2m - p \\ 0 \end{pmatrix} = 1$. It is the first number in the $(2m - p)$th row of Pascal's triangle.

   C. $\begin{pmatrix} 2m - p \\ 0 \end{pmatrix} = 0$. It is the $(2m - p)$th number in the 0th row of Pascal's triangle.

   D. $\begin{pmatrix} 2m - p \\ 0 \end{pmatrix} = 1$. It is the $(2m - p)$th number in the 1st row of Pascal's triangle.

Exercises 4–7: Calculate the requested term using Pascal's triangle.

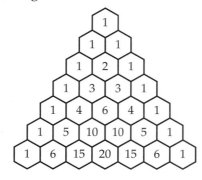

4. The third term in $(a + b)^7$.

5. The last term in $(a + b)^7$.

6. The second term in $(a + b)^6$.

7. The fourth term in $(a + b)^6$.

Exercises 8–15: Calculate the requested term.

8. The fourth term in $(3x + y)^4$.

9. The third term in $(3x + y)^4$.

10. The fifth term in $(2z - w)^5$.

11. The third term in $(2z - w)^5$.

12. The fourth term in $(p - q^2)^6$.

13. The third term in $(p - q^2)^6$.

14. The fifth term in $(-2k + 3m^3)^7$.

15. The third term in $(-2k + 3m^3)^7$.

Exercises 16–17: Expand.

16. $(2 + \sqrt{x})^3$

17. $(5 - 2\sqrt{x})^3$

Exercises 18–23: Evaluate.

18. $\dfrac{(0!)(9!)}{7!}$

19. $\dfrac{13!}{9!}$

20. $\begin{pmatrix} 13 \\ 11 \end{pmatrix}$

21. $\begin{pmatrix} 7 \\ 4 \end{pmatrix}$

22. $\begin{pmatrix} 5 \\ 2 \end{pmatrix}$

23. $\begin{pmatrix} 8 \\ 4 \end{pmatrix}$

Exercises 24–27: State the requested term.

24. In $(a + b)^{27}$, the term with b to the 25th power.

25. In $(a + b)^{18}$, the term with b to the 16th power.

26. In $(a + b)^{12}$, the term with b to the 9th power.

27. In $(a + b)^{14}$, the term with b to the 11th power.

Exercises 28–29: State the requested term.

28. In $(2x - y)^{14}$, the term where y is raised to the 12th power.

29. In $(-x + 2y)^{11}$, the term where y is raised to the 4th power.

Practice Problems continue . . .

Practice Problems continued . . .

30. **MP 3, 6** A student's completed solution for the 5th term in the binomial expansion of $(2x - a)^7$ is shown below. Identify the errors in the student's work.

5th term in $(2x - a)^7 = \binom{7}{5}(2x^2)(a^5)$

$$= \frac{7!}{5!(7 - 5)!}(2x^2)(a^5)$$

$$= \frac{7 \cdot 6}{2 \cdot 1}(2x^2)(a^5)$$

$$= 42x^2a^5$$

31. Prove $(m + n)! = m! + n!$ or provide a counterexample.

32. **MP 3, 7** Use Pascal's triangle to explain why $\binom{n}{k} = \binom{n}{n - k}$. Prove this algebraically.

33. Choose a large integer n and compute the nth partial sum given by $\sum_{k=0}^{n} \frac{1}{k!}$. Make an educated guess as to the value of $\sum_{k=0}^{\infty} \frac{1}{k!}$.

34. Solve the equation $\sum_{k=0}^{6} \left(\binom{6}{k} x^{6-k} 2^k \right) = 0$.

35. Solve the equation $\sum_{k=0}^{5} \left(\binom{5}{k} x^{5-k} (-3)^k \right) = 32$.

36. **MP 3, 6** Prove $\binom{n}{k} = \left(\frac{n - k + 1}{k} \right)\binom{n}{k - 1}$.

37. **MP 3, 6** Prove $\binom{n}{k} = \binom{n - 1}{k - 1} + \binom{n - 1}{k}$.

Chapter 8 Key Ideas

8.1 Arithmetic Sequences

- A sequence is an ordered list of numbers. By "ordered," we mean that it matters which number comes first, which comes second, and so on. A number in a sequence is called a *term*. The notation, $a_1, a_2, a_3, \ldots$, is used to describe sequences. The subscripted number is called the *index* and describes the place of the term in the sequence. The general term of a sequence is a_n, where the index is indicated with the variable n. The general term represents any term in a sequence and is often used in equations.

- In an arithmetic sequence, each term equals the sum of the preceding term and a constant called the *common difference*. The definition of an arithmetic sequence is the formula $a_n = a_{n-1} + d$ where a_n is the general term in the sequence, a_{n-1} is the term before a_n, and d is the common difference. This is a recursive formula.

- The explicit formula for the general term in an arithmetic sequence is $a_n = a_1 + (n - 1)d$ where a_1 is the first term in the sequence, and d is the common difference.

- The slope of a line that passes through the graph of an arithmetic sequence equals the common difference of the sequence.

8.2 Arithmetic Series

- When the terms of a sequence are added together, the resulting expression is a series. Adding the terms of an arithmetic sequence creates an arithmetic series.

- A series can be written using sigma notation. The Greek letter Σ (sigma) indicates a sum, and is called the *summation sign*. The summand is the expression for the nth term of the sequence. The variable n is called the index of the summation, and is always an integer. The initial value of n is stated below Σ, and the value of n is increased by 1 to create each term, until the value above Σ is reached. The value above Σ is infinity for an infinite series.

- The sum of the first n terms of a series is denoted by S_n. This is called the *nth partial sum of a series*. For an arithmetic series, $S_n = \frac{n}{2}(a_1 + a_n)$.

8.3 Geometric Sequences

- In a geometric sequence, each term equals the product of the preceding term and a constant called the common ratio. As with arithmetic sequences, the terms of a geometric sequence are often referred to using the notation $a_1, a_2, a_3, \ldots$, with a_n representing the general term.
- The definition of a geometric sequence is the formula: $a_n = a_{n-1} \cdot r$ where a_n is the general term in the sequence, a_{n-1} is the term before a_n, and r is the common ratio.
- The formula for the general term in a geometric sequence is $a_n = a_1 r^{n-1}$ where a_1 is the first term in the sequence, and r is the common ratio.

8.4 Geometric Series

- Adding the terms of a geometric sequence creates a geometric series. As with an arithmetic series, S_n is the sum of the first n terms of a geometric series. The formula for calculating the nth partial sum of a geometric series is $S_n = \frac{a_1(1 - r^n)}{1 - r}$.
- An infinite geometric series is an expression for the sum of the terms in an infinite geometric sequence. The sum of an infinite series, if it exists, is denoted as S. An infinite geometric series has a sum when $|r| < 1$. If the sum exists, $S = \frac{a_1}{1 - r}$.

8.5 Binomial Theorem

- A binomial expansion is created by raising a binomial like $a + b$ to a power, n. The coefficients of the terms are called *binomial coefficients*.
- Pascal's triangle is a triangular array of numbers where the outside edges are all 1, and each other number is the sum of the two numbers directly above it. The top point of Pascal's triangle is considered row 0, and it has only one number in it: 1. The numbers in a row of Pascal's triangle are the same as the coefficients of the terms in the binomial expansion of $(a + b)^n$, where n corresponds to the row number.
- Factorial notation is an efficient way to write products of integers. To calculate $n!$, start with n, subtract 1 repeatedly to calculate the other factors, stopping at 1, and multiply all of the factors: $n! = n \cdot (n - 1) \cdot (n - 2) \cdot \ldots \cdot 3 \cdot 2 \cdot 1$. The factorial $0!$ is defined as 1.
- The binomial coefficient for n and k is written as $\binom{n}{k}$, and is read as "n choose k". It is defined as $\binom{n}{k} = \frac{n!}{k!(n - k)!}$.
- The binomial theorem states that the binomial coefficient $\binom{n}{k}$ is the number at position $k + 1$ in row n of Pascal's triangle.

CHAPTER 8 REVIEW

1. Assume the pattern continues in the sequence 17, 10, 5, … . Is the sequence arithmetic, geometric, or neither?

   A. Arithmetic
   B. Geometric
   C. Neither

2. What is the index of the term 8 in the sequence 4, −2, 6, −8, 8, −32, 10, −128, 12?

3. The general term in a sequence is described by $a_n = n^2 - 1$. Find a_7.

4. The eighteenth term in an arithmetic sequence is 89, and the common difference is −16. What is the nineteenth term in the sequence?

5. What is the next term in the arithmetic sequence −2, 5, 12, 19, … ?

6. Write an expression for the general term in the arithmetic sequence 52, 56, 60, 64, … .

7. Find the 11th term in the sequence −9, −21, −33, −45, … .

8. Consider the famous Fibonacci sequence: 1, 1, 2, 3, 5, 8, 13, … . Use the pattern to find the recursive formula for the series and calculate the next term.

9. Write the series for the sequence 1, 3, 9, 27.

10. Expand the series $\sum_{n=1}^{5} (3n - 1)$.

11. For the geometric series $5 + (-10) + 20 + \dots$, what is S_7?

12. Evaluate $\sum_{n=1}^{6} 224\left(\frac{1}{2}\right)^{n-1}$.

13. Calculate S for an infinite geometric series with $a_1 = 30$ and $r = \frac{3}{5}$.

14. Calculate the sum of the infinite geometric series $112 + (-84) + 63 + \dots$.

15. Write the first three terms in the expansion of $(2x + y)^5$.

16. Compute 5!

17. Compute $\dfrac{12!}{10!}$

18. What is the value of $\begin{pmatrix} 13 \\ 3 \end{pmatrix}$?

19. Sketch the graph of $a_n = 7 - 3(n - 1)$.

20. Sketch the graph of $a_n = 6\left(\frac{2}{3}\right)^{n-1}$.

21. Complete the table and plot the points (n, S_n) on the coordinate system. Then use the infinite series formula to find the value of the infinite series for $a_n = (7)\left(-\frac{3}{5}\right)^{n-1}$.

Index n	1	2	3	4	5	6	7
Sequence a_n							
Partial sums S_n							

22. **MP 1** Taking the reciprocal of each term of an arithmetic sequence creates a *harmonic sequence*. For example, the reciprocals of the terms of the arithmetic sequence 1, 2, 3, … create the harmonic sequence $\frac{1}{1}, \frac{1}{2}, \frac{1}{3}, \dots$. A harmonic sequence begins $3, \frac{3}{2}, 1, \frac{3}{4}, \dots$. What is the general form for this harmonic sequence? Use this to determine the 99th term.

23. **MP 2, 4** Use the diagram below to make a sketch for the sequence of partial sums at least for the first 5 terms of the arithmetic sequence $a_n = -1 + 2n$. Then determine the 12th term of the sequence of partial sums (i.e., the 12th partial sum of a_n).

24. The seventh term in a geometric sequence is $\frac{7}{2}$ and the common ratio is 6. What is the eighth term?

Chapter Review continues . . .

25. Write an expression for the general term in the geometric sequence -224, -56, -14, -3.5, ...

26. The first term in a geometric sequence is 405. To get the next term, you divide by 3. What is the fifth term in the sequence?

27. What is the sixth term in the geometric sequence that starts $4x$, $20x^2$, $100x^3$, ... ?

28. **MP 2, 6** A convergent infinite geometric series starts with 4, and the sum is 8. What is the sum of the first three terms?

29. **MP 2, 7** Add the entries of the first few rows in Pascal's triangle and make a conjecture about the sum of the entries in the nth row as a function of n. That is, find $f(n)$ for $\sum_{i=0}^{n} \binom{n}{i} = f(n)$. Test your formula by comparing it with the result from the sum of binomial coefficients for $n = 7$.

30. **MP 7, 8** Write the expansion for $\left(\sqrt{a} + 4x\right)^3 \left(\sqrt{a} - 4x\right)^3$.

Cumulative Review
for Chapters 1–8

1. Solve $2^x + 2^{x-1} = 96$.

   A. 2

   B. 5

   C. 6

   D. 32

2. Factor completely: $3x^4 - 27x^2 + 5x^4 - 45x^2$

3. Is $(-3, 6, 0)$ a solution to the system of equations?

   $2x + y = z; x + 3 = z; z - 4x = 2y$

4. Solve the system $y = 2x$ and $\dfrac{x^2}{8} - \dfrac{y^2}{64} = 1$ using substitution. Show the process and state the solutions.

5. **MP 6, 7** Solve the system $2x^2 + 4y^2 = 108$ and $x^2 + y^2 = 45$ using elimination. Show the process and state the solutions.

6. **MP 1, 2, 4** On a quarter-mile track, two runners start at the same position and time. One person runs 6-minute miles and the other runs 8-minute miles. When will they be together at the same position on the track?

7. Divide $\dfrac{x + 35}{x + 11}$. Write your answer as $1 + R(x)$ where $R(x)$ is a rational expression.

Exercises 8–9: Simplify.

8. $\dfrac{w^{\frac{1}{6}}}{w^{\frac{2}{3}}} \cdot w^{\frac{3}{4}}$

9. $\dfrac{\sqrt[7]{36}}{\sqrt[7]{4}}$

Exercises 10–11: Solve.

10. $\sqrt{x} - 4 = 12$

11. $\sqrt{x} - 6 = 7$

12. What is the volume of a cube with each face having a surface area of $291 + 154\sqrt{2}$ centimeters? The side length has the form $a + b\sqrt{c}$. Give your answer in exact radical form.

13. **MP 4, 5** Determine whether a linear, quadratic, or radical function is "best" used to model the given table of data. Justify your answer. What might be associated with this data?

x	y
1	5
2	5.6
4	6.6
7	7.9
10	9.0

Exercises 14–17: Solve. If there is no solution, say so.

14. $3^{2x} = 3^{x+2}$

15. $5^{x-1} = 5^{3x-7}$

16. $5^x + 3 \cdot 5^{x-2} = 140$

17. **MP 2, 7** $4^x - 2^{x+1} - 48 = 0$ (Hint: Let $t = 2^x$. Then solve a quadratic equation for t.)

18. What is $(f - g)(5)$ if $f(x) = -3x - 1$ and $g(x) = 4x - 11$?

19. What is $\left(\dfrac{f}{g}\right)(4)$ if $f(x) = x + 6$ and $g(x) = -3x - 8$?

Exercises 20–21: Restate the following as exponential equations.

20. $y = \log_{15} 2$

21. $\log_3 81 = 4$

Exercises 22–23: State the answer to the nearest thousandth. Use a calculator or a spreadsheet.

22. $\log 14$

23. $\log 0.2$

24. Evaluate $\ln \dfrac{1}{e^{-5}}$.

25. Restate as an exponential equation: $\ln a = 2$

26. Restate as a logarithmic equation: $e^{2k+1} = 15$

27. Write the series in expanded form:

$$\sum_{n=1}^{8} (5n - 3)$$

28. What is S_6 for the geometric series $-4 + 12 + (-36) + \dots$?

29. Calculate S for an infinite geometric series with $a_1 = -8$ and $r = \dfrac{2}{3}$.

30. **MP 4, 8** A county fair is holding a pool tournament for cash prizes. First place receives $400, second place receives $350, and third place receives $300. Prizes continue to be awarded following this pattern until the prize amount reaches 0. What is the total amount of cash awarded to the tournament players, and how many prizes are given? Assume there are enough players such that all cash prizes are awarded.

Chapter Content

Vocabulary

adjacent leg	hypotenuse	radian measure
amplitude	midline	reference angle
angle of rotation	opposite leg	secant
central angle	period	sine
cosecant	periodic function	tangent
cosine	phase identity	trigonometric identity
cotangent	phase shift	trigonometric ratio
coterminal	Pythagorean identity	trigonometry
frequency	Pythagorean theorem	unit circle
horizontal scaling	radian	vertical scaling

LESSON 9.1

9.1 Geometry Review: Right Triangles

Right Triangle Basics

A *right triangle* is a triangle with one angle equal to 90°, which is called a *right angle*. The two sides that meet at the right angle are called *legs*, and the side of the triangle opposite the right angle is called the **hypotenuse**. It is typical to call the legs a and b, and the hypotenuse c.

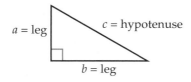

The **Pythagorean theorem** states that in a right triangle, the hypotenuse squared equals the sum of the squares of the legs, $c^2 = a^2 + b^2$.

> **Pythagorean theorem**
> $$a^2 + b^2 = c^2$$

You may find yourself calculating the length of a hypotenuse frequently. You may see the equation for the hypotenuse's length stated as $c = \sqrt{a^2 + b^2}$. We can also apply a similar idea to calculate the length of a leg, $a = \sqrt{c^2 - b^2}$.

> The converse of the Pythagorean theorem is also true. In any triangle, if the lengths of the 3 sides, a, b, c, satisfy the equation $a^2 + b^2 = c^2$, then the triangle is a right triangle and the side of length c is the hypotenuse.

MODEL PROBLEMS

1. What is the length of the hypotenuse of a right triangle with legs 9 and 12?

SOLUTION

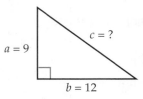

$a^2 + b^2 = c^2$ The Pythagorean theorem states that the sum of the squares
$9^2 + 12^2 = c^2$ of the legs equals the square of the hypotenuse. The legs have
               lengths 9 and 12, so substitute those values in the equation.

$81 + 144 = c^2$ Evaluate. Square 9 and 12, getting 81 and 144, and add. The result is 225.
$\quad\;\; 225 = c^2$

$c = \sqrt{225} = 15$ Since c^2 is equal to 225, c is the square root of 225, which is 15.

2. Is a triangle with sides of length 3 meters, 4 meters, and 5 meters a right triangle?

SOLUTION

If the sides of a triangle $3^2 + 4^2 \stackrel{?}{=} 5^2$ The longest side must be the hypotenuse,
have lengths, a, b, c that   since its square is the sum of the
satisfy $a^2 + b^2 = c^2$ squares of the legs. If this triangle is a
right triangle, the side of length 5 meters
must be the hypotenuse, c. Enter the
values into the Pythagorean theorem.

> We use the converse of the Pythagorean theorem to determine if this is a right triangle.

Then the triangle is a $9 + 16 \stackrel{?}{=} 25$ Square 3, 4, and 5, and add the squares 9 and 16. Their sum,
right triangle $25 = 25$ 25, equals the square of 5, confirming that this is a right
triangle.

3. A leg of a right triangle is 12 and the hypotenuse is 13. How long is the other leg?

SOLUTION

Start with Pythagorean theorem	$a^2 + b^2 = c^2$	Start with the Pythagorean theorem.
Solve for a^2	$a^2 = c^2 - b^2$	Solve the equation for a^2. Subtract b^2 from both sides.
Substitute hypotenuse for c and leg for b	$a^2 = 13^2 - 12^2$	Substitute in the length of the hypotenuse, 13, and the length of the leg, 12.
	$a^2 = 169 - 144$ $a^2 = 25$ $a = 5$	Square the numbers and subtract, then take the positive square root, since lengths are positive. The length of the leg is 5.

PRACTICE

1. Which of the following sets of side lengths cannot form a right triangle?

   A.   3, 4, 5
   B.   5, 12, 13
   C.   8, 15, 17
   D.   5, 6, 8

2. A triangle has sides $a = 4$, $b = 5$, and $c = 6$. Is it a right triangle?

   A.   Yes
   B.   No
   C.   Not enough information to determine

Practice Problems continue . . .

Practice Problems continued . . .

3. A triangle has sides 1, 2, and 5. Is it a right triangle?

   A. Yes

   B. No

   C. Not enough information to determine

4. What is the length of the hypotenuse of a right triangle with legs 6 and 8?

5. A right triangle has legs 8 and 15. What is the length of the hypotenuse?

6. A right triangle has one leg of length 14 and a hypotenuse of length 50. What is the length of the other leg?

7. A right triangle has a leg 8 and hypotenuse 17. What is the length of the other leg?

8. A right triangle has two legs, one with length 8 and the other with length 2. What is the length of the hypotenuse?

9. A right triangle has one leg of length 5 and a hypotenuse of length $\sqrt{125}$. What is the length of the other leg?

10. A right triangle has a hypotenuse of length 12 and one leg with length 6. What is the length of the other leg?

11. What is the length of the hypotenuse of a right triangle with legs $a = 5$ and $b = 5$?

12. A 19-foot ladder leans against a wall. If the base of the ladder is 10 feet from the wall, how far up the wall is the top of the ladder?

13. **MP 2** To get from his house to the grocery store, Peter must drive 6 miles directly east and then 8 miles directly north. How far is Peter's house from the grocery store, as the crow flies?

Special Right Triangles

A triangle can be described by the number of sides and angles that are congruent and the measures of its angles. One way a triangle can be described is by the measure of its largest angle.

Acute
All angles less than 90°

Right
Has a right (90°) angle

Obtuse
Has an angle greater than 90°

Another property of a triangle is the number of congruent sides or congruent angles it has.

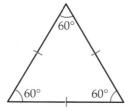
Equilateral triangles have:

- all sides congruent
- three congruent angles

Isosceles triangles have:

- at least two congruent sides
- at least two congruent angles

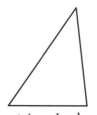
Scalene triangles have:

- no congruent sides
- no congruent angles

We use the Pythagorean theorem to determine the lengths of the sides of two specific right triangles, 45-45-90 and 30-60-90 triangles.

45-45-90 Triangles

Remember that any triangle with two sides of the same length is an isosceles triangle. In such triangles the acute angles are equal, so the angles of isosceles right triangles measure 45°, 45°, and 90°. For this reason, isosceles right triangles are sometimes referred to as 45-45-90 triangles.

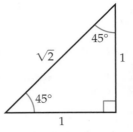

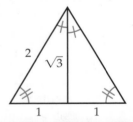

All 45-45-90 triangles are similar, so their pairs of corresponding sides are proportional. The ratio of the hypotenuse to a leg is $\sqrt{2} : 1$ in an isosceles right triangle.

We use sides of length 1 to calculate the hypotenuse. The ratio of the hypotenuse to the legs will be the same for any isosceles right triangle, since all isosceles right triangles are similar.

$c^2 = 1^2 + 1^2$ Use the Pythagorean theorem to state the relationship
$c^2 = 2$ between the legs and the hypotenuse c.
$c = \sqrt{2}$ Solve the equation. The length of the hypotenuse is $\sqrt{2}$.

30-60-90 Triangles

Another special right triangle has acute angles measuring 30° and 60°. This is called a 30-60-90 triangle. The short leg is opposite the smaller, 30° angle.

Again, we have the length of one leg as 1 for simplicity's sake. The ratios here apply to any 30-60-90 triangle, since all these triangles are similar.

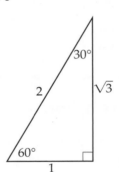

In a 30-60-90 triangle, the ratio of the shorter leg to the hypotenuse is 1 : 2. The ratio of the longer leg to the hypotenuse is $\dfrac{\sqrt{3}}{2}$.

We can use the diagram to the right to explain the lengths of the sides. We construct a congruent triangle to form an equilateral triangle (since the two base angles are 60°, the upper angle must be 60° as well). We assume the sides of the equilateral triangle have length 2. The vertical leg bisects the base, forming a right angle, and each of the two smaller triangles has a horizontal leg length of 1. The Pythagorean theorem enables us to conclude the vertical leg has a length of the square root of 3.

MODEL PROBLEMS

1. What are the lengths of the legs of this triangle?

$\sqrt{72}$

SOLUTION

45-45-90 triangle ratio

This is a 45-45-90 triangle, since the two legs are shown as congruent and it is a right triangle. The ratio of the sides opposite the 45° angles to the side opposite the right angle is $1 : 1 : \sqrt{2}$.

Write ratio $\dfrac{\text{hypotenuse}}{\text{leg}} = \dfrac{\sqrt{2}}{1}$ Write the ratio of the hypotenuse to a leg.

Solve for leg $\text{leg} = \dfrac{\text{hypotenuse}}{\sqrt{2}}$ Solve for a leg.

Evaluate $\text{leg} = \dfrac{\sqrt{72}}{\sqrt{2}} = \sqrt{\dfrac{72}{2}} = \sqrt{36} = 6$ Substitute, divide radicals, and simplify.

Model Problems continue . . .

2. What are the angles in this triangle?

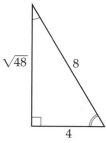

SOLUTION

Simplify $\sqrt{48} = \sqrt{16 \cdot 3} = 4\sqrt{3}$ In the triangle, the longer leg is $\sqrt{48}$. Simplify this to $4\sqrt{3}$.

Divide all sides by 4

$\dfrac{4}{4} = 1$ Divide each side by 4.

$\dfrac{4\sqrt{3}}{4} = \sqrt{3}$

$\dfrac{8}{4} = 2$

30-60-90 triangle $1 : \sqrt{3} : 2$ This is the ratio of the sides of a 30-60-90 triangle.

3. Jolene has a ramp that she wants to make into a jump. She is curious how high off the ground it will be if it makes a 30° angle compared to a 60° angle from the ground. She would like to know the answer to the nearest tenth of a foot.

SOLUTION

Draw triangles

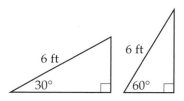

Draw the two cases of a 30° and 60° triangle.

Use 30° ratio   30° opposite leg to hypotenuse = 1 : 2

$\dfrac{x}{6} = \dfrac{1}{2}$

This is the ratio of the leg opposite the 30° angle to the hypotenuse in a 30-60-90 triangle.

Evaluate $x = 6 \cdot \dfrac{1}{2} = 3$ feet

The 30° leg is one-half the length of the hypotenuse. Multiply, and calculate that the end of the ramp would be 3 feet high.

Calculate the height with the 60° angle

60° opposite leg to hypotenuse = $\sqrt{3} : 2$

$\dfrac{x}{6} = \dfrac{\sqrt{3}}{2}$

$x = 6 \cdot \dfrac{\sqrt{3}}{2} \approx 5.2$ feet

Rounded to the nearest tenth of a foot, the end of the ramp is about 5.2 feet high when the ramp makes a 60° angle with the ground.

We can check the answers for being reasonable. The 60° jump is higher than the 30° jump, which makes sense. Also, both lengths are less than the hypotenuse, which also makes sense.

Model Problems continue . . .

4. **MP 2, 4** It is 90 feet from home plate to first base, and the same distance between any two consecutive bases. How far does a catcher have to throw from home plate to second base, to the nearest foot?

SOLUTION

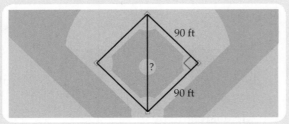

Draw isosceles right triangle

Start by recognizing that the indicated base paths form two legs of an isosceles right triangle. Both are 90 feet.

Ratio

$$\text{hypotenuse} : \text{leg} = \sqrt{2} : 1$$

This is the ratio of the hypotenuse to the legs of an isosceles right triangle.

Multiply leg by ratio

$$\frac{\text{hypotenuse}}{\text{leg}} = \frac{\sqrt{2}}{1}$$

$$\text{hypotenuse} = \frac{\sqrt{2}}{1} \text{leg}$$

$$\text{hypotenuse} = \sqrt{2} \cdot 90 \approx 127 \text{ feet}$$

Multiply 90 by the ratio, and round to the nearest foot. The catcher needs to throw the ball 127 feet. To check this answer, we could check that indeed $90^2 + 90^2 \approx 127^2$.

PRACTICE

1. If the sides of a right triangle measure 8, $8\sqrt{3}$, and 16, what is the measure of the smallest interior angle of the triangle?

    A. 30°   C. 60°

    B. 45°   D. 90°

2. The area of a 30-60-90 triangle is $18\sqrt{3}$. How long is the shortest side of the triangle?

    A. 6   C. 12

    B. $6\sqrt{3}$ D. $9\sqrt{3}$

3. A triangle has sides that measure 2, $2\sqrt{3}$, and 4. This triangle is best described as a(n)

    A. 30-60-90 triangle.

    B. Scalene obtuse triangle.

    C. Scalene acute triangle.

    D. Isosceles right triangle.

4. The hypotenuse of an isosceles right triangle has a length of $3\sqrt{2}$. What is the length of a leg?

5. The leg opposite the 30° angle of a 30-60-90 triangle has a length of 5. What is the length of the hypotenuse?

6. The leg opposite the 30° angle of a 30-60-90 triangle has a length of 4. What is the length of the hypotenuse?

7. The leg opposite the 60° angle of a 30-60-90 triangle has a length of $7\sqrt{3}$. What is the length of the hypotenuse?

8. The leg opposite the 60° angle of a 30-60-90 triangle has a length of $11\sqrt{3}$. What is the length of the hypotenuse?

9. The leg opposite the 60° angle of a 30-60-90 triangle has a length of $3\sqrt{3}$. What is the length of the hypotenuse?

10. One leg of an isosceles right triangle measures 1 unit. What is the exact length of the hypotenuse of this triangle?

11. The hypotenuse of an isosceles right triangle has a length of $5\sqrt{2}$. What is the length of a leg?

12. The hypotenuse of an isosceles right triangle has a length of $\sqrt{18}$. What is the length of a leg?

Practice Problems continue . . .

13. The hypotenuse of an isosceles right triangle has a length of 8. What is the length of a leg?

14. The hypotenuse of an isosceles right triangle has a length of $12\sqrt{2}$. What is the length of a leg?

15. A right triangle has a hypotenuse that measures 2 cm and a base that measures 1 cm. What is the exact length of its height?

16. In a 30-60-90 triangle, the hypotenuse measures 12 inches. What is the length of the shorter leg?

17. In a 45-45-90 triangle, the hypotenuse measures $7\sqrt{2}$ centimeters. What is the length of one leg?

18. The longer leg of a 30-60-90 triangle measures $\sqrt{75}$ units. How long is the shorter leg?

19. The hypotenuse of a 30-60-90 triangle measures 22 units. How long is the leg opposite the 60° angle?

20. An isosceles right triangle has a hypotenuse of $3\sqrt{2}$. Sketch the triangle and label the measures of all three angles. Then state the length of each of the legs.

21. Sketch a 30-60-90 triangle with a hypotenuse of 6. Label the measures of all three angles, as well as the lengths of both legs.

22. A square courtyard is crossed by two diagonal footpaths that connect its corners. One side of the courtyard measures 120 feet.

   a Make a sketch of the situation.

   b Find the length of one diagonal footpath, to the nearest tenth of a foot.

23. On a fast-pitch softball field, it is 60 feet from home plate to first base, and the same distance between any two consecutive bases. How far does a catcher have to throw from home plate to second base, to the nearest foot?

24. Joel has an 8-foot-long ramp that he wants to make into a jump. He wants the jump to be as high as possible, as long as it's not higher than 7 feet. Should he use a 30° or 60° angle between the ground and board? Round to the nearest tenth.

25. Mr. Nichols built a ramp over his front steps so he could move a piano into his house. The ramp makes a 30° angle with the ground and reaches a height of 4.25 feet at the top of the steps. How long is the ramp?

26. The perimeter of an equilateral triangle is 42 feet. What is the exact length of its altitude?

27. An obtuse isosceles triangle has a vertex angle that measures 120°, and its two congruent sides each measure 8 centimeters. How long is the altitude of the triangle, in centimeters?

28. **MP 1, 3** Is it possible for the lengths of all three sides in a 45-45-90 triangle to be integers? Why or why not?

29. **MP 2** The diagonal of a rectangle is equal to twice the length of the base of the rectangle. What is the measure of the smallest angle of a triangle formed by the base, height, and diagonal of the rectangle?

30. What type(s) of triangles are formed within a 30-60-90 triangle when the altitude connecting the right angle to the hypotenuse is constructed? Explain your reasoning.

31. Write a word problem based on a 30-60-90 triangle. Make sure to include a solution to the problem you have written.

32. **MP 2, 3** Assuming that the legs of an isosceles right triangle each measure x, show that the length of the hypotenuse will be $x\sqrt{2}$.

33. An artist is designing a window. The window will be a square within a square, with the interior square formed by connecting the midpoints of the sides of the outer square. If the outer square has a perimeter of 80 inches, what is the area of the interior square?

34. The legs of an isosceles right triangle each measure 6 feet. An altitude of the triangle is constructed, connecting the triangle's right angle and its hypotenuse. What is the exact length of the altitude, in feet?

35. **MP 2** The interior of a regular hexagon can be divided into 6 congruent, equilateral triangles. If the perimeter of the hexagon is 60 units, what is its exact area, in square units?

9.2 Geometry Review: Trigonometric Functions

Trigonometric Ratios

Trigonometry is the study of the relationships of the sides and angles of triangles. Ratios of the sides of triangles play a crucial role in trigonometry.

Trigonometric ratios are the ratios of the sides of a right triangle defined in connection with an acute angle in the triangle. We will call that acute angle $\angle A$. The **adjacent leg** is next to angle A. The hypotenuse and the adjacent leg form $\angle A$. The **opposite leg** is the other leg, which lies across from $\angle A$.

The **sine**, **cosine**, and **tangent** are the most commonly used trigonometric ratios.

Sine of A $\sin A = \dfrac{\text{length of opposite leg}}{\text{length of hypotenuse}}$	The sine of $\angle A$ is the ratio of the lengths of the leg opposite to $\angle A$ and the hypotenuse. The abbreviation for the sine is "sin."
Cosine of A $\cos A = \dfrac{\text{length of adjacent leg}}{\text{length of hypotenuse}}$	The cosine of $\angle A$ is the ratio of the lengths of the leg adjacent to $\angle A$ and the hypotenuse. The abbreviation for the cosine is "cos."
Tangent of A $\tan A = \dfrac{\text{length of opposite leg}}{\text{length of adjacent leg}}$	The tangent of $\angle A$ is the ratio of the lengths of the leg opposite to $\angle A$ and the leg adjacent to $\angle A$. The abbreviation for the tangent is "tan."

The classic way to remember the ratios: SOH CAH TOA. It is **S**ine **O**pposite **H**ypotenuse, **C**osine **A**djacent **H**ypotenuse, and **T**angent **O**pposite **A**djacent.

Trigonometric ratios are an outcome of similar right triangles. We examine the side ratios for two similar triangles, and show that the ratios depend only on the angles of the triangles. If two right triangles are similar, then the values of their trigonometric ratios will be equal, since the ratios only depend on the acute angle measures.

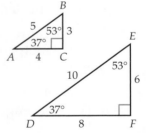

- $\triangle ABC$ and $\triangle DEF$ are similar

  By definition of similar triangles, all corresponding angles are congruent and corresponding sides are proportional.

- The corresponding side ratios are equal: $\dfrac{BC}{AB} = \dfrac{EF}{DE} = \dfrac{3}{5}, \dfrac{BC}{AC} = \dfrac{EF}{DF} = \dfrac{3}{4}, \dfrac{AC}{AB} = \dfrac{DF}{DE} = \dfrac{4}{5}$

  Calculate the ratio of the sides in one triangle and compare it to the ratio of the corresponding sides in the other triangle. The ratios are equal. This is true for any pair of side ratios between the two triangles.

- Trigonometric function: $\dfrac{AC}{AB} = \dfrac{DF}{DE} = \sin 53°$

  Trigonometric ratios are side ratios that reference specific sides related to one of the acute angles. For example, $\dfrac{AC}{AB}$ and $\dfrac{DF}{DE}$ are the ratios of the opposite leg to the hypotenuse with respect to the 53° angle. This is the sine of 53°.

The values of many trigonometric functions are irrational numbers. This means their digits continue forever with no pattern. We use the "approximately equals" symbol, ≈, to indicate we are rounding their values to the nearest thousandth.

 In this activity, experiment with right triangles and the sine, cosine, and tangent functions. You can drag vertices A or B to change the triangle.

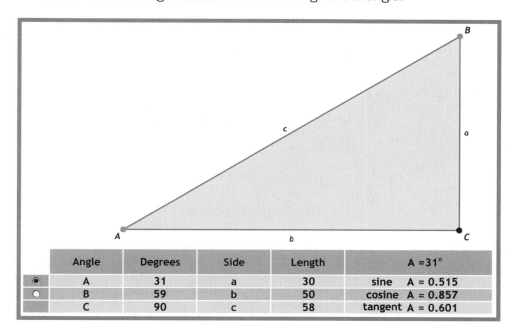

Angle	Degrees	Side	Length	A =31°
A	31	a	30	sine A = 0.515
B	59	b	50	cosine A = 0.857
C	90	c	58	tangent A = 0.601

You can use a calculator to evaluate the sine, cosine, and tangent of angles. Press the SIN, COS, or TAN button, enter the angle, and press the equals key to calculate the function.

MODEL PROBLEMS

1. What are the sine, cosine, and tangent of A?

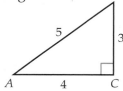

SOLUTION

Sine of A $\sin A = \dfrac{\text{length of opposite leg}}{\text{length of hypotenuse}} = \dfrac{3}{5}$ The sine of ∠A is the ratio of the lengths of the opposite leg and the hypotenuse.

Cosine of A $\cos A = \dfrac{\text{length of adjacent leg}}{\text{length of hypotenuse}} = \dfrac{4}{5}$ The cosine of ∠A is the ratio of the lengths of the adjacent leg and the hypotenuse.

Tangent of A $\tan A = \dfrac{\text{length of opposite leg}}{\text{length of adjacent leg}} = \dfrac{3}{4}$ The tangent of ∠A is the ratio of the lengths of the opposite leg and the adjacent leg.

Model Problems continue . . .

2. If $\tan \theta = \dfrac{15}{8}$, what is $\sin \theta$?

SOLUTION

Use definition of tangent	$\tan \theta = \dfrac{\text{opposite}}{\text{adjacent}} = \dfrac{15}{8}$	Start with the definition of the tangent, substituting the given values.

Draw triangle

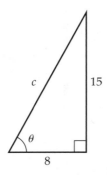

Draw a right triangle with an angle θ, whose tangent is $\dfrac{15}{8}$, which means the opposite leg has length 15 and the adjacent leg has length 8.

Pythagorean theorem	$c^2 = 15^2 + 8^2 = 289$ $c = 17$	To calculate the sine of angle θ, we need the length of the hypotenuse. Use the Pythagorean theorem to calculate the hypotenuse.
Use definition of sine	$\sin \theta = \dfrac{\text{opposite}}{\text{hypotenuse}} = \dfrac{15}{17}$	Apply the definition of the sine of θ.

 3. MP 2, 4 A snowboarder wants to build a jump that is at a 40° angle from the horizontal. She has a 6-foot-long wooden board with which to make the jump. How high should she raise the end of the board off the ground, to the nearest hundredth of a foot?

SOLUTION

Draw diagram

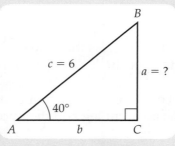

The jump will be 6 feet long and the designer wants a 40° angle. She needs to calculate a to find how high the end of the jump should be.

Use definition of sine	$\sin A = \dfrac{\text{opposite}}{\text{hypotenuse}}$ $\text{opposite} = (\sin A)(\text{hypotenuse})$	Apply the definition of the sine of A. Solve for the opposite leg, since that is the unknown.
Substitute and evaluate	$a \approx (0.6428)(6)$ $a \approx 3.86$	Let a be the length of the opposite leg, $A = 40°$, and 6 is the length of the hypotenuse. Since $\sin 40°$ is approximately 0.6428, a is about 3.86 feet. The end of the board should be propped up about 3.86 feet.

Sine, Cosine, and Complementary Angles

In right triangles, the two acute angles are always complementary. Because of this, the sine and cosine ratios have a special relationship. See if you can figure it out by looking at the table without reading ahead. All numbers are rounded to the nearest thousandth.

$m\angle A$	$m\angle B$	sin A	cos A	sin B	cos B
10°	80°	0.174	0.985	0.985	0.174
20°	70°	0.342	0.940	0.940	0.342
30°	60°	0.500	0.866	0.866	0.500
40°	50°	0.643	0.766	0.766	0.643
50°	40°	0.766	0.643	0.643	0.766
60°	30°	0.866	0.500	0.500	0.866
70°	20°	0.940	0.342	0.342	0.940
80°	10°	0.985	0.174	0.174	0.985

As you may have noticed, the sine of one angle is the cosine of its complementary angle, and vice versa. For instance, look at the cosine of 20° and the sine of 70°.

We discuss this relationship further by examining a general right triangle.

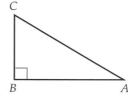

Find sin A	$\sin A = \dfrac{\text{opposite}}{\text{hypotenuse}}$
	$\sin A = \dfrac{BC}{AC}$

Find the sine of $\angle A$, using the appropriate trigonometric ratio.

Find cos C	$\cos C = \dfrac{\text{adjacent}}{\text{hypotenuse}}$
	$\cos C = \dfrac{BC}{AC}$

Find the cosine of $\angle C$ using the appropriate trigonometric ratio.

$\sin A = \cos C$ $\angle A$'s opposite side is the same as $\angle C$'s adjacent side.

Because the *opposite side* from $\angle A$ is the same side as the *adjacent side* to $\angle C$, the trigonometric ratios are equal.

MODEL PROBLEMS

1. Calculate the sine, cosine, and tangent of 40°.

SOLUTION

$\sin 40° \approx 0.643$ Use a calculator to determine the value of sin 40°. It is approximately 0.643. The value of the sine of this angle is irrational, so the digits continue forever.

$\cos 40° \approx 0.766$ The cos 40° is approximately 0.766.

$\tan 40° \approx 0.839$ The tan 40° is approximately 0.839.

> The values of some trigonometric functions are rational. For instance, the tangent of 45° is 1, since it is the ratio of two equal sides in an isosceles triangle.

Model Problems continue . . .

2. a What is the length of a, to the nearest tenth?

b What is the length of b, to the nearest tenth?

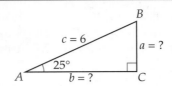

SOLUTION

a Definition of sine $\qquad \dfrac{\text{opposite}}{\text{hypotenuse}} = \sin A \qquad$ The sine equals the opposite leg divided by the hypotenuse.

Substitute $\qquad \dfrac{a}{6} = \sin 25° \qquad$ The angle is 25°. Substitute and calculate the sine of the angle.

$$\dfrac{a}{6} \approx 0.423$$

Solve $\qquad 6 \cdot \dfrac{a}{6} = 6 \cdot \sin 25° \qquad$ Solve for a by multiplying both sides of the equation by 6. Round the answer to the nearest tenth.

$$a \approx 2.5$$

> With a calculated, there are a variety of ways to calculate b. We could use the Pythagorean theorem since we know the length of a leg and the hypotenuse, or we could use the cosine of 25°.

b Calculate $m\angle B$

$$m\angle A + m\angle B + m\angle C = 180°$$
$$m\angle B = 180° - 90° - 25°$$
$$m\angle B = 65°$$

One way to calculate the length of the leg b is to calculate $m\angle B$. Since the measure of the angles sum to 180°, $m\angle B = 65°$.

Use definition of sine to calculate b

$$\dfrac{\text{opposite}}{\text{hypotenuse}} = \sin B$$

$$\text{opposite} = \sin B \cdot \text{hypotenuse}$$

Use the definition of the sine. Solve the equation for the opposite leg by multiplying both sides of the equation by the hypotenuse.

Solve

$$b = (\sin 65°)(6)$$
$$b \approx (0.906)(6) \approx 5.4$$

Substitute in the values we know from the diagram. The measure of $\angle B$ is 65°, and the hypotenuse is 6. The leg opposite $\angle B$ is b. b to the nearest tenth is 5.4. We can check the answer using the Pythagorean theorem. Since $2.5^2 + 5.4^2 \approx 6^2$, the answer is correct.

3. What is the length of the hypotenuse, to the nearest tenth?

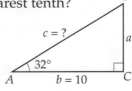

SOLUTION

Definition of cosine $\qquad \dfrac{\text{adjacent}}{\text{hypotenuse}} = \cos A \qquad$ Since we know the length of the adjacent leg, use the cosine ratio.

Substitute $\qquad \dfrac{10}{c} = \cos 32° \qquad$ The angle is 32°. Substitute and calculate the cosine of the angle.

$$\dfrac{10}{c} \approx 0.848$$

Solve $\qquad c \cdot \dfrac{10}{c} \approx c \cdot 0.848 \qquad$ Solve the equation. First, remove c as the denominator of a fraction. Multiply both sides by c. Divide both sides by 0.848. Rounded to the nearest tenth, c is approximately 11.8.

$$10 \approx c \cdot 0.848$$
$$11.8 \approx c$$

Model Problems continue . . .

4. MP 2, 4 Ted is estimating the height of the Space Needle using the angle of 75° between his line of sight and the horizontal. Based on this diagram, how tall is the Space Needle? The angle between a horizontal line and the line of sight to an object above the horizontal line is called the *angle of elevation*. In this problem, that angle is 75°. Surveyors use angles of elevation to estimate the heights of objects that cannot be easily measured directly. We ignore Ted's height in this estimate.

SOLUTION

Definition of tangent	$\tan A = \dfrac{\text{opposite}}{\text{adjacent}}$ $\text{opposite} = (\tan A)(\text{adjacent})$		Use the diagram. The tangent of $\angle A$ is the opposite leg divided by the adjacent leg. Solve for the opposite leg.
Substitute and evaluate	$a \approx (3.73)(50)$ $a \approx 186.5$ meters		Substitute a for the length of the opposite leg, 75° for the measure of $\angle A$, and 50 for the length of the adjacent leg. The tangent is approximately 3.73. The tower is approximately 186.5 meters tall. The calculation is close to the actual height of the tower, which is about 184 meters.

5. MP 2, 4 The angle at which an airplane descends is the *angle of depression*. It is a downward angle from the horizontal. An airplane's path of descent is at a 15° angle from the horizontal. The airplane is 3 miles above the ground. To the nearest tenth of a mile, how far does it travel before it reaches the ground?

SOLUTION

Draw diagram	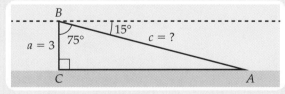	Draw the descent of the airplane. It is 3 miles above the ground. It is flying at a 15° angle from the horizontal. We want to calculate c, the distance the plane travels before it lands.
Calculate angle	$B = 90° - 15° = 75°$	The two angles sum to 90°. Subtract to calculate that $B = 75°$.
Definition of cosine	$\cos B = \dfrac{\text{adjacent}}{\text{hypotenuse}}$ $\text{hypotenuse} = \dfrac{\text{adjacent}}{\cos B}$	Use the definition of cosine, solving the equation for the hypotenuse.
Substitute	$c = \dfrac{3}{\cos 75°}$	Substitute c for the hypotenuse, 3 for the length of the adjacent leg, and 75° for B.
Substitute value of $\cos 75°$	$c \approx \dfrac{3}{0.2588}$ $c \approx 11.6$ miles	Use a calculator to find the value of $\cos 75°$ to the nearest ten thousandth. Substitute that and divide. The plane travels 11.6 miles before it lands.

Model Problems continue . . .

6. **MP 2, 4** Two measurements of angles of elevation to a mountain summit are made as shown in the diagram. There is a distance of 3930 feet between the two points from which the measurements are made. How tall is the mountain?

a Write equations solved for *b* using angles of elevation.

b Use the equations from part **a** to solve for *a*.

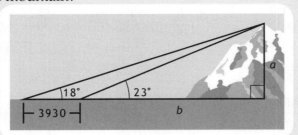

This example illustrates a technique that surveyors use, taking two measures of the angle of elevation to the top of the mountain to calculate the height of a mountain.

SOLUTION

a First equation

$$\tan 23° = \frac{\text{opposite}}{\text{adjacent}} = \frac{a}{b}$$

To find an equation that involves the measuring position closer to the mountain, where the angle is 23°, we can use the tangent of angle $\theta = 23°$, which equals $\frac{\text{opposite}}{\text{adjacent}}$. Let *a* represent the mountain height, and let *b* represent the horizontal distance.

Solve first equation for *b*

$$b(\tan 23°) = a$$
$$b = \frac{a}{\tan 23°}$$

Solve the first equation for *b*.

Second equation

$$\tan 18° = \frac{\text{opposite}}{\text{adjacent}} = \frac{a}{b + 3930}$$

The equation describes the situation at the farther measuring position. The horizontal distance increases by 3930, the distance in feet between the two measuring positions. The angle is 18° at this point.

Solve second equation for *b*

$$\tan 18° = \frac{a}{b + 3930}$$
$$b = \frac{a}{\tan 18°} - 3930$$

Solve the second equation for *b* by multiplying both sides of the equation by $b + 3930$.

b Set right sides equal

$$\frac{a}{\tan 18°} - 3930 = \frac{a}{\tan 23°}$$

Set the first and second equations equal to each other, since both equaled *b*.

Solve for *a*

$$(\tan 23°)(a) - (\tan 23°)(3930)(\tan 18°) = (\tan 18°)(a)$$
$$(\tan 23°)(a) - (\tan 18°)(a) = (\tan 23°)(3930)(\tan 18°)$$
$$a(\tan 23° - \tan 18°) = (\tan 23°)(3930)(\tan 18°)$$
$$a = \frac{(\tan 23°)(3930)(\tan 18°)}{\tan 23° - \tan 18°}$$

Solve for *a*. Multiply both sides by tan 18° and tan 23° to eliminate the fractions. Move the *a* terms to one side of the equation and the constants to the other. Factor out *a*. Divide both sides of the equation by the expression that *a* is multiplied by.

Substitute and evaluate

$$a \approx \frac{0.4245 \cdot 3930 \cdot 0.3249}{0.4245 - 0.3249}$$
$$a \approx 5440 \text{ feet high}$$

Substitute and evaluate. The mountain is about 5440 feet high.

Model Problems continue . . .

7. **MP 7** If $\cos A = \dfrac{15}{17}$, what is $\sin A$?

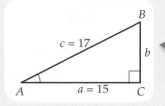

The triangle we draw is one possible triangle, given the stated value of the cosine. Any other similar triangle would be possible, such as one with lengths of 16, 30, and 34. Since the sides are proportional, it does not change the value of the sine ratio.

SOLUTION

Definition of cosine	$\cos A = \dfrac{\text{adjacent}}{\text{hypotenuse}} = \dfrac{15}{17}$	Start with the definition of the cosine, the length of the adjacent leg divided by the length of the hypotenuse.
Pythagorean theorem	$15^2 + b^2 = 17^2$ $b^2 = 289 - 225$ $b = 8$	To calculate the sine, we need the length of the other leg. Use the Pythagorean theorem to calculate that the leg has length 8.
Definition of sine	$\sin A = \dfrac{\text{opposite}}{\text{hypotenuse}} = \dfrac{8}{17}$	The sine is the length of the opposite leg divided by the length of the hypotenuse. Enter the values for the opposite leg and the hypotenuse. The sine of $\angle A = \dfrac{8}{17}$.

Sine, Cosine, and Tangent for Special Triangles

The values of the sine, cosine, and tangent in 30-60-90 and 45-45-90 triangles are frequently used. We show how to calculate them.

30-60-90 Triangle: 30° angle

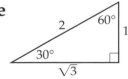

$\sin 30° = \dfrac{\text{opposite}}{\text{hypotenuse}} = \dfrac{1}{2}$

For a 30° angle, use the 30-60-90 triangle shown to calculate the trigonometric ratios. The sine equals the length of the opposite leg divided by the length of the hypotenuse, which means the sine of 30° is $\dfrac{1}{2}$.

$\cos 30° = \dfrac{\text{adjacent}}{\text{hypotenuse}} = \dfrac{\sqrt{3}}{2}$

The length of the leg adjacent to the 30° angle is $\sqrt{3}$. The cosine equals the length of the adjacent leg divided by the length of the hypotenuse, which means the cosine of 30° is $\dfrac{\sqrt{3}}{2}$.

$\tan 30° = \dfrac{\text{opposite}}{\text{adjacent}} = \dfrac{1}{\sqrt{3}} \cdot \dfrac{\sqrt{3}}{\sqrt{3}} = \dfrac{\sqrt{3}}{3}$

The tangent equals the length of the opposite leg divided by the length of the adjacent leg, which means the tangent of 30° equals $\dfrac{\sqrt{3}}{3}$.

30-60-90 Triangle: 60° angle

Rotate the diagram to calculate these ratios for a 60° angle.

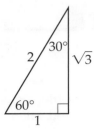

$$\sin 60° = \frac{\text{opposite}}{\text{hypotenuse}} = \frac{\sqrt{3}}{2}$$

For a 60° angle, use the 30-60-90 triangle above to calculate the sine. The sine equals the length of the leg opposite the 60° angle divided by the length of the hypotenuse, which means the sine of 60° is $\frac{\sqrt{3}}{2}$.

$$\cos 60° = \frac{\text{adjacent}}{\text{hypotenuse}} = \frac{1}{2}$$

As always, the cosine equals the length of the leg adjacent to the 60° angle divided by the length of the hypotenuse. The cosine of 60° is $\frac{1}{2}$.

$$\tan 60° = \frac{\text{opposite}}{\text{adjacent}} = \frac{\sqrt{3}}{1} = \sqrt{3}$$

And as always, the tangent is the length of the opposite leg divided by the length of the adjacent leg. The tangent of 60° is $\sqrt{3}$.

45-45-90 Triangles

We now calculate the same ratios for an isosceles right triangle. We calculated the length of the hypotenuse using the Pythagorean theorem.

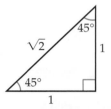

$$\sin 45° = \frac{1}{\sqrt{2}} = \frac{\sqrt{2}}{2}$$

For a 45° angle, use the 45-45-90 triangle shown to calculate the trigonometric ratios. The length of each leg is 1, and the length of the hypotenuse is $\sqrt{2}$. The sine equals the opposite leg divided by the length of the hypotenuse.

$$\cos 45° = \frac{1}{\sqrt{2}} = \frac{\sqrt{2}}{2}$$

The cosine equals the adjacent leg's length over the hypotenuse's length. It has the same value as the sine, since both legs have the same length.

$$\tan 45° = \frac{1}{1} = 1$$

The tangent equals the opposite leg's length over the adjacent's. Since the lengths are the same, $\tan 45° = 1$.

You will start to recognize the values for the trigonometric ratios for 30°, 45°, and 60° angles. These are ratios that you may want to refer to frequently, so we summarize them in a table.

θ	$\sin \theta$	$\cos \theta$	$\tan \theta$
30°	$\frac{1}{2}\sqrt{1} = \frac{1}{2}$	$\frac{1}{2}\sqrt{3} = \frac{\sqrt{3}}{2}$	$\sqrt{\frac{1}{3}} = \frac{\sqrt{3}}{3}$
45°	$\frac{1}{2}\sqrt{2} = \frac{\sqrt{2}}{2}$	$\frac{1}{2}\sqrt{2} = \frac{\sqrt{2}}{2}$	$\sqrt{\frac{2}{2}} = 1$
60°	$\frac{1}{2}\sqrt{3} = \frac{\sqrt{3}}{2}$	$\frac{1}{2}\sqrt{1} = \frac{1}{2}$	$\sqrt{\frac{3}{1}} = \sqrt{3}$

1. *A* is an acute angle and $\cos A = \dfrac{1}{2}$.

What is the measure of *A*, in degrees?

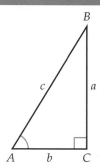

SOLUTION

Use definition of cosine $\qquad \cos A = \dfrac{\text{adjacent}}{\text{hypotenuse}} = \dfrac{1}{2}$

Start with the definition of the cosine, the length of the adjacent leg divided by the length of the hypotenuse. Use the value of the cosine stated in the problem. The adjacent leg has a length of 1 and the hypotenuse has a length of 2.

30-60-90 triangle $\qquad m\angle A = 60°$

In any 30-60-90 triangle, the hypotenuse is twice as long as the short leg, so this is a 30-60-90 triangle. Based on these lengths, angle *A* must be the 60° angle.

2. The leg opposite angle *B* is $\sqrt{2}$ long, and the hypotenuse has a length of 2. What is the measure of $\angle B$?

SOLUTION

Calculate the ratio $\qquad \sin B = \dfrac{\text{opposite}}{\text{hypotenuse}} = \dfrac{\sqrt{2}}{2}$

Calculate the sine of the angle since you know the opposite leg and hypotenuse.

Evaluate $\qquad m\angle B = 45°$

Complete the calculation.

PRACTICE

1. For an acute angle in a right triangle, the cosine of the angle is equal to:

A. $\dfrac{\text{length of opposite side}}{\text{length of adjacent side}}$

B. $\dfrac{\text{length of hypotenuse}}{\text{length of adjacent side}}$

C. $\dfrac{\text{length of adjacent side}}{\text{length of hypotenuse}}$

D. $\dfrac{\text{length of opposite side}}{\text{length of hypotenuse}}$

2. Which ratio is equal to cos 32°?

A. sin 32°   C. sin 58°

B. −cos 32°   D. cos 58°

3. In a right triangle, $\sin A = \dfrac{7}{11}$, where the two numbers are actual lengths. If you needed to state the value of cos *A*, for which of the following sides of the triangle, relative to angle *A*, would you need to find the length?

A. Opposite   C. Hypotenuse

B. Adjacent   D. Height

4. The value of $\cos B = \dfrac{4}{5}$. What is the value of sin *B*?

A. $\dfrac{3}{5}$ C. $\dfrac{5}{4}$

B. $\dfrac{3}{4}$ D. $\dfrac{4}{3}$

Practice Problems continue . . .

5. What is the value of tan A, rounded to the nearest thousandth, when $m\angle A = 16°$?

A. 0.28

B. 0.286

C. 0.287

D. 2.868

6. Which of the following is the value of cos A, if angle A measures 60°?

A. 0.5

B. $2\sqrt{2}$

C. $\dfrac{\sqrt{3}}{2}$

D. 1

Exercises 7–16: Determine the value of each function. Give your answer to the nearest thousandth.

7. cos 42°

8. tan 65°

9. sin 59°

10. sin 56°

11. sin 8°

12. sin 28°

13. tan 21°

14. cos 13°

15. tan 68°

16. cos 61°

17. What is the length of side a in the triangle below? State your answer to the nearest tenth.

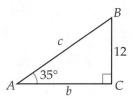

18. What is the length of side c in the triangle below? State your answer to the nearest tenth.

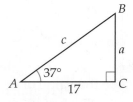

19. What is the length of side c in the triangle below? State your answer to the nearest tenth.

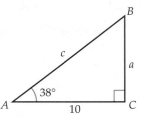

20. If $\cos A = \dfrac{8}{17}$, what is sin A?

21. In a right triangle with acute angles C and D, the value of $\sin D = \dfrac{10}{26}$. Find the value of sin C. Express your answer as a fraction.

Exercises 22–23: Use the diagram below to answer the questions.

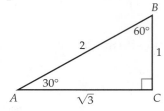

22. What is sin 60°? State the exact value.

23. What is tan 60°? State the exact value.

24. Sketch $\triangle ABC$, where angle B is the right angle, $\sin A = \dfrac{4}{5}$, and $\tan A = \dfrac{4}{3}$.

25. Gretchen stands 10 meters from the base of a tree. She measures the angle to the top of the tree from the ground to be 60°. What is the height of the tree, to the nearest tenth of a meter?

26. A guy-wire is used to connect the top of a radio antenna to an anchor on the ground. The guy-wire is 120 meters long, and it forms an angle of elevation between the ground and the top of the antenna of 70°. How tall is the radio antenna, to the nearest whole meter?

27. A carpenter uses a 10-foot ladder. When he rests the top of the ladder against the wall, the ladder makes a 65° angle with the floor. How far up the wall does the top of the ladder reach? Round your answer to the nearest tenth of a foot.

Practice Problems continue . . .

28. The leg opposite angle B is $\sqrt{2}$ long, and the hypotenuse has a length of 2 units. What is the measure of $\angle B$?

Exercises 29–31: Use the diagram to answer the following questions.

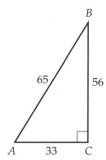

29. What is the cosine of angle A in the triangle? Write your answer as a fraction.

30. What is the tangent of angle A in the triangle above? Write your answer as a fraction.

31. What is the sine of angle A in the triangle above? Write your answer as a fraction.

Exercises 32–33: Use the diagram below to answer the questions.

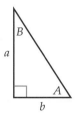

32. What is tan B of the triangle shown if $a = 8$ and $b = 4$? State your answer as an exact expression.

33. What is tan B of the triangle shown if $a = 8$ and $b = 5$? State your answer as an exact expression.

34. MP 7 For what degree measure are the sine and cosine of an angle equal to each other?

35. MP 7 As the measure of an angle A increases from 1° to 89°, what happens to the value of the sine of A? Explain your reasoning.

36. Is it possible for the cosine of an angle in a right triangle to be equal to 2? Why or why not?

37. Is it possible for the sine of an acute angle in a right triangle to be equal to 1? Explain your reasoning.

38. MP 3 Using the triangle below, Ivan wrote the following equation to find the height of the triangle: $\sin 40° = \dfrac{x}{15}$. Is Ivan's work correct? Explain your reasoning.

39. A right triangle has a hypotenuse of 12. How long is the leg adjacent to angle A if the angle's measure is 30°? State your answer to the nearest hundredth.

40. Sketch triangle DEF, which has a right angle at E. Label the length of side DE as 10 inches and the length of hypotenuse DF as 18 inches. Find and label the length of side EF and the measure of angle F. Round all answers to the nearest integer.

41. Standing 140 meters from a building, a surveyor measures the angle from the ground to a balcony as 13°. How high is the balcony? Give your answer to the nearest tenth of a meter.

42. Carrie measures the angle from the ground to the top of a tree as 50°. If she is 20 meters from the base of the tree, how tall is the tree? Give your answer to the nearest tenth of a meter.

43. The angle of elevation from a point on a gym floor to the top of a rope ladder hanging from the ceiling is 40°. The distance from the same point on the floor to the base of the ladder is 30 feet. How long is the ladder, to the nearest tenth of a foot?

44. The pilot of a plane sitting on the tarmac at an airport looks up at the top of the control tower at an angle of 15°. If the pilot is 300 feet horizontally from the tower, how far above his head is the top of the tower? Round your answer to the nearest foot.

Practice Problems continue . . .

45. Clayton is building a bicycle ramp. He wants the angle of the ramp to be 20°. If the length of the board is 8 feet, how high off the ground is the highest part of the ramp, to the nearest hundredth of a foot?

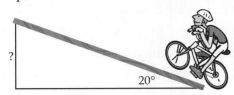

46. A contractor is building a wheelchair ramp to provide access to a building. The ramp must make an angle of 8° with the ground and must rise to a height of three feet at the other end. How long will the slanted part of the ramp be, to the nearest tenth of a foot?

47. **MP 2** A boat is anchored in a part of a lake that has a uniform depth. The rope connecting the boat to its anchor is 60 feet long and makes an angle of 30° with the bottom of the lake. Make a sketch of this situation, and state which trigonometric ratio could be used to find the depth of the lake.

48. In triangle *ABC*, angle *C* is a right angle. If $\sin A = \dfrac{3}{8}$, find $\cos B$.

49. What is sin *A* of the triangle below if $a = 4$ and $b = \sqrt{65}$?

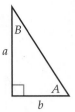

50. An equilateral triangle has sides that measure 4 feet each. What is the exact height of the triangle, in feet?

51. Create a word problem that can be solved using the tangent ratio. Show the solution to the problem you have written.

52. Prove that the tangent of an angle is equal to the angle's sine divided by its cosine, or $\tan A = \dfrac{\sin A}{\cos A}$.

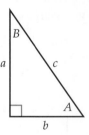

LESSON 9.3

9.3 Angles of Rotation and Trigonometric Functions

An angle can be created by rotating a ray. In this case, the angle is called an **angle of rotation**. To create an angle of rotation, start with a ray at the positive *x*-axis. This is called the *initial side* of the angle. As the ray rotates, it creates an angle. We call the final location of this ray the *terminal side*.

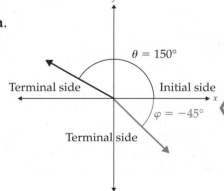

A full rotation is 360°. Positive rotation is counterclockwise, and negative rotation is clockwise.

The measure of an angle of rotation is determined by how far the ray rotates by the direction of rotation: counterclockwise is positive and clockwise is negative. If the ray rotates in the counterclockwise direction, the measure of the angle is positive. The measure of the angle θ in the diagram above is 150°. If the ray rotates in the clockwise direction, the measure of the angle is negative. The measure of the angle φ in the diagram above is −45°. There are 360 degrees in one full rotation, so one degree of rotation is $\dfrac{1}{360}$ of one full rotation.

An angle can be created by rotating a ray more than one full rotation, so it is possible that two different angles could be described by the same ray. Such angles are called **coterminal**. Two angles are coterminal if they have the same terminal side. 120°, 480°, and −240° are coterminal angles.

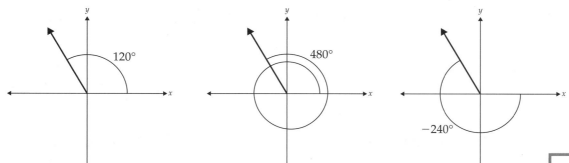

We can create coterminal angles by rotating an additional 360°, or by using a negative angle. The measures of any two coterminal angles differ by a multiple of 360°. For example: 480° = 120° + 360° **or** 480° = −240° + 2 · 360°.

> The terminal sides of angles that are multiples of 90°, such as 0°, 180°, and 270°, lie on the x- or y-axis.

MODEL PROBLEMS

Exercises 1–3: In which quadrant is the terminal side of each angle?

1. 230°　　**SOLUTION**

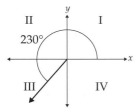

In quadrant III
Rotate past 180° counterclockwise, and then 50° more to get to 230°. This angle lies between 180° and 270°. An angle with measure 230° lies in the third quadrant.

2. −30°　　**SOLUTION**

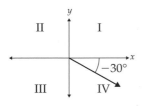

In quadrant IV
An angle of measure −30° (rotating 30° clockwise) lies in the fourth quadrant.

3. 270°　　**SOLUTION**

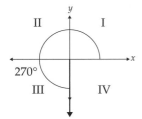

On y-axis
An angle of 270° points straight down, along the y-axis.

Reference Angles and Trigonometric Functions

The **reference angle** is the acute angle between the terminal side of an angle and the positive or negative x-axis. References angles range from $0°$ to $90°$.

> Diagrams are one way to calculate reference angles. Formulas can also be used to calculate reference angles.

- For angles in the second quadrant, between $90°$ and $180°$, the reference angle can be calculated by subtracting the angle from $180°$.
- For angles in the third quadrant, between $180°$ and $270°$, subtract $180°$ from the angle to calculate the reference angle.
- For angles in the fourth quadrant, between $270°$ and $360°$, subtract the angle from $360°$ to calculate the reference angle.

MODEL PROBLEMS

Exercises 1–2: Determine the reference angle for each given angle.

1. $300°$ **SOLUTION**

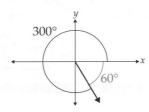

The reference angle for an angle of rotation is the acute angle between the terminal side and the x-axis. For an angle of $300°$, the reference angle is $60°$.

2. $-210°$ **SOLUTION**

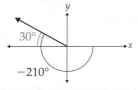

For an angle of rotation $-210°$, the reference angle is $30°$.

Angles of Rotation and Trigonometric Functions

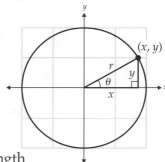

The values of trigonometric functions can be calculated for angles of any measure. The definitions of the trigonometric functions for angles of rotation are based on the right triangle definitions of the trigonometric ratios. The trigonometric functions for the angle θ are defined using any point (x, y) on the terminal side of the angle. It sweeps out a circle with the point always the same distance r from the origin.

The x-coordinate is the length of the adjacent leg. The y-coordinate is the length of the opposite leg. The x-axis and the vertical segment from the x-axis to the point (x, y) create a right triangle. The distance from the origin to the point (x, y) is the radius r. This is also the hypotenuse of the right triangle. The trigonometric functions are defined in terms of x, y, and r.

$\sin \theta = \dfrac{y}{r}$ The sine of θ is y divided by r. This is the same ratio as the opposite leg divided by the hypotenuse.

$\cos \theta = \dfrac{x}{r}$ The cosine of θ is x divided by r. This is the same ratio as the adjacent leg divided by the hypotenuse.

$\tan \theta = \dfrac{y}{x}$ The tangent of θ is y divided by x. This is the same ratio as the opposite leg divided by the adjacent leg.

1. State $-310°$ as an angle between $0°$ and $360°$.

SOLUTION

Calculate measure of reference angle

$\varphi = -310° + 360°$
$\varphi = 50°$

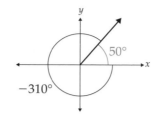

In this case, add $360°$ to the negative measure of the angle, $-310°$, to calculate the measure of the reference angle, which is $50°$, since it is in the first quadrant.

2. State $840°$ as an angle between $0°$ and $360°$ and state its reference angle.

SOLUTION

Subtract multiple of $360°$

$\varphi = 840° - 2(360)°$
$\varphi = 840° - 720°$
$\varphi = 120°$

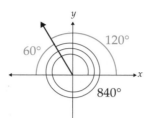

In this case, subtract $720°$, a multiple of $360°$, to calculate an angle between $0°$ and $360°$.

Calculate measure of reference angle

$\varphi = 60°$

Note the acute angle from the x-axis.

3. **MP 1** The terminal side of an angle θ passes through the point $(6, 8)$. Use the distance formula to calculate r and then calculate the sine, cosine, and tangent of θ.

SOLUTION

Draw diagram

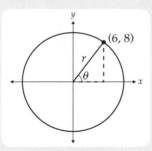

We need to calculate r. To do so, draw a diagram with a ray passing through $(6, 8)$.

Calculate r

$r = \sqrt{x^2 + y^2}$
$r = \sqrt{6^2 + 8^2}$
$r = 10$

Apply the Pythagorean theorem to find r. Substitute the coordinates of the point $(6, 8)$ to find the value for r is 10.

Calculate sine

$\sin \theta = \dfrac{y}{r} = \dfrac{8}{10} = \dfrac{4}{5}$

$\sin \theta$ is equivalent to the y-coordinate of the point divided by r.

Calculate cosine

$\cos \theta = \dfrac{x}{r} = \dfrac{6}{10} = \dfrac{3}{5}$

$\cos \theta$ is equivalent to the x-coordinate of the point divided by r.

Calculate tangent

$\tan \theta = \dfrac{y}{x} = \dfrac{8}{6} = \dfrac{4}{3}$

$\tan \theta$ is equivalent to the y-coordinate of the point divided by the x-coordinate.

Model Problems continue . . .

4. The terminal side of an angle θ passes through the point $(12, -9)$. What are the sine, cosine, and tangent of θ?

SOLUTION

Draw diagram

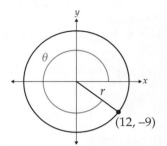

We need to calculate r. To do so, draw a diagram with a ray passing through $(12, -9)$ and the angle of rotation θ.

> In model problem 4, the terminal ray is not in the first quadrant, so be careful with signs.

Calculate r

$$r = \sqrt{x^2 + y^2}$$
$$r = \sqrt{12^2 + (-9)^2}$$
$$r = 15$$

Use the distance formula to find the distance r between the point $(12, -9)$ and the origin, $(0, 0)$.

Calculate sine

$$\sin \theta = \frac{y}{r} = \frac{-9}{15} = -\frac{3}{5}$$

Since the sine of θ equals the y-coordinate of the point divided by the distance r, substitute those values and simplify.

Calculate cosine

$$\cos \theta = \frac{x}{r} = \frac{12}{15} = \frac{4}{5}$$

Since the cosine of θ equals the x-coordinate of the point divided by r, substitute those values and simplify.

Calculate tangent

$$\tan \theta = \frac{y}{x} = \frac{-9}{12} = -\frac{3}{4}$$

Since the tangent of θ equals the y-coordinate of the point divided by the x-coordinate, substitute those values and simplify.

5. What are the sine, cosine, and tangent of $210°$?

SOLUTION

Draw diagram

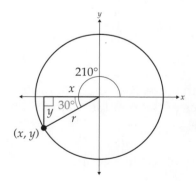

Draw the angle of rotation of $210°$. In the third quadrant, the x- and y-coordinates are negative. The value of r is always positive.

We use a reference angle to calculate the sine, cosine, and tangent of $210°$, an angle in the third quadrant. The reference angle of $30°$ has the same absolute values for these trigonometric functions as does $210°$. To put it another way, we calculate the value of the trigonometric functions for $30°$, and then by considering the quadrant of $210°$, determine the signs of the functions' values.

sin, cos, tan

$$\sin \theta = \frac{y}{r}; \text{ negative}$$

$$\cos \theta = \frac{x}{r}; \text{ negative}$$

$$\tan \theta = \frac{y}{x}; \text{ positive}$$

The sine of $210°$ is negative y divided by positive r, so it is negative. Similarly, $\cos 210°$ is negative and $\tan 210°$ is positive.

Model Problems continue . . .

Reference angle	$210° - 180° = 30°$	The reference angle is the acute angle between the terminal side and the x-axis, which is 30°.
Calculate sine	$\sin 210° = -\sin 30° = -\dfrac{1}{2}$	Calculate the trigonometric functions of 210°. The values of the three functions are the same as the values for 30°, except for sign. We determined the signs of the functions above, and we use them here. The sine of 30° is $\dfrac{1}{2}$, so the sine of 210° is $-\dfrac{1}{2}$.
Calculate cosine	$\cos 210° = -\cos 30° = -\dfrac{\sqrt{3}}{2}$	The cosine of 210° equals the opposite of the cosine of 30°.
Calculate tangent	$\tan 210° = \tan 30° = \dfrac{\sqrt{3}}{3}$	The tangent of 210° has the same value as the tangent of 30°.

6. What are the sine and cosine of 315°?

SOLUTION

Draw diagram	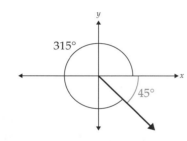	The angle of rotation, 315°, is in the fourth quadrant, where the x-coordinate is positive and the y-coordinate is negative. Since the y-coordinate of any point in the fourth quadrant is negative and r is always positive, sin 315° is negative.
Reference angle	reference angle = 45°	The reference angle is 45° from the x-axis.
State sine of reference angle	$\sin \theta = \dfrac{y}{r}$ $\sin 45° = \dfrac{\sqrt{2}}{2}$	The sine of $45° = \dfrac{\sqrt{2}}{2}$.
Calculate sin 315°	$\sin 315° = -\dfrac{\sqrt{2}}{2}$	The sine of 315° is negative.
Calculate cos 315°	$\cos 45° = \dfrac{\sqrt{2}}{2}$ $\cos 315° = \dfrac{\sqrt{2}}{2}$	In the fourth quadrant, the x-coordinate is positive and r is positive, as always, which means the cosine in that quadrant is positive. The cosine of 315° has the same value as cos 45°, which is $\dfrac{\sqrt{2}}{2}$. Since the cosine is positive in the fourth quadrant, cos 315° equals positive $\dfrac{\sqrt{2}}{2}$.

PRACTICE

1. Which of the following are coterminal with $-50°$? Select all that apply.

   A. $-310°$ D. $250°$
   B. $-150°$ E. 310
   C. $50°$

2. Which of the following are coterminal with $101°$? Select all that apply.

   A. $-619°$ D. $361°$
   B. $-101°$ E. $461°$
   C. $111°$

3. Which of the following angles are coterminal with $72°$? Select all that apply.

   A. $-648°$ C. $792°$
   B. $162°$ D. $432°$

4. Which of the following angles are coterminal with $-21°$? Select all that apply.

   A. $21°$ C. $0°$
   B. $339°$ D. $-381°$

5. Which pairs of the following angles are coterminal? Select all that apply.

   A. $-110°$ and $250°$
   B. $215°$ and $-105°$
   C. $55°$ and $765°$
   D. $40°$ and $760°$

6. In what quadrant is the terminal side of $-323°$?

   A. Quadrant I   C. Quadrant III
   B. Quadrant II   D. Quadrant IV

7. In what quadrant is the terminal side of $845°$?

   A. Quadrant I   C. Quadrant III
   B. Quadrant II   D. Quadrant IV

8. If $\sin \theta = \dfrac{\sqrt{3}}{2}$ and θ is in quadrant I, what is $\sin 2\theta$?

   A. $\dfrac{1}{2}$ C. $\sqrt{3}$

   B. $\dfrac{\sqrt{3}}{2}$ D. Not enough information

9. If $\sin \theta = -\dfrac{5}{13}$ and $\cos \theta > 0$, then in which quadrant is θ?

   A. Quadrant I   C. Quadrant III
   B. Quadrant II   D. Quadrant IV

Exercises 10–20: State the reference angle for each angle θ.

10. $\theta = 150°$

11. $\theta = -135°$

12. $\theta = -165°$

13. $\theta = 330°$

14. $\theta = -150°$

15. $\theta = 210°$

16. $\theta = 475°$

17. $\theta = -50°$

18. $\theta = 375°$

19. $\theta = 360°$

20. $\theta = -210°$

21. The terminal side of an angle θ passes through the point $(4, 9)$. What are the sine and cosine of θ?

22. The terminal side of an angle θ passes through the point $(5, 10)$. What are the sine, cosine, and tangent of θ?

23. The terminal side of angle θ passes through the point $(-8, 6)$. What is $\cos \theta$?

24. The terminal side of angle θ passes through the point $(5, -7)$. What is $\tan \theta$?

Exercises 25–26: State the acute angle defined by each function.

25. $\sin x = \dfrac{\sqrt{3}}{2}$

26. $\cos x = \dfrac{\sqrt{3}}{2}$

Practice Problems continue . . .

Exercises 27–29: State the requested ratio based on the diagram. The ratio may be undefined.

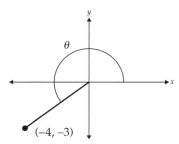

27. sin θ

28. cos θ

29. tan θ

Exercises 30–32: State the requested ratio based on the diagram. The ratio may be undefined.

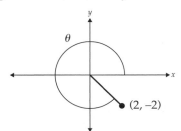

30. sin θ

31. cos θ

32. tan θ

Exercises 33–35: State the requested ratio based on the diagram. The ratio may be undefined.

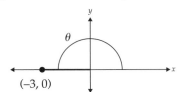

33. sin θ

34. cos θ

35. tan θ

Exercises 36–37: State the requested ratio based on the diagram. The ratio may be undefined.

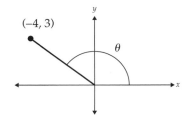

36. cos θ

37. tan θ

Exercises 38–43: Find all angles θ, with $0° \leq θ < 360°$, which make the statement true.

38. $\cos θ = 0$

39. $\cos θ = -1$

40. $\sin θ = \dfrac{\sqrt{2}}{2}$

41. $\sin θ = -\dfrac{\sqrt{2}}{2}$

42. $\tan θ = 0$

43. $\tan θ = 1$

44. a A wheel with a dot on its edge rolls on the ground. The radius of the wheel is 15 inches. When the dot is at the position shown below, at an angle of 112°, what is the distance of the dot above the ground, to the nearest tenth of an inch?

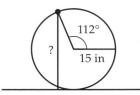

b The same wheel as in part **a** rotates so the dot is at the position shown below, at an angle of 308°. What is the distance of the dot above the ground, to the nearest tenth of an inch?

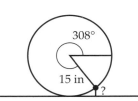

45. **MP 1, 4, 6** A bicycle wheel with a radius of 13 inches has a valve cap positioned at the highest point of the wheel. If the wheel is spun 750° in one direction, how high is the valve cap above the ground? Round your answer to the nearest tenth of an inch.

46. **MP 1, 4, 6** A child gets on a Ferris wheel ride directly below the center. The wheel has a radius of 30 feet. His mom takes a picture at the instant the wheel has just rotated 254° counterclockwise. What is the displacement of the child from his initial position to the position when the picture is taken, i.e., the straight-line distance between the two positions? Round your answer to the nearest tenth of a foot.

9.3 Angles of Rotation and Trigonometric Functions **413**

Radian Measure of Angles

Instead of degrees, an angle can be measured in units called **radians**. The radian measure of an angle is defined using a circle whose center is at the vertex of the angle. This angle is called a **central angle**, shown as θ in the diagram to the right.

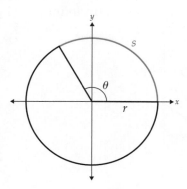

One radian is defined as the angle created when the arc length equals the radius. The **radian measure** of the angle equals the ratio of the length of the arc intercepted by the angle to the radius of the circle.

For a circle with its center at the angle's vertex:

r = radius   To find the radian measure of an angle θ, construct a circle of radius r whose center is at the vertex of the angle.

s = arc length   The angle intercepts an arc of length s on the circle.

$\theta = \dfrac{s}{r}$ The radian measure of the angle θ is the ratio of the arc length to the radius, or $\dfrac{s}{r}$.

The circumference of a circle with radius r is $2\pi r$. When the radius of a circle is 1, the circumference and the arc length of the full circle are both 2π. This means that the radian measure of a 360° angle is 2π. Since 360° equals 2π radians, 180° equals π radians. Later, we will graph trigonometric functions using the unit circle. A unit circle has a radius of 1.

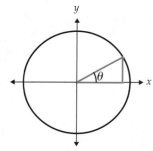   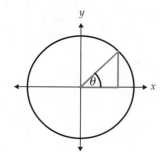   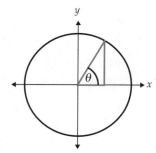

$\theta = 30° = \dfrac{\pi}{6} = 0.52$ radians $\theta = 45° = \dfrac{\pi}{4} = 0.79$ radians $\theta = 60° = \dfrac{\pi}{3} = 1.05$ radians

The conversion factors enable you to convert from degrees to radians and radians to degrees:

Degrees to radians
To convert degrees to radians, multiply by $\dfrac{\pi \text{ radians}}{180°}$.

Radians to degrees
To convert radians to degrees, multiply by $\dfrac{180°}{\pi \text{ radians}}$.

In this activity, convert between degrees and radians, and vice versa.

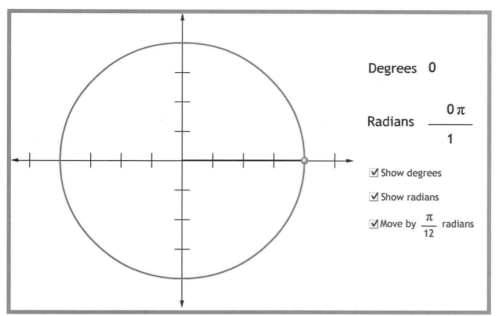

 We show one of the three similar activities below. Use the activities to become familiar with common radian measures.

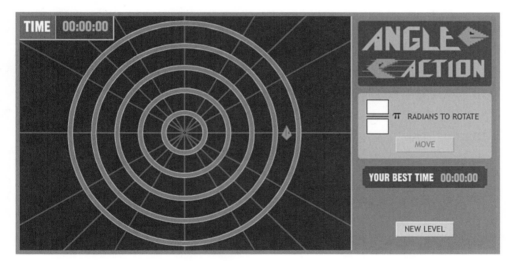

MODEL PROBLEMS

Exercises 1–2: Convert each radian measure to degrees.

1. 1 radian   **SOLUTION**

$$1 \text{ radian} \cdot \frac{180°}{\pi \text{ radians}} \approx 57.3°$$

To convert radians to degrees, we multiply the number of radians by the fraction $\frac{180°}{\pi \text{ radians}}$.

2. $-\frac{5}{4}\pi$ radians   **SOLUTION**

$$-\frac{5}{4}\pi \cdot \frac{180°}{\pi \text{ radians}} = -225°$$

We do a similar operation on another angle.

PRACTICE

Exercises 1–6: State each angle in radians in terms of π.

1. $-15°$

2. $-20°$

3. $-18°$

4. $-80°$

5. $480°$

6. $540°$

Exercises 7–15: Convert the radian measures to degrees, rounded to the nearest degree.

7. $\dfrac{8\pi}{3}$

8. $\dfrac{2\pi}{5}$

9. -3π

10. $\dfrac{\pi}{5}$

11. $\dfrac{5\pi}{6}$

12. $-\dfrac{9\pi}{4}$

13. $\dfrac{5\pi}{12}$

14. $\dfrac{7\pi}{15}$

15. $\dfrac{14\pi}{9}$

Exercises 16–23: State each angle to the nearest hundredth of a radian.

16. $78°$

17. $-27°$

18. $627°$

19. $-198°$

20. $726°$

21. $10°$

22. $270°$

23. $140°$

Exercises 24–31: Convert the radian measures to the nearest tenth of a degree.

24. 1.25

25. 5.8

26. 3.7

27. 7.9

28. 10.6

29. -2.6

30. -3.6

31. 1.7

32. MP 6 A circle has radius 8. What is the arc length of the segment cut by a central angle with measure $\dfrac{6\pi}{7}$ radians? State your answer as an exact expression.

33. MP 6 A circle has radius 2. What is the arc length of the segment cut by a central angle with measure $\dfrac{13\pi}{12}$ radians? State your answer as an exact expression.

34. What angle, in radians, does the hour hand make with the positive x-axis?

35. MP 2, 6 A clock starts at midnight. It is now 1 P.M. What angle has the hour hand swept through during that time? Hint: Use a sign to indicate the direction of motion.

36. You sleep for 24 hours. State the motion of the hour hand in radian measure. Hint: Use a sign to indicate the direction of motion.

9.4 Trigonometric Functions and the Unit Circle

The Unit Circle

A **unit circle** has a radius of 1, which means $r = 1$ for any point on the circle. We assume it is centered at the origin. Recall that $\cos \theta = \frac{x}{r}$ and $\sin \theta = \frac{y}{r}$. For a unit circle, with $r = 1$, the equations simplify to $\cos \theta = \frac{x}{1} = x$ and $\sin \theta = \frac{y}{1} = y$. The tangent still equals $\frac{y}{x}$ since r never figured into its calculation.

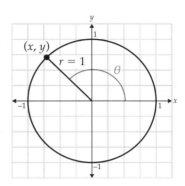

On a unit circle:

- The x-coordinate equals $\cos \theta$.
- The y-coordinate equals $\sin \theta$.
- r equals 1.

 In this activity, experiment with the unit circle, coordinates, and trigonometric functions.

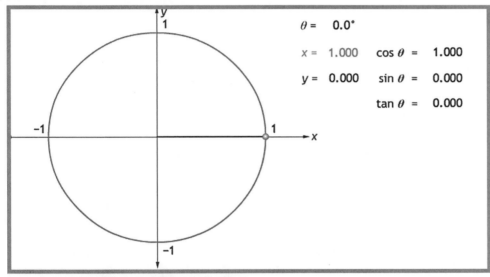

$\theta = \quad 0.0°$

$x = \quad 1.000 \qquad \cos \theta = \quad 1.000$

$y = \quad 0.000 \qquad \sin \theta = \quad 0.000$

$\qquad\qquad\qquad\qquad \tan \theta = \quad 0.000$

MODEL PROBLEMS

1. Calculate the cosine, sine, and tangent of the angle defined by $\left(-\frac{3}{5}, \frac{4}{5} \right)$.

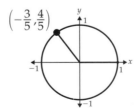

SOLUTION

$\cos \theta = x = -\dfrac{3}{5}$

$\sin \theta = y = \dfrac{4}{5}$

Substitute the x- and y-coordinates of the point and calculate the sine and cosine of θ, which in this case (a unit circle) equal the x- and y-values.

$\tan \theta = \dfrac{y}{x} = \dfrac{4/5}{-3/5} = -\dfrac{4}{3}$ Find the tangent, which equals y divided by x.

Model Problems continue . . .

2. The x-coordinate of a point on a unit circle is given.
What is the y-coordinate there?

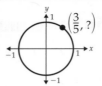

SOLUTION

Pythagorean theorem	$x^2 + y^2 = r^2$	The x-coordinate is one leg on a right triangle. Use the Pythagorean theorem to calculate the other.
Solve for y	$y = \sqrt{r^2 - x^2}$	Solve for y.
Substitute and evaluate	$y = \sqrt{1^2 - \left(\dfrac{3}{5}\right)^2}$	Substitute and evaluate. The y-coordinate on the unit circle is $\dfrac{4}{5}$.
	$y = \sqrt{1 - \dfrac{9}{25}} = \dfrac{4}{5}$	

3. Given the y-coordinate of a point on the unit circle, find the sine, cosine, and tangent of the angle.

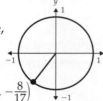

SOLUTION

$\sin\theta = y$-coordinate	$\sin\theta = -\dfrac{8}{17}$	On a unit circle, the sine of the angle equals the y-coordinate.
Solve the Pythagorean theorem for x	$x = \sqrt{r^2 - y^2}$	Solve for x.
Negative sign reflects quadrant of x	$x = -\sqrt{1^2 - \left(-\dfrac{8}{17}\right)^2}$	Note that x is negative based on its location (in the third quadrant).
	$x = -\sqrt{1 - \dfrac{64}{289}} = -\dfrac{15}{17}$	
$\cos\theta = x$-coordinate	$\cos\theta = -\dfrac{15}{17}$	On a unit circle, the cosine of the angle is the x-coordinate.
$\tan\theta = \dfrac{y}{x}$	$\tan\theta = \dfrac{-\dfrac{8}{17}}{-\dfrac{15}{17}} = \dfrac{8}{15}$	In all cases, the tangent is the ratio of the coordinates.

4. What are the sine, cosine, and tangent of 180°?

SOLUTION

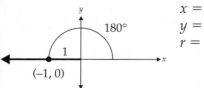

$x = -1$
$y = 0$
$r = 1$

Start with a diagram for an angle of 180°. This is a straight angle, where the terminal side lies on the left side of the x-axis. The terminal side of the angle passes through the point $(-1, 0)$ on the unit circle.

Model Problems continue . . .

Sine, cosine, tangent	$\sin 180° = \dfrac{y}{r} = \dfrac{0}{1} = 0$ $\cos 180° = \dfrac{x}{r} = \dfrac{-1}{1} = -1$ $\tan 180° = \dfrac{y}{x} = \dfrac{0}{-1} = 0$	Calculate the sine, cosine, and tangent of 180° using the values of x, y, and r. All of these functions are defined for 180°.

Trigonometric Identities

Some equations involving trigonometric functions of an angle θ are true for any value of θ. Such equations are called **trigonometric identities**.

We can use the Pythagorean theorem to show a relationship between the sine and cosine. We know that $x^2 + y^2 = r^2$, since the sum of each leg squared equals the hypotenuse squared. Using the unit circle, we know $\cos \theta = \dfrac{x}{r}$ and $\sin \theta = \dfrac{y}{r}$, and we can write $\cos^2 \theta + \sin^2 \theta = 1$. (These squares are usually written as $\sin^2 \theta$ and $\cos^2 \theta$, which are equivalent to $(\sin \theta)^2$ and $(\cos \theta)^2$.)

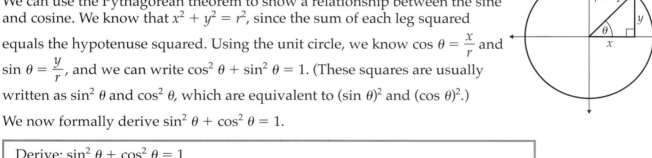

We now formally derive $\sin^2 \theta + \cos^2 \theta = 1$.

Derive: $\sin^2 \theta + \cos^2 \theta = 1$		
Start with the Pythagorean theorem	$x^2 + y^2 = r^2$ $\dfrac{y^2 + x^2}{r^2} = \dfrac{r^2}{r^2}$ $\dfrac{y^2 + x^2}{r^2} = 1$	Begin with the triangle that has a hypotenuse of length r starting at the origin and ending at the point (x, y) and an angle θ between the hypotenuse and the x-axis. Use the Pythagorean theorem to write an equation relating x, y, and r. We want to derive an equation that is equal to 1, so divide both sides by r^2 to get 1 on the right side. We can do this because r^2 is a non-zero constant.
Separate into fractions	$\dfrac{y^2}{r^2} + \dfrac{x^2}{r^2} = 1$ $\left(\dfrac{y}{r}\right)^2 + \left(\dfrac{x}{r}\right)^2 = 1$	Divide each term of the numerator by the denominator, r^2, to separate the fraction into two terms. Then use the rules of exponents to group each term with a single exponent.
Use definitions of $\sin \theta$ and $\cos \theta$	$(\sin \theta)^2 + (\cos \theta)^2 = 1$ $\sin^2 \theta + \cos^2 \theta = 1$	Use the definitions of sine, $\sin \theta = \dfrac{y}{r}$, and cosine, $\cos \theta = \dfrac{x}{r}$, for the angle θ to replace the terms in the equation. We have now arrived at the trigonometric identity.

Because the identity $\sin^2 \theta + \cos^2 \theta = 1$ is derived using the Pythagorean theorem, it is sometimes called a **Pythagorean identity**. Two other Pythagorean identities are often used. We state all three of these identities below. They can be derived using the definitions of the reciprocal trigonometric functions.

$\sin^2 \theta + \cos^2 \theta = 1$

$1 + \tan^2 \theta = \sec^2 \theta$ — You can derive this identity by dividing both sides of the first identity by $\cos^2 \theta$.

$\cot^2 \theta + 1 = \csc^2 \theta$ — You can derive this identity by dividing both sides of the first identity by $\sin^2 \theta$.

> *sec*, *cot*, and *csc* are reciprocal trigonometric functions. You will learn more about these in lesson 9.6.

MODEL PROBLEMS

1. If θ is an acute angle and $\sin \theta = \dfrac{1}{3}$, what is $\cos \theta$?

SOLUTION

Trigonometric identity	$\sin^2 \theta + \cos^2 \theta = 1$	State the trigonometric identity.
Solve for $\cos^2 \theta$	$\cos^2 \theta = 1 - \sin^2 \theta$	Solve the identity for $\cos^2 \theta$.
Substitute for $\sin \theta$	$\cos^2 \theta = 1 - \left(\dfrac{1}{3}\right)^2$	Substitute the value $\sin \theta = \dfrac{1}{3}$.
	$\cos^2 \theta = \dfrac{8}{9}$	
Take square root	$\cos \theta = \sqrt{\dfrac{8}{9}}$ $\cos \theta = \dfrac{2\sqrt{2}}{3}$	Take the positive square root of both sides, since θ is an acute angle, and the cosine of an acute angle is positive. Simplify the radical expression.

2. **MP 6** Show that $\tan \theta = \dfrac{\sin \theta}{\cos \theta}$.

SOLUTION

Use definitions of sine and cosine	$\tan \theta = \dfrac{\sin \theta}{\cos \theta}$ $\tan \theta = \dfrac{\left(\dfrac{\text{opposite}}{\text{hypotenuse}}\right)}{\left(\dfrac{\text{adjacent}}{\text{hypotenuse}}\right)}$	Start by substituting the definitions of the sine and cosine functions.
Simplify	$\tan \theta = \dfrac{\text{opposite}}{\text{hypotenuse}} \cdot \dfrac{\text{hypotenuse}}{\text{adjacent}}$ $\tan \theta = \dfrac{\text{opposite}}{\text{adjacent}}$	To simplify the fraction, multiply the numerator by the inverse of the denominator. The hypotenuse terms cancel out. We are left with the definition of tangent.

Model Problems continue . . .

3. On a unit circle, $\sin \theta = \dfrac{12}{13}$ and θ is acute. What does the cosine of this angle equal?

SOLUTION

Relation of trigonometric functions	$\cos^2 \theta + \sin^2 \theta = 1$	We derived this relationship earlier.
Solve for cosine	$\cos \theta = \sqrt{1 - \sin^2 \theta}$	Solve for the cosine.
Substitute and evaluate	$\cos \theta = \sqrt{1 - \left(\dfrac{12}{13}\right)^2}$ $\cos \theta = \dfrac{5}{13}$	Substitute and evaluate. The cosine equals $\dfrac{5}{13}$.

Trigonometric Functions and the Unit Circle

We want to use the unit circle to express the values of sine, cosine, and tangent for $\pi - z$ and $\pi + z$, terms of the sine, cosine, and tangent for z, where z is any real number.

1. Locate angle *z* and corresponding point

We pick an angle z and locate its coordinates on the unit circle. We call these coordinates (x, y).

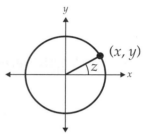

2. Locate $\pi - z$

We locate $\pi - z$. Note that $\pi - z$ makes the same angle from the horizontal as z. Since $\pi - z$ makes the same angle from the horizontal as z, the corresponding point on the unit circle is $(-x, y)$.

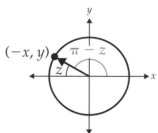

3. Sign of trigonometric functions

Sine

$\sin(\pi - z) = \sin z$ since they both have the same y-coordinate. For the unit circle, the sine equals the y-coordinate.

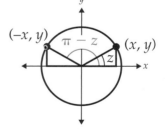

Cosine

The x-coordinates are opposites, so $\cos(\pi - z) = -\cos z$. Multiplying by -1 gets us the opposite.

Tangent

The tangent equals the y-coordinate divided by the x-coordinate. Since the y-coordinates are the same and the x-coordinates are opposites here, $\tan(\pi - z) = \dfrac{y}{-x} = -\tan z$.

We can use a similar approach for $\pi + z$:

1. Locate angle z and corresponding point

We pick an angle z and locate its coordinates on the unit circle. We call these coordinates (x, y).

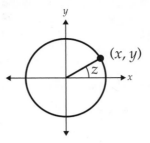

2. Locate π + z

We locate $\pi + z$. Note that $\pi + z$ makes the same size angle from the horizontal as z, but on the opposite side of the x-axis. Since z is the same angle from the horizontal, the corresponding point on the unit circle is $(-x, -y)$.

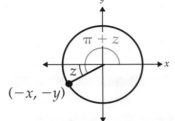

3. Sign of trigonometric functions

Sine

$\sin(\pi + z) = -\sin z$ since they have the opposite y-coordinates. For the unit circle, the sine equals the y-coordinate. Multiplying by -1 gets us the opposite.

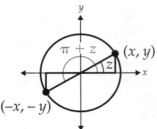

Cosine

The x-coordinates are also opposites, so $\cos(\pi + z) = -\cos z$.

Tangent

$\tan(\pi + z) = \dfrac{-y}{-x} = \tan z$. It is the same as $\tan z$. It is the ratio of the opposite x- and y-coordinates, which equals the ratio of the coordinates themselves.

MODEL PROBLEM

On the unit circle, the terminal side of an angle θ passes through the point $(-a, -b)$. Both a and b are positive and $a \neq b$. Which is true?

A. $\tan \theta = \dfrac{-a}{-b}$ 　　　　C. $\tan \theta = \dfrac{b}{a}$

B. $\cos \theta = $ positive 　　　　D. $\sin \theta = $ positive

SOLUTION

A. The tangent of the angle is $\dfrac{-b}{-a} = \dfrac{b}{a}$.

B. The cosine of the angle is $\dfrac{-a}{1}$, which is negative.

C. **Correct answer.** The tangent of the angle is $\dfrac{y}{x} = \dfrac{-b}{-a} = \dfrac{b}{a}$.

D. The sine of the angle is $\dfrac{-b}{1}$, which is negative.

PRACTICE

1. **MP 7** The angle shown below on the unit circle is $\frac{\pi}{3}$. The circle is dilated by a factor of 6. What is the measure of the angle after the dilation?

A. $\frac{\pi}{6}$

B. $\frac{\pi}{3}$

C. $\frac{\pi}{18}$

D. 2π

2. On the unit circle, the terminal side of an angle θ passes through the point $(a, -b)$. Both a and b are positive. Which is *not* true?

A. $\sin \theta = -b$

B. $\tan \theta = $ negative

C. $\cos \theta = a$

D. $\frac{\sin \theta}{\cos \theta} = $ positive

3. **MP 8** Use a unit circle to complete the table below for all values of cos x.

	0	$\frac{\pi}{2}$	π	$\frac{3\pi}{2}$	2π
cos x					

4. The angle θ corresponds to the angle between the positive x-axis and the line between the origin and the point $\left(\frac{-7}{25}, \frac{-24}{25}\right)$ on the unit circle. State your answers as exact expressions.

a What is tan θ?

b What is sin θ?

c What is cos θ?

5. The angle θ corresponds to the angle between the positive x-axis and the line between the origin and the point $\left(\frac{15}{17}, -\frac{8}{17}\right)$ on the unit circle. State your answers as exact expressions.

a What is sin θ?

b What is tan θ?

c What is cos θ?

6. sin $\theta = x$. What is cos θ? (Assume θ is acute.)

7. cos $\theta = x$. What is sin θ? (Assume θ is acute.)

8. cos $\theta = x$. What is tan θ? (Assume θ is acute.)

9. Give an example of angles $0° \leq A < 90°$ and $0° \leq B < 90°$ such that $\sin (A + B) = \sin A + \sin B$.

10. Give an example of angles $0° \leq A < 90°$ and $0° \leq B < 90°$ such that $\cos (A + B) = (\cos A)(\cos B)$.

11. **MP 3, 6** Show that $1 \leq |\cos \theta| + |\sin \theta| \leq \sqrt{3}$ for any angle θ. Hint: Square $|\cos \theta| + |\sin \theta|$ and use the Pythagorean identity $\cos^2 \theta + \sin^2 \theta = 1$.

12. **MP 5** Given that $\sin \theta = \frac{3}{8}$, and θ is an obtuse angle less than π radians, use the Pythagorean identity to find the exact value of cos θ.

13. **MP 2, 7** Use the Pythagorean identity to discuss the limits on the magnitude of sine and cosine values, and their relationship to each other.

• Multi-Part PROBLEM Practice •

MP 6, 7 **a** If $\cos \theta = \frac{4}{7}$, what are two possible values for sin θ?

b Why are there two possible answers to part **a**?

c If $\sin \theta = \frac{3}{8}$, what is $\sin \left(\frac{\pi}{2} - \theta\right)$?

d Explain how you got your answer to part **c**.

9.5 Trigonometric Function Graphs

Properties of Trigonometric Function Graphs

Functions that have a pattern that repeats over and over are called **periodic functions**. The graph of the function repeats its pattern indefinitely. Many functions are not periodic. For instance, linear and exponential functions do not have a repeating form, so they are not periodic. Trigonometric functions are periodic functions.

Period

The **period** is the interval on which the graph repeats once. A cycle of a periodic function is the smallest repeating unit of its graph. A period is the interval of the independent variable (x) that contains a single cycle. The graph of a sine function has a period of 2π, as shown in the diagram. This means it repeats its pattern, or completes a cycle, every 2π units as you move from left to right or from right to left. In this type of graph, high points are called *peaks* and low points are called *troughs*.

> The period can be calculated as the distance from any x-value to the closest x-value for which the graph starts to repeat. It is often convenient to use two adjacent peaks or two adjacent troughs.

Frequency

The **frequency** is the number of cycles contained in one unit interval of the independent variable (x). The frequency is the reciprocal of the period. For instance, if a function has a period of 4π, then the frequency is $\dfrac{1}{4\pi}$.

Midline

A **midline** is a horizontal line about which a periodic function *oscillates*. It is the graph's vertical midpoint. In the graph of $y = \sin x$, the midline is the line $y = 0$ (the horizontal axis of the graph).

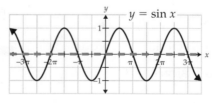

> The midline is halfway between the peaks and the troughs.

In the graph of $y = \sin x + 2$, the midline is $y = 2$. The graph has been shifted up 2, and the graph is oscillates about the line $y = 2$.

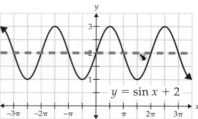

Amplitude

The **amplitude** is the distance from the midline of the graph to its highest or lowest point, or the distance to a peak or a trough. We show the amplitude of the parent functions sin x and cos x. The maximum value of both sin x and cos x is 1, and the minimum value is -1. These values occur at a point such as π radians, for cos x, and $\frac{\pi}{2}$ radians, for sin x. The amplitude of these functions is 1, or the distance between their midline (the x-axis) and a peak or trough.

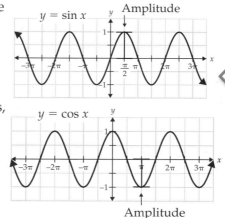

One way to calculate the amplitude is to measure the distance from peak to trough and divide by two. As a distance, the amplitude is always positive.

End Behavior

The end behavior of trigonometric functions is to extend infinitely along the x-axis, unless the domain of the function is restricted. The range of the function will be determined by the y-coordinates of a peak and a trough, which are functions of the amplitude and midline.

MODEL PROBLEMS

1. State the amplitude of $y = 2 \sin x$.

SOLUTION

| Calculate distance from midline | Amplitude = 2 | The amplitude is the maximum distance from the midline, or x-axis in this case. |

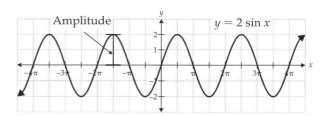

2. State the period of $y = \cos 2x$.

SOLUTION

| Calculate period | Period = π | The distance from peak to peak is the period. From the graph, the period is π. |

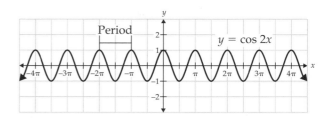

Graphs Using the Unit Circle

Cosine and sine are the *sinusoidal functions*. How can you graph a sine or cosine function? One way is to use the unit circle. We start with the sine function and graph the angle θ, in radians, on the horizontal axis and the sine of that angle on the vertical. Remember, on a unit circle, the y-coordinate equals the sine of an angle and the x-coordinate equals the cosine of an angle.

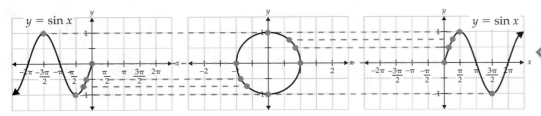

The sine and cosine are periodic functions because the pattern of the graph repeats over and over and over. The unit circle explains why the sine and cosine functions are periodic: After one revolution of the circle is made, the pattern repeats. Each time we trace a path around the circle, we create the same graph.

The circle can also explain the period of the function, or how long it takes to create one complete pattern of the graph. One complete revolution of a circle is 2π radians, and that is the period of the function.

x	y
0°	$\sin 0 = 0$
30°	$\sin \dfrac{\pi}{6} = 0.5$
45°	$\sin \dfrac{\pi}{4} \approx 0.7$
90°	$\sin \dfrac{\pi}{2} = 1$
135°	$\sin \dfrac{3\pi}{4} \approx 0.7$
180°	$\sin \pi \approx 0$
270°	$\sin \dfrac{3\pi}{2} = -1$
360°	$\sin 2\pi = 0$

> Sine is an odd function because it is symmetric about the origin, which means it can be rotated 180° about the origin and remain the same graph. To put it another way, $\sin (-x) = -\sin x$.

θ	$\cos \theta$
0	1
$\dfrac{\pi}{4}$	≈ 0.7
$\dfrac{\pi}{2}$	0
$\dfrac{3\pi}{4}$	≈ 0.7
π	-1
$\dfrac{3\pi}{2}$	0
2π	1

Now, we graph the cosine function, $y = \cos x$. We graph it by evaluating the cosine function using radian values for θ. Again, you can consider cosine as the x-coordinates on the unit circle. For instance, the coordinates at $\theta = 0$ are $(1, 0)$, so $\cos 0 = 1$. At $\theta = \dfrac{\pi}{2}$ (or 90°), the coordinates are $(0, 1)$, so $\cos \dfrac{\pi}{2} = 0$. The cosine function also has a period of 2π, which is a complete revolution of the circle. Each trip around the circle produces a graph with the same pattern.

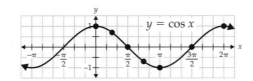

> The cosine function is an even function because it is symmetric about the y-axis. To put it another way, $\cos (-x) = \cos x$.

The graphs of the sine and cosine are similar, but it is helpful to note some differences. The graph of the sine passes through the origin $(0, 0)$, and increases to the right from there to $\dfrac{\pi}{2}$. The graph of the cosine has a maximum at $x = 0$ and decreases to zero at $x = \pi$. On the other hand, the graphs of the two functions have the same period and general shape. As we discuss later, one graph can be created by translating the other.

Scaling Trigonometric Function Graphs

Horizontal Scaling

As with other functions, trigonometric functions can be scaled. We use the cosine function as the parent function to discuss the concept of **horizontal scaling**. Scaling horizontally means that you can squeeze points like peaks closer together, or stretch them farther apart. This changes the period of a function.

We show $y = \cos x$ horizontally scaled by a factor of $\frac{1}{4}$. This pushes the peaks closer together. In other words, it reduces the period by a factor of 4, and since the frequency is the reciprocal of the period, it increases the frequency by a factor of 4.

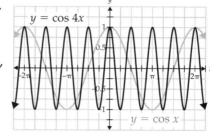

We show $y = \cos x$ horizontally scaled by a factor of 4. This pushes the peaks farther apart. In other words, it increases the period by a factor of 4.

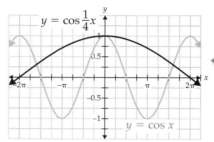

A periodic function of the form $f(kx)$ changes the period of $f(x)$, scaling its period, by a factor of $\frac{1}{|k|}$. If k's sign is changed, the graph reflects about the y-axis, but a change in sign does not affect its period. If $|k| > 1$, the graph is horizontally compressed, and if $|k| < 1$, it is horizontally stretched.

Vertical Scaling

We use the sine function as the parent function to discuss the concept of **vertical scaling**. This changes the amplitude of a function. We show $y = \sin x$ and $y = 3 \sin x$. $y = 3 \sin x$ is vertically taller than the parent function.

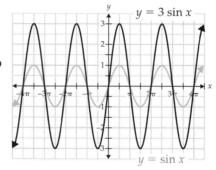

We show $y = \sin x$ and $y = \frac{1}{2} \sin x$.

$y = \frac{1}{2} \sin x$ is vertically shorter than the parent function. The constant multiplying the function either stretches it vertically, making the function's graph taller, or it squeezes it vertically, making it shorter.

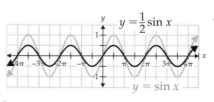

In general, the amplitude of $a \sin x$ or $a \cos x$ is $|a|$, the absolute value of a. We use the absolute value since the amplitude is a distance, and cannot be negative. When $|a|$ is greater than 1, it stretches the graph, making it taller than the parent graph. When $|a|$ is less than 1, it squeezes the graph, making it shorter than the parent graph. With $k(f(x))$, the graph scales vertically by the factor $|k|$. A negative value of k also reflects the graph through the x-axis.

In this activity, you are challenged to match graphs by changing *a* and *b*.

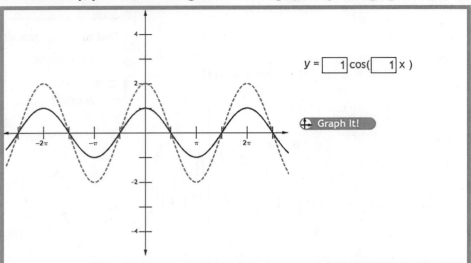

$$y = \boxed{1}\cos(\boxed{1}x\,)$$

⊕ Graph It!

 In this activity, experiment with two changes to a function, *f(kx)* and *k(f(x))*.

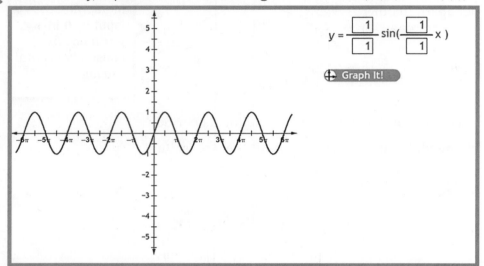

$$y = \frac{\boxed{1}}{\boxed{1}}\sin(-\frac{\boxed{1}}{\boxed{1}}x\,)$$

⊕ Graph It!

MODEL PROBLEMS

1. Graph $y = \dfrac{1}{2}\cos 3x$ compared to the parent function $y = \cos x$.

SOLUTION

Amplitude scaled by $\dfrac{1}{2}$	$a = \dfrac{1}{2}$	Multiplying the output of a function, or the function itself, by a number scales it vertically; it stretches or compresses it along the *y*-axis. The output is multiplied by $\dfrac{1}{2}$, compressing its amplitude.

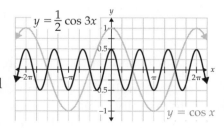

Period scaled by $\dfrac{1}{3}$	$b = 3$	Multiplying the input of a function by a number scales it horizontally; it stretches or compresses it along the *x*-axis. The input is multiplied by 3, compressing the graph horizontally.

Model Problems continue . . .

2. Graph $y = \frac{1}{2}\sin\frac{1}{3}x$ compared to the parent function $y = \sin x$.

SOLUTION

Amplitude $y = \frac{1}{2}\sin\frac{1}{3}x$ The coefficient of the sine is $\frac{1}{2}$, so $a = \frac{1}{2}$. Shrink the graph of $\sin x$

$\quad\quad\quad\quad$ Amplitude $= |a|$ vertically by a factor of $\frac{1}{2}$, cutting its height in half.

$\quad\quad\quad\quad a = \frac{1}{2}$

Period   Period $= \frac{2\pi}{b}$ The value of b, the coefficient of the input x, is $\frac{1}{3}$. That means the

$\quad\quad\quad\quad b = \frac{1}{3}$ period is stretched by a factor of 3, becoming 6π.

$\quad\quad\quad\quad \frac{2\pi}{b} = \frac{2\pi}{1/3} = 6\pi$

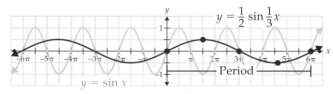

To stretch the graph horizontally, a period should start at the x-intercept $x = 0$ and finish at the x-intercept $x = 6\pi$. This is three times the length of the period of $\sin x$. Mark an x-intercept also at 3π, which is halfway. The maximum and minimum values occur halfway between the x-intercepts.

Plot these points. The y-values are $\frac{1}{2}$ and $-\frac{1}{2}$ at these points.

3. Graph $y = -3\cos\frac{1}{4}x$.

SOLUTION

Amplitude $y = -3\cos\frac{1}{4}x$ The amplitude of the graph is 3. This will help us plot points. Start

$\quad\quad\quad\quad$ Amplitude $= |a|$ with $\cos 0$. It equals 1, and we multiply by -3 to calculate the

$\quad\quad\quad\quad |a| = 3$ y-coordinate. Since the amplitude is 3, we know this will be the lowest point on the graph.

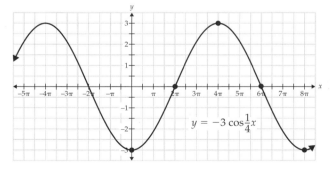

x	y
0	-3
2π	0
4π	3
6π	0
8π	-3

With $x = 2\pi$, calculate $\cos\frac{\pi}{2}$, which is 0. Calculate for $x = 4\pi$. $\cos\pi$ equals -1. Multiply by -3 to get 3. This is the maximum height of the function since the amplitude is 3. Plot the points for $x = 6\pi$ and $x = 8\pi$. Connect the points with the curve.

PRACTICE

1. What is the period of the function $y = -2 \sin 8x$?

   A. $\dfrac{\pi}{8}$ C. 8

   B. $\dfrac{\pi}{4}$ D. 16π

2. Which of the following functions best represents the graph below?

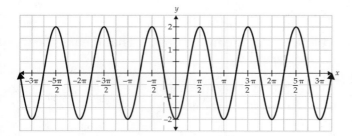

   A. $y = -3 \cos 2x$

   B. $y = -2 \cos \dfrac{1}{2}x$

   C. $y = -2 \cos 2x$

   D. $y = \dfrac{1}{2} \cos x$

3. $\sin \dfrac{\pi}{4} \approx 0.707$. What is $\sin \dfrac{9\pi}{4}$?

4. $\cos \dfrac{3\pi}{5} \approx -0.309$. What is $\cos \dfrac{13\pi}{5}$?

5. $\sin \dfrac{2\pi}{7} \approx 0.782$. What is $\sin \dfrac{16\pi}{7}$?

Exercises 6–8: Determine the amplitude of each function.

6. $24 \sin 3\pi x$

7. $6 \cos 9x$

8. $13 \sin 7\pi x$

Exercises 9–11: Determine the period of each function.

9. $5 \cos 3x$

10. $\dfrac{1}{2} \sin \pi x$

11. $2 \cos \dfrac{1}{5}x$

Exercises 12–20: Determine the amplitude, period, and maximum and minimum values for each function.

12. $f(x) = \cos 2x$

13. $f(x) = 2 \cos 3x$

14. $f(x) = 2 \cos 5x$

15. $f(x) = 4 \cos \pi x$

16. $f(x) = 3 \cos 3\pi x$

17. $f(x) = \dfrac{1}{4} \cos 4\pi x$

18. $f(x) = 2 \sin \pi x$

19. $f(x) = 6 \sin \dfrac{7}{3}x$

20. $f(x) = 7 \sin \dfrac{\pi}{3}x$

Exercises 21–24: State an equation of the form $y = a \sin bx$ that matches the description.

21. Maximum value is 2, minimum value is -2, and the period is 2π.

22. Maximum value is 4, minimum value is -4, and the period is π.

23. Maximum value is 0.5, minimum value is -0.5, and the period is 2.

24. Maximum value is 413, minimum value is -413, and the period is 0.1π.

25. Graph $y = 2.5 \sin x$ from $x = -4\pi$ to 4π

26. Graph $y = 4 \cos \pi x$ from $x = -10$ to 10

27. Graph $y = 1.5 \cos 2x$ from $x = -\pi$ to π

28. Graph $y = 5 \sin 2\pi x$ from $x = -5$ to 5

29. What is the equation of the graph shown? State your answer using the sine function.

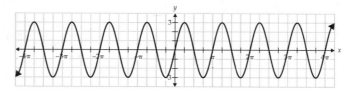

Practice Problems continue . . .

Practice Problems continued . . .

30. What is the equation of the graph shown? State your answer using the cosine function.

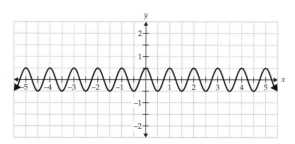

31. **MP 1, 2, 4** A puck, attached to a spring, is held 4 inches from its equilibrium position. Once the puck is let go, the puck returns to its initial position in 5 seconds. Assuming the system is undamped (the oscillations continue forever without losing amplitude), write the equation that represents the displacement, d, in inches from its equilibrium position as a function of time, t, in seconds. The function of time is a sine or cosine function, and $t = 0$ when the puck is released.

Translating Trigonometric Function Graphs

As with other functions, when a constant k is added to the parent function $f(x)$ to create the function $f(x) + k$, the graph is translated up by k. All the points are vertically shifted by k (and if k is negative, the graph shifts down).

With the graphs of the sine and cosine functions, we also discuss shifting the midline, since we draw points from there based on the graph's amplitude. The constant k, of course, shifts the midline by k units as well.

As with other graphs, when a constant is subtracted from the input of a function $f(x - h)$, the graph is translated to the right by h. This means that all points on the graph, including peaks and troughs, are translated by h units.

> A constant that creates a horizontal translation of a sinusoidal function has a specific name, the *phase* of the function, and the resulting horizontal shift is called a **phase shift**. The graph is translated by the phase shift h.

 In this activity, experiment with translating trigonometric function graphs.

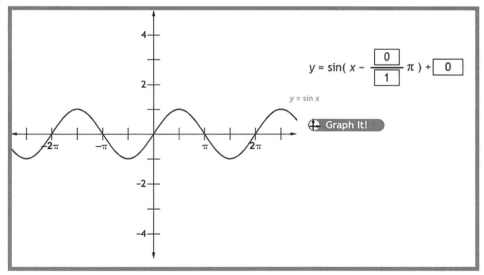

In this activity, match the graph by filling in values for *h* and *k*.

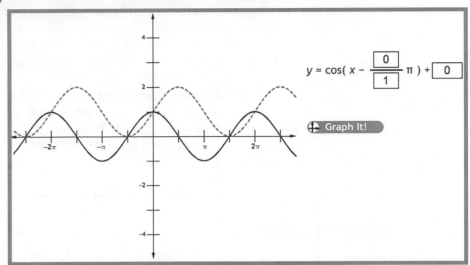

$$y = \cos\left(x - \frac{\boxed{0}}{\boxed{1}}\pi\right) + \boxed{0}$$

Graph It!

MODEL PROBLEMS

1. Graph $y = \sin x - 3$ compared to the parent function $y = \sin x$.

SOLUTION

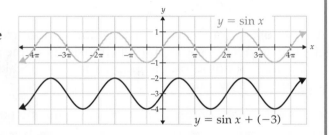

Determine sign of *k*	$y = \sin x + k$ $y = \sin x + (-3)$	Restate the equation so that the constant is added. This puts it in the form $f(x) + k$.
Translates graph down 3		Since the constant added to the function is negative, the graph shifts down 3 units.

2. Graph $y = \cos\left(x - \dfrac{\pi}{4}\right)$ compared to the parent function $y = \cos x$.

SOLUTION

Translates graph horizontally by *h*	$y = \cos(x - h)$	The phase shift is the constant *h* subtracted from *x*. It translates the graph right if *h* is positive or left if *h* is negative.
Graph $\cos(x - h)$	$\cos\left(x - \dfrac{\pi}{4}\right)$	For the function $\cos\left(x - \dfrac{\pi}{4}\right)$, the phase shift *h* is $\dfrac{\pi}{4}$. The phase shift is positive, so it translates the graph to the right by the distance $\dfrac{\pi}{4}$.

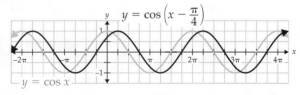

Model Problems continue . . .

3. Graph a sine function with a phase shift of $-\dfrac{\pi}{2}$ compared to the parent function $y = \sin x$.

SOLUTION

Identify phase shift, h

$y = \sin(x - h)$

$y = \sin\left(x - \left(-\dfrac{\pi}{2}\right)\right) = \sin\left(x + \dfrac{\pi}{2}\right)$

The phase shift is the constant subtracted from x, so in this case the phase shift is $-\dfrac{\pi}{2}$.

Graph

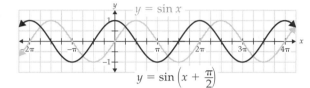

$y = \sin\left(x + \dfrac{\pi}{2}\right)$

The phase shift is negative, so it translates the graph to the left by the distance $\dfrac{\pi}{2}$.

4. Write an equation for the graph using the sine function.

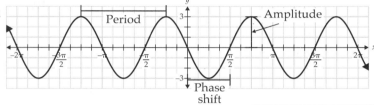

SOLUTION

Use sine as parent function

$y = a \sin b(x - h)$

The problem asks us to use sine as the parent function. We show the form of the function. We need to determine the values of a, b, and h.

> This form of the trigonometric function uses variables for scaling (*a* and *b*) and translation (*h*).

Amplitude a

$a = 3$

The graph has not been vertically shifted. The amplitude of the graph is 3, the height of a peak. This gives us the value for a.

Use period to determine b

$\text{Period} = \pi = \dfrac{2\pi}{b}$

$\dfrac{2\pi}{\pi} = 2$

$b = 2$

The period of the graph is π. That is the distance between two adjacent peaks. The period is 2π divided by b. Write this as an equation and solve for b, which is 2.

Phase shift h

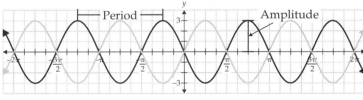

$h = \dfrac{\pi}{2}$

We show with a gray line the sine function with no phase shift. We need to shift the gray line graph. It will be shifted by the phase shift. The graph we are trying to match starts at 0 and decreases. The graph with no phase shift has that property at $\dfrac{\pi}{2}$. We need to shift the gray graph by $\dfrac{\pi}{2}$ to the right. This is the phase shift. This value equals h and it will be subtracted from x.

Substitute a, b, h

$y = 3 \sin 2\left(x - \dfrac{\pi}{2}\right)$

We now have the values for a, b, and h, which we substitute in the equation.

Model Problems continue . . .

5. Graph $y = 4 \cos \frac{2}{3}\left(x - \frac{3\pi}{4}\right)$.

SOLUTION

Calculate period

$$y = 4 \cos \frac{2}{3}\left(x - \frac{3\pi}{4}\right)$$

Calculate the period. The variable b is the coefficient of the input.

$$\text{Period} = \frac{2\pi}{b} = \frac{2\pi}{\left(\frac{2}{3}\right)} = 3\pi$$

Calculate amplitude

$$|a| = 4$$

The amplitude equals $|a|$, the coefficient of the function.

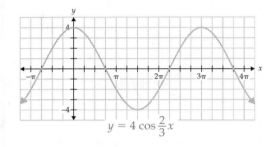

We can start our graph. It is a cosine function so it starts at its maximum value, the amplitude 4. It has a period of 3π, so the next peak is at 3π.

Phase shift to right

$$h = \frac{3\pi}{4}$$

The phase is the constant subtracted from x, so in this case the phase is $\frac{3\pi}{4}$.

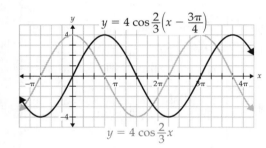

The graph is phase shifted to the right. The graph shifts $\frac{3\pi}{4}$ to the right.

 6. **MP 2, 4** When an object moves in *simple harmonic motion*, its position can be described using the sine or cosine function. Many objects can exhibit simple harmonic motion, from molecules in a solid, to pendulums, to moons in a circular orbit when viewed "on edge." A puck moves on a frictionless air hockey table in simple harmonic motion. Write an equation for the puck's position, y, as a function of time, t, given the graph.

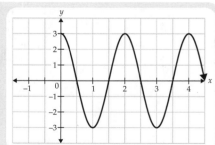

SOLUTION

Sine or cosine?   To write an equation for the puck's position, determine the amplitude and period from the graph. At $x = 0$, y is at its greatest value. This is true for the cosine function.

Amplitude $a = 3$ The amplitude of the graph is 3. This gives us the value for a.

Model Problems continue . . .

Midline	$y = 0$	The graph is vertically centered at $y = 0$.
Use period to determine b	$\text{period} = \dfrac{2\pi}{b} = 2$ $b = \pi$	The period is 2 because the distance between adjacent peaks is 2. The period is 2π divided by b. We write this as an equation and solve for b, which *is* π.
Substitute a, b	$y = 3 \cos \pi t$	Substitute the values for a and b in the equation.

Sine and Cosine Identities

Some identities can help us graph the sine and cosine functions. These identities are called **phase identities**. They translate the graph of the function to the left or right.

We start with the graphs of the sine function and cosine function. These are two different graphs.

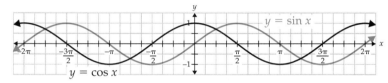

But if we translate the cosine graph $\dfrac{\pi}{2}$ units to the right, the graphs will coincide. We can state this relationship as an identity, $\cos\left(x - \dfrac{\pi}{2}\right) = \sin x$.

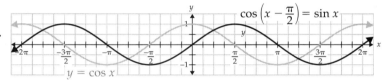

If we take the sine function and translate it $\dfrac{\pi}{2}$ units to the left, the graph matches the graph of the cosine function. This leads to the second identity, $\cos x = \sin\left(x + \dfrac{\pi}{2}\right)$.

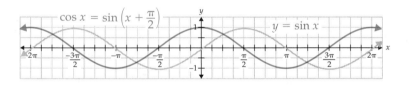

 In this activity, experiment with a sine and cosine identity using the graphing tool.

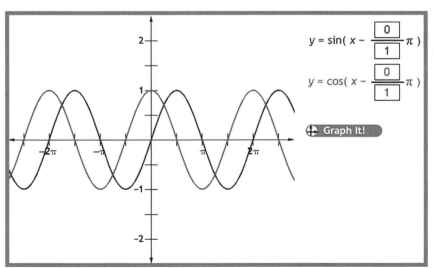

$$y = \sin\left(x - \frac{\boxed{0}}{\boxed{1}}\pi \right)$$

$$y = \cos\left(x - \frac{\boxed{0}}{\boxed{1}}\pi \right)$$

⊕ Graph It!

We also use graphs to show two identities that involve the same function. We can show two other identities. We graph both $-\cos x$ and $\cos x$.

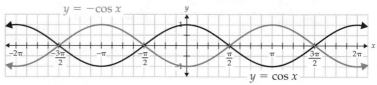

If we shift the graph of the cosine function π units to the left or right, the two graphs coincide. Subtracting π gives the same result as adding π, since the difference between $-\pi$ and $+\pi$ is 2π, which is equal to one period, thus mapping the left shift onto the right shift. This leads to the identity $-\cos x = \cos(x + \pi) = \cos(x - \pi)$.

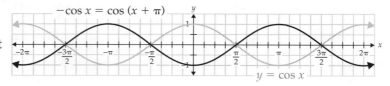

We can do the same with the sine function. We graph both the sine function and the opposite of that function.

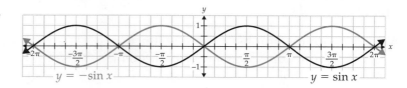

We again shift π units to the left to show the identity $-\sin x = \sin(x + \pi)$.

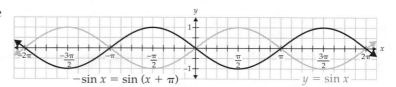

Graph of the Tangent Function

To graph the tangent function, we could just plot points until we were sure we had a good idea of the shape of the curve. However, to reduce the number of points we have to plot, we consider some properties of the tangent.

Since the tangent is the sine divided by the cosine, we must consider values of x for which $\cos x$ is 0, since at these points the tangent is undefined. At these values, the graph of the tangent will have vertical asymptotes, lines which the graph approaches but never reaches. To identify these points, we graph the cosine function.

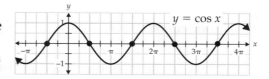

- Definition of tangent $\qquad \tan x = \dfrac{\sin x}{\cos x}$

  Since the tangent is the sine divided by the cosine, it is undefined when the cosine has the value 0.

- Asymptotes for tangent $\qquad x = \ldots, -\dfrac{3\pi}{2}, -\dfrac{\pi}{2}, \dfrac{\pi}{2}, \dfrac{3\pi}{2}, \ldots$

  $\cos x = 0$ at $\dfrac{\pi}{2}$, and then 0 again every π additional units left and right along the x-axis. Using the graph, we state the values of x that will result in asymptotes for the tangent.

We also use the locations of the asymptotes to determine the period of the tangent function. Adjacent asymptotes are separated by π, so the period is π. We more formally derive the period next. Using our analysis, we need only five points to draw a graph.

- Draw
  asymptotes
  and plot
  points

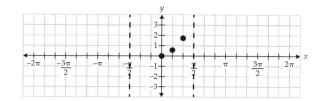

We use the facts about the tangent function to graph it. We draw asymptotes based on our analysis above of their locations. We plot 3 points for the interval from 0 to the first asymptote. The function is undefined at $\frac{\pi}{2}$.

- Tangent is
  symmetric
  about origin

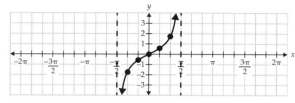

We plot some points between $-\frac{\pi}{2}$ and 0, and we draw the curve that passes through these points. The graph is symmetric about the origin. This shows the function is odd.

- Period is π

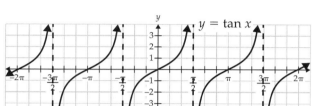

Finally, since the period of the tangent is π, we repeat the graph every π units.

MODEL PROBLEM

Graph $y = \tan 2x$ compared to the parent function $y = \tan x$.

SOLUTION

Compare functions

$y = \tan 2x$ versus $y = \tan x$

The variable b in the two functions is different, $b = 2$ versus $b = 1$. This means that the period is also different.

Period

$\text{Period} = \frac{\pi}{b} = \frac{\pi}{2}$

The period of the tangent is π, so calculate the period of this function by dividing π by b, which is 2. Squeeze the graph horizontally so the period is $\frac{\pi}{2}$.

Graph

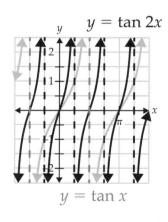

1. Which of the following is true about the graph of $y = -12 + 19 \cos (x - 7)$ compared to the graph of $y = 19 \cos (x - 7)$?

   A. It is shifted up by 7.
   B. It is shifted down by 7.
   C. It is shifted up by 12.
   D. It is shifted down by 12.
   E. It is shifted up by 19.
   F. It is shifted down by 19.

2. Which of the following is true about the graph of $y = 4 - 15 \cos (x + 3)$ compared to the graph of $y = -15 \cos (x + 3)$?

   A. It is shifted up by 3.
   B. It is shifted down by 3.
   C. It is shifted up by 4.
   D. It is shifted down by 4.
   E. It is shifted up by 15.
   F. It is shifted down by 15.

3. Which of the following is true about the graph of $y = -25 - 8 \sin (x - 2)$ compared to the graph of $y = -8 \sin (x - 2)$?

   A. It is shifted up by 2.
   B. It is shifted down by 2.
   C. It is shifted up by 8.
   D. It is shifted down by 8.
   E. It is shifted up by 25.
   F. It is shifted down by 25.

4. Given the function $y = \sin x$, which of the following represents the translation of $\frac{\pi}{8}$ units to the right?

   A. $\sin x - \frac{\pi}{8}$
   B. $\sin x + \frac{\pi}{8}$
   C. $\sin \left(x - \frac{\pi}{8} \right)$
   D. $\sin \left(x + \frac{\pi}{8} \right)$

5. Given $f(x) = \sin x$, which of the following could represent the given graph?

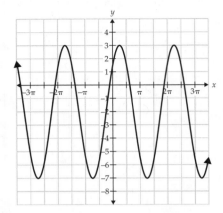

   A. $f(x) = 2f \left(x - \frac{\pi}{4} \right) - 5$
   B. $f(x) = 2f \left(x + \frac{\pi}{2} \right) + 5$
   C. $f(x) = 5f \left(x + \frac{\pi}{4} \right) - 2$
   D. $f(x) = 5f \left(x - \frac{\pi}{2} \right) - 2$

6. Which of the following is equivalent to $\cos (2x - \pi)$?

   A. $-\cos 2x$
   B. $\cos 2x$
   C. $2 \cos (x - \pi)$
   D. $2 \cos \left(x - \frac{\pi}{2} \right)$

7. **MP 2, 7** Which function has a graph whose phase shift is twice the period?

   A. $y = \cos 8 \left(x - \frac{\pi}{2} \right)$
   B. $y = \cos \left(x - \frac{\pi}{2} \right) + \frac{\pi}{4}$
   C. $y = \cos 4 \left(x - \frac{\pi}{2} \right)$
   D. $y = \frac{\pi}{4} \cos \left(x - \frac{\pi}{2} \right)$

Practice Problems continue . . .

8. If the tangent function is undefined at $x = a$, which of the following must be true?

    A. $a = 0$

    B. $\cos a = 0$

    C. $\sin a = 0$

    D. $\tan (a + \pi) = 0$

9. **MP 2, 7** Briefly describe what each letter represents in the function $y = a \sin b(x - c) + d$.

Exercises 10–16: Determine the phase shift of each function, including its sign.

10. $y = 2 + 10 \cos (x - 5)$

11. $y = -3 + \cos (x - 11)$

12. $y = 12 + 3 \cos (x - 6)$

13. $y = \sin \left(x - \dfrac{\pi}{8} \right)$

14. $y = \cos (x + \pi)$

15. $y = 2 \sin \left(x + \dfrac{\pi}{2} \right) - 1$

16. $y = 3 \cos \left(x - \dfrac{\pi}{8} \right) + 2$

Exercises 17–20: Graph each function from $x = -2\pi$ to 2π.

17. $y = 2 \sin \left(x - \dfrac{\pi}{4} \right)$

18. $y = 2 \sin 4\left(x - \dfrac{\pi}{4} \right) - 1$

19. $y = 3 \cos 2\left(x + \dfrac{\pi}{2} \right)$

20. $y = 3 \cos 2\left(x + \dfrac{\pi}{2} \right) + 2$

Exercises 21–26: Write a function in the form $y = a \sin b(x - c) + d$ that matches each description of the changes to the parent function $y = \sin x$.

21. Shifted down by 5, has a period of $\dfrac{\pi}{3}$, and shifted to the left by 9.

22. Shifted down down by 4, has a period of $\dfrac{\pi}{6}$, and shifted to the right by 8.

23. Peaks at 3, a period of π, and shifted left by $\dfrac{\pi}{2}$.

24. Amplitude of 4, a period of 2, and shifted right by 3.

25. Peaks at 1, a period of 2π, and shifted left by $\dfrac{\pi}{8}$.

26. Amplitude of 6, a period of $\dfrac{\pi}{4}$, and shifted right by π.

Exercises 27–31: Write a function in the form $y = a \cos b(x - c) + d$ that matches each description of the changes to the parent function $y = \cos x$.

27. Shifted up by 1, has a period of $\dfrac{\pi}{5}$, and shifted to the right by 6.

28. Amplitude of 1, a period of $\dfrac{\pi}{5}$, and shifted left by $\dfrac{\pi}{20}$.

29. Amplitude of 3, a period of $\dfrac{\pi}{2}$, and shifted right by $\dfrac{3\pi}{4}$.

30. Amplitude of 5, a period of 1, and shifted right by 4.

31. Amplitude of 2, a period of $\dfrac{1}{2}$, and shifted left by $\dfrac{3}{4}$.

Exercises 32–38: Write an equation for the graph shown. State your answer in the form $y = a \sin b(x - h) + k$ where $a > 0$ and $-\pi < h \le \pi$.

32. Assume the function is not shifted horizontally.

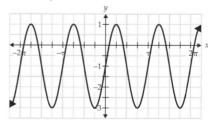

33. The horizontal shift should be between $-\dfrac{\pi}{2}$ and $\dfrac{\pi}{2}$.

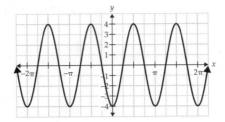

34.

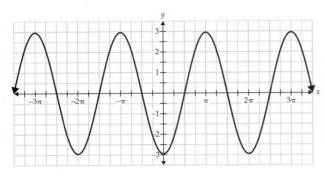

35.

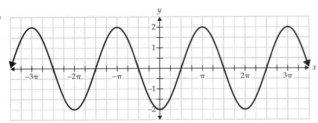

36.

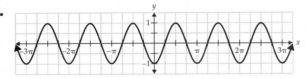

37.

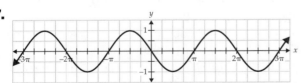

38.

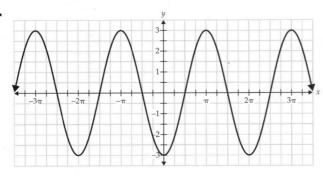

Exercises 39–42: State an equation of the form $y = a \sin bx + c$ that matches each description.

39. Maximum value is 5, minimum value is 1, and the period is 2π.

40. Maximum value is -3, minimum value is -5, and the period is 4π.

41. Maximum value is 10, minimum value is 4, and the period is 4.

42. Maxmum value is 0, minimum value is -1, and the period is 6.

Exercises 43–45: Find the smallest non-negative values of a and b such that the given line intersects the trigonometric function graph at an adjacent maximum and minimum pair. Then make a sketch of the two functions on the same set of axes.

43. $y = \dfrac{1}{2}x$; $y = \sin (a(x + b))$

44. $y = x$; $y = \cos (a(x + b))$

45. $y = -\dfrac{1}{2}x + 2$; $y = \cos (a(x + b))$

46. **MP 3, 7** Two of Gina's group members have a dispute over the phase shift of the graph $y = 2 \sin (5x + \pi) - 1$. One says that the phase shift is π units to the left, while the other says that it is $\dfrac{\pi}{5}$ units to the left. Which member is correct? Explain.

47. Write a cosine function equivalent to $f(x) = 2 \sin (3x + \pi)$, with phase shift between $-\pi$ and π.

48. Write a sine function equivalent to $f(x) = 5 \cos (2x - 3\pi)$, with phase shift between $-\pi$ and π.

49. Find all the points of intersection of the graphs $y = \cos x$ and $y = \sin x$.

50. **MP 3, 7** Can you perform horizontal and vertical translations to the tangent functions in the same way as sinusoidal functions? Explain.

MP 2, 4 The tidal variations at a spot in Puget Sound can be loosely modeled by the equation $y = 7 \sin \frac{\pi}{6}(x - 1) + 6$, where x is time in hours after midnight and y is water level in feet.

a Graph the equation.

b Explain the "real-life" meaning of
  (i) the 7
  (ii) the $\frac{\pi}{6}$
  (iii) the −1
  (iv) the 6

c When does the first high tide after midnight occur?

d When does the first low tide after midnight occur?

LESSON 9.6

9.6 Optional: Reciprocal Trigonometric Functions

Cosecant, Secant, and Cotangent

The **cosecant**, **secant**, and **cotangent** are trigonometric ratios that are the reciprocals of the sine, cosine, and tangent.

Cosecant of θ	$\csc \theta = \dfrac{1}{\sin \theta} = \dfrac{\text{hypotenuse}}{\text{opposite}}$	The cosecant of θ is the reciprocal of the sine of θ. The abbreviation for the cosecant is "csc."
Secant of θ	$\sec \theta = \dfrac{1}{\cos \theta} = \dfrac{\text{hypotenuse}}{\text{adjacent}}$	The secant of an angle θ is the reciprocal of the cosine of θ. The abbreviation for the secant is "sec."
Cotangent of θ	$\cot \theta = \dfrac{1}{\tan \theta} = \dfrac{\text{adjacent}}{\text{opposite}}$	The cotangent of an angle θ is the reciprocal of the tangent of θ. The abbreviation for the cotangent is "cot."

1. What are the cosecant, secant, and cotangent of 30°? 60°?

SOLUTION

$\csc 30° = \dfrac{1}{\sin 30°} = \dfrac{1}{\left(\dfrac{1}{2}\right)} = 2$ — The cosecant is the reciprocal of the sine. The sine of 30° is $\dfrac{1}{2}$. Take the reciprocal, and calculate that the cosecant of 30° = 2.

$\sec 30° = \dfrac{1}{\cos 30°} = \dfrac{1}{\left(\dfrac{\sqrt{3}}{2}\right)} = \dfrac{2\sqrt{3}}{3}$ — The secant is the reciprocal of the cosine. The cosine of 30° is $\dfrac{\sqrt{3}}{2}$. Take the reciprocal and rationalize the denominator by multiplying numerator and denominator by $\sqrt{3}$. The secant of 30° = $\dfrac{2\sqrt{3}}{3}$.

$\cot 30° = \dfrac{1}{\tan 30°} = \sqrt{3}$ — The cotangent is the reciprocal of the tangent. The tangent of 30° is $\dfrac{\sqrt{3}}{3}$. Take the reciprocal and simplify the fraction. The cotangent of 30° = $\sqrt{3}$.

$\csc 60° = \dfrac{1}{\sin 60°} = \dfrac{1}{\left(\dfrac{\sqrt{3}}{2}\right)} = \dfrac{2}{\sqrt{3}} = \dfrac{2\sqrt{3}}{3}$ — Use the value of sin 60° and the relationship between sine and cosecant to find csc 60°. To rationalize the expression, multiply the numerator and the denominator by $\sqrt{3}$.

$\sec 60° = \dfrac{1}{\cos 60°} = \dfrac{1}{\left(\dfrac{1}{2}\right)} = 2$ — Use the value of cos 60° and the relationship between cosine and secant to find sec 60°.

$\cot 60° = \dfrac{1}{\tan 60°} = \dfrac{1}{\sqrt{3}} = \dfrac{\sqrt{3}}{3}$ — Use the value of tan 60° and the relationship between tangent and cotangent to find cot 60°. To rationalize the expression, multiply the numerator and the denominator by $\sqrt{3}$.

2. In a right triangle, θ is one of the acute angles. If $\sin \theta = \dfrac{5}{13}$, what are the values of the other five trigonometric ratios for angle θ?

    a Determine the lengths of the sides of a right triangle where the sine of one angle is $\dfrac{5}{13}$.

    b Calculate cosine and tangent for θ.

    c Calculate secant, cosecant, and cotangent for θ.

SOLUTION

a Use definition of sine

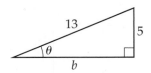

$\sin \theta = \dfrac{\text{opposite}}{\text{hypotenuse}} = \dfrac{5}{13}$

Draw a right triangle where $\sin \theta$ is $\dfrac{5}{13}$. Since the sine is the opposite leg divided by the hypotenuse, set the length of the leg opposite angle θ to 5 and the length of the hypotenuse to 13.

Model Problems continue . . .

| Pythagorean theorem | $5^2 + b^2 = 13^2$
 $b^2 = 144$
 $b = \sqrt{144} = 12$ | To calculate the length of the leg b, use the Pythagorean theorem. The length of leg b is the square root of 144, which is 12. |

b Cosine of θ $\quad \cos\theta = \dfrac{\text{adjacent}}{\text{hypotenuse}} = \dfrac{12}{13}$ $\quad$ The $\cos\theta$ is the ratio of the lengths of the side adjacent to θ and the hypotenuse. In this triangle, that is $\dfrac{12}{13}$.

Tangent of θ $\quad \tan\theta = \dfrac{\text{opposite}}{\text{adjacent}} = \dfrac{5}{12}$ $\quad$ The $\tan\theta$ is the ratio of the lengths of the side opposite to θ and the side adjacent to θ. In this triangle, that is $\dfrac{5}{12}$.

c Cosecant of θ $\quad \csc\theta = \dfrac{1}{\sin\theta} = \dfrac{\text{hypotenuse}}{\text{opposite}} = \dfrac{13}{5}$ $\quad$ The $\csc\theta$ is the reciprocal of $\sin\theta$. You can also calculate the cosecant as the hypotenuse divided by the opposite leg.

Secant of θ $\quad \sec\theta = \dfrac{1}{\cos\theta} = \dfrac{\text{hypotenuse}}{\text{adjacent}} = \dfrac{13}{12}$ $\quad$ The $\sec\theta$ is the reciprocal of $\cos\theta$. You can also calculate the secant as the hypotenuse divided by the adjacent leg.

Cotangent of θ $\quad \cot\theta = \dfrac{1}{\tan\theta} = \dfrac{\text{adjacent}}{\text{opposite}} = \dfrac{12}{5}$ $\quad$ The $\cot\theta$ is the reciprocal of $\tan\theta$. You can also calculate the cotangent as the adjacent leg divided by the opposite leg.

3. **MP 1** What are the cosecant, secant, and cotangent of 180°?

SOLUTION

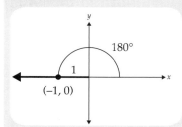

At 180°, $x = -1$, $y = 0$, and $r = 1$ on the unit circle.

Cosecant, secant, cotangent

$\csc 180° = \dfrac{r}{y} = \dfrac{1}{0}$ undefined

$\sec 180° = \dfrac{r}{x} = \dfrac{1}{-1} = -1$

$\cot 180° = \dfrac{x}{y} = \dfrac{1}{0}$ undefined

The cosecant, secant, and cotangent are reciprocals of the sine, cosine, and tangent. For 180°, the secant is -1, but the cosecant and cotangent result in denominators of 0, so they are undefined.

Reciprocal Trigonometric Function Graphs

To graph the cotangent, secant, and cosecant functions, we could plot points, or determine the period and other characteristics of each function to reduce the number of points to plot. Instead, the approach we use is to recognize that these three functions are the reciprocals of functions we have already graphed. That is,

$$\cot x = \frac{1}{\tan x}, \sec x = \frac{1}{\cos x}, \text{ and } \csc x = \frac{1}{\sin x}.$$

We will graph $\cot x = \dfrac{1}{\tan x}$ together. You will graph the other reciprocal functions in the model problems. The cotangent is the reciprocal of the tangent. To graph the cotangent function, we start with the graph of the tangent function.

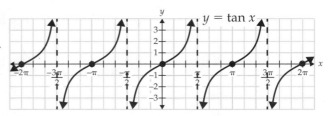

- **Definition of cotangent** $\cot x = \dfrac{1}{\tan x}$

  When the cotangent function equals 1 or −1, so does its reciprocal function.

- **Asymptotes for cotangent** $x = \ldots, 0, \pi, 2\pi, 3\pi, \ldots$

  Because the reciprocal of 0 is undefined, there is an asymptote for the cotangent function when $\tan x = 0$. This occurs at 0 and then again every π additional units along the x-axis. Using the graph, we state the values of x that will result in asymptotes for the cotangent.

- **Draw asymptotes and plot points**

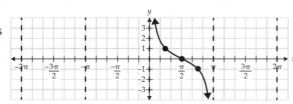

  We use the facts about the cotangent function to graph it. We draw asymptotes based on our analysis above of their locations. For $x = \dfrac{\pi}{4}$, the tangent is 1, and so is the cotangent, since the reciprocal of 1 is 1. At $x = \dfrac{\pi}{2}$, the tangent is undefined, but the cotangent has value 0. At $x = \dfrac{3\pi}{4}$, the tangent function has a value of −1. The reciprocal of −1 is −1.

- **Period is π**

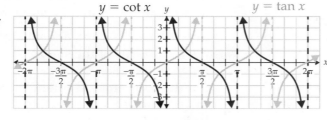

  The period of the tangent function is π. The cotangent will have the same period.

1. Graph sec x.

SOLUTION

Use graph
of cosine

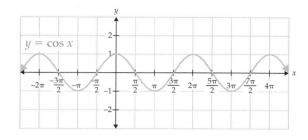

In a fashion similar to how we drew the cotangent function, we draw the graph of the secant as the reciprocal of the cosine. Start with the graph of the cosine function. When the cosine function is 0, the secant function is undefined and it approaches an asymptote. The cosine function is equal to 0 at $x = \ldots, -\dfrac{3\pi}{2}, -\dfrac{\pi}{2}, \dfrac{\pi}{2}, \dfrac{3\pi}{2}, \ldots$.

Draw
asymptotes
and plot
points

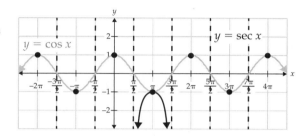

Start at 0 radians, where the cosine equals 1. The reciprocal of 1 is 1, so the secant function equals 1 there also. $\cos \pi = -1$, so its reciprocal has the same value. The graphs intersect again at 2π, where both equal 1. Because the absolute value of the cosine is never greater than one, its reciprocal, the secant, will never have a value between -1 and 1. When the cosine function equals 1 or -1, so does its reciprocal function.

Period is 2π

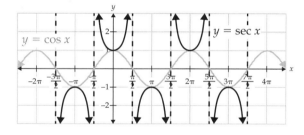

The period of the cosine function is 2π, so repeat the secant function with the same period.

2. Graph csc x.

SOLUTION

Use graph of sine

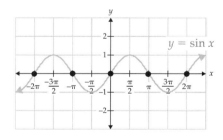

The cosecant is the reciprocal of the sine function. We will explain its graphing more rapidly, since it is very similar to graphing the secant function. There will be asymptotes where the sine function equals 0.

Draw graph

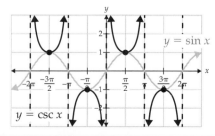

Draw the cosecant graph, which has asymptotes as shown and equals the reciprocal of the sine function at all points. When the sine function equals 1 or -1, so does its reciprocal function.

PRACTICE

1. The sin $\theta = \dfrac{4}{5}$. Evaluate the cotangent of the angle θ.

   A. $\cot \theta = \dfrac{3}{4}$ C. $\cot \theta = \dfrac{3}{5}$

   B. $\cot \theta = \dfrac{4}{3}$ D. $\cot \theta = \dfrac{5}{3}$

Exercises 2–7: Use the right triangle to answer the following questions.

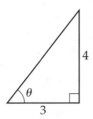

2. What is the sine of the angle θ?

3. What is the cosine of the angle θ?

4. What is the tangent of the angle θ?

5. What is the secant of the angle θ?

6. What is the cosecant of the angle θ?

7. What is the cotangent of the angle θ?

Exercises 8–13: Use the right triangle to answer the following questions.

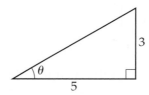

8. What is the sine of the angle θ?

9. What is the cosine of the angle θ?

10. What is the tangent of the angle θ?

11. What is the cosecant of the angle θ?

12. What is the secant of the angle θ?

13. What is the cotangent of the angle θ?

Exercises 14–18: A right triangle has an acute angle with a sine of $\dfrac{3}{5}$. State your answers using fractions.

14. What is the cosine of the angle?

15. What is the tangent of the angle?

16. What is the cosecant of the angle?

17. What is the secant of the angle?

18. What is the cotangent of the angle?

Exercises 19–23: A right triangle has an acute angle with a cosine of $\dfrac{3}{4}$. State your answers using simplified radicals.

19. What is the sine of the angle?

20. What is the tangent of the angle?

21. What is the cosecant of the angle?

22. What is the secant of the angle?

23. What is the cotangent of the angle?

Exercises 24–26: Evaluate. Express your answer to the nearest hundredth.

24. $\csc (-12)°$

25. $\cot 249°$

26. $\sec 146°$

Exercises 27–30: Determine whether the graphs can be described by the secant, cosecant, tangent, or cotangent function. Justify your answer.

27.

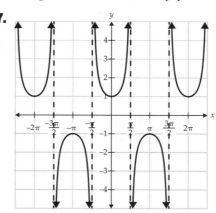

Practice Problems continue . . .

Practice Problems continued . . .

28.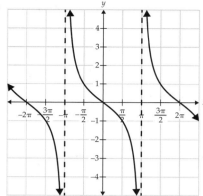

29.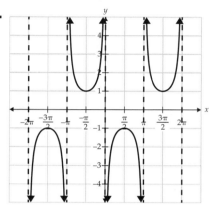

30.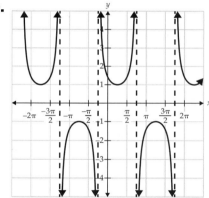

31. **MP 2, 3, 7** What do you notice about the relationship between the secant and cosecant functions?

Exercises 32–33: Sketch each trigonometric function for the domain $-2\pi \le x \le 2\pi$.

32. $y = 2 \csc\left(x - \dfrac{\pi}{2}\right)$

33. $y = 3 \sec\left(x + \dfrac{\pi}{2}\right)$

34. **MP 2, 7** A right triangle has an acute angle A, and $\sin A = z$. Write a formula for $\sec A$ in terms of z.

35. **MP 7** The angle θ corresponds to the angle between the positive x-axis and the line between the origin and the point $\left(\dfrac{15}{17}, -\dfrac{8}{17}\right)$ on the unit circle. What is $\csc \theta$? State your answer as an exact expression.

9.7 Modeling with Functions

You have now seen all the different types of functions you will encounter in this textbook: linear, quadratic, polynomial, rational, exponential, logarithmic, and trigonometric functions. Different types of functions can be used to model data.

MODEL PROBLEMS

1. Determine the model that best fits the data. Explain how you arrived at your solution.

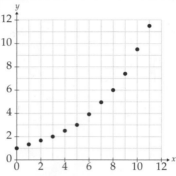

SOLUTION

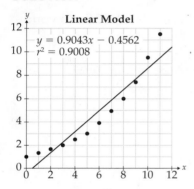

We use a spreadsheet program to find the regression curves. We try a linear model. It has a fairly high r^2 of 0.9. However, if x were to continue to increase in value, the linear model would be more challenged to model the data.

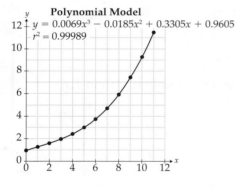

Next, we try a third-degree polynomial. It provides a model that is very close—it has an r^2 greater than 0.99. Polynomial models can often provide high r^2 due to their flexibility. We used a third degree (greatest power is 3) to model the function.

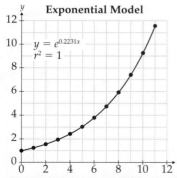

Finally, we try an exponential model. The data came from an exponential function, so all of its data points are on the graph of the function. The r^2 value is 1. This model fits the data the best. The spreadsheet likes to use the natural logarithm (with e the natural logarithm's base) for exponential functions. The base could be converted to 1.25, which is what we used ourselves. There is an important point here: If data looks like the graph of a function you know, try that function. The graph does not look linear, of course, and it looks like it could be exponential.

Model Problems continue . . .

2. Determine the model that best fits the data. Explain how you arrived at your solution.

x	y
2.00	1.50
3.00	1.33
4.00	1.26
5.00	1.14
6.00	1.13
7.00	1.08
8.00	1.08
9.00	1.03
10.00	0.93
11.00	1.02
12.00	1.00
13.00	0.99

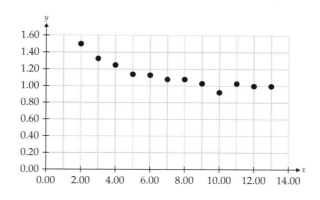

SOLUTION

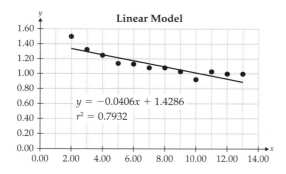

We use a spreadsheet and start with a linear model. The r^2 is about 0.79, which is not bad, but far from perfect. Perhaps the relationship between the variables is not linear.

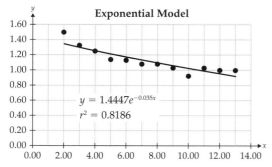

The data might look like an exponential function with a base less than 1. We try that. (Again, the spreadsheet prefers to use e as its base; note the negative power, which makes the base less than 1.) The model has a moderate r^2.

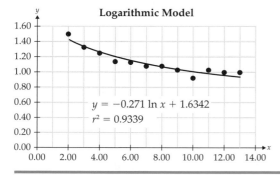

That makes logarithms a good model to try. The spreadsheet prefers to use natural logs, as shown in the logarithmic model. It has a very high r^2.

Model Problems continue . . .

3. Determine the model that best fits the data. Explain how you arrived at your solution.

x	y
-3.14	1.00
-2.36	-0.41
-1.57	-1.00
-0.79	-0.41
0.00	1.00
0.79	2.41
1.57	3.00
2.36	2.41
3.14	1.00
3.93	-0.41
4.71	-1.00
5.50	-0.41

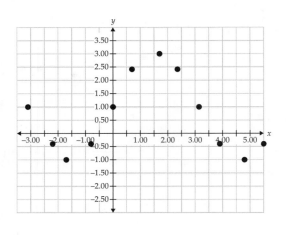

> It helps to consider what the graph may look like, instead of simply trying functions. The graph looks like the graph of a sine function, so that is an appropriate function to try.

SOLUTION

We could write a trigonometric function to model the data by looking at the graph above. It has a midline of 1, an amplitude of 2, and seems to have a frequency of about $\frac{1}{6}$ of a cycle per unit, which means it has a period of about 6. To calculate the coefficient of x in the trigonometric function, we divide 2π by the period, 6, and will round to 1. It can be modeled with $y = 2\sin x + 1$.

If we do not recognize that, we can try functions such as linear or polynomial, but they will not be very close to the data points. Spreadsheets do not provide trigonometric functions for modeling data, but the data (such as the position of a particle in a wave over time) is modeled with a trigonometric function.

Linear Model

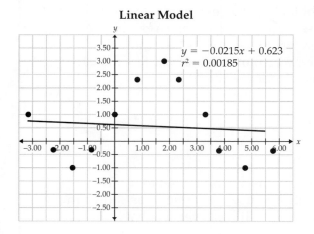

$y = -0.0215x + 0.623$
$r^2 = 0.00185$

We try a linear function, but unsurprisingly, its r^2 is very low. The graph does not look like the graph of a linear function.

Model Problems continue . . .

Polynomial Model

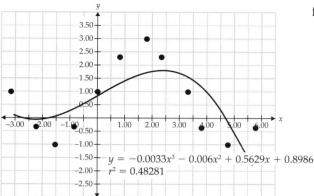

$y = -0.0033x^3 - 0.006x^2 + 0.5629x + 0.8986$
$r^2 = 0.48281$

We try a polynomial model of degree 3. It has a fairly low r^2.

Polynomial Model

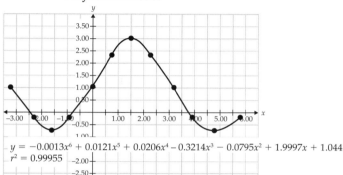

$y = -0.0013x^6 + 0.0121x^5 + 0.0206x^4 - 0.3214x^3 - 0.0795x^2 + 1.9997x + 1.044$
$r^2 = 0.99955$

We could increase the degree of the polynomial that the spreadsheet can use. If we allow it to use a sixth-degree polynomial, the model has a very high r^2. But we should caution you strongly: This is true for this range of data. With no additional information about the system being modeled, we cannot predict what happens when the range is extended. The two well-fitting models here—the trigonometric and the polynomial—each predict very different behavior outside the given range, and each prediction, or neither, might be correct. Only the data can tell us.

PRACTICE

1. A student models two data sets with linear models. For which data set should the student expect a lower r^2 value?

Graph 1

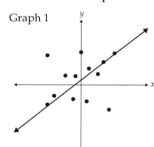

Graph 2

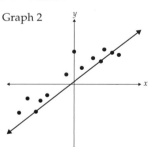

   A. Graph 1 because three points appear to lie exactly on the line.

   B. Graph 2 because more data points are closer to the line.

   C. Graph 1 because there are more points far away from the model than there are in Graph 2.

   D. Graph 2 because more points appear to lie on the line than in Graph 1.

2. Which of the following function types is the best fit for the data points graphed below?

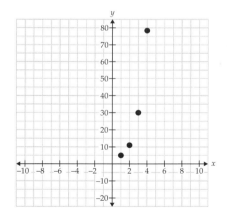

   A. Linear

   B. Polynomial

   C. Sine

   D. Logarithmic

Practice Problems continue . . .

3. Which graph could represent a non-linear polynomial function?

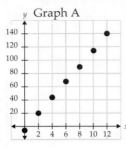

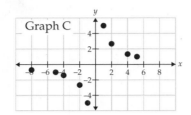

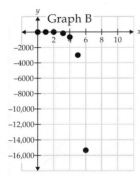

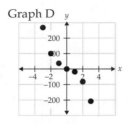

A. Graph A   C. Graph C
B. Graph B   D. Graph D

4. Which type of function is shown in the graph?

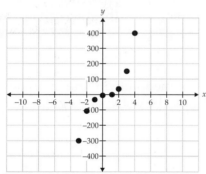

A. Exponential
B. Logarithmic
C. Linear
D. Polynomial

5. Which type of function, of the choices given, will best model the data plotted in the graph below?

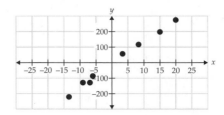

A. Logarithmic
B. Polynomial
C. Linear
D. Exponential

6. Which type of function, of the choices given, will best model the data plotted in the graph below?

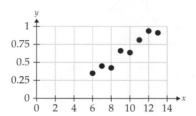

A. Sine
B. Tangent
C. Linear
D. Exponential

7. Which type of function, of the choices given, will best model the data plotted in the graph below?

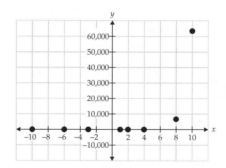

A. Polynomial
B. Exponential
C. Linear
D. Logarithmic

Practice Problems continue . . .

Practice Problems continued . . .

Exercises 8–9: Identify the type of function (linear, polynomial, exponential, or trigonometric) that provides the best fit for the data points given in the table. Justify your answer.

8.

x	y
−4	2340
−3	553
−2	36
−1	−9
0	4
1	45
2	468
3	2011
4	5796

9.

x	y
0	1
2	5
4	18
6	62
8	258
10	1026
12	4090
14	16,390

MP 5 Exercises 10–16: Graph the data points shown in the table. Based on the graph's appearance, provide a conjecture for the type of function represented by the data (linear, polynomial, logarithmic, or exponential). Explore the possible functions using a trend line. State the best fit function, in equation form, and state the r^2 value.

10.

x	y
3	20
6	38
11	68
14	86
20	122
25	152
28	170
30	182

11.

x	y
2	12
4	84
6	260
8	588
10	1116
12	1892
14	2964
16	4380

12.

x	y
2	0.60
4	0.90
6	1.08
8	1.20
10	1.30
12	1.38
14	1.45
16	1.51

13.

x	y
0	1
2	5
4	16
6	68
8	260
10	1018
12	5001
14	16,388

14.

x	y
0	4
3	23
6	79
9	165
12	296
15	456
18	656
21	890

Practice Problems continue . . .

15.

x	y
1	0.80
2	0.86
3	0.94
4	0.98
5	1.02
6	1.06
7	1.09
8	1.11

16.

x	y
1	9
3	228
5	1021
7	2790
9	5908
11	10,763
13	17,735
15	27,215

17. What are the most likely types of functions represented by the data points in the graph shown? Explain your reasoning.

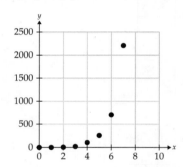

18. What are the most likely types of functions represented by the data points in the graph shown? Explain your reasoning.

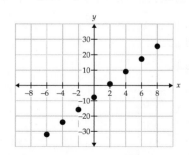

19. What are the most likely types of functions represented by the data points in the graph shown? Explain your reasoning.

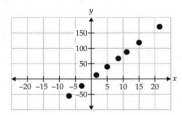

20. What are the most likely types of functions represented by the data points in the graph shown? Explain your reasoning.

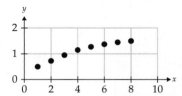

21. What are the most likely types of functions represented by the data points in the graph shown? Explain your reasoning.

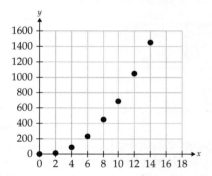

22. **MP 3** Eric states, "An experiment to measure the relationship between two variables produces a data set. The best fit trend line for this data set has an r^2 value of 1. This means the trend line describes the relationship between the variables." Is Eric's statement correct?

Practice Problems continue . . .

Practice Problems continued . . .

23. Decide if the function, which includes the points shown in the table, is a polynomial function or a cosine function. Identify the type of function and justify your decision.

x	y
-1	-0.99
0.68	-0.03
2	0.96
-4	1
5	-0.91
8	0.84
-5	0.54
-9.2	0.47

24. **MP 2, 3** In your own words, explain the meaning of an r^2 value, or the coefficient of determination.

25. In your own words, explain the meaning of the line of best fit, or trend line.

26. Create a table of values that would be best modeled by a linear function.

27. Create a table of values that would be best modeled by a logarithmic function.

28. **MP 4, 7** The bar graph represents the average rainfall in inches each month in Seattle, WA. Use a cosine or sine function to model the average rainfall, R, at any given time, t, in monthly intervals, where $t = 1$ represents January 15 and $t = 12$ represents December 15. Assume a full cycle period of 12 months. Note that because the average rainfall is not symmetric in the 12-month cycle, your model may be a bit inaccurate.

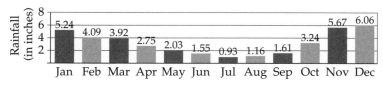

Chapter 9 Key Ideas

9.1 Geometry Review: Right Triangles

- An isosceles right triangle is an isosceles triangle with a right angle. The acute angles of an isosceles right triangle are equal, so the angles of the triangle are 45°, 45°, and 90°. For this reason, the isosceles right triangle is also called a 45-45-90 triangle. An isosceles right triangle with legs of length 1 has a hypotenuse of length $\sqrt{2}$.

- The 30-60-90 triangle has acute angles of 30° and 60°. A 30-60-90 triangle with a short leg of length 1 has a hypotenuse with a length of 2 and a longer leg, opposite the 60° angle, with a length of $\sqrt{3}$.

9.2 Geometry Review: Trigonometric Functions

- The sine, cosine, and tangent are trigonometric ratios, which are the ratios of the sides of a right triangle defined in connection with an acute angle in the triangle. For an acute angle θ, each ratio is:

$$\sin \theta = \frac{\text{length of opposite leg}}{\text{length of hypotenuse}}, \cos \theta = \frac{\text{length of adjacent leg}}{\text{length of hypotenuse}}, \text{ and } \tan \theta = \frac{\text{length of opposite leg}}{\text{length of adjacent leg}}.$$

9.3 Angles of Rotation and Trigonometric Functions

- An angle of rotation is created by rotating a ray from its initial side on the positive x-axis. The terminal side of the angle is where the ray stops. The measure of an angle of rotation is determined by how far the ray rotates, and in what direction. Positive rotation is counterclockwise, and negative rotation is clockwise. A full rotation is 360°.

- Coterminal angles can be created when a rotation greater than 360° is made. Coterminal angles have the same terminal side, and their measures differ by a multiple of 360°.

- The reference angle for an angle of rotation (other than a multiple of 90°) is the acute angle between the terminal side and the x-axis. A reference angle is used to calculate the trigonometric values.

- The values of trigonometric functions can be calculated for angles of any measure. The sine, cosine, and tangent of an angle of rotation θ are defined using the coordinates of any point (x, y) on the terminal side of the angle, and the distance r from the origin to the point.

- Angles can be measured in units called *radians*. The radian measure of an angle is defined using a circle whose center is at the vertex of the angle. The radian measure is the ratio of the length of the arc intercepted by the angle to the radius of the circle.

9.4 Trigonometric Functions and the Unit Circle

- The trigonometric functions on the unit circle can be defined as functions of angles defined by (x, y) coordinates and a circle with a radius of 1. The x-coordinate equals $\cos \theta$. The y-coordinate equals $\sin \theta$.

- Some equations involving trigonometric functions of an angle θ are true for any value of θ. Such equations are called *trigonometric identities*. The main trigonometric identities are $\sin^2 \theta + \cos^2 \theta = 1$, $1 + \tan^2 \theta = \sec^2 \theta$, and $\cot^2 \theta + 1 = \csc^2 \theta$.

9.5 Trigonometric Function Graphs

- A periodic function is one whose graph repeats. A cycle of a periodic function is the smallest repeating unit of its graph. A period is the interval of the independent variable (x) that contains a single cycle.

- Sine and cosine are *sinusoidal functions*. The graphs of the sine and cosine functions are smooth curves with periods of 2π. The period of a sinusoidal function is 2π divided by b, the factor that is the coefficient of the input x.

- The maximum value of both $\sin x$ and $\cos x$ is 1, and the minimum value is -1. The amplitude of these functions is 1, the maximum distance of the function's graph from the x-axis. The amplitude of $a \sin x$ or $a \cos x$ equals $|a|$.

- Multiplying the function $\sin x$ or $\cos x$ by a scales its graph vertically. Multiplying the input x by a factor b scales the graph horizontally, changing its period.

- When a constant is added to a function, $f(x) + k$, the graph is shifted up by k. When a constant is subtracted from the input of a function, $f(x - h)$, the graph is shifted to the right by h. This remains true for trigonometric functions.

- Some identities can help us graph the sine and cosine functions. These identities are called *phase identities*. They translate the graph of the function to the left or right.

- To graph the tangent function, we consider some properties of the tangent. Since the tangent is the sine divided by the cosine, we must consider values of x for which $\cos x$ is 0 and the tangent is undefined. At these values, the graph of the tangent will have vertical asymptotes, lines which the graph approaches but never reaches.

9.6 Optional: Reciprocal Trigonometric Functions

- The cosecant, secant, and cotangent are trigonometric ratios that are the reciprocals of the sine, cosine, and tangent. For angle θ, each ratio can be defined: $\csc \theta = \dfrac{1}{\sin \theta}$, $\sec \theta = \dfrac{1}{\cos \theta}$, and $\cot \theta = \dfrac{1}{\tan \theta}$.

- To graph the cotangent, secant, and cosecant functions, recognize that they are the reciprocal functions of the tangent, cosine, and sine functions.

9.7 Modeling with Functions

- Functions can be used to fit data sets. Use the shape of the scatter plot to narrow down which function to test. Function models with higher r^2 values are better fits for the data.

CHAPTER 9 REVIEW

1. Which of the following are coterminal with 170°? Select all that apply.

   A. −190°   D. 370°

   B. −170°   E. 890°

   C. 190°

2. Which pairs of the following angles are coterminal? Select all that apply.

   A. 125° and 465°   C. −75° and 315°

   B. 150° and 510°   D. 70° and −290°

3. If $\cos \theta = -\dfrac{5}{13}$ and $\sin \theta > 0$, then in which quadrant is θ?

   A. Quadrant I   C. Quadrant III

   B. Quadrant II   D. Quadrant IV

Exercises 4–8: State the reference angle for each angle θ.

4. $\theta = 290°$

5. $\theta = 330°$

6. $\theta = 350°$

7. $\theta = -220°$

8. $\theta = -330°$

9. The terminal side of angle θ passes through the point $(-5, -12)$. What is $\sin \theta$? State your answer as an exact expression.

Exercises 10–13: State the acute angle defined by the function.

10. $\sin x = 0.5$

11. $\cos x = 0.5$

12. $\tan x = 1$

13. $\cos x = \dfrac{\sqrt{2}}{2}$

14. A right triangle's hypotenuse starts at the origin and ends at the point (2, 6), with one leg on the x-axis. Angle θ is between the hypotenuse and the positive x-axis. What is the value of $\tan \theta$?

Exercises 15–18: State each angle in radians in terms of π.

15. 90°

16. 30°

17. 45°

18. 60°

Exercises 19–22: Convert the radian measures to degrees.

19. $\dfrac{\pi}{3}$

20. $\dfrac{\pi}{12}$

21. $\dfrac{\pi}{18}$

22. $\dfrac{3\pi}{8}$

23. A circle has radius 4. What is the arc length of the segment cut by a central angle with measure $\dfrac{5\pi}{9}$ radians? State your answer as an exact expression.

24. Determine the amplitude, period, maximum and minimum values of $f(x) = \sin 5x$.

25. **MP 1, 2** Derive a formula for the straight line distance from the maximum to the minimum values of a sinusoidal function in terms of the amplitude A and period T.

26. Write an equation for the graph below using the cosine function. Assume the function is not shifted horizontally.

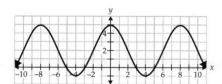

27. **MP 2, 6** Write an equation for the graph below using the cosine function. Assume the function is not shifted horizontally.

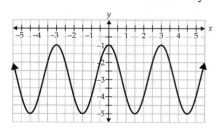

Chapter Review continues . . .

28. Write an equation for the sinusoidal function below using the cosine function. The horizontal shift should be between -2π and $+2\pi$.

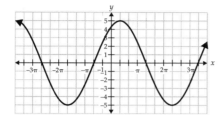

29. Write an equation for the sinusoidal function below using the sine function. The horizontal shift should be between -4π and $+4\pi$.

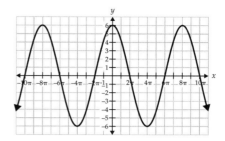

30. **MP 4, 7** Use the table to write a sinusoidal function to model the mean temperature, T, in Seattle, WA, at any given time, t, in monthly intervals, where $t = 1$ represents January 15 and $t = 12$ represents December 15. Assume the temperature is similar to a cosine or sine curve with a full cycle period of 12 months. You may assume the maximum temperature occurs either in July or August.

Month	Ave. High	Ave. Low	Mean	Ave. Precip.	Record High	Record Low
Jan	47°F	36°F	41°F	5.24 in	64°F (1981)	16°F (1980)
Feb	51°F	37°F	44°F	4.09 in	70°F (1986)	11°F (1989)
Mar	55°F	39°F	47°F	3.92 in	74°F (1995)	23°F (1989)
Apr	59°F	43°F	51°F	2.75 in	85°F (1976)	32°F (1997)
May	65°F	48°F	57°F	2.03 in	88°F (1973)	38°F (1996)
Jun	70°F	53°F	61°F	1.55 in	93°F (1995)	42°F (1991)
Jul	75°F	56°F	66°F	0.93 in	96°F (1991)	47°F (1979)
Aug	75°F	57°F	66°F	1.16 in	94°F (1996)	48°F (1980)
Sep	70°F	53°F	61°F	1.61 in	91°F (1988)	41°F (1985)
Oct	60°F	46°F	53°F	3.24 in	82°F (1991)	31°F (1991)
Nov	52°F	40°F	46°F	5.67 in	71°F (1980)	13°F (1985)
Dec	47°F	36°F	41°F	6.06 in	65°F (1980)	12°F (1983)

1. Which of the following is the inverse of

$$f(x) = \frac{3 - 2x}{x - 4}?$$

A. $f^{-1}(x) = \dfrac{2x - 3}{4 - x}$

B. $f^{-1}(x) = \dfrac{4 - 2x}{x + 3}$

C. $f^{-1}(x) = \dfrac{4x + 3}{x + 2}$

D. The inverse does not exist.

2. If $f(x) = 3x - 2$, what is $f(f(f(1)))$?

A. -1 C. 2

B. 1 D. 3

3. In a right triangle, $\tan \theta = \dfrac{y}{x}$. Which is $\sin \theta$?

A. $\dfrac{x}{x^2 + y^2}$

B. $\dfrac{x}{\sqrt{x^2 + y^2}}$

C. $\dfrac{\sqrt{x^2 + y^2}}{x}$

D. $\dfrac{y}{\sqrt{x^2 + y^2}}$

4. If $(b + 2)(b + 5) = -3b - 15$ and $a = 4b - 10$, find the value of a.

5. Factor: $(x + 4)(x - 5) - 11x + 56$

Exercises 6–8: Simplify each expression.

6. $\dfrac{x^2 + 2x - 3}{x^2 - 9}$

7. $\sqrt{2x^2 + 16x + 32}$

8. $\sqrt{-5} \cdot \sqrt{2}$

Exercises 9–10: Solve each equation.

9. $4^{\sqrt{x-3}} + 64 = 20 \cdot 2^{\sqrt{x-3}}$

10. $\dfrac{1}{64} = (\sqrt{2})^x$

11. What is $(f \cdot g)(x)$ if $f(x) = x - 8$ and $g(x) = x - 2$?

12. Restate as a logarithmic equation: $e^k = 16.2$

Exercises 13–16: State as a single logarithm.

13. $\log_3 13 + \log_3 3$

14. $\log_4 6 - \log_4 5$

15. $\log_b 32 - \log_b 8$

16. $\log_{35} 77 - \log_{35} 7$

17. **MP 6** pH is a measure of the acidity or alkalinity of a solution, and it equals $-\log [\text{H}^+]$, where H^+ is the hydrogen ion concentration measured in moles per liter. For instance, oven cleaner has a hydrogen ion concentration of about 2×10^{-13} moles per liter, so its pH equals $(-\log 2) + 13$, which is 12.7. What is the pH of coffee, which has a hydrogen ion concentration of about 8.7×10^{-6}? State the answer to the nearest tenth.

18. Express $2 \log_7 5 + 3 \log_7 2 - \log_7 4$ as a logarithm of a single number.

19. Find the 16th term in the sequence: $-30, -22, -14, -6\ldots$.

20. Write the series in expanded form:

$$\sum_{n=4}^{9} (-3n + 16)$$

21. **MP 4, 5** A small business sells \$28,000 worth of hair care products during its first year of operation. The owner decides to set a goal of increasing annual sales by \$3500 each year thereafter. Assuming the goal is met, what is the total revenue in its first 10 years of operation?

22. The first term in a geometric sequence is 30. To get the next term, you multiply by 2. What is the sixth term in the sequence?

23. **MP 3, 8** Prove that the infinite harmonic series $\frac{1}{2} + \frac{1}{3} + \frac{1}{4} + \ldots$ has no sum (that is, it does not converge). In the series, the number in the denominator increases by 1 each term. To do this, group the terms of the series as $\frac{1}{2}, \frac{1}{3} + \frac{1}{4}, \frac{1}{5} + \frac{1}{6} + \frac{1}{7} + \frac{1}{8}$, and so on, and show that each of these sums is greater than or equal to $\frac{1}{2}$.

24. For positive integers n, how do the expansions of $(a + b)^n$ and $(a - b)^n$ differ?

25. What angle, in radians, does the hour hand make with the positive x-axis?

26. State $\sin \theta$ based on the diagram. The ratio may be undefined.

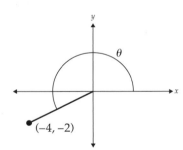

27. What is the equation of the graph shown? State your answer using the cosine function.

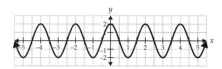

28. **MP 4, 6** A person gets on a Ferris wheel with a radius of 27 meters at its lowest position. If the ride took 4 minutes and made 30 complete revolutions, write an equation that represents the vertical displacement, d, in meters from the center of the Ferris wheel as a function of time, t, in minutes.

29. **MP 2, 3** Use the triangle below to answer the questions.

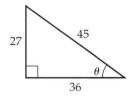

a Prove that the triangle is a right triangle by using the Pythagorean theorem.

b Show that the values in the triangle satisfy the trigonometric identity $\sin^2 \theta + \cos^2 \theta = 1$.

c Describe a similarity with the Pythagorean theorem and the identity $\sin^2 \theta + \cos^2 \theta = 1$.

Chapter Content

Lessons	Standards

Vocabulary

addition rule	experimental study	outcome
bias	independent event	placebo
binomial distribution	independently combined probability model	probability
coefficient of variation	lurking variable	proportion
complement	margin of error	randomization
compound event	medical trial	sample space
conditional probability	multiplication rule	side effect
confidence interval	mutually exclusive	standard deviation
confidence level	normal curve	subtraction rule
dependent events	normal distribution	survey
event	observation	theoretical probability
experimental probability	observational study	two-way table

LESSON 10.1

10.1 Introduction to Probability

Experimental Probability

You have learned previously that **probability** is the study of how likely it is that some **event** or set of events will occur. There are two ways to determine the probability of an event: *experimental probability* or *theoretical probability*.

Experimental probability is based on observation. Say you toss a coin 100 times and record the outcome each time. Each of those results, also called **outcomes**, is an **observation**. Based on the observations, you can calculate an experimental probability that some event or set of events occurs.

$$P(A) = \frac{\text{\# of times event } A \text{ occurs}}{\text{\# of observations}}$$

The experimental probability of an event A, $P(A)$, equals the number of times A occurs, divided by the total number of observations.

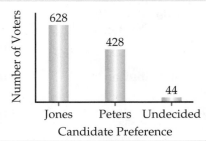

MODEL PROBLEM

MP 2 What is the probability a person prefers candidate Jones, based on the data of a survey of people about their preferences for candidates in an election?

SOLUTION

Formula for experimental probability

$$P(A) = \frac{\text{\# of times event } A \text{ occurs}}{\text{\# of observations}}$$

$$P(\text{Jones}) = \frac{\text{\# of people who prefer Jones}}{\text{\# of people surveyed}}$$

The probability a person prefers Jones equals the number of people who prefer Jones divided by the number of people surveyed.

Substitute $$P(\text{Jones}) = \frac{628}{628 + 428 + 44} = \frac{628}{1100} = 0.57$$ The chart says 628 people prefer Jones, so put that in the numerator and divide.

Theoretical Probability and Sample Spaces

Unlike experimental probability, which is determined from observations, **theoretical probability** is determined using reasoning and analysis. In theoretical probability, we assume that all outcomes are equally likely. Classic examples include the outcomes from flipping a fair coin, rolling a fair number cube, drawing a single card from a well-shuffled deck, spinning a fair spinner, etc.

Suppose you flip a fair coin and then roll a fair six-sided number cube. What is the probability that the outcome is (Heads (H), 5)? To begin answering this question, we need to determine the **sample space**, which is the set of all possible outcomes of some action. The sample space is shown below.

H, 1	H, 4	T, 1	T, 4
H, 2	H, 5	T, 2	T, 5
H, 3	H, 6	T, 3	T, 6

We can see there are 12 possible outcomes and of those, only one is (H, 5). To calculate the probability of this event, we use the following formula:

$$P(A) = \frac{\text{\# of outcomes of event } A}{\text{\# of outcomes in the sample space}}$$

Theoretical probability equals the number of ways an event can occur divided by the number of possible outcomes.

Thus, $P(\text{H}, 5)$ is $= \dfrac{1}{12}$, which is about 8.3%. Note that as a decimal, probability is always a value between 0 and 1. Recall that decimal values can be converted to percents by multiplying the decimal by 100.

We show one of four similar activities below. In these activities, you can simulate hundreds or even thousands of coin tosses. If two coins are tossed, the theoretical probability is that 50% of the time, the outcome is one heads and one tails. The theoretical probability for both heads is 25%, and the theoretical probability for both tails is 25%. Complete 4 simulations of tossing coins. Do the probabilities you observe match the model discussed above? Does this make you question the model? Conduct this same experiment 5 times. How often do the outcomes match the theoretical model? Then run the simulation 100 times, and do this 5 times. How close are the probabilities you observe to the theoretical model? Then run the simulation about 1000 times (you may want to let it run in the background as you work on another task—and if it runs more than 1000 times, that's fine). How does the additional data work to help you support or reject the theoretical model?

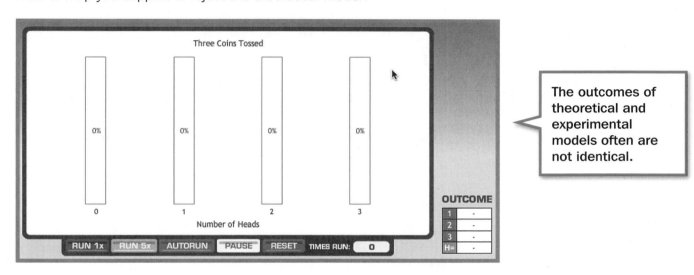

The outcomes of theoretical and experimental models often are not identical.

MODEL PROBLEMS

1. Say you have a fair coin and 4 equally sized cards that are red, green, blue, and yellow, respectively. You close your eyes and draw a card, and then you flip the coin.
   a   What is the sample space for this problem?
   b   What is the probability that the outcome is (Blue, Heads)?

SOLUTION

a   Create the sample space

	Heads	Tails
Red	(Red, Heads)	(Red, Tails)
Green	(Green, Heads)	(Green, Tails)
Blue	(Blue, Heads)	(Blue, Tails)
Yellow	(Yellow, Heads)	(Yellow, Tails)

b   Use the data

There is only one outcome that is (Blue, Heads) out of the 8 outcomes in the sample space.

Then $P(\text{Blue, Heads}) = \dfrac{1}{8} = 12.5\%$.

Model Problems continue . . .

2. You have a fair spinner numbered 1 through 3 and a small bag containing a red chip, a blue chip, and a purple chip. You spin the spinner and then select one of the chips from the bag without looking.

   a What is the probability that the spinner lands on an odd number <u>and</u> you select a red chip from the bag?

   b What is the probability that you spin an odd number <u>or</u> select a red chip from the bag?

   c Explain why these two events, odd number <u>and</u> red chip, an odd number <u>or</u> red chip, do not have the same probability of occurring.

SOLUTION

a Create the sample space

	Red (R)	Blue (B)	Purple (P)
1	(1, R)	(1, B)	(1, P)
2	(2, R)	(2, B)	(2, P)
3	(3, R)	(3, B)	(3, P)

Use the sample space

There are 2 outcomes in which you spin an odd number and select a red card. Since there are 9 possible outcomes, $P(\text{Odd, R})$ is $\frac{2}{9} \approx 22\%$.

b Count the number of times the events of interest occur and compute probability

The outcomes of "spin an odd number or select a red card" include (1, R); (2, R); (3, R); (1, B); (3, B); (1, P); and (3, P). The probability of spinning an odd number or drawing a red card is $\frac{7}{9} \approx 78\%$.

c Interpret your sample space and probabilities

In part **a**, both events must occur for the outcome to count. There are only two outcomes in which an odd number is spun <u>and</u> a red chip is drawn. In part **b**, either event occurring counts that outcome in the probability. Since there are more outcomes with either an odd number or a red card, that probability is greater.

Model Problems continue . . .

3. **MP 1, 5, 7** **a** If you roll a pair of dice, what is the probability that the *total* on the two dice will be 7?
b Graph the outcome—the sums of the two dice—based on their frequency of occurring. If you were given only the frequency graph of the outcomes, what conclusion could you draw about the probabilities associated with rolling a pair of dice?

SOLUTION

a Create sample space

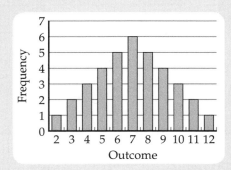

The sample space represents all the possible outcomes when two dice are rolled. To make it easier to see all the outcomes in the sample space, we use one green die and one black die. For instance, the outcome on the upper right, 1, 6, means the green die came up 1 and the black die came up 6.

Count number of times event occurs

Number of times dice total 7 is 6

All the outcomes where the dice total 7 are circled. There are 6 such outcomes.

Count total number of outcomes

36 outcomes

There are 36 outcomes in the sample space.

Compute probability

$$P(7) = \frac{6}{36} = \frac{1}{6}$$

The probability of the dice totaling 7 is $\frac{6}{36}$, or $\frac{1}{6}$, because there are 6 outcomes where the dice total 7 and 36 outcomes in the sample space.

b Sample space distribution

Use the sample space to graph the frequencies of various outcomes. For instance, there is one cell in the sample space with an outcome of a sum of 2, so put up a bar of height 1. Continue for each outcome. If you were to examine only the frequency graph of the outcomes, you would know that the sum with the highest probability is 7, and that the probabilities of the remaining sums are symmetric about 7.

Simulations

In the theoretical probabilities listed on page 467, we imagined performing a single repetition of an experiment with equally likely outcomes. For example, we considered flipping a coin one time and then drawing a single card and recorded the outcome. What if we decided to perform multiple repetitions, called *iterations*, of our experiment? We could flip a coin and then draw a card 25 times, recording the result each time. This could show us if one outcome was more likely than another, but it wouldn't give us the whole picture of an outcome's probability. What if we decided to flip a coin and then draw a card for 20 sets of 25 iterations? Or 50 sets of 25 iterations? Or 100 sets of 25 iterations? Each time we perform and record the results of another set of iterations, we draw closer and closer to the true experimental probability of each possible outcome in the sample space. Performing experiments like these helps us to determine the true probability that an event or set of events will occur (or not occur). We can also compare our experimental outcome with the theoretical probability to test the assumptions we used to calculate the theoretical probability. These experiments can also help us to determine whether a number cube, coin, or spinner is truly fair, which is the usual assumption in a calculation of a theoretical probability. Of course, it is quite time consuming to sit and flip a coin, then draw a card, and record the results hundreds of times. To help us with the process, we use technology to perform the simulation and automatically record and graph the results.

MODEL PROBLEMS

1. A circular spinner is divided into five sectors. A student spun the arrow on the spinner 25 times and recorded that the arrow stopped on the space marked "1" a total of 3 times out of 25 spins. To determine if the spinner was fair, the student then used a program to simulate the number of times the arrow stopped on the number 1 in 25 spins of a fair spinner equally divided into five sections. The results of 1,000 trials of the simulation are shown below. Based on the results of the simulation, is there statistical evidence that the spinner is fair? Why or why not?

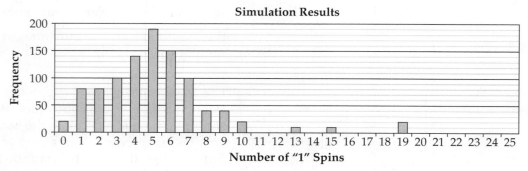

SOLUTION

Interpret the graph: When spinning a fair spinner, each of the outcomes is theoretically equally likely. Thus, when the outcome choices are 1, 2, 3, 4, or 5, we should land on the number 1 about 20% of the time. In each iteration, we spun the spinner 25 times and 20% of 25 is 5. In this graph, we see that the spinner head landed on the desired outcome $\frac{190}{1,000} = 19\%$ of the time.

Since 19% is close to the theoretical 20% we are looking for, we can be fairly certain the spinner is fair.

Another type of simple simulation involves using coins, cards, a spinner, or some other type of device that produces equally likely outcomes to simulate a certain outcome as in the next model problem.

Model Problems continue . . .

2. **MP 2, 4** 78% of the students in a town go to one school, and the rest go to another. The city council wants to decide which school will get a new football field based on the probability of some chance outcome, where the probability matches the student percents.

> Different simulations with different probabilities, such as a deck of 52 cards or a coin toss, can be used to model decisions.

a How might they do this by flipping a coin?

b How about using a deck of playing cards?

SOLUTION

a Coin

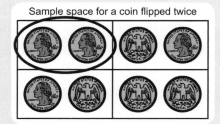

Sample space for a coin flipped twice

Create a sample space for a coin flipped twice. The probability of two heads is 1 out of 4 outcomes, or 25%. The probability of any of the other 3 outcomes is 3 out of 4, or 75%. That is not exactly 78%, but close.

If anything but heads twice, then the 78% school gets it.

Two heads has 25% probability, not 22%. Are there better ways to use a coin? Yes. For instance, the probability of tossing a coin 8 times and obtaining any outcome other than 3 heads and 5 tails is 78%. You're welcome to show this by counting in the sample space.

b Cards

Remove 2 cards (leaving 50)
Write "78% school" on 39 of the cards
Pick a card, any card

$$\frac{39}{50} = 78\%$$

The probability of picking a "78% school" card is exactly 78%.

In this activity, solve various probability problems. With each question, you risk money. If you are correct, you win it. If not, you lose it.

PRACTICE

1. A jar contains 4 white, 14 blue, 18 yellow, and 7 red jellybeans. Suppose that you draw out 3 jellybeans and they are yellow, blue, and yellow. If you don't replace those 3 jellybeans, what is the probability that your 4th draw results in a yellow jellybean?

   A. $\dfrac{9}{20}$ C. $\dfrac{2}{5}$

   B. $\dfrac{18}{43}$ D. $\dfrac{3}{40}$

2. Annelise randomly draws a card from a well-shuffled, standard 52-card deck, and then she flips a coin. Which of the following statements is true?

   I. The probability of drawing a jack of spades is $\dfrac{1}{52}$.

   II. The probability of the coin landing on heads is $\dfrac{1}{2}$.

   III. The probability of drawing a diamond is $\dfrac{1}{4}$.

   A. I only
   B. II only
   C. I and II only
   D. I, II, and III

3. What is the probability that two six-sided dice numbered from 1 to 6 will sum to 4?

   A. $\dfrac{1}{6}$ C. $\dfrac{1}{12}$

   B. $\dfrac{1}{9}$ D. $\dfrac{1}{18}$

4. The tally below shows the number of times that Jim and Rob won games of checkers. What is the experimental probability that Rob beats Jim in future games?

   Jim: I I I I I I I I I
   Rob: I I I I I

5. What is the theoretical probability of getting one tail and one head when you flip a coin twice?

6. If you flip a fair coin and then roll a fair 6-sided number cube, what is the probability that the outcome is (tails, odd number)?

7. Shanta states that the probability of rolling 2 fair, six-sided number cubes and having their faces show a sum of 7 is the same as the probability of rolling doubles (both number cubes show a 1, both show a 2, etc.). Is she correct?

8. What is the theoretical probability of rolling a prime number with a single die?

9. What is the probability that when you roll two dice, they total 10?

10. Suppose you roll two four-sided dice, numbered from 1 to 4.

    a What is the most likely sum of the dice?
    b What is the probability that the dice will total 7?

11. What is the probability that when you roll two six-sided dice, they total 5?

12. Last year in November it rained 18 days, snowed 2 days, and there was no precipitation on the other 10 days. Based on those observations, what is the experimental probability that it will rain on a random day in November of this year?

13. The theoretical probability of flipping a coin and landing on heads is 50%. Mrs. Nuria has each of her 30 students flip the same coin once and records that it landed on heads 18 times and tails 12 times. Are these results enough to conclude the coin is not fair? Why or why not?

14. You pour out half a bag of jelly beans, and 17 of the 25 are red. Then you return them to the bag. What is the experimental probability of randomly pulling out a red jelly bean from the bag?

15. Valeri surveys 52 people and determines that 14 of them would vote for Rodriguez for president. How could Valeri design an experiment, based on the probability of some chance outcome, where the probability matches the results of his survey?

Practice Problems continue . . .

470 Chapter 10: Probability

Practice Problems continued . . .

16. Lule is playing a game with her brother. She notices that of the 3 color choices available on the spinner, each occupying $\frac{1}{3}$ of the circle, the arrowhead lands on blue more often than $\frac{1}{3}$ of the time. Lule suspects the spinner is not fair, so she runs a computer simulation with 1,000 iterations of 50 spins. The results are shown above. Is Lule's spinner fair? Why or why not?

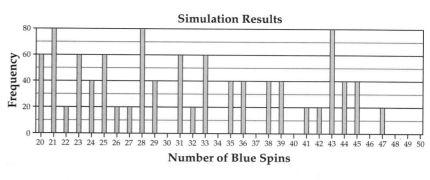

17. A bag contains two kinds of fruit, peaches and apples. The probability of picking a peach is 0.4, and there are 60 peaches. How many apples are in the bag?

18. A bag contains two kinds of fruit, oranges and pears. The probability of picking an orange is 0.3, and there are 24 oranges. How many pears are in the bag?

19. Consider rolling two three-sided dice.

  a Fill in the sample space for the two three-sided dice.

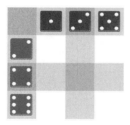

  b What is the probability of an even total, stated as a percent?

  c What is the probability of an odd total, stated as a percent?

  d What is the probability of the dice totaling 5, stated as a fraction?

  e What is the probability the total will be prime?

20. Create a sample space to answer the questions below. There are two five-sided dice. The numbers on each die go from one to five.

  a What is the probability that the dice sum to 4?

  b What is the probability that the dice sum to an even number?

  c What is the probability that the dice sum to an odd number?

  d What is the probability that the dice sum to 8 or a larger number?

21. The draft in a professional sports association wants to determine a random method for awarding the first pick to one of the bottom two teams. If they want the team with the worst record to have a two-thirds chance of getting the first draft pick, how would you use a die to determine which team gets the first draft?

Exercises 22–24: There are two six-sided dice. The numbers on each die go from one to six.

22. What is the probability that the sum and product of the dice are the same?

23. What is the probability that the sum is greater than the product of the dice?

24. What is the probability that the product is at least 5 greater than the sum of the dice?

25. Ten balls numbered from 0 to 9 are consecutively placed in a bingo wheel. A person rolls the wheel and draws a ball, places it back in the wheel, and draws another ball.

  a How many possible ways can the sum of the two drawn balls be equal to 10?

  b Based on part **a**, determine the probability that the sum is 10.

  c A person rolls the wheel and draws two balls without replacement. How many possible ways can the sum be 10?

  d Based on part **c**, determine the probability that the sum is 10.

  e Explain how the results of the scenarios in parts **a**–**b** differ from parts **c**–**d**.

26. Kim was given a fair six-sided die. She did an experiment by rolling the die exactly 30 times, resulting in each number appearing 5 times each, confirming the theoretical probabilities. She then states that for any $6n$ rolls, the number 2 will appear exactly n times. Is her statement correct? Explain.

Practice Problems continue . . .

10.1 Introduction to Probability **471**

Practice Problems continued . . .

27. What are some of the uses of finding probabilities through experiments?

28. What are some of the disadvantages of using experimental probabilities?

29. **MP 3** How might you use probability to your advantage in board games involving dice?

30. Explain how you might perform experiments and use probabilities to predict the weather on a given day.

31. A report states that approximately 5.3 people live in a single dwelling in India. If you randomly survey 1000 homes, how many people do you expect to find?

32. A study finds that each household in the United States owns an estimated 2.28 cars. If you randomly survey 5000 households, how many cars should you expect to find?

33. **MP 4** At a party, one of the 18 guests will be given a special prize. To choose the winner, each guest has an envelope, and one envelope contains a card saying "You are the winner!" The guests open the envelopes one at a time. Seven guests have opened their envelopes, with no winners before Christy's turn. What is the probability that out of the remaining envelopes, Christy's has the winning paper?

34. **MP 2** Lucky you. You have acquired two fake quarters, one that has heads on both sides and one that has tails on both sides. You put them in your pocket with a genuine quarter, draw out one coin at random, and place it on a table. The side you can see is heads. What is the probability the other side is also heads?

LESSON 10.2

10.2 Independent Events, the Multiplication Rule, and Compound Events

Independent Events and the Multiplication Rule

In probability, we are often interested in the likelihood that more than one event occurs. One way we can represent the relationship among events is by using "and" probability. For example, we might want to know the probability that a student earns an A on our math review assignment and earns an A on the associated math test.

There are different methods to display data associated with "and" events. One way is to use a **two-way table**, which is a visual representation of the different possible relationships between two categorical variables.

	Earned A on Review Assignment	Did Not Earn A on Review Assignment	Total
Earned A on Test	12	5	17
Did Not Earn A on Test	4	9	13
Total	16	14	30

Another way we might display the relationship among "and" events is to use a Venn diagram, as shown on the next page. The expression $P(A \text{ and } B)$ is the probability of both events A and B occurring. This set is the area in the diagram where A and B overlap. The intersection of A and B is written $A \cap B$, so $P(A \cap B)$ is the probability that both A and B occur. In this case, let event A be "earning an A on the review assignment" and let event B be "earning an A on the test."

Then, according to the two-way table on the previous page,

$P(A) = \dfrac{16}{30} \approx 0.53$, $P(B) = \dfrac{17}{30} \approx 0.57$, and $P(A \cap B) = \dfrac{12}{30} = 0.40$.

This information is represented on the Venn diagram to the right.

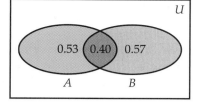

If one of the events that we are interested in depends on the other event occurring, we say those events are **dependent events**. The example above of earning an A on a math review assignment and earning an A on the associated math test are dependent events. In contrast, **independent events** are events in which the outcome of one has no effect on the probability of another occurring. Another way to state this is that the fact that one event occurs does not affect the probability of the other occurring.

The probability that two independent events both occur can be calculated using the **multiplication rule**: The probability that both events occur equals the product of the probabilities of the two events. In fact, this is the definition of independent events: the events A and B are independent if and only if $P(A \text{ and } B) = P(A) \cdot P(B)$.

> Multiplication rule:
> With two independent events A and B, $P(A \text{ and } B) = P(A) \cdot P(B)$.

If the multiplication rule holds, two events are independent. If it does not, they are dependent.

One can recognize if two events are independent using this rule. For instance, let us say the probability of "rain" is 0.3 and "carrying an umbrella" is 0.1. If the probability of both is 0.05, the events are not independent. If they were independent, the product would be $0.3 \cdot 0.1 = 0.03$.

On the other hand, let's assume the probability of taking a green marble from a bag is 0.4 and the probability of drawing a diamond card from a deck is 0.25. If the probability of doing both is 0.1, the events are independent, since $0.4 \cdot 0.25 = 0.1$. These two events occurring together would be considered an **independently combined probability model**.

In this activity, solve various probability problems that get harder and harder! With each question, you risk money. If you are correct, you win it. If not, you lose it.

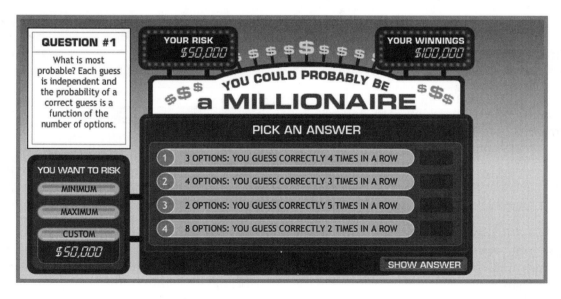

1. The two-way table below depicts the events "enrolled in a high school calculus class" and "has a part-time job" for the student body of Springfield Senior High School. Prove the events "enrolled in a high school calculus class" and "has a part-time job" are dependent.

	Has a Part-Time Job	Does Not Have a Part-Time Job	Total
Enrolled in Calculus	200	170	370
Not Enrolled in Calculus	300	330	630
Total	500	500	1,000

SOLUTION

If the events are independent, we know the multiplication rule will be true. Otherwise, the events are dependent.

Apply the multiplication rule. In this case, event A is "enrolled in high school calculus" and event B is "has a part-time job." So,

$$P(A \cap B) \overset{?}{=} P(A) \cdot P(B)$$

$$\frac{200}{1000} \overset{?}{=} \frac{370}{1000} \cdot \frac{500}{1000}$$

$$0.20 \neq 0.185$$

Since the left-hand side does not equal the right-hand side, the multiplication rule does not hold and the events are dependent.

2. Suppose that you know the events "always wears a seatbelt" and "listens to the radio in the car" are independent events.

   If P(always wears a seatbelt) = 0.89 and P(always wears a seatbelt $\cap$ listens to the radio in the car) = 0.55, what is P(listens to the radio)?

SOLUTION

We know the events are independent, so we can apply the multiplication rule to solve for P(listens to the radio).

We substitute and solve for the unknown probability:

$$P(A \cap B) = P(A) \cdot P(B)$$

$$0.55 = 0.89 \cdot [P(B)]$$

$$0.62 \approx P(B)$$

$$62\% = P(B)$$

3. There is a 30% chance Julie will work on Saturday and a 70% chance of rain. There is a 50% chance her favorite hockey team will win that evening. If the events are independent, what is the probability that on Saturday Julie works in the rain and her hockey team wins?

> The multiplication rule can apply to 3, 4, or however many independent events there are. Their probabilities can be multiplied as long as they are independent.

SOLUTION

Multiplication rule

$P(A$ and B and $C)$
A = Julie works
B = It rains
C = Team wins

A represents the event that Julie works, B the event that it rains, and C the event that her hockey team wins. Calculate the probability that all three occur. Since the events are independent, use the multiplication rule.

Model Problems continue . . .

Substitute and evaluate	$P(A) = 30\% = 0.3$ $P(B) = 70\% = 0.7$ $P(C) = 50\% = 0.5$ $P(A \text{ and } B \text{ and } C) = 0.3 \cdot 0.7 \cdot 0.5$ $P(A \text{ and } B \text{ and } C) = 0.105$ $P(A \text{ and } B \text{ and } C) = 10.5\%$	Write the probabilities and multiply. The probability of Julie working in the rain and her hockey team winning is 10.5%.

4. A chain department store opened a new location in a town with a population of 1,000 people. Prior to their grand opening, the company marketing department used a mailing list to send out an advertisement to half of the residents, which included a coupon for 20% off a single item. When the store opened, they counted the number of people who attended and whether or not they had received a coupon. The segregated data follows.

	Attended Store Opening	Did Not Attend Store Opening	Total
Received a Coupon	470	30	500
Did Not Receive a Coupon	325	175	500
Total	795	205	1,000

a Are the events "attended store opening" and "received a coupon" independent or dependent? Justify your answer using probabilities calculated from the table.

b What can we conclude about the events "attended store opening" and "received a coupon" based on this table?

SOLUTION

a We use the multiplication rule to determine independence

If the events are independent, then the multiplication rule will hold true.

Let event A = Attended store opening
Let event B = Received a coupon

$$P(A \cap B) \stackrel{?}{=} P(A) \cdot P(B)$$

$$\frac{470}{1000} \stackrel{?}{=} \frac{795}{1000} \cdot \frac{500}{1000}$$

$$0.47 \neq 0.3975$$

Since the left-hand side is not equal to the right-hand side, the multiplication rule does not hold and the events are dependent.

b Use the two-way table to calculate probabilities and to draw a conclusion

Out of 1,000 people, half received a coupon. Of those 500 people, 470 attended the store's opening and 30 did not. It is tempting to conclude that receiving the coupon caused residents to attend the opening, but dependence is not equivalent to causation. The best we can say is that receiving the coupon increased the likelihood that a randomly selected town resident attended the store's opening.

> Remember:
> Dependence ≠ Causation

Compound Events

In lesson 10.1 we discussed the probability of two simple events happening together, such as the outcomes that occur when we flip a fair coin and draw a card from a well-shuffled deck. Although we did not formally define it as such, a composition of two or more events such as these is called a **compound event**. We can easily calculate the probability of compound events.

MODEL PROBLEMS

1. If you draw 5 cards from a well-shuffled deck, what is the experimental probability that at least one of those cards is both a club and a numbered card?

SOLUTION

Use a simulation

Let's imagine a simulation. Five cards are drawn, with each card returned to the deck before the next card is drawn. Repeat the 5-card draw three more times. Now imagine that among the four 5-card draws there are two draws in which at least one card is a numbered club: two successes in a sample space of four tries.

Calculate probability

$P(\text{club and numbered card}) = \dfrac{2}{4} = 0.5$ The simulation showed an experimental probability of 0.5 that if you draw 5 cards at a time with replacement, you will get at least one numbered club card.

> Is the theoretical probability of this occurring equal to 0.5? No! This is an experimental procedure. If we did several hundred draws, the empirical result would become close to the theoretical probability.

2. The events A, B, C, D, and E are all independent. The probability of event A occurring is a; the probability of B occurring is b; the probability of C occurring is c; and so on. The probability of all these events occurring is

- A. $a + b + c + d + e$
- B. $1 - (a + b + c + d + e)$
- C. The product of a, b, c, d, and e.
- D. $\dfrac{1}{a \cdot b \cdot c \cdot d \cdot e}$

SOLUTION

A. This is the probability of events A or B or C or D or E occurring.

B. This is the complement of A or B or C or D or E occurring.

C. **Correct answer.** Since the probability of each event is independent, their probabilities can be multiplied. Using the multiplication rule, the probability of all of the events occurring is $P(\text{all events}) = a \cdot b \cdot c \cdot d \cdot e$.

D. This is the reciprocal of the probability of all of the events occurring.   *Model Problems continue . . .*

3. **MP 2, 4** A breed of dog can be white, black, or chocolate-colored. 25% of the breed will be chocolate-colored, and that is the color we want. What is the probability that if we visit a breeder who has a litter of 6 puppies, we will find a puppy that is chocolate-colored that we will take home and love?

SOLUTION

Use simulation

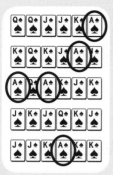

Use cards as a simulation system. We use 4 cards (the jack, queen, king, and ace of spades), with the ace representing the 25% probability of a chocolate-colored puppy. Draw the cards with replacement—once a card is drawn, it is replaced back to the four cards. This means for each draw of the cards, there is always a 25% possibility of the ace, which represents a 25% probability of chocolate-colored. Six draws simulate the six-puppy litter. Perform five simulations to get a reasonable amount of data. Our results are on the left.

Calculate
probability
$$P(\text{chocolate puppy in the litter}) = \frac{4}{5} = 0.8$$

Four of the five times, there were one or more chocolate-colored puppies. Again, this is a small experimental sample space so it should not be used to draw any conclusion.

---

4. Suppose that you flip a fair coin more than once. What is the probability that

  a the coin comes up heads four times in a row?

  b the coin comes up tails six times in a row?

1st flip   2nd flip   3rd flip   4th flip

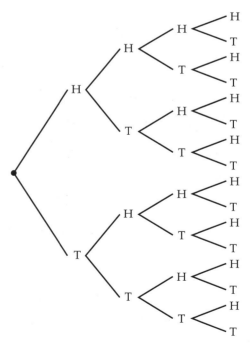

SOLUTION

a To determine the probability of this event, we need to find the sample space. Listing all the possible outcomes by hand can get tedious and it would be easy to make a mistake. Since this is a compound event of simple probability, we can use a tree diagram to help us. Let H = a result of heads and T = a result of tails.

Reading the branches of the tree, we can see that the sample space for this compound event is:

HHHH	HTHH	THHH	TTHH
HHHT	HTHT	THTT	TTHT
HHTH	HTTH	THTH	TTTH
HHTT	HTTT	THTT	TTTT

There are 16 outcomes in this sample space and only 1 that is all heads. $P(\text{HHHH}) = \frac{1}{16} = 6.25\%$.

Model Problems continue . . .

b We can create a tree diagram that incorporates the outcomes for 6 flips of a coin, or we can reason through the problem using the tree diagram for 4 flips of a fair coin to help us.

When we flip the coin once, there are 2 outcomes in the sample space, (H)eads or (T)ails. If we flip the coin twice, there are 4 outcomes: (HH), (HT), (TH), or (TT). Likewise, if we flip three times, there are 8 outcomes, and we found that if we flip the coin 4 times, that results in 16 outcomes in the sample space. Continuing the pattern:

1 flip = 2 outcomes

2 flips = 4 outcomes

3 flips = 8 outcomes

4 flips = 16 outcomes

5 flips = 32 outcomes

6 flips = 64 outcomes

If we flip a coin 6 times, there are 64 outcomes. Notice that no matter how many times we flip the coin, there is only one outcome that is all tails; we can reason that the same will be true for 6 flips.

Thus, $P(TTTTTT) = \dfrac{1}{64} = 1.5625\%$.

PRACTICE

1. Patrick rolls a die and flips a coin. What is the probability he will roll a 6 and get heads?

   A. $\dfrac{1}{12}$ C. $\dfrac{1}{2}$

   B. $\dfrac{1}{6}$ D. $\dfrac{2}{3}$

2. A jar contains a ratio of 2 green to 3 blue to 5 white marbles. What is the probability of selecting a green marble first, a blue marble second, and a white marble last?

   A. $\dfrac{1}{24}$

   B. $\dfrac{2}{57}$

   C. $\dfrac{3}{100}$

   D.   Not enough information

3. The probability a randomly selected individual has green eyes is 0.02. The probability that a randomly selected individual has brown hair is 0.25. If eye color is independent from hair color, what is the probability that a randomly selected person will have green eyes and brown hair?

4. Suppose that the type of car you drive is independent from your favorite fruit. If the probability that a randomly selected person drives a red car is 0.10 and the probability that a randomly selected individual likes oranges best and drives a red car is 0.08, what is the probability that a randomly selected person likes oranges best?

Exercises 5–10: Find the probabilities. Assume a number cube has six sides.

5. What is the probability of rolling a number cube and getting the number 6 three times in a row?

6. What is the probability of rolling a number cube and getting the number 2 four times in a row?

7. What is the probability of a number cube coming up an even number three times in a row?

8. What is the probability of a number cube coming up an odd number four times in a row?

9. What is the probability of rolling a number 2 or greater three times in a row?

Practice Problems continue . . .

10. What is the probability of rolling a number 4 or less four times in a row?

11. Suppose that you are a clerk in a convenience store. Let A be the event that the first customer you help pays with a credit card, and let B be the event that the second customer you help pays with cash. What is $P(A \cap B)$?

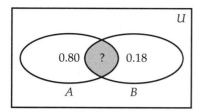

12. The following two-way table represents the Friday night plans and respective GPAs of the senior class of an American high school.

	Goes Out on Friday Nights	Stays In on Friday Nights	Total
Has a GPA of 3.0 or Greater	130	378	508
Has a GPA Less Than 3.0	292	200	492
Total	422	578	1,000

   a Are the events "goes out on Friday nights" and "has a GPA less than 3.0" independent? Why or why not?

   b Suppose we would like the events "has a GPA of 3.0 or greater" and "goes out on Friday nights" to be independent. How would the value in the highlighted cell need to change, assuming the numbers in the Total column and row do not change?

13. What is the probability that you flip a coin and it comes up heads, tails, tails, heads, in that order?

14. You simultaneously flip a coin and roll a six-sided die. What is the probability that the coin turns up heads and you roll a prime number? Remember that 1 is not prime.

15. There are 5 green marbles, 3 blue marbles, and 2 red marbles in a bag. If you pick 1 marble and then pick a second without replacing the first, what is the probability you will pick 2 blue marbles?

16. An insurance agent sells car insurance and life insurance. The probability that a randomly selected client has car insurance is 85%. The probability that a randomly selected client has life insurance is 30%. What is the probability that a randomly selected client has both car and life insurance?

17. An algebra class consists of 18 male students and 12 female students. Each day, the teacher randomly selects 3 students from the class to present their work on a problem. What is the probability that the teacher randomly selects 3 female students, if no one student can be selected twice?

18. A player's union is negotiating new contracts. The probability that they reach an agreement on a pay increase is 30%, the probability that an agreement is reached on work hours is 53%, and the probability that an agreement is reached on both issues is 16%. Are the events "pay increase" and "work hours" independent? How do you know?

19. **MP 2, 4** A batter is taking batting practice. The probability she hits a ball is 0.4, that she swings and misses is 0.3, that she does not swing is 0.25, and that she is hit by the ball is 0.05. Each swing is an independent event.

   a What is the probability that she hits the ball two times in a row?

   b What is the probability that she swings and misses three times in a row?

   c What is the probability she hits the ball, and then swings and misses two times in a row?

   d What is the probability that she does not swing twice in a row, and then gets hit by a ball?

Practice Problems continue . . .

20. MP 2, 4 The probability that a randomly selected person will vote for Coleman is $\frac{1}{2}$, for Mareike is $\frac{1}{3}$, and for Alban is $\frac{1}{6}$.

A computer randomly dials telephone numbers to ask voters whom they prefer.

a What is the probability of hearing Coleman followed by Mareike?

b What is the probability of hearing Mareike three times in a row?

c What is the probability of hearing Alban, Alban, Mareike?

d What is the probability of hearing Mareike, Mareike, and then Coleman?

21. You are playing a game with a die where you only move if the die comes up an even number. How many times must you roll the die so that the probability of rolling an even number every time is less than 0.1?

22. You are playing a game with a die where you get a bonus every time you roll a 5 or a 6. How many times must you roll the die so that the probability of getting a bonus every time is less than 0.05?

23. There are 25 jelly beans: 16 blue, 5 green, and 4 red. You take jelly beans from a bag and give them to a friend, who eats them.

a What is the probability of first drawing a green bean then a red?

b What is the probability of first drawing a green bean followed by a blue?

c What is the probability of first drawing a red bean then a green?

d What is the probability of first drawing a blue bean followed by a green?

e What is the probability of the first two jelly beans being green?

f What is the probability of the first two jelly beans being red?

24. Estimate the probability of obtaining an odd prime from the roll of a single die by rolling the die 30 times. Remember that 1 is not a prime number. How close is your experimental probability to the theoretical probability? Is your experimental probability a good indicator of future outcomes? Explain.

25. The probability of an arrow hitting a region on the target below is proportional to the area of that region of the target. All triangles in the image are equilateral. Each shot is independent, and all shots hit the target.

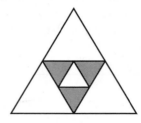

a What is the probability that three consecutive shots fired will hit the shaded region? State your answer in decimal form.

b What is the probability that three consecutive shots fired will hit the white region? State your answer in decimal form.

26. Suppose you draw four cards in succession from a deck, putting each card back after you draw it. Make a prediction about the probability of drawing a diamond as one of the four cards. Repeat this experiment 20 times and record the number of times you draw a diamond as one of the 4 drawn cards. Are you surprised by your experimental probability?

27. Sketch a Venn diagram that represents the probability of *A* and *B* and *C*.

28. Explain why $P(A \text{ and } B \text{ and } C) \leq P(A \text{ and } B)$, where *A*, *B*, and *C* are independent events.

29. Give an example of 3 events, *A*, *B*, and *C*, in which *A* and *B* are dependent and *B* and *C* are independent.

30. MP 2, 5 Stu has five pairs of matching socks in his drawer, each pair a different color. He picks two socks at random from the drawer. What is the probability he picked a matching pair?

31. MP 2, 5 Given an eight-sided die numbered from 3 to 10, find the probability that a prime smaller than 6 will appear at least once in five rolls.

10.3 Addition and Subtraction Rules

"Or" and the Addition Rule

Similar to how we can use the word "and" in probability, we can use the word "or" to mean at least one of a set of events occurs. Probabilities that use the word "or" are written $P(A \cup B)$ and represent the probability of A or B occurring. An example is the probability that you wear red socks or you wear jeans to school.

We can use a Venn diagram to illustrate the concept of "or." The probability of A or B occurring is the entire region covered by the two ovals; it is the union of A and B. The probability of A or B occurring is written as $A \cup B$.

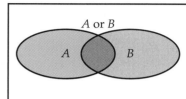

We can use the diagram to derive the **addition rule**, which is used to calculate $P(A$ or $B)$. As the diagram shows, the probability equals the sum of the probability of A occurring and the probability of B occurring, but minus the probability of both A and B occurring, $P(A$ and $B)$, so as not to double count the events in the overlapping region of the Venn diagram.

> Addition rule:
> $$P(A \cup B) = P(A) + P(B) - P(A \text{ and } B)$$

MODEL PROBLEMS

1. **MP 2, 4** A corporation manufacturing a car notes that 20% of potential customers would pay for a convertible, 30% would pay for the premium sound system, and 5% would pay for both. What is the probability that a customer would pay for a convertible or the premium sound system?

SOLUTION

Define terms $P(C)$ = probability customers would pay for convertible = 20%
$P(S)$ = probability customers would pay for premium sound system = 30%
$P(C$ and $S)$ = 5%

Addition rule	$P(A$ or $B) = P(A) + P(B) - P(A$ and $B)$ $P(C$ or $S) = P(C) + P(S) - P(C$ and $S)$	Restate the addition rule using the variables from the problem.
Substitute and evaluate	$P(C$ or $S) = 0.2 + 0.3 - 0.5$ $P(C$ or $S) = 0.45 = 45\%$	Substitute given values. The probability that customers would buy a convertible or premium sound system is 45%. As we would expect, this is less than the simple sum of 20% and 30%, since a part of the simple sum double counts the customers who would pay for both. The subtraction removes the doubling of the count.

Model Problems continue . . .

2. Of 100 students surveyed, 95 like chocolate or raisins, 35 like both chocolate and raisins, and 40 like raisins. How many students like chocolate?

SOLUTION

State probabilities	C = likes chocolate R = likes raisins $P(C \text{ or } R) = \dfrac{95}{100} = 0.95$ $P(C \text{ and } R) = \dfrac{35}{100} = 0.35$ $P(R) = \dfrac{40}{100} = 0.4$	The probability that a student likes certain foods equals the number of students who like those foods divided by the total number of students.
Addition rule	$P(C \text{ or } R) = P(C) + P(R) - P(C \text{ and } R)$	State the addition rule with C and R.
Substitute probabilities	$0.95 = P(C) + 0.4 - 0.35$	Substitute the known probabilities.
Solve for $P(C)$	$P(C) = 0.9$	Solve for $P(C)$, the probability that a student likes chocolate.
Find number of students who like chocolate	$P(C) = \dfrac{\text{chocolate likers}}{\text{total students}}$ $0.9 = \dfrac{\text{chocolate likers}}{100}$ chocolate likers = 90 out of 100	By definition, the probability that students like chocolate equals the number of "chocolate likers" divided by the total number of students. Using this survey, we can conclude there are a lot of chocolate fans out there because the probability that a student likes chocolate is 0.9.

Mutually Exclusive Events and the Addition Rule

Two events are **mutually exclusive** if it is impossible for them both to occur at the same time. For instance, if you roll a number cube once, it cannot result in an outcome of both 3 and 5. Mutually exclusive events are sometimes referred to as *disjoint sets* because their intersection is the empty set, as shown in the Venn diagram to the right.

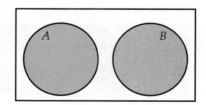

Since $P(A \cap B) = \varnothing$ for mutually exclusive events, we can simplify the addition rule for these events:

> Addition Rule for Mutually Exclusive Events
> $$P(A \cup B) = P(A) + P(B)$$

In a board game, a spinner has a 0.3 probability of saying "draw again," a 0.2 probability of saying "return to start," and a 0.5 probability of saying "take $200 from the bank." Only one outcome is possible per spin. On a given spin, what is the probability of "draw again" or "take $200 from the bank" being the results?

SOLUTION

Define terms

$P(D)$ = draw again = 0.3
$P(M)$ = take $200 = 0.5

Addition rule for mutually exclusive events

$P(D \text{ or } M) = P(D) + P(M)$

Substitute and evaluate

$P(D \text{ or } M) = 0.3 + 0.5 = 0.8$

The Subtraction Rule

The sum of the probabilities of all possible outcomes of an event equals 1. For instance, the probability of obtaining a heads on a coin toss is 0.5, the probability of tails (the only other possible outcome) is 0.5, and $0.5 + 0.5 = 1$. Heads is the **complement** of tails. If A is the event, the complement of A is what is *not* in A.

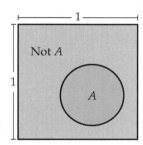

We can use a Venn diagram to illustrate the concept of "not." The probability of "not A" is covered by the gray region. Take the entire area of the square, which is equal to 1, and subtract the circle A to get "not A."

We state the **subtraction rule**:

Subtraction rule:
$P(\text{not } A) = 1 - P(A)$

> The subtraction rule states: The probability that the event A will *not* occur equals one minus the probability that A will occur.

1. There is a 25% probability that it will rain tomorrow. The probability that it will not rain tomorrow is

A. Unknowable from this information
B. 0.25

C. The reciprocal of 0.25
D. 0.75

SOLUTION

A. The probability that it will not rain tomorrow is the complement of the probability that it will rain tomorrow. Since the probability that it will rain tomorrow is 0.25, $P(\text{not rain}) = 1 - 0.25 = 0.75$.

B. This is the probability that it will rain tomorrow.

C. The complement is not found by taking the reciprocal.

D. **Correct answer.** As explained above, $P(\text{not rain}) = 1 - 0.25 = 0.75$.

Model Problems continue . . .

2. Let event A be the probability that a randomly selected person prefers the color green, and let event B be the probability a randomly selected person prefers to wear sandals. If $P(A) = 0.40$, $P(B) = 0.20$, and the probability that a randomly selected person prefers both the color green and wearing sandals equals 0.10, what is the probability that a randomly selected individual is a member of the complement of $(A \cup B)$?

SOLUTION

Addition rule	$P(A \cup B) = P(A) + P(B) - P(A \cap B)$ $P(A \cup B) = 0.40 + 0.20 - 0.13$ $P(A \cup B) = 0.47$	First, we must determine the probability that a randomly selected person is a member of $(A \cup B)$.
Subtraction rule	$P(\text{not } A \cup B) = 1 - P(A \cup B)$ $P(\text{not } A \cup B) = 1 - 0.47$ $P(\text{not } A \cup B) = 0.53$	Now we can use the subtraction rule to determine the probability that a randomly selected person is in the complement of $(A \cup B)$.
State your answer	The probability that a randomly selected person does not prefer green or does not prefer wearing sandals (or both) is 0.53.	

3. If a football player is from an NCAA school, the probability of that athlete being drafted into the National Football League (NFL) after college is about 1.6%. What is the probability that a football player from an NCAA school is not drafted into the NFL?

SOLUTION

Subtraction rule	$P(A) = $ probability drafted $P(A) = 0.016$ $P(\text{not } A) = 1 - P(A)$ $P(\text{not } A) = 1 - 0.016$ $P(\text{not } A) = 0.984$	Use the subtraction rule. $P(A)$ represents the probability that a football player from an NCAA school is drafted into the NFL after college. Substitute that value, as a decimal, into the equation and solve.
State your answer	A football player from an NCAA school has about a 98% probability of not being drafted into the NFL after college.	

4. Suppose a couple has 4 biological children. None of the children are multiples (twins, triplets, etc.). What is the probability that at least one of their children is a girl?

SOLUTION

Subtraction rule	$P(\text{not } A) = 1 - P(A)$ $A = $ all boys not $A = $ at least one girl	It is easier to calculate the probability of this event using the subtraction rule because we can quickly calculate the probability the couple has no girls (all 4 children are boys) and then we can subtract that probability from 1, which will give us the probability that the couple has at least one girl.
Use the multiplication rule to calculate $P(A)$	$P(A) = \dfrac{1}{2} \cdot \dfrac{1}{2} \cdot \dfrac{1}{2} \cdot \dfrac{1}{2} = \dfrac{1}{16}$	To calculate the probability of having a boy each time, apply the multiplication rule, since each child's birth is an independent event. We assume that the couple has a 50% chance of having a boy (or girl). The probability of having 4 boys is $\dfrac{1}{16}$.
Substitute and evaluate	$P(\text{not } A) = 1 - \dfrac{1}{16}$ $P(\text{not } A) = \dfrac{15}{16}$	In the subtraction rule, substitute in the probability of all boys, which is $\dfrac{1}{16}$. The probability of at least one of the couple's children being a girl is $\dfrac{15}{16}$.

PRACTICE

1. The probability that a male German shepherd weighs more than 77 pounds is 0.70. The probability that a male German shepherd weighs less than 50 pounds is 0.15. What is the probability that a male German shepherd weighs more than 77 pounds or less than 50 pounds?

A. 0.75 C. 0.55
B. 0.85 D. 0.65

2. There are two types of red berries growing in the forest. One red berry is poisonous and the other is not. On average, if you pick 50 red berries, 42 are fine to eat. What is the probability of picking a poisonous red berry?

A. 0.16 C. 0.24
B. 0.42 D. 0.48

3. If you roll a pair of number cubes, there is a 1 in 6 chance that you will roll doubles (both number cubes show the same number). What is the probability that the two number cubes do not show doubles?

A. $\frac{1}{3}$ C. $\frac{5}{36}$

B. $\frac{1}{2}$ D. $\frac{5}{6}$

4. At a summer camp, there are 20 climbing ropes. Five of the ropes are thicker than 10 mm, six are waterproof, and one rope is both thicker than 10 mm and waterproof. What is the probability of a randomly selected rope being thicker than 10 mm or waterproof?

A. $\frac{1}{4}$ C. $\frac{1}{2}$

B. $\frac{3}{10}$ D. $\frac{11}{20}$

5. A promotional giveaway offers three destinations: Las Vegas, Hawaii, or San Diego. Each customer is allowed to choose only one destination. The probability that a randomly selected customer chooses Las Vegas is 0.60, and the probability a randomly selected customer chooses Hawaii is 0.25. What is the probability that a randomly selected customer chooses San Diego?

A. 0.85 C. 0.15
B. 0.35 D. 0.55

6. The probability that a randomly selected student's favorite sport is hockey is 0.18. The probability that a randomly selected student's favorite sport is baseball is 0.21. The probability that a randomly selected student likes both hockey and baseball is 0.07. What is the probability that a randomly selected student likes neither hockey nor baseball?

7. A bag contains 12 marbles. Four of the marbles are purple, two are green, and 6 are yellow. What is the probability that you randomly select one of the marbles that isn't green?

8. In the Westland housing subdivision, the probability that a randomly selected house has exactly 4 bedrooms is 0.52. The probability that a randomly selected house in Westland has exactly 2 bathrooms is 0.22. The probability that a randomly selected house has both 4 bedrooms and two bathrooms is 0.11. What is the probability that a randomly selected house in Westland has exactly 4 bedrooms or exactly 2 bathrooms?

9. In a box of 20 filled chocolates, 8 pieces have only nuts, 9 pieces have only nougat, and 3 pieces have both nuts and nougat. What is the probability that a randomly selected piece of candy contains nuts?

10. In a diner, the probability that a random customer orders a cheeseburger is 0.65, that they order fries is 0.55, and that they order both a cheeseburger and fries is 0.35. What is the probability that a randomly selected customer orders neither a cheeseburger nor fries?

Practice Problems continue . . .

Practice Problems continued . . .

11. Each time she visits her favorite amusement park, Melati rides two roller coasters, the Ricochet and the Monster. Sometimes she is able to get right on the rides, and other times she must wait in line. The probability that Melati will need to wait in line to ride the Ricochet is P(ricochet) = 0.55. The probability that she must wait in line to ride the Monster is P(monster) = 0.28. The probability that she must wait for both rides is 0.43. Suppose that we randomly select one day that Melati is at the amusement park.

   a Describe, in words, the event P(not ricochet, monster).

   b Calculate the probability you described in part **a**.

   c Calculate P(ricochet or monster) and interpret your result in context.

Exercises 12–15: Write the complement of the statements without using any words of negation.

12. More than half of the students take part in extracurricular activities.

13. The probability of randomly selecting a positive number from a set of real numbers.

14. All adults exercise at least 30 minutes each day.

15. The probability that two die rolls land on at least one odd number.

16. **MP 2, 3** A teacher in a 25-student class curves the grades so that only 6 students receive A's. Joan calculated that the probability that three randomly selected students will all get A's is $\frac{6}{25} \cdot \frac{5}{24} \cdot \frac{4}{23} = \frac{1}{115}$. Then Joan states that the probability that none of these students will get A's is $1 - \frac{1}{115} = \frac{114}{115}$.

Is Joan correct? Why or why not?

17. **MP 1, 2** On a television game show, there are three curtains, A, B, and C. Behind one curtain is a brand-new car, and behind the other two are a live goat and a fruitcake from the previous holiday season. You are a contestant on the show and have won the right to pick a curtain and get the prize behind it. You pick curtain B. Before it is opened, the host opens curtain A, revealing the goat, and gives you the opportunity to switch to curtain C. Before curtain A was opened, the probability you would win the car was $\frac{1}{3}$. After the curtain was opened, what is the probability if you don't switch? and if you do switch? Note: This problem has created much debate and discussion, which can be found on the Internet.

18. **MP 7** Show algebraically that $P(A) = P(\text{not}(\text{not } A))$.

19. **MP 3** Suppose that you have two events, A and B. If $P(A) = 0$, are A and B mutually exclusive? Support your answer with algebraic reasoning.

20. **MP 2** Determine if:
$P((A \text{ or } B) \text{ and } C) = P(A \text{ or } (B \text{ and } C))$

• Multi-Part PROBLEM Practice •

MP 2, 4 From a group of high school seniors surveyed to find out their plans after graduating, 67% said they would be attending college, 42% said they planned to move away from home, and 21% said they planned to do both.

a What is the probability that a student surveyed will attend college or move away from home?
b Given the probabilities of the student attending college (67%) and of the student moving away from home (42%), how do you know that there will be some students who plan to do both?
c What is the minimum percentage of students who could have answered that they plan to both attend college and move away from home?
d Is there a maximum percentage of students who could have answered yes to both questions? If so, what is it?

10.4 Conditional Probability

There are many times an event will be influenced by whether or not a related event has occurred. This is the idea of **conditional probability**, or the probability that an event A occurs given that event B has occurred. The formula below is used to calculate conditional probability.

Conditional probability:

$$P(A|B) = \frac{P(A \text{ and } B)}{P(B)}$$

> This is a formula for calculating the probability that A occurs, given B has occurred. It equals the probability that both A *and* B occur, divided by the probability that B occurs.

For example, consider the probability that a professional athlete will improve their on-field performance given that they practice an additional two hours each week. It is reasonable to consider that the probability of professional athletes improving their on-field performance is higher for those who take on extra practice hours than for those who do not. If we let event A be the event that a professional athlete improves their on-field performance and event B is the event that they engage in an additional two hours of practice each week, then the conditional probability statement is: $P(A|B) = P(\text{improved on-field performance}|\text{additional two hours of weekly practice})$.

We can use a Venn diagram to illustrate this probability concept. In the diagram, the oval represents the number of times event A occurs; the circle represents the number of times that B occurs; and the shaded overlap represents the number of times events A and B both occur.

The conditional probability of A given B is the fraction of B's outcomes that also belong to A out of all of B. This is the shaded overlapping region divided by the entire circle. And equally true is the fact that the conditional probability of B given A is the fraction of A's outcomes that also belong to B out of all of A. Again, this is the shaded overlapping region divided by the entire oval.

Note that $P(A|B)$ is not necessarily equal to $P(B|A)$. For example:

The probability B occurs given that A has occurred is: $P(B|A) = \dfrac{P(A \text{ and } B)}{P(A)}$

The probability that A occurs given that B has occurred is: $P(A|B) = \dfrac{P(A \text{ and } B)}{P(B)}$

If we refer to the Venn diagram above, we can see that either the oval or the circle divides the overlapping region, and since their sizes can be unequal, the conditional probabilities can differ.

Conditional Probability and Independent Events

Recall from previous lessons in this chapter that events are independent if the probability of one occurring does not affect the probability of the others occurring. If events are independent, we can show that the following conditional probability relationships are true:

For independent events A and B:

$$P(A|B) = P(A) \text{ and } P(B|A) = P(B)$$

Algebraically, from the definition of independent events, we know that if A and B are independent, then $P(A \cap B) = P(A) \cdot P(B)$. The conditional probability of independent events A and B is then:

$P(A\|B) = \dfrac{P(A \cap B)}{P(B)}$	Start with the conditional probability formula.
$P(A\|B) = \dfrac{P(A) \cdot P\cancel{(B)}}{\cancel{P(B)}}$	Since events A and B are independent, we can substitute for $P(A \cap B)$ and simplify.
$P(A\|B) = P(A)$	We have shown the relationship is true for $P(A\|B)$.

> The reasoning for $P(B \mid A) = P(B)$ is similar.

We can also use this idea to show that events are dependent by demonstrating that the relationship $P(A|B) = P(A)$ does not hold.

Events that are not independent

If $P(A) \neq P(A|B)$, then the events are not independent.

MODEL PROBLEMS

1. In the diagram to the right, the numbers represent the number of events in each bounded area. The conditional probability of A occurring given that B has occurred is

   A. 0.40   C. 0.25

   B. 0.20   D. 0.625

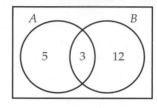

SOLUTION

We can see from the diagram that there are 20 events in our sample space. Then $P(A \cap B) = \dfrac{3}{20}$,

and the probability of B occurring (with or without A) is $P(B) = \dfrac{15}{20}$. Now we can calculate

$P(A|B) = \dfrac{P(A \cap B)}{P(B)}$ to find that $P(A|B) = \dfrac{\frac{3}{20}}{\frac{15}{20}} = \dfrac{1}{5} = 0.20$.

2. In a certain manufacturing process, 96% of the parts produced by machine G are not defective. If the events *a randomly selected part from machine G is not defective* and *a randomly selected part from machine G is the color blue* are independent, what you do know about the probability that a randomly selected blue part from machine G will not be defective? Justify your answer.

SOLUTION

Since the events are defined to be independent, knowing that the selected part is blue does not affect the probability that the part is not defective. This means that the probability that a selected blue part from machine G is not defective is also 96%.

Model Problems continue . . .

3. In a midwestern city, if a high school basketball player is a center, the probability that he or she is left-handed is 18%. On any given team, 20% of the players are centers. What percent are left-handed centers?

SOLUTION

Define the events

A = being left-handed
B = being a center

Start by defining event A and event B.

Use probability notation to state the given information

$P(B) = 0.20$
$P(A|B) = 0.18$

Restate the problem using probability notation.

Use the conditional probability formula

$$P(A|B) = \frac{P(A \cap B)}{P(B)}$$

$$0.18 = \frac{P(A \cap B)}{0.20}$$

$$0.036 = P(A \cap B)$$

Substitute the known probabilities and solve for $P(A \cap B)$. The result shows that about 3.6% of players on a team are left-handed centers.

4. In a certain region of the country, the probability that a woman naturally conceives twins is about 2.2%, and the probability that she conceives triplets is about 0.8%. Based on these numbers, what is the probability that a woman has conceived twins given that she is carrying more than one baby?

SOLUTION

Define the events

A = having twins
B = carrying more than one baby

Use probability notation to state the given information

$$P(A|B) = \frac{P(A \cap B)}{P(B)}$$

$$P(A|B) = \frac{0.022}{0.022 + 0.008}$$

$$P(A|B) = 0.73$$

State the answer

Given that a woman is carrying more than one baby, the probability that she is having twins is about 73%.

Conditional Probability and Two-Way Tables

In lesson 10.2 we defined two-way tables, which are also sometimes called *frequency tables*. These tables can be used to organize data and to determine independence, and we can use them to calculate conditional probability.

Consider the following example: Merryweather Auto Insurance Company performed a study to determine the number of claims filed by 1,000 randomly selected drivers they insured over the last year. They segregated their data by the driver's age. The results are listed on the next page.

	0 Claims	1 Claim	2 Claims	3+ Claims	Totals
Age 16–24	35	41	37	14	127
Age 25–34	66	34	59	19	178
Age 35–44	126	187	36	16	365
Age 45+	273	38	18	1	330
Totals	500	300	150	50	1,000

We can use the table to easily calculate conditional probability. For instance, say we want to know the probability that a driver filed 2 claims given that the driver was aged 25–34, $P(2 \text{ claims} | 25\text{–}34)$. We can read these values from the table, using the total number of drivers surveyed, to find that $P(2 \text{ claims} \cap 25\text{–}34) = \dfrac{59}{1000} = 0.59$ and $P(25\text{–}34) = \dfrac{178}{1000} = 0.178$. Then $P(2 \text{ claims} | 25\text{–}34) = \dfrac{0.059}{0.178} = 0.331$, or about 33.1%.

MODEL PROBLEM

MP 2, 4 Late in the evening on April 14, 1912, the British ocean liner *Titanic* hit an iceberg and then sank the following morning. The table shows the distribution of survivors and non-survivors according to their class as a passenger.

	Survived	Did Not Survive	Total
1st Class	201	123	324
2nd Class	118	166	284
3rd Class	181	528	709
Total	500	817	1317

a What is the probability that a passenger survived given that they were a first-class passenger?

b What is the probability that a passenger was a second-class passenger given that they did not survive?

c Was the chance (probability) for survival the same for first-, second-, and third-class passengers? Explain.

SOLUTION

a Conditional probability

$P(A \mid B) = \dfrac{P(A \text{ and } B)}{P(B)}$

Use the equation to find the probability of A occurring given that B has occurred.

Assign probabilities

$P(S) = \text{surviving}$
$P(N) = \text{not surviving}$
$P(1) = \text{1st class}$
$P(2) = \text{2nd class}$
$P(3) = \text{3rd class}$

Assign each of the possibilities a variable.

Substitute

$P(S|1) = \dfrac{P(S \text{ and } 1)}{P(1)}$

Write the equation using the given variables.

Calculate probabilities

$P(S \text{ and } 1) = \dfrac{201}{1317} = 0.153$

$P(1) = \dfrac{324}{1317} = 0.246$

Find the probability that a passenger was both in first class and survived. Then find the probability that a passenger was in first class.

Divide

$P(S|1) = \dfrac{0.153}{0.246} = 0.622$

The probability that a passenger survived given they were in first class was 0.622, or about 62%.

Model Problem continues . . .

b Conditional probability equation

$$P(A|B) = \frac{P(A \text{ and } B)}{P(B)}$$

Again, we want to find the probability of *A* given that *B* occurs.

Substitute probabilities

$$P(2|N) = \frac{P(2 \text{ and } N)}{P(N)}$$

This time, we want to know the probability that a passenger was in second class given that they were among the non-survivors.

Calculate probabilities

$$P(2 \text{ and } N) = \frac{166}{1317} = 0.126$$

$$P(N) = \frac{817}{1317} = 0.620$$

Calculate the probability of being a second-class passenger who did not survive, and the probability of not surviving.

Divide

$$P(2|N) = \frac{0.126}{0.620} = 0.203$$

The probability that a passenger was in second class given that they did not survive was 0.203, or a little over 20%.

c To determine whether a passenger's class played any role in his or her chance for survival, compare the probability that a passenger survived, given that they were in first, second, or third class.

Calculate for 1st class

$$P(S|1) = \frac{P(S \text{ and } 1)}{P(1)} = 0.618$$

We performed this calculation in part **a**.

Calculate for 2nd class

$$P(S|2) = \frac{P(S \text{ and } 2)}{P(2)}$$

$$P(S|2) = \frac{118/1317}{284/1317} = \frac{0.0896}{0.2156}$$

$$P(S|2) = 0.4156 = 0.416$$

A passenger had close to a 42% chance of survival given they were a second-class passenger.

Calculate for 3rd class

$$P(S|3) = \frac{P(S \text{ and } 3)}{P(3)}$$

$$P(S|3) = \frac{181/1317}{709/1317} = \frac{0.137}{0.538}$$

$$P(S|3) = 0.255$$

Given that a passenger was in third class, he/she had about a 25.5% chance of survival. It appears there definitely was a greater chance of survival if the passenger was in a higher class.

PRACTICE

1. The junior class at Ashlake High School took both their Algebra 2 final and Chemistry final on the same day. If 60% of students passed both finals, and 75% of students passed the Algebra 2 final, what percent of the students who passed Algebra 2 also passed Chemistry?

A. 15%   C. 80%

B. 45%   D. 90%

2. Suppose a red die and a blue die are rolled. What is the probability that the red die shows a 3 given that the sum of the two dice is 4?

A. $\frac{1}{3}$ C. $\frac{1}{12}$

B. $\frac{1}{6}$ D. $\frac{1}{36}$

Practice Problems continue . . .

3. Out of 100 cars on a new-car lot, 60 have air conditioning, 50 have an automatic transmission, and 25 cars have both.

    a What is the percentage of cars that have air conditioning given that they have an automatic transmission?

    b What is the percentage of cars that have an automatic transmission given that they have air conditioning?

Exercises 4–7: Use the two-way table below to answer the following questions. Round each answer to the nearest whole percent.

The two-way table below reflects the actual number of post-high school degrees earned in 2009–2010 by people in the United States as reported by the Bureau of Labor and Statistics. The data is grouped by race.

	White	Black	Hispanic	Asian	Totals
Associate's	552,863	113,905	112,211	44,021	823,000
Bachelor's	1,167,499	164,844	140,316	117,422	1,590,081
Master's	445,038	76,458	43,535	42,072	607,103
Totals	2,165,400	355,207	296,062	203,515	3,020,184

4. Find the probability that a person has an associate's degree given that person is white.

5. What is the probability that a person who has earned a master's degree is Hispanic?

6. What is the probability that a person with a bachelor's degree is Asian?

7. What is the probability that a person has earned a post-high school degree given that person is Black?

8. An aquarium contains 200 fish. There are 135 blue fish, 85 fish that are yellow, and 52 fish that are both blue and yellow.

    a If you catch a fish that is yellow, what is the probability that it also has blue coloration?

    b If you catch a fish that is blue, what is the probability that it also has yellow coloration?

9. The probability that it is snowing is 35%. The probability that it is snowing and your car will not start is 15%. If it is snowing, what is the probability that your car will not start?

Exercises 10–12: Use the two-way table below to answer the following questions. Round each answer to the nearest whole percent.

A medical researcher is investigating which of three treatments, A, B, or C, best relieves the symptoms of a chronic disease. The results are shown below.

	Treatment A	Treatment B	Treatment C	Totals
Showed Improvement	293	72	203	568
Did Not Show Improvement	107	328	197	632
Totals	400	400	400	1,200

10. Find the probability that a patient showed improvement given they were taking treatment A.

11. What is the probability that a patient taking treatment C did not show improvement?

12. Are the events *taking treatment B* and *showed improvement* independent? Why or why not?

Practice Problems continue . . .

Practice Problems continued . . .

13. A typical bag of a popular chocolate candy contains 50 pieces in the following color assortment: 24% blue, 20% orange, 16% green, 14% yellow, 13% red, and 13% brown. Suppose you open a typical bag of this candy a remove one green candy from the bag. What is the probability that you draw a second green candy from the bag given the first one was green?

14. In a board game where properties are bought and sold, the probability that player 1 will own three certain adjacent properties is 31%. The probability that player 2 will land on one of these properties on her next turn is 22%. What is the probability that player 2 will land on one of these properties given that player 1 owns them all?

Exercises 15–18: Use the two-way table below to answer the following questions.

A manufacturing company has three machines that all make the same part for a door assembly. A sampling of these parts was taken from each machine and tested to see if the part was defective or not defective. The results are below.

	Machine A	Machine B	Machine C	Totals
Defective	3	8	1	12
Not Defective	197	192	199	588
Totals	200	200	200	600

15. Given that the part came from Machine A, what is the probability it is defective?

16. Find the probability that a part is not defective given that it came from Machine C.

17. Given that it came from Machine B, what is the probability a part is defective?

18. Show that the events *part is defective* and *part came from Machine A* are not independent.

---

19. **MP 3** What must be true of events A and B if $P(A|B) = P(B|A)$?

20. Define conditional probability in your own words.

21. **MP 2, 5** Jar A contains x red marbles and y blue marbles. Jar B contains all blue marbles. If one jar is randomly chosen and a marble is then picked out, what is the probability the marble is red given it is taken from jar A? What is the probability the marble is blue?

22. **MP 1, 2** If Zandee studies for her test, the probability that she will pass is 83%. If she does not study, she has only a 67% probability of passing the test. The probability that she studied given that she passes the test is 92%. What is the probability that Zandee studied for the test? Round your answer to the nearest whole percent.

Exercises 23–25: Use the two-way table below to answer the following questions. Round each answer to the nearest whole percent.

There are 300 seniors at Bellmere Senior High School who are enrolled in elective science classes as shown below.

	Physics	Chemistry	Total
Males	100	68	168
Females	71	61	132
Total	171	129	300

23. What is the probability that a senior student chosen at random is male given that student is enrolled in chemistry?

24. What is the probability that a senior student chosen at random is enrolled in physics given that student is female?

25. Are the events *gender* and *science elective selection* independent? Justify your answer.

LESSON 10.5

10.5 **The Normal Distribution**

We briefly pause our studies of probability to discuss graphical representations of data sets, such as the ones that generated the two-way tables earlier in this chapter. As we will see shortly, these two concepts, probability and graphical representation, are connected.

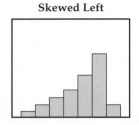
Skewed Left

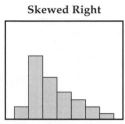
Skewed Right

Some types of data sets, when graphed in quadrant I of the coordinate plane, produce a skewed distribution, which is a distribution with the majority of its values residing at the left- or right-hand side of the graph. Examples of skewed graphs are shown to the right.

Other data sets, however, produce what is known as a **normal distribution**, which is a bell-shaped graph that associates an event with the probability that the event occurs. In a normal distribution, many of the values cluster around the mean, represented in mathematics by the Greek letter mu, μ, which is located at the peak of the graph. The remaining values then taper off, in a roughly symmetric manner, toward the extreme values at the ends of the curve. Many natural phenomena can be approximately modeled with a normal distribution, so understanding this type of curve is very useful. The graph on the right is a normal distribution with $\mu = 8$.

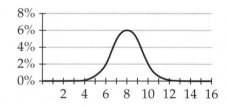

The mean is the peak of the graph.

Normal distributions require the collection of a large amount of data, such as by performing an experiment many times. Say, for example, that we wanted to know the average height of college freshman males in the United States. We could survey 5,000 randomly chosen male college freshmen in the United States and calculate the mean height, to the nearest inch. We could then graph the results and create a sampling distribution. We see that this data creates a roughly symmetric bell curve.

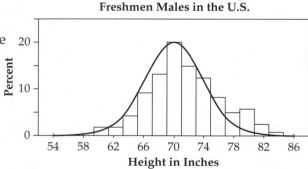
Average Heights of College Freshmen Males in the U.S.

Suppose that we were able to perform our survey of 5,000 randomly chosen male college freshmen in the United States twice. If we graphed the results of both surveys, would the sampling distributions be identical? No, they would not be. In considering data, we must take into account variability among data sets. When we can model data using a **normal curve**, we can measure the variability (or spread of the data) using the **standard deviation**, which is symbolized in mathematics by the Greek letter sigma, σ. Note that we cannot measure the variability in data with a right- or left-hand skew using the standard deviation.

494 Chapter 10: Probability

In the sampling distributions below, we can see that the curve on the right has a larger standard deviation than the curve on the left. There are several factors that might explain the variability in this data. For example, defining our population as college freshmen males means that we are surveying traditional college students, aged 18–24, who may not have reached their full adult height, as well as non-traditional students who did not attend college immediately after high school, who are at their full adult height. There may also be regional differences in height due to ancestry or local nutrition. This survey may also include international students, who may naturally be shorter or taller than an average American male.

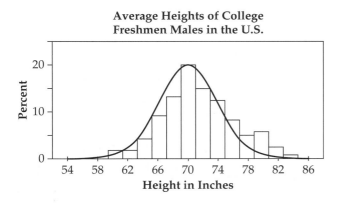

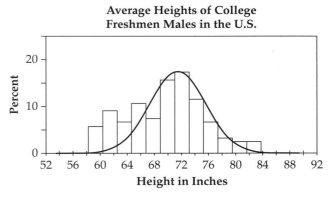

Instead of a sampling distribution, let us now consider the theoretical standard normal distribution with a mean of $\mu = 0$ and a standard deviation of $\sigma = 1$, as shown below. The numbers on the horizontal axis represent how far, in terms of standard deviation, the data is from the mean. For any normal distribution, about 68% of the data will fall within 1 standard deviation of the mean. Notice that this percentage is symmetrically distributed with 34% on each side of the mean value. An additional 27% of the data, with 13.5% on each side of the mean, will fall between 1 and 2 standard deviations of the mean; to represent this, we usually say that 95% of all the data in a normal distribution is within 2 standard deviations of the mean. The remaining 5% of the data is more than two standard deviations from the mean, with 2.5% on each side. Remember this curve; it will be quite important later in this section.

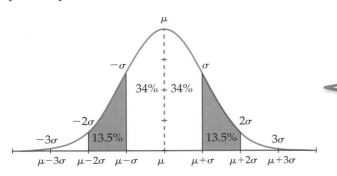

To calculate the range of data one standard deviation away from the mean, add and subtract the value of a standard deviation to and from the mean. To calculate two standard deviations, multiply the standard deviation by 2, and add and subtract that from the mean.

Normal curves can be used to describe many different sets of data including heights, weights, grades, sizes of items produced by a machine, the time it takes for a standardized process to be completed, and more.

As you have seen in previous courses, two data sets can have the same mean but different ranges (recall that range is also a measure of variability). Likewise, two data sets can have the same standard deviation but different means. We can compare data sets like these by computing the **coefficient of variation**, which is the ratio of the standard deviation to the mean. Doing so will allow us to mentally picture the normal curve that fits each data set. For example, lets say that we have two similar data sets, both normally distributed. Set A has a standard deviation of 5 and a mean of 10; set B has a standard deviation of 5 and a mean of 1,000. The coefficient of variation for set A is $\frac{5}{10} = \frac{1}{2}$, and for set B it is $\frac{5}{1000} = \frac{1}{200}$. This tells us that set A is more widely distributed than set B.

MODEL PROBLEMS

1. **MP 2** The average mass of a group of wombats is 15 kilograms, with a standard deviation of 1.25 kilograms. Graph the normally distributed data.

> If you know the mean of some data, its standard deviation, and that it is normally distributed, you can graph the data.

SOLUTION

Mean is peak of graph	15	The problem states that the average (or mean) mass of a wombat is 15 kilograms. That is the peak of the graph.
About 68% of data is within one standard deviation	$15 + 1.25 = 16.25$ $15 - 1.25 = 13.75$	The problem states the standard deviation is 1.25 kilograms. Add and subtract that value. We know this will include about 68% of the data, and we use the standard shape of a normal curve.
About 95% of data is within two standard deviations	$15 + 2.5 = 17.5$ $15 - 2.5 = 12.5$	Multiply 1.25 by two to calculate two standard deviations. Add and subtract that product, 2.5, from the mean. Plot points based on the shape of the curve and knowing about 95% of the data is within two standard deviations.
Graph curve	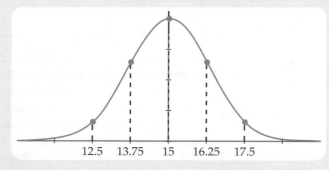	Since 95% of the data falls within two standard deviations, the rest falls outside this region. Draw the rest of the graph, which represents the remaining 5% of the data.

Model Problems continue . . .

2. The mean score is 80 and the standard deviation is 5.

   a What is the probability that a student had a test score above 90?

   b What is the probability that a student had a score between 75 and 85?

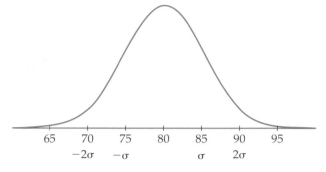

SOLUTION

a Score greater than 90

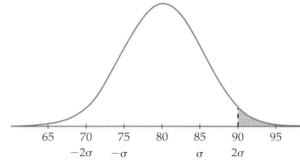

The test scores above 90 are greater than two standard deviations from the mean. Two standard deviations away on one side of the mean is 2.5% of the data.

b Score between 75 and 85

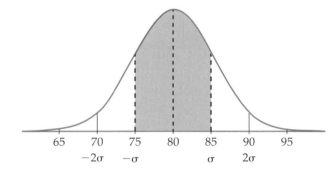

These scores fall within one standard deviation on either side of the mean. That is 68% of the data.

3. In data distribution A, the mean is 40 and the standard deviation is 5. In data distribution B, the mean is 800 and the standard deviation is 50. By considering the ratio of the standard deviation to the mean, determine which distribution has the more widely distributed data.

SOLUTION

Find the ratio for distribution A	$A = \dfrac{\text{standard dev}}{\text{mean}}$ $A = \dfrac{5}{40} = 0.125$	Find the ratio of the standard deviation to the mean for distribution A, first as a fraction, then as a decimal.
Find the ratio for distribution B	$B = \dfrac{\text{standard dev}}{\text{mean}}$ $B = \dfrac{50}{800} = 0.0625$	Find the ratio of the standard deviation to the mean for distribution B, first as a fraction, then as a decimal.
Identify the larger ratio	$0.125 > 0.0625$ $A > B$	The distribution with the larger ratio of standard deviation to mean has the more widely distributed data. Distribution A has the more widely distributed data.

We show one of two similar activities below. In the activities, we simulate tossing coins, and count the number of heads we see. The data is not continuous—the number of heads has to be an integer, which is why the graph is made up of bars. However, it can be shown that as the number of outcomes increases, a binomial distribution can increasingly be better described by a normal distribution. It can be shown that a normal distribution describes a binomial distribution as the number of outcomes increases. As you can see, you can also change the probability of heads in the simulation. For instance, you can decide that 70% of the time, the result of a coin toss is heads. With a probability of heads 70%, is the data consistent with a model of normal distribution? How does increasing the number of coins change the distribution?

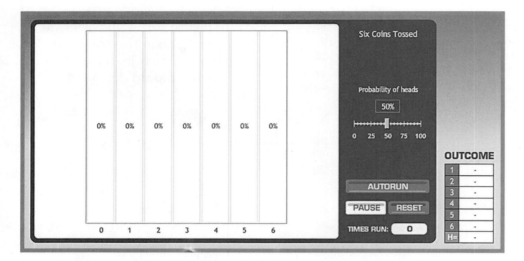

A **binomial distribution** results from a collection of data with two possible outcomes, each equally likely. Tossing a coin is an example of binomial distribution.

 In this activity, simulate the results from a science experiment where the landing location of a projectile is recorded. Data like this is often normally distributed. Let's say a lab report states the data is consistent with a model indicating the data is normally distributed. Would you agree with the report's conclusion? Why or why not? We would suggest allowing the simulation to record hundreds of results.

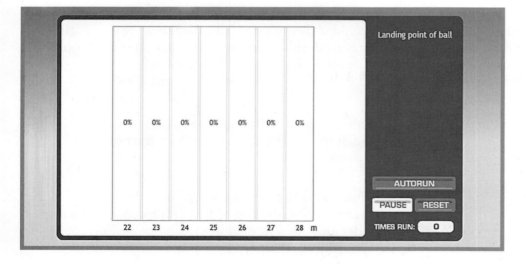

Approximating the Area Under the Normal Curve: z-Scores

Let's return to our normal curve that represents the heights of 5,000 randomly selected male college freshmen in the United States. The mean of this distribution is $\mu = 70$ inches, and we will tell you that the standard deviation is 4 inches. Suppose that we randomly select one male college freshman in the United States. What is the probability that his height is less than 74 inches?

We begin this problem by sketching the normal curve. Notice that the curve and the horizontal axis form a space that has area. We can use the area to calculate the probability of an event approximated by a normal distribution by determining the area it occupies under the curve. We mark the mean and the value of the random variable we are interested in; in this case, 70 and 74. We want to know if the randomly selected person's height is less than 74 inches, so we shade to the left of 74 as shown. The shaded region is the area we will find. Since the total area under the curve is 1.00 (100%), we can use the standard normal curve that we discussed on page 495 to approximate the probability that $x < 74$. At this point in your mathematical career, you do not have the tools to directly calculate this area by hand; instead, we will use a z-chart, a calculator, or a spreadsheet to help us.

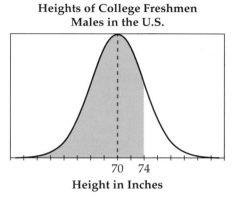

Heights of College Freshmen Males in the U.S.

70 74

Height in Inches

Calculation Using a z-Score Chart

First, we must convert our real-world data to the theoretical normal distribution. This is easier than it sounds, and the process standardizes the data so we can calculate the area as well as make comparisons across data sets. We use the z-score formula, shown below.

> Converting to the Standard Normal Distribution:
> $$z = \frac{x - \mu}{\sigma}$$

> For our data, $x = 74$, $\mu = 70$, and $\sigma = 4$, then:
>
> Substitute $\quad z = \dfrac{74 - 70}{4}$
>
> Simplify $\quad z = 1.0$

On the standard normal distribution, a value of $x = 74$ is equivalent to $z = 1.0$. Since we want to know $x < 74$, we want to find the probability that $z < 1.0$.

We look at the chart on pages 500–501. The green column labeled **z** is z-scores precise to the tenth; we use the green row across the top of the chart to increase our precision to the nearest hundredth. The entries in the body of the chart reflect the cumulative probability under the curve up to that particular z-score. Follow the row labeled 1.0 to the column labeled 0.00. The cumulative probability for $z = 1.0$ is 0.8413, so we know the probability that a randomly selected college freshman male in the United States is less than 74 inches tall is 84.13%.

Standard Normal Curve Areas

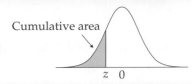

Cumulative area

z	0.00	0.01	0.02	0.03	0.04	0.05	0.06	0.07	0.08	0.09
−3.8	0.0001	0.0001	0.0001	0.0001	0.0001	0.0001	0.0001	0.0001	0.0001	0.0001
−3.7	0.0001	0.0001	0.0001	0.0001	0.0001	0.0001	0.0001	0.0001	0.0001	0.0001
−3.6	0.0002	0.0002	0.0001	0.0001	0.0001	0.0001	0.0001	0.0001	0.0001	0.0001
−3.5	0.0002	0.0002	0.0002	0.0002	0.0002	0.0002	0.0002	0.0002	0.0002	0.0002
−3.4	0.0003	0.0003	0.0003	0.0003	0.0003	0.0003	0.0003	0.0003	0.0003	0.0002
−3.3	0.0005	0.0005	0.0005	0.0004	0.0004	0.0004	0.0004	0.0004	0.0004	0.0003
−3.2	0.0007	0.0007	0.0006	0.0006	0.0006	0.0006	0.0006	0.0005	0.0005	0.0005
−3.1	0.0010	0.0009	0.0009	0.0009	0.0008	0.0008	0.0008	0.0008	0.0007	0.0007
−3.0	0.0013	0.0013	0.0013	0.0012	0.0012	0.0011	0.0011	0.0011	0.0010	0.0010
−2.9	0.0019	0.0018	0.0018	0.0017	0.0016	0.0016	0.0015	0.0015	0.0014	0.0014
−2.8	0.0026	0.0025	0.0024	0.0023	0.0023	0.0022	0.0021	0.0021	0.0020	0.0019
−2.7	0.0035	0.0034	0.0033	0.0032	0.0031	0.0030	0.0029	0.0028	0.0027	0.0026
−2.6	0.0047	0.0045	0.0044	0.0043	0.0041	0.0040	0.0039	0.0038	0.0037	0.0036
−2.5	0.0062	0.0060	0.0059	0.0057	0.0055	0.0054	0.0052	0.0051	0.0049	0.0048
−2.4	0.0082	0.0080	0.0078	0.0075	0.0073	0.0071	0.0069	0.0068	0.0066	0.0064
−2.3	0.0107	0.0104	0.0102	0.0099	0.0096	0.0094	0.0091	0.0089	0.0087	0.0084
−2.2	0.0139	0.0136	0.0132	0.0129	0.0125	0.0122	0.0119	0.0116	0.0113	0.0110
−2.1	0.0179	0.0174	0.0160	0.0166	0.0162	0.0158	0.0154	0.0150	0.0146	0.0143
−2.0	0.0228	0.0222	0.0217	0.0212	0.0207	0.0202	0.0197	0.0192	0.0188	0.0183
−1.9	0.0287	0.0281	0.0274	0.0268	0.0262	0.0256	0.0250	0.0244	0.0239	0.0233
−1.8	0.0359	0.0351	0.0344	0.0336	0.0329	0.0322	0.0314	0.0307	0.0301	0.0294
−1.7	0.0446	0.0436	0.0427	0.0418	0.0409	0.0401	0.0392	0.0384	0.0375	0.0367
−1.6	0.0548	0.0537	0.0526	0.0516	0.0505	0.0495	0.0485	0.0475	0.0465	0.0455
−1.5	0.0668	0.0655	0.0643	0.0630	0.0618	0.0606	0.0594	0.0582	0.0571	0.0599
−1.4	0.0808	0.0793	0.0778	0.0764	0.0749	0.0735	0.0721	0.0708	0.0694	0.0681
−1.3	0.0968	0.0951	0.0934	0.0918	0.0901	0.0885	0.0869	0.0853	0.0838	0.0823
−1.2	0.1151	0.1131	0.1112	0.1093	0.1075	0.1056	0.1038	0.1020	0.1003	0.0985
−1.1	0.1357	0.1335	0.1314	0.1292	0.1271	0.1251	0.1230	0.1210	0.1190	0.1170
−1.0	0.1587	0.1562	0.1539	0.1515	0.1492	0.1469	0.1446	0.1423	0.1401	0.1379
−0.9	0.1841	0.1814	0.1788	0.1762	0.1736	0.1711	0.1685	0.1660	0.1635	0.1611
−0.8	0.2119	0.2090	0.2061	0.2033	0.2005	0.1977	0.1949	0.1922	0.1894	0.1867
−0.7	0.2420	0.2389	0.2358	0.2327	0.2296	0.2266	0.2236	0.2206	0.2177	0.2148
−0.6	0.2743	0.2709	0.2676	0.2643	0.2611	0.2578	0.2546	0.2514	0.2483	0.2451
−0.5	0.3085	0.3050	0.3015	0.2981	0.2946	0.2912	0.2877	0.2843	0.2810	0.2776
−0.4	0.3446	0.3409	0.3372	0.3336	0.3300	0.3264	0.3228	0.3192	0.3156	0.3121
−0.3	0.3821	0.3783	0.3745	0.3707	0.3669	0.3632	0.3594	0.3557	0.3520	0.3483
−0.2	0.4207	0.4168	0.4129	0.4090	0.4052	0.4013	0.3974	0.3936	0.3897	0.3859
−0.1	0.4602	0.4562	0.4522	0.4483	0.4443	0.4404	0.4364	0.4325	0.4286	0.4247
−0.0	0.5000	0.4960	0.4920	0.4880	0.4840	0.4801	0.4761	0.4721	0.4681	0.4641

z	0.00	0.01	0.02	0.03	0.04	0.05	0.06	0.07	0.08	0.09
0.0	0.5000	0.5040	0.5080	0.5120	0.5160	0.5199	0.5239	0.5279	0.5319	0.5359
0.1	0.5398	0.5438	0.5478	0.5517	0.5557	0.5596	0.5636	0.5675	0.5714	0.5753
0.2	0.5793	0.5832	0.5871	0.5910	0.5948	0.5987	0.6026	0.6064	0.6103	0.6141
0.3	0.6179	0.6217	0.6255	0.6293	0.6331	0.6368	0.6406	0.6443	0.6480	0.6517
0.4	0.6554	0.6591	0.6628	0.6664	0.6700	0.6736	0.6772	0.6808	0.6844	0.6879
0.5	0.6915	0.6950	0.6985	0.7019	0.7054	0.7088	0.7123	0.7157	0.7190	0.7224
0.6	0.7257	0.7291	0.7324	0.7357	0.7389	0.7422	0.7454	0.7486	0.7517	0.7549
0.7	0.7580	0.7611	0.7642	0.7673	0.7704	0.7734	0.7764	0.7794	0.7823	0.7852
0.8	0.7881	0.7910	0.7939	0.7967	0.7995	0.8023	0.8051	0.8078	0.8106	0.8133
0.9	0.8159	0.8186	0.8212	0.8238	0.8264	0.8289	0.8315	0.8340	0.8365	0.8389
1.0	0.8413	0.8438	0.8461	0.8485	0.8508	0.8531	0.8554	0.8577	0.8599	0.8621
1.1	0.8643	0.8665	0.8686	0.8708	0.8729	0.8749	0.8770	0.8790	0.8810	0.8830
1.2	0.8849	0.8869	0.8888	0.8907	0.8925	0.8944	0.8962	0.8980	0.8997	0.9015
1.3	0.9032	0.9049	0.9066	0.9082	0.9099	0.9115	0.9131	0.9147	0.9162	0.9177
1.4	0.9192	0.9207	0.9222	0.9236	0.9251	0.9265	0.9279	0.9292	0.9306	0.9319
1.5	0.9332	0.9345	0.9357	0.9370	0.9382	0.9394	0.9406	0.9418	0.9429	0.9441
1.6	0.9452	0.9463	0.9474	0.9484	0.9495	0.9505	0.9515	0.9525	0.9535	0.9545
1.7	0.9554	0.9564	0.9573	0.9582	0.9591	0.9599	0.9608	0.9616	0.9625	0.9633
1.8	0.9641	0.9649	0.9656	0.9664	0.9671	0.9678	0.9686	0.9693	0.9699	0.9706
1.9	0.9713	0.9719	0.9726	0.9732	0.9738	0.9744	0.9750	0.9756	0.9761	0.9767
2.0	0.9772	0.9778	0.9783	0.9788	0.9793	0.9798	0.9803	0.9808	0.9812	0.9817
2.1	0.9821	0.9826	0.9830	0.9834	0.9838	0.9842	0.9846	0.9850	0.9854	0.9857
2.2	0.9861	0.9864	0.9868	0.9871	0.9875	0.9878	0.9881	0.9884	0.9887	0.9890
2.3	0.9893	0.9896	0.9898	0.9901	0.9904	0.9906	0.9909	0.9911	0.9913	0.9916
2.4	0.9918	0.9920	0.9922	0.9925	0.9927	0.9929	0.9931	0.9932	0.9934	0.9936
2.5	0.9938	0.9940	0.9941	0.9943	0.9945	0.9946	0.9948	0.9949	0.9951	0.9952
2.6	0.9953	0.9955	0.9956	0.9957	0.9959	0.9960	0.9961	0.9962	0.9963	0.9964
2.7	0.9965	0.9966	0.9967	0.9968	0.9969	0.9970	0.9971	0.9972	0.9973	0.9974
2.8	0.9974	0.9975	0.9976	0.9977	0.9977	0.9978	0.9979	0.9979	0.9980	0.9981
2.9	0.9981	0.9982	0.9982	0.9983	0.9984	0.9984	0.9985	0.9985	0.9986	0.9986
3.0	0.9987	0.9987	0.9987	0.9988	0.9988	0.9989	0.9989	0.9989	0.9990	0.9990
3.1	0.9990	0.9991	0.9991	0.9991	0.9992	0.9992	0.9992	0.9992	0.9993	0.9993
3.2	0.9993	0.9993	0.9994	0.9994	0.9994	0.9994	0.9994	0.9995	0.9995	0.9995
3.3	0.9995	0.9995	0.9995	0.9996	0.9996	0.9996	0.9996	0.9996	0.9996	0.9997
3.4	0.9997	0.9997	0.9997	0.9997	0.9997	0.9997	0.9997	0.9997	0.9997	0.9998
3.5	0.9998	0.9998	0.9998	0.9998	0.9998	0.9998	0.9998	0.9998	0.9998	0.9998
3.6	0.9998	0.9998	0.9999	0.9999	0.9999	0.9999	0.9999	0.9999	0.9999	0.9999
3.7	0.9999	0.9999	0.9999	0.9999	0.9999	0.9999	0.9999	0.9999	0.9999	0.9999
3.8	0.9999	0.9999	0.9999	0.9999	0.9999	0.9999	0.9999	0.9999	0.9999	0.9999

z-Score Calculation Using a Graphing Calculator

Calculating z-scores with the aid of a printed chart is relatively simple if the chart is available. In cases where a chart is not provided, we can perform the same calculation using our graphing calculators. For this type of operation, we do not need to convert the random variable to a standard z-score by hand; the calculator will do this for us.

Again, suppose that we randomly select one male college freshman in the United States. What is the probability that his height is between 68 and 74 inches if $\mu = 70$ and $\sigma = 4$?

1. **Find the probability.** Here we want to know the probability that the random variable x falls between 68 and 74 inches, so $68 \leq x \leq 74$. On your graphing calculator, press [2nd][VARS] **2:normalcdf(lower boundary, upper boundary, mean, standard deviation)**. In this case, the key sequence is **normalcdf(68, 74, 70, 4)**. We see that the probability of the outcomes between $68 \leq x \leq 74$ is approximately 0.5328.

```
normalcdf(68,74,
70,4)
            .532807
```

2. **Graph and shade the region.** Use [Y=] to get to the equation entry screen and select one of the Y variable lines. Enter the key sequence as described in step 1. For the window parameters, make Xmin the mean minus three times the standard deviation $(70 - (3 \cdot 4) = 58)$, and Xmax the mean plus three times the standard deviation $(70 + (3 \cdot 4) = 82)$. Once the window is set, press [2nd] [VARS] [DRAW] **1:ShadeNorm(lower boundary, upper boundary, mean, standard deviation)**. Press [GRAPH] to graph the normal distribution. The graph confirms our calculation from step 1; the probability of outcomes between $68 \leq s \leq 74$ is approximately 0.5328.

```
WINDOW
 Xmin=58
 Xmax=82
 Xscl=5
 Ymin=-.01
 Ymax=.03
 Yscl=.01
 Xres=1
```

```
Area=.532807
low=64      up=74
```

Calculation Using a Spreadsheet

We can perform these same types of calculations using a spreadsheet. It is sometimes easier to work with a large data set in a spreadsheet rather than by hand or by using the graphing calculator.

1. **Determine mean and standard deviation.** Enter your data in the spreadsheet and use the **AVERAGE** and **STDEV.P** functions to calculate the mean and the standard deviation. We've done this in cells B1 and B2.

	A	B
1	Mean	70.775
2	Standard Deviation	4.9319748
3		

2. **Calculate y-values.** Use the normal distribution function to generate the curve: **=NORM.DIST(x, mean, standard deviation, FALSE)**. We show one cell as an example of how the formula is displayed. This plots the probability of an x-value located in cell A7 of the normal distribution. The function looks to cell B1 for the mean and to cell B2 for the standard deviation. The B1 means that the function will always use the number in column B, row 1. FALSE means that we want the probability of that value, not the cumulative probability of all the values up to B7. Use the handle to fill all the cells in column B.

	A	B	C	D
1	Mean	70.775		
2	Standard Deviation	4.9319748		
3				
4				
5	x-values	y-values		
6	60	0.0074378		
7	61	=NORM.DIST(A7,B1,B2,FALSE)		
8	62	0.0166147		
9	64	0.0314897		
10	65	0.0407534		
11	67	0.0603492		
12	68	0.069047		

3. Use scatterplot with line option to generate the curve. Select the data under the labels *x*-values and *y*-values, and then graph the distribution using a scatterplot, selecting the line option to show the curve.

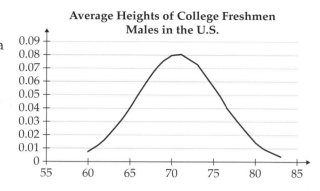

Average Heights of College Freshmen Males in the U.S.

MODEL PROBLEMS

1. University presidents receive a housing provision that averages $32,658. Assume that a normal distribution applies and that the standard deviation is $5,500. What is the minimum annual housing provision for the 10% of college presidents receiving the largest provision?

SOLUTION

In this problem, we would like to know the value of the random variable that produces the probability that a randomly selected college president receives a housing provision that is in the top 10% of provisions. We will solve this using our calculator, but to understand the situation, it is helpful to draw it.

Sketch and label the normal distribution.

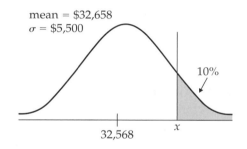

mean = $32,658
σ = $5,500

10%

32,568

x

Since the calculator reads probability from the left-hand side over and the total area under the curve is 1.00, we must subtract to find the unshaded area under the curve.

$1.00 - 0.10 = 0.90$

Now we can use the calculator to find the random variable given a probability of 0.90 with a mean of $32,658 and a standard deviation of $5,500.

Press [2nd] [VARS]
3:invNorm(probability, mean, standard deviation)

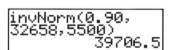

invNorm(0.90,
32658,5500)
            39706.5

Restate the answer in terms of the problem.

The minimum annual housing provision for the 10% of college presidents receiving the largest provision is $39,706.50.

Model Problems continue . . .

2. Mensa is the international society for individuals with a high IQ. To be a Mensa member, a person must earn a score of 132 or higher on the Stanford-Binet Intelligence Test. Suppose that IQ scores are normally distributed with a mean of 100 and a standard deviation of 15. What is the probability that a randomly selected person qualifies for Mensa membership?

SOLUTION

As always, when confronted with a question about the normal distribution, it is helpful to sketch the situation before jumping immediately to a solution strategy.

Sketch and label the normal distribution. Here we are being asked the probability that a randomly selected person has an IQ of 132 or greater on a specific scale. We are trying to calculate the shaded area.

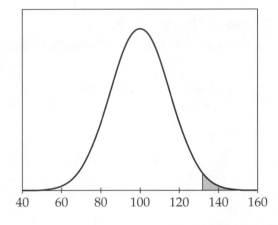

To solve this using our calculator, we must play a little trick. Notice from the drawing that there is no upper limit to enter; the tail of the distribution stretches to infinity. To input this into the calculator, we enter the largest number most calculators can compute, 10^{99} , which looks like 1E99 on the calculator. E is entered by pressing [2nd] [,].

Press [2nd] [VARS]
2:normalcdf(lower boundary, upper boundary, mean, standard deviation)

```
normalcdf(132,
1E99,100,15)
    0.0164486368
```

Restate the answer in terms of the problem.

The probability that a randomly selected person qualifies for Mensa membership is approximately 1.65%.

PRACTICE

1. The results of a math exam follow a normal distribution with mean p and standard deviation m. What is the probability that your friend who took the math exam had a score between $p - m$ and p?

A. 95%

B. 68%

C. 34%

D. m%

2. Use the following graph of a normal distribution to answer the questions below.

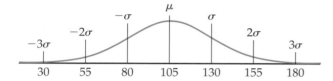

a What z-score is associated with the random variable $x = 92$?

b If a z-score of 1.96 is calculated using the formula for converting to a standard normal distribution, what was the value of x?

c What z-score is associated with a cumulative probability of 20%? What is the x-value that produces that probability?

3. Use the graph of a normal distribution to answer the following questions.

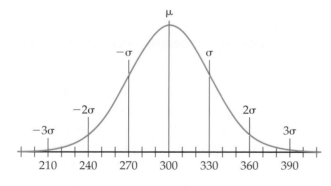

a Approximately what percentage of the data is above 300?

b Approximately what percentage of the data lies between 240 and 300?

c Approximately what percentage of the data is below 240 or above 360?

4. **MP 4** The distribution of ball-bearing diameters produced by a certain machine is approximately normal with a mean of 20 mm and a standard deviation of 4 mm.

a About what percentage of the ball bearings will have diameters between 16 mm and 24 mm? Round to the nearest percent.

b About what percentage of the ball bearings will have diameters between 12 mm and 28 mm? Round to the nearest percent.

c About what percentage of the ball bearings will have diameters between 16 mm and 28 mm? Round to the nearest tenth of a percent.

5. **MP 5, 7** Use the graph of a normal distribution to answer the following questions.

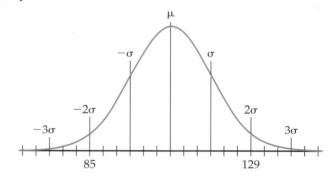

a What is the mean of the distribution?

b What is the standard deviation of the distribution?

c About 68% of the data is found between what two values that are displaced equally from the mean on either side?

d What is the probability that a random value is between 85 and 129? Round your answer to the nearest hundredth.

Exercises 6–8: Determine whether each scenario results in a normal or non-normal distribution. Justify your answer.

6. Selecting a volunteer from a group of 30 students.

7. The sum of the toss of two six-sided dice.

8. The number of years people live.

Practice Problems continue . . .

9. Describe in your own words what it means for a set of data to be normally distributed. (A sketch may be helpful in your explanation.)

10. In 2014, American college seniors graduated from school with an average student loan debt of $29,400. Assume this debt is normally distributed with a standard deviation of $6,500.

    a What is the probability that a randomly selected person who graduated college in 2014 has a student loan debt of less than $25,000?

    b What percent of these college graduates have student loan debt between $27,000 and $32,000?

    c The uppermost 5% of student loan debt is in excess of what amount?

11. The last digit of a telephone number is not normally distributed. Give an example of a different set of data that is not normally distributed.

12. Research a few natural phenomena in which the data can be represented by a normal curve.

13. **MP 2, 4** The game warden for an ocean sanctuary wants sports fishermen to release the smallest and biggest fish that they catch. They must release fish that weigh less than 27 lb or more than 33 lb. Statisticians calculated these guidelines to ensure that only those fish with weights in the middle 68% of the population are caught. Assuming the weights of fish in the sanctuary are normally distributed, what is the mean and standard deviation of the weights of fish in the sanctuary, in pounds?

14. In the 2014 regular season, the Detroit Lions scored an average of 20.1 points per game with a standard deviation of 3.2 points. If the number of points scored per game is normally distributed across the season, what is the probability that the Lions scored more than 21 points in a randomly selected 2014 regular season game?

15. Mrs. Andrews gave a math quiz to her 190 Algebra 2 students. The quiz scores were normally distributed with a mean of 8.2 points and a standard deviation of 1.6 points. At least how many points did each of the top 10% of students earn on the quiz?

16. For a set of data, the mean is 5.2, and the ratio of the standard deviation to the mean is 0.25. What is the standard deviation for this set of data?

17. A zookeeper is doing a presentation on small mammals. She originally planned to display data about the animals' weights using kilograms, but has now decided to use grams. When the weights of the animals were measured in kilograms, the ratio of the standard deviation to the mean for the group was 0.34. What is the ratio of the standard deviation to the mean when their weights are measured in grams?

18. A tire manufacturer estimates the mean life of one of their tires to be about 50,000 miles if properly inflated and cared for. The standard deviation is about 3,500 miles. What percentage of tires manufactured by this company will have a useful life of more than 52,000 miles?

19. **MP 2, 3** Pedro examined two sets of data and determined that they had different means but the same standard deviation. He says that this means the data sets will have a similar spread. Is he correct? Why or why not?

20. If you are presented with a frequency graph of data that have been grouped into intervals before they were graphed, is it possible to calculate the mean and standard deviation of the data? Explain your reasoning.

21. Five hundred employees at one company were asked about their commuting habits. The data on the distance of their commutes was determined to be normally distributed, with 68% of the workers' daily commutes ranging between 14 and 38 miles.

    a What is the mean distance that a surveyed worker commutes daily, assuming that the given values are displaced equally from the mean on either side?

    b What is the standard deviation for the commuting data?

    c What set of commuting ranges that are symmetric about the mean are composed of the extreme 5% of commuters?

Practice Problems continue . . .

22. **MP 2, 4** Ms. Stine teaches high school algebra to a total of 176 students. The scores on her last midterm were normally distributed, with a mean score of 74.3 and a standard distribution of 9.6.

   a Approximately how many students scored between 74 and 84?

   b What is the probability that a randomly selected student scored between 84 and 93.5?

   c What percentage of students likely scored above 93.5?

   d If one of Ms. Stine's classes has a mean score of 86 with a standard deviation of 6.5, what can you conclude about one or more of her other classes? Give a reason why this might occur.

23. **MP 2, 4, 5** Based upon 50 years of data, the annual rainfall for Damp City, U.S.A., had a normal distribution with mean 43.5 inches and standard deviation of 4.7 inches.

   a What is the probability of any given year having less than 34 inches?

   b What rainfall range, symmetric about the mean, contains 68% of the years?

   c Use a spreadsheet or graphing calculator to estimate the probability that a given year had between 45 and 48 inches of rainfall. Round your answer to the nearest tenth of a percent.

LESSON 10.6

10.6 Statistical Studies and Randomization

Oftentimes, we have a question we would like answered, such as what a population's opinion is on a certain issue, whether a new educational method is more successful than current methodologies, or if a new experimental drug effectively combats a disease. To find the answers to these questions, we rely on research and statistics. *Statistics* is formally defined as the science of collecting and analyzing numerical data, usually in large quantities, for the purpose of making inferences (drawing conclusions) about the population from which the sample is drawn. There are several methods we can use to collect the data we seek, including surveys, observational studies, and experimental studies. In this lesson, we define some of these data collection methods and discuss their natural benefits and biases.

> The *population* is the set of all elements of interest in a particular study. A *sample* is a subset drawn from the population.

Surveys, Observational Studies, and Experimental Studies

A **survey** is a method of gathering data where all participants answer the same questionnaire. Surveys are often used because they are simple to administer and can gather information across a wide range of variables. It is also relatively easy to organize the collected data because all of the survey responses are in the same format. Disadvantages of collecting data via a survey include the fact that responses are voluntary. Additionally, the accuracy of the survey depends on each participant's honesty as well as their interpretation of the question and the available responses. Also, certain subgroups of the population may be more likely to respond to certain surveys; for example, people with strong feelings, either positive or negative, about a certain issue may be more likely to respond than people who are not as interested. For these reasons, surveys are the least effective data collection method, but we do often rely on them to learn about social and political opinions.

> A *questionnaire* is a set of questions with predefined answers to be asked of a number of people in order to gather information or opinions.

In an **observational study**, a researcher observes the participants as they are, without any type of intervention or influence. For instance, a researcher might wish to determine if there is a link between eating foods high in protein and weight loss. To conduct an observational study, the researcher would find participants who already eat a protein-rich diet and observe their weight over time. At no time would the researcher directly influence the diet eaten by the participants; she would only gather the data and investigate possible correlations. Observational studies are beneficial because they provide access to people in real-life contexts. They can also provide an in-depth understanding of situations not easily measured by surveys. A pitfall of observational studies is that the researcher must avoid *observer bias*, which is when a researcher unconsciously influences the participants in the observation. These studies are also quite time-consuming. Note that a survey is considered a type of observational study because the researcher simply observes the answers to the questionnaire and does not attempt to influence the answers.

In both surveys and observational studies, there is no direct manipulation of the participants by the researcher. This is in contrast to an **experimental study**, where the researcher intentionally imposes a treatment, procedure, or program on the participants and then measures outcome(s). Perhaps the best-known experimental studies are medical trials.

A **medical trial** is a test of a new medication on humans. A sample is assembled and the participants are divided into groups. One group is given the experimental treatment, while the other group, called the *control group*, is given a placebo. Over time, aspects of the health of all members in both groups are measured. If the participants who received the treatment show more positive results than those who received the placebo, then the treatment may be beneficial.

> A **placebo** has no medical benefit but physically resembles the drug being tested.

To use the vocabulary of conditional probability, let H represent a healthy patient and let D represent a medication. For an effective medicine, $P(H|D) >> P(H)$, which means that the probability of a patient taking the medication becoming healthy is significantly greater than the probability that a patient becomes healthy whether they are taking the medication or not. If $P(H|D) \leq P(H)$, then the medication is having no effect, or perhaps even a negative effect, and it should not be marketed or sold.

In these trials, researchers also measure the **side effects** of the treatment. A side effect is a result of the treatment that is outside its intended purpose. For example, a drug designed to reduce blood pressure might harm the liver or cause bone weakening.

These tests are often conducted so that neither the participants nor the researchers know whether the participant has received the treatment or the placebo. This is called a *double-blind methodology*, and it is one of the major advantages of an experimental study. In this way, observer bias is eliminated. Other advantages include researcher control over variables and being able to determine a cause-and-effect relationship. This type of research, however, is very time-consuming, expensive, and complicated.

Randomization and Lurking Variables

No matter the type of data collection method used, it is important to ensure that the participants included in the sample reflect the overall population. To this end, statisticians and researchers use **randomization**, which is the process of randomly selecting individuals to participate in a survey or observational study, or assigning participants to groups through the use of chance methods, such as flipping a coin or using a random number generator. In surveys and other observational studies, randomization helps to minimize the effects of selection **bias**, which happens when the group selected does not accurately reflect the overall population. In experimental studies, randomization also ensures that there is no systematic difference between the participants receiving the treatment and those who receive the placebo.

It is important to reiterate that unless the data comes from an experimental study, no cause-and-effect relationship can be established. Surveys and observational studies can only establish an association among the variables considered. However, when studying variables that appear to have an association, researchers must be very careful to account for any lurking variable(s). A **lurking variable** is one that causes two other variables to have what appears to be a relationship even though there is not one. A classic example of this phenomenon is that as ice cream sales increase, the number of drowning accidents increases. Can we conclude that ice cream sales cause drowning accidents? No, of course not. The lurking variable here is time of year. More ice cream is sold in the summer than in the winter, and there is more opportunity for drowning in the summer than in the winter. A well-designed experiment includes randomization and features that allow researchers to eliminate lurking variables as an explanation for the observed relationship.

MODEL PROBLEMS

1. For your statistics class, you must survey residents in your town to determine their preferences of dogs or cats for a pet. Explain why each of the following populations would or would not exhibit bias:

   a) Residents of an apartment complex
   b) People at a dog park
   c) Shoppers at a grocery store
   d) Students at your high school

SOLUTION

Answers will vary. We list one possible solution for each situation.

a) Residents of an apartment complex	Many more apartments allow cats as pets than allow dogs. This population is likely to be biased toward cats.
b) People at a dog park	It's not likely that anyone would visit a dog park who did not like dogs. This population is certain to be biased toward dogs.
c) Shoppers at a grocery store	This is most likely an unbiased population because everyone needs groceries.
d) Students at your high school	This is also most likely an unbiased population, unless you know something about your school that would change this.

Model Problems continue . . .

2. MP 2, 4 A new drug is intended to end a type of rash. You read a report about a small, early trial with 50 patients. Of the 30 who get the drug, 18 have their rash disappear and 4 report severe headaches. Of the 20 who get a placebo, 13 have their rash disappear and 3 report severe headaches.

a Does the drug seem to be working?

b Does it seem to be causing severe headaches?

c Based on the data, should the FDA approve the drug?

SOLUTION

a Create frequency table

	Rash Disappears	Rash Remains	Total
Drug	18	12	30
Placebo	13	7	20

Record the outcomes in a frequency table.

Calculate conditional frequencies

	Rash Disappears	Rash Remains
Drug	60%	40%
Placebo	65%	35%

Calculate a conditional frequency table. In other words, calculate the percent of people who received the drug who had the rash disappear.

Example: $\dfrac{18 \text{ had rash disappear}}{30 \text{ received drug}} = 60\%$

Analyze the data

In this small trial, the drug does not seem to be helping. The rash disappears in 60% of the patients taking the drug, while it disappears in 65% of those not taking the drug. The rash disappears "on its own" in 65% of the cases. With a survey of only 50 patients, it seems unwise to draw the conclusion that the drug causes the rash to remain. For instance, if only two more people had reported success with the drug, both groups would be approximately the same. On the other hand, although this is a small group, it is not consistent with a model that shows the drug has a positive effect, which of course is the model the drug company hopes is true. Our hypothesis from this data is that the probability of the rash disappearing is independent of taking the drug. If a person took the drug or not, the resulting probability seems to be roughly the same.

b Create frequency table

	Severe Headaches	No Severe Headaches	Total
Drug	4	26	30
Placebo	3	17	20

Record the outcomes in a frequency table.

Calculate conditional frequencies

	Severe Headaches	No Severe Headaches
Drug	13%	87%
Placebo	15%	85%

Calculate a conditional frequency table. In other words, calculate the percent of people that received the drug who had severe headaches.

Example: $\dfrac{4 \text{ had severe headaches}}{30 \text{ received drug}} = 13\%$

Model Problems continue . . .

Analyze the data	13% of those who received the drug had severe headaches, but 15% of those who did not receive the drug also had severe headaches. The drug does not seem to be increasing the number of people with severe headaches. People have severe headaches whether they take the drug or not. Again, the resulting probability seems to be independent of the drug. To put it another way: $P(A)$ is about the same as $P(A|B)$, with A having a headache and B having taken the drug.

c The FDA should not approve the drug. Those using the placebo had a better outcome than those using the drug. The effect is both minor and negative.

3. An emergency room found that of the people they treated for sprained or broken wrists, 70% had injured their right wrist and 30% had injured their left wrist. Why might this occur?

SOLUTION

There are more people who are right-handed than there are people who are left-handed, so people may be more likely to reach out with the right hand while falling.

PRACTICE

1. A researcher doing a project on recycling wants to determine the amount of trash produced by a household in Monroe County in one day. Which of the following methods of selecting households for his study will lead to the least bias?

A. Asking for participants at a local meeting on environmental issues

B. Randomly selecting households from a recent census that lists the addresses of all residential units in the county

C. Choosing all the households in a large apartment complex

D. Running an ad on a local country radio station, asking for volunteers

2. Anthony is doing an experiment while blindfolded. He tosses two similarly shaped objects and then reaches out to touch one of them. Which of the differences below is most likely to increase his chance of touching one object over the other?

A. Color   C. Cost

B. Size   D. Texture

3. You are giving a survey to students. In which of the following surveys would it matter on which day of the week the student was taking the survey? Select all that apply.

A. Finding out if the student was going out that night

B. Finding out the student's birthday

C. Finding out how much homework the student had been assigned that day

D. Finding out the student's hat size

4. A drug being tested in a medical trial is manufactured as a red pill, and it has a distinct bitter taste. Would a green pill with no taste make a good placebo for this trial? Why or why not?

5. In an experimental study on a new allergy drug, a coin is flipped to determine whether a participant should be placed in a group receiving the drug or in a group receiving the placebo. Using a coin flip to assign participants to study groups accomplishes what crucial element of an experimental study?

Practice Problems continue . . .

6. In a study of a blood pressure medication, many participants reported developing itchy rashes on their arms and legs. What term is used to refer to results like this, which are caused by a drug but are not related to its main purpose?

7. **MP 3** In the context of a survey, what is bias?

8. For a survey of a sample of typical voters in a town, which location would likely result in the least biased results: a supermarket, a baseball game, or a senior center?

9. A city collected data about the number of firefighters sent to fight fires and the amount of property damage that resulted. The mayor noticed that the greater the number of firefighters involved in a call, the greater the amount of resulting property damage. He concluded that sending more firefighters to a call would result in more property damage. Is this a valid conclusion? Why or why not?

10. A school offered an optional, free SAT prep class for juniors. Students could choose whether to attend the class. Juniors who took the class, on average, scored 300 points higher on the SAT than their classmates who did not attend the class. The principal says this proves the class is very successful and should be offered again next year.

    a State at least one reason the principal might be wrong about the class.

    b State one way enrollment in the SAT prep class could have been changed to provide a better measurement of the relationship between taking the SAT prep class and a student's score on the SAT.

11. An airport needs to order a new X-ray machine for luggage, and a survey is conducted to determine the size of the average suitcase. Fifteen business travelers have their suitcases measured. Describe why this survey may exhibit bias.

12. **MP 3** Two college students are collecting data on which sport is more popular among students: basketball or football. Jarrod surveys all of the students in the marching band that performs for football games. Brad surveys all of the students in a freshmen residence hall. Which student's survey has less bias and should give more accurate results?

13. What is one possible disadvantage of allowing patients to choose whether they receive a drug treatment or a placebo?

14. Mike asks his 9 friends who sit at his lunch table if they will vote for him for class treasurer. They all say that they will vote for him, so Mike is confident he will be the next treasurer. Describe why the survey of his friends may not give him an accurate prediction.

15. The library receives a donation to buy new books for the library. The head librarian surveys people at a retirement center and children at the local elementary school to decide what types of books the library should order. Is the survey biased? Why or why not?

16. A company tested a new asthma medication with a double-blind trial. Of the 180 test subjects, 100 received the new medication and 80 received a placebo. Of the test subjects who received the medication, 70 reported they had fewer asthma attacks during the testing period than prior to the test. Of the test subjects receiving the placebo, 20 reported they had fewer asthma attacks during the test period.

    a What percentage of subjects receiving the new medication reported fewer asthma attacks?

    b What percentage of subjects receiving the placebo reported fewer asthma attacks?

    c **MP 3, 6** Does the drug appear to be decreasing the incidence of asthma attacks? Support your answer.

Exercises 17–21: Explain why the population described for the given survey is biased.

17. For a survey on the merits of gambling, the population is the citizens of Las Vegas.

18. For a survey on weather preferences, the population is the citizens of Seattle.

19. For a survey on sleep habits, the population is high school students.

20. For a survey on favorite TV shows, the population is high school students.

Practice Problems continue . . .

21. For a survey on favorite cars, the population is people exiting a grocery store on weekdays between 10:00 A.M. and 2:00 P.M.

22. MP 3, 4 You have been asked to collect data about how a typical voter in your town feels about building a new fire station to service the northern section of the town. State three types of bias you need to avoid in selecting voters for your survey.

23. MP 3, 4, 5 A drug was developed to treat eczema, a skin condition. Some people who take the new drug report a side effect of severe headaches. Researchers decide to conduct a trial and compare the drug and a placebo to determine if the headaches may be related to the drug. There are 120 people enrolled in the trial. Of the 54 receive the drug, 15 of them report having severe headaches. Of the 66 receive the placebo, 17 of them report severe headaches. Does the drug appear to cause headaches?

24. Explain why using a double-blind methodology in a medical trial might be preferable to allowing researchers to know which participants have or have not received a placebo.

• Multi-Part PROBLEM Practice •

MP 1, 3, 4 You want to survey members of your community to see if the town wants to pass a law to raise the minimum wage.

a Determine whether each of the following locations would be likely to provide a biased or unbiased population to survey:

  i.   The corner pub
  ii. The country club
  iii. The grocery store
  iv. A game of the town's minor league baseball team

b Turns out, the baseball game is where everybody goes. There is a wide cross section of citizens from all socioeconomic levels. Of the 1000 people, you can only survey 100. How could you use decks of cards to choose the 100 people?

c Determine another method for randomly selecting 100 of the 1000 people that is a fair method.

LESSON 10.7

10.7 Means, Proportions, Confidence Intervals, and Margin of Error

In the previous lesson, we saw some different ways in which we can gather data and how randomization can be used to ensure the validity of the data collection process. In this lesson, we discuss some of the analysis procedures data is put through after it is collected.

Means and Proportions

Often, statisticians or researchers are interested in defining a value that describes some characteristic of the population they're studying. To this end, *measures of central tendency* are used. The most common measures of central tendency are mean, median, and mode, which you have studied in previous math classes. Recall that the mean is a data set's average value, the median is the middle value, and the mode is the value that occurs the most often.

A measure related to mean, median, and mode is **proportion**, p, which is the fraction of the total collected data that possesses the characteristic in which we are interested. For example, suppose that we are interested in knowing the proportion of high school freshmen in a metro area that participate in after-school activities. If our collected data reflects that 65 out of 100 high school freshmen in that metro area participate in after-school activities, the proportion, $p = \dfrac{65}{100} = 0.65$. We can also compute np, the proportion of high school freshmen in that metro area who do not participate in after-school activities: $np = 1 - p = 1 - 0.65 = 0.35$.

> The notation *np* refers to the proportion of the total collected data that does not possess the desired characteristic.

Calculating Proportions:

$$p = \frac{\text{number with characteristic}}{\text{total number}}$$

$$np = \frac{\text{number without characteristic}}{\text{total number}} = 1 - p$$

For any set of collected data, we can calculate the mean or a proportion, depending on what we are trying to determine.

MODEL PROBLEM

Members of a school board are considering spending some of the district budget on upgraded technology for the middle school math classrooms. To determine if the community supports this idea, a survey is conducted which shows that 160 out of 400 survey participants support spending money to update technology in the middle school math classrooms. What is the proportion of participants that support this idea?

A.	0.16	C.	0.60
B.	0.40	D.	0.82

SOLUTION

Calculate p, the proportion of participants who support upgraded technology in middle school math classrooms

$$p = \frac{160}{400} = 0.40$$

The correct answer is B.

Confidence Interval and Margin of Error

When analyzing a data set, the calculated mean or proportion gives us an incomplete snapshot of the data. This is because data is spread out around the mean value or proportion. In order to quantify and account for this spread, we determine a measure of variability such as the *standard deviation*. Calculation of the standard deviation is beyond the scope of this course, but it is important that you understand its definition and how its value affects other calculations, such as margin of error and confidence intervals. We will use an election poll scenario to illustrate these concepts.

> *Standard deviation*, abbreviated S. D., is the numerical value that is used to indicate how widely values in a data set vary. The higher the standard deviation, the more widely the values vary.

Suppose that a local election poll results in 52% of the respondents for Mr. Cooper and 48% for Ms. Raimundo. The poll is reported with a margin of error of plus or minus 2 percentage points at a 95% confidence level. The results are being reported with terms that are parameters in statistics; they are used to state how confident a statistician is in the results of her survey.

Margin of error • Plus or minus a constant	The margin of error provides the values that are added to and subtracted from a reported statistic to account for possible error due to sampling. This value is a function of the standard deviation, so the higher the standard deviation, the higher the margin of error and vice versa. A two-percentage-point margin of error does not mean plus or minus 2% of the result—when the result itself is a percentage—but rather $(37 \pm 2)\%$ for a result of 37%.
Confidence level • A percent	The confidence level gives a sense of how likely the true value for a parameter is to be within the margin of error of the statistic. It states the percent of times, if the study were conducted multiple times, that the true value would be within the margin of error.
Confidence interval • A range of values	The confidence interval is the range of values that is found by adding the margin of error to and subtracting it from the statistic at the given confidence level.

For instance, perhaps the pollster in this scenario surveyed 1,500 people out of the larger population and found that $p = \dfrac{780}{1500} = 0.52$ of them said they would vote for Cooper. The standard deviation of the survey is not reported, but the margin of error, 2 percentage points, is. We know the confidence level is 95%. We can interpret these parameters to mean that if the survey were conducted multiple times within the same population, 95% of the results would fall between 50% and 54%, i.e., $(52 \pm 2)\%$, of survey respondents preferring Cooper. This also means that 5% of the time, the survey results will be outside the confidence interval of 50% − 54%.

A poll says that 58% of voters will vote for Thieu, plus or minus 3 percentage points, and the pollster is 90% confident of his results. State the margin of error, the confidence level, and the confidence interval.

SOLUTION

Margin of error	Plus or minus 3 percentage points at 90%	The poll said that the results were accurate to within plus or minus 3 percentage points at a 90% confidence level. The margin of error is 3 percentage points.
Confidence level	90%	The pollster says he has a 90% confidence level.
Confidence interval at 90% confidence level	58% ± 3 percentage points 55% to 61% at 90% confidence level	Add and subtract the margin of error to 58% to calculate the confidence interval.

Computing the Margin of Error

We now explain how to compute the margin of error for means and for proportions. Different types of statistics have different techniques for computing margin of error.

If the mean, standard deviation, and number of participants in a sample are known, the margin of error can be estimated using the following formula:

$$\text{margin of error} = \frac{2 \cdot \text{standard deviation}}{\sqrt{N}}$$

N = sample size

This formula assumes that the data are normally distributed (see lesson 10.5) and that the confidence level is 95%. In this formula, it is easy to see how the standard deviation affects the margin of error—the higher the deviation, the higher the margin of error and vice versa. It is also easy to see that as the sample size, N, increases, the margin of error decreases. This is due to the division by $\sqrt{N}$.

If, instead of working with the mean of a data set, you are working with a proportion, the margin of error can be calculated using this formula:

$$\text{margin of error} = 2\sqrt{\frac{p(1-p)}{N}}$$

N = sample size
p = survey results as a decimal, not percent

This method assumes that the data have a *binomial distribution*. This type of distribution differs from the normal distribution discussed in lesson 10.5; however, if we repeat a statistical study a sufficient number of times with a large enough sample size, the binomial distribution can be approximated by the normal distribution. As such, the mean becomes equivalent to the value of p and the formula above gives the margin error for a confidence level of 95%. Again, it is easy to see how the margin of error is affected by the number of participants in the sample—the larger the sample, the smaller the resulting margin of error.

> How does one reduce the margin of error? One way is to increase the size of the survey. With everything else being equal, a larger survey will have a smaller margin of error.

1. Of 500 surveyed, 47% prefer SuperGloss Shampoo. What is the margin of error at a 95% confidence level?

SOLUTION

Use the formula $\quad$ margin of error $= 2\sqrt{\dfrac{p(1-p)}{N}}$

Start with the formula and substitute 0.47 for the 47% stated in the problem, and substitute 500 for N.

$$p = 47\% = 0.47$$
$$N = 500$$

$$\text{margin of error} = 2\sqrt{\frac{0.47(1 - 0.47)}{500}}$$

Margin of error $\quad$ margin of error $\approx 0.045 = 4.5$ percentage points

Compute the margin of error in percentage points.

Confidence interval $\quad$ $(47 - 4.5)\%$, $(47 + 4.5)\%$
$(42.5\%, 51.5\%)$

Calculate the 95% confidence interval.

2. The mass of 150 chimpanzees had a standard deviation of 1.25 kilograms. At a 95% confidence level, what is the margin of error?

SOLUTION

Use the formula $\quad\quad$ margin of error $= \dfrac{2 \cdot \text{standard deviation}}{\sqrt{N}}$

Start with the formula and substitute.

$$\text{standard deviation} = 1.25$$
$$N = 150$$

$$\text{margin of error} = \frac{2 \cdot 1.25}{\sqrt{150}}$$

Margin of error $\quad\quad$ margin of error ≈ 0.20 kilograms

Compute the margin of error.

The margin of error is an important statistical measure. It defines the maximum expected difference between the true population parameter and the estimate provided by the statistical study. For a study repeated a sufficient number of times, either through real-time questioning or by simulation, the margin of error can help us determine whether the results we observe are so unusual that they wouldn't happen by chance.

Divinda's Divine Snacks is thinking about producing a new snack mix variety. The company will produce the new snack mix if at least 28% of people who eat snack mix will buy the product. Fifty people who eat snack mix are randomly selected to take a blind taste test of products X, Y, and the new snack mix. Ten participants preferred the new snack mix to products X and Y. Divinda's Divine Snacks then devises a simulation where the computer repeatedly took samples of size 50 from a population with a true proportion of 0.28 for those who prefer Divinda's Snack Mix. The company will compare the results of the simulation to the results of their taste test. Each dot in the graph to the right represents the proportion of people who preferred Divinda's new product.

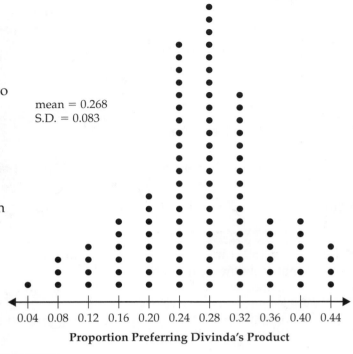

mean = 0.268
S.D. = 0.083

Proportion Preferring Divinda's Product

a   Assume the data are normally distributed. If the company wants to be 95% confident of its results, does the sample proportion, 10 out of 50, fall within the margin of error developed from the simulation? Justify your answer.

b   Divinda's Divine Snacks decided to continue developing the new product even though only 10 out of 50 participants preferred its brand of snack mix in the taste test. Describe how the simulation data could be used to support this decision.

SOLUTION

a   Calculate the margin of error predicted by the simulation.

We use the margin of error formula, $2 \cdot \sqrt{\dfrac{p(1-p)}{N}}$ where $p = 0.268$, to find that $2 \cdot \sqrt{\dfrac{0.268(1-0.268)}{50}} = 0.125$.

Interpret the margin of error.

The margin of error indicates that 95% of the observations fall within ± 0.125 of the mean simulated proportion, 0.268. The sample proportion, 0.20, falls within this margin of error.

b   The company has evidence that the population proportion could be at least 28%. As seen in the dot plot, a sample proportion of 0.20 (10 out of 50) or less could be obtained several times, even when the true proportion is 0.28, due to sampling variability. Given this and the results of the taste test, product development should continue at this time.

In this activity, the results of a voting survey are shown. Two candidates are running for office. You control how many people are polled. We set rules (theoretical probabilities) for the outcomes, but the experimental results you get are randomly generated, like drawing a card from a deck to see if it is a club.

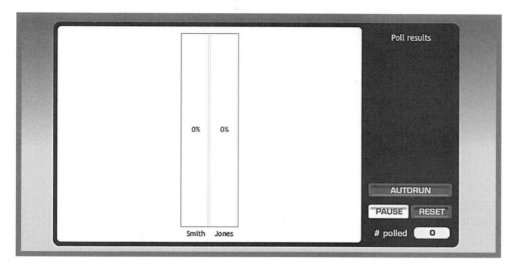

 In this activity, view the results of an experimental drug trial. Some study members receive a placebo, while others receive the experimental drug. The members are either cured or not cured. We set rules (theoretical probabilities) for the outcomes, but the experimental results you get are randomly generated, like drawing a card from a deck to see if it is a club.

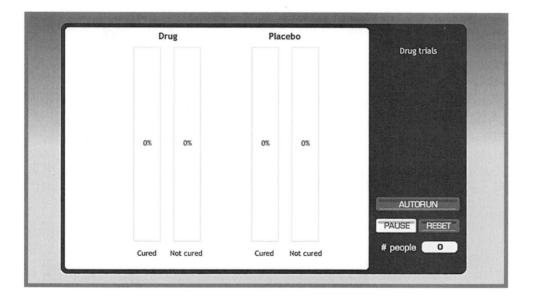

1. A survey of a sample of registered voters reports that 47%, with a margin of error of plus or minus 2 percentage points, are expected to vote for the Democratic candidate in an election. Based on the results of this survey, what percentage of votes would the Democratic candidate not be likely to receive?

   A. 45%
   B. 48%
   C. 49%
   D. 50%

2. In a medical trial with 70 patients, 40 received the experimental drug. What proportion of the patients did not receive the experimental medication?

   A. $\frac{3}{7}$ C. $\frac{2}{7}$

   B. $\frac{4}{7}$ D. $\frac{5}{7}$

3. A simulation estimates the standard deviation of a sample proportion to be 0.062 when the sample size is 85. What is the margin of error?
   A. 0.352
   B. 0.249
   C. 0.134
   D. 0.031

4. A pollster takes a poll of 200 voters in a small town and finds that the incumbent, Mayor Parsons, will receive 54% of the vote, with a margin of error of 4 percentage points at 90% confidence level. If all 1000 residents of the town were surveyed, 51.1% would say they would vote for Parsons. Is the actual population value within the margin of error of the statistic?

   A. Yes
   B. No

5. You are given the formula to find the margin of error: $2\sqrt{\frac{p(1-p)}{N}}$. Which example best describes what happens to the margin of error as N increases?

   A. The margin of error in a political survey will increase as more people are surveyed.
   B. The margin of error in a medical study will decrease if fewer people participate in the study.
   C. The margin of error will be two times larger than the number of people participating in a shopping survey.
   D. The margin of error will decrease as more people are polled for an automobile survey.

6. 1,000 voters are surveyed, and 62% prefer the candidate from the "Math for All" party. What is the margin of error at a 95% confidence level? Round your answer to the nearest tenth of a percentage point.

7. The heights of 225 plants are measured, and the standard deviation is 3.75 cm. At a 95% confidence level, what is the margin of error?

8. A poll says that 62% of voters support an increase in social services spending, plus or minus 4 percentage points. The pollster is 90% confident of his results. State the margin of error, the confidence level, and the confidence interval.

Practice Problems continue . . .

9. Anneka owns a small T-shirt printing business. She currently offers 8 different solid colored T-shirt choices and is considering expanding to 10 solid color varieties. She will move forward with her plan if she is 95% confident that 35% of her customers will buy at least one of the two new color choices. She conducts a survey and finds that 13 of 50 people will buy at least one of the two new colors. To see if her results are indicative of the true proportion of the population that will buy the two new colors, Anneka then devises a simulation where the computer repeatedly takes samples of size 50 from a population with a true proportion of 0.35 for those who would buy at least one of the two new colors. Anneka will compare the results of the simulation to the results of her survey. Each dot in the graph below represents the proportion of people who would buy at least one of the two new colors.

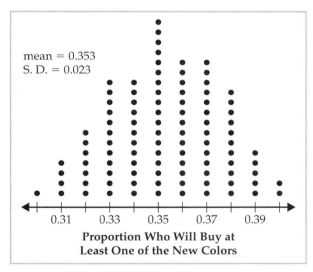

mean = 0.353
S. D. = 0.023

Proportion Who Will Buy at
Least One of the New Colors

Should Anneka move ahead with her plan of expanding to 10 solid color choices for her T-shirts? Justify your answer.

10. Laelia weighed 25 five-pound bags of flour and found their average weight to be 5.15 with a standard deviation of 0.84 pounds. At a 95% confidence level, what is the margin of error?

11. A manufacturing plant makes a certain part for automobile engines. The average length of the part is 3.25 cm. The floor supervisor is 95% confident that 92% of these parts that are stamped out by machine K are 3.25 cm in length, plus or minus 3 percentage points. What is the floor supervisor's confidence interval for her estimate of 92%?

12. A college psychology professor theorizes that 45% of her students spent at least 15 hours studying for the last exam. She conducts a survey and finds that 19 of her 50 students spent at least 15 hours studying for the exam. The professor then devises a simulation where the computer repeatedly took samples of size 50 from a population of students with a true proportion of 0.45. She will compare the results of the simulation to the results of her survey to determine the validity of her hypothesis. Each dot in the graph below represents the proportion of students who studied at least 15 hours for the exam.

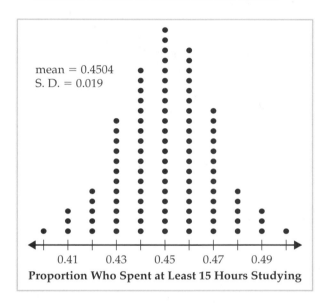

mean = 0.4504
S. D. = 0.019

Proportion Who Spent at Least 15 Hours Studying

With 95% confidence, what conclusions can the psychology professor draw about her hypothesis that at least 45% of her students spent 15 hours studying for the last exam?

13. The manufacturer of a candy coated chocolate states that in a standard bag of their product, 38% of the candies are red. Fishel opens 30 standard-sized bags of the product and finds that 32% of the candies were red. What is Fishel's margin of error at a 95% confidence level? How does this experimental result compare with the manufacturer's claim?

14. A survey of a sample of supermarket shoppers reported that 44% buy generic mustard, with a margin of error of plus or minus 5 percentage points. What is the maximum percentage of all shoppers that the survey predicts will buy generic mustard?

Practice Problems continue . . .

15. A survey of 100 people shopping for a new car indicated that 16% planned to buy a hybrid vehicle, with a margin of error of plus or minus 3 percentage points. Based on the survey, what range of all people buying a new car could be expected to buy a hybrid?

16. In a close race for a seat on the local school board, a poll of registered voters reported that Candidate A led Candidate B by 52% to 48%, with a margin of error of plus or minus 6 percentage points. Does the survey predict Candidate A will win the election? Support your answer.

17. The confidence interval for the experimental results of a coin toss is 90%. If the coin toss experiment was conducted 10 times, how many times would the experimental results be expected to fall outside the margin of error?

18. As the number of trials run on a coin toss simulator increases, what happens to the margin of error?

19. A group of students in a science class is using a simulator to model inheritance of different genetic traits. One trait they are testing is leaf shape, and they have determined that a group of plants should, theoretically, have pointy leaves 25% of the time and round leaves 75% of the time. The students run their simulation 500 times and determine that 140 plants have pointy leaves. What percentage of plants in the simulation have leaves that are pointy?

20. With 95% confidence, a researcher expects between 9% and 13% of the units of a new product to fail during the first year of use. Express this estimate as a single percentage with a plus or minus margin of error.

21. A government researcher hypothesizes that 50% of the homes in a certain county have basements. He surveys the records of home purchases for the last year in that county and finds that 20 out of 50 homes purchased have a basement. The researcher then devises a simulation where the computer repeatedly took samples of size 50 from a population with a true proportion of 0.50. The researcher will compare the results of the simulation to the results of his survey. Each dot in the graph below represents the proportion of homes with a basement.

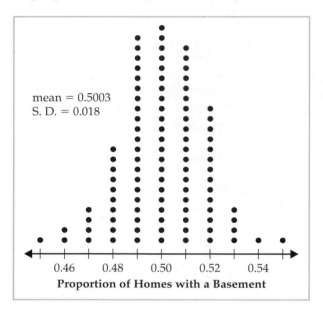

Based on the results of the simulation, can the researcher conclude that at least 50% of the homes in this county have a basement? Justify your answer.

22. MP 2, 3 A polling company conducted a survey of 50 people who were running in a local road race. Based on the runners' estimations of their finishing times, the polling company expected 57% of the runners, plus or minus 4 percentage points, to finish the race in under 2 hours. Their confidence interval for the results was 70%. During the event, 63% of runners finished in under two hours. The race organizer says the polling company did a lousy job because the actual results of the race fell outside their margin of error. Do you agree? Support your answer.

Practice Problems continue . . .

Practice Problems continued . . .

23. Cherice conducted a survey of the type of music most preferred by 500 of her peers. She found that 185 prefer pop music, 200 like rock music, 150 most like rap music, and 35 enjoy country. What is the margin of error for students who like rap music?

24. **MP 2** The confidence level for the results of a survey is $k\%$. What is the chance the actual results will fall outside the margin of error?

Chapter 10 Key Ideas

10.1 Introduction to Probability

- Experimental probability is calculated by recording the outcomes of a series of observations. The probability of an event A, $P(A)$, equals the number of times A is observed, divided by the number of observations.

- A sample space is the set of all possible outcomes of an event. Theoretical probability equals the number of ways an event can occur divided by the number of outcomes in the sample space, given the outcomes are all equally likely.

10.2 Independent Events, the Multiplication Rule, and Compound Events

- In probability, the word "and" means that all events occur.

- Two events are independent if the occurrence of one event does not affect the probability that the other event will occur.

- The multiplication rule for independent events states that $P(A \cap B) = P(A) \cdot P(B)$.

10.3 Addition and Subtraction Rules

- "Or" means at least one of a set of events occurs. The addition rule is used to calculate the probability $P(A \text{ or } B)$. It says $P(A \text{ or } B) = P(A) + P(B) - P(A \text{ and } B)$.

- Two events are mutually exclusive if it is impossible for them both to occur. If A and B are mutually exclusive events, $P(A \text{ and } B) = 0$ and $P(A \text{ or } B) = P(A) + P(B)$.

- The sum of the probabilities of all the outcomes of an event equals 1. The probability $P(\text{not } A)$ is the probability that the event A does not occur. To calculate it, use the relation: $P(\text{not } A) = 1 - P(A)$. Another name for mutually exclusive events is disjoint sets.

10.4 Conditional Probability

- Conditional probability is the probability that the event A occurs, given that event B has already occurred. A conditional probability is written $P(A|B)$. The formula that follows is used to calculate it: $P(A|B) = \dfrac{P(A \text{ and } B)}{P(B)}$.

10.5 The Normal Distribution

- Normal distribution is a pattern of data that represents many random variables; its graph has a symmetrical, bell-shaped curve.

- Calculating the area under part of a normal curve allows one to determine the probability of an outcome, or range of outcomes, of an event that has a normal distribution of outcomes.

10.6 Statistical Studies and Randomization

- There are several different methods to gather data, including surveys, observational studies, and experimental studies.
- Randomization is an essential process whereby participants are randomly selected for studies or randomly grouped once chosen to minimize selection bias.
- Cause-and-effect conclusions can only be drawn from experimental studies.
- Researchers must account for lurking variables when drawing conclusions based on their collected data.

10.7 Means, Proportions, Confidence Intervals, and Margin of Error

- We use the data from a statistical study to estimate a population mean or proportion.
- Means and proportions are values that describe characteristics of the population being studied.
- Standard deviation is a measure of the variability, or spread, of the data.
- The margin of error is a value typically added to and subtracted from either the mean or proportion. It is related to the standard deviation, and it provides a range of values for the variable of interest at some confidence level. The range of values is called the confidence interval.

CHAPTER 10 REVIEW

1. Which of the following numbers could be probabilities? Select all that apply.

A. $\dfrac{4}{3}$ D. -0.4

B. $\dfrac{3}{4}$ E. 2

C. 0.999

2. In the graph of the sample space below, the height of the bar for the outcome "6" is

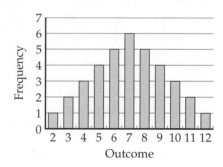

A. 4   C. 6

B. 5   D. 7

3. Which of the pairs of events below are independent? Select all that apply.

A. A coin coming up heads, and then the same coin coming up tails.
B. The weather being sunny and people carrying umbrellas.
C. Drawing a 5 from a deck of cards, replacing it in the deck, and then drawing a queen.
D. Drawing a red gumdrop from a bag, eating it, and then drawing a blue gumdrop.

4. The probability that event Z occurs is 0.4; the probability that event K occurs is 0.5; and the probability that events Z and K both occur is 0.2. This means

A. The probability of Z is conditional on the probability of K.
B. The probability of K is conditional on the probability of Z.
C. The two events are independent.
D. The event Z is the complement of the event K.

Chapter Review continues . . .

5. Laetitia is relating probability and sets. She states: "In probability, we can compute the probability that *A* and *B* may occur. We might also compute the probability that *X* or *Y* may occur." To relate this to sets, Laetitia should say,

  A. "The probability of *A* and *B* occurring is a union of two sets, and the probability of *X* or *Y* occurring is an intersection of two sets."

  B. "The probability of *A* and *B* occurring is an intersection of two sets, and the probability of *X* or *Y* occurring is the union of two sets."

  C. "The probability of *A* and *B* occurring is the complement of two sets, and the probability of *X* or *Y* occurring is the intersection of two sets."

  D. "The probability of *A* and *B* occurring is a union of two sets, and the probability of *X* or *Y* occurring is the complement of two sets."

6. Robert is finding the probability of randomly drawing a queen or diamond from a deck of 52 cards. His solution steps are stated below.

Step 1: $P(A \text{ or } B) = P(A) + P(B) - P(A \text{ and } B)$

Step 2: $P(A \text{ or } B) = \dfrac{4}{52} + \dfrac{13}{52} - \dfrac{1}{52}$

Step 3: $P(A \text{ or } B) = \dfrac{4}{13}$

Which is the first incorrect step shown above, if there are any errors at all?

  A. Step 1
  B. Step 2
  C. Step 3
  D. All the steps are correct.

7. **MP 4, 5** Customers order one or two scoops of ice cream at the corner store. The probability that the store serves a chocolate scoop is 0.4; the probability that a customer orders two scoops is 0.3; and the probability that they order two chocolate scoops is 0.1. What is the probability they order chocolate or two scoops?

8. **MP 4, 7** There is a 70% chance that it will rain, and a 30% chance that the temperature will be above 80°F. There is a 20% chance that it will rain and the temperature will be above 80°F. What is the probability that it will rain or the temperature will be above 80°F?

9. Create a sample space to answer the questions below. There are two six-sided dice. The numbers on one die are even (2, 4, 6, 8, 10, 12) and the numbers on the other are odd (1, 3, 5, 7, 9, 11).

  a What is the probability that the dice sum to 7?
  b What is the probability that the dice sum to an even number?
  c What is the probability that the dice sum to an odd number?
  d What is the probability that the dice sum to 8 or a larger number?

Exercises 10–12: Sketch the graph to represent the sample space.

10. The sum of two 5-sided dice.

11. The sum of two 8-sided dice.

12. The number of heads when flipping 3 fair coins.

13. **MP 4, 7** A survey asked people which days of the week they usually go grocery shopping. 70% of those surveyed went grocery shopping on Saturday or Sunday, 50% went shopping on Saturday, and 30% went shopping on Sunday. What percentage of people went shopping on both Saturday and Sunday?

14. An efficiency researcher collected data about the number of miles that ten different types of cars can drive on a single gallon of gasoline. She calculated the mean miles per gallon for the cars, as well as the standard deviation for the data set. Another researcher in Canada asked if the first researcher could convert her measurements to kilometers per liter, which will change the mean and the standard deviation of the data. Will the conversion affect the ratio of the standard deviation to the mean? Explain your reasoning.

15. Shaquille (Shaq) O'Neal played 20 seasons in the National Basketball League. Over that time, he amassed 8,890 regular season defensive rebounds (DRB). Suppose he averaged 7.4 DRB per regular season game with a standard deviation of 2.3 DRB. If his number of DRB per game is normally distributed across his career, what is the probability that Shaq gained more than 12 DRB in a randomly selected regular season game?

16. In Data Set M, the mean is 32 centimeters, and the standard deviation is 4 centimeters. What piece of information can be used to compare the spread of data in Data Set M to the data in Data Set S, which has a different mean and a different standard deviation?

17. Azra is considering buying a treadmill. He knows that the average life of a treadmill from a certain manufacturer is about 10,000 miles with a standard deviation of 1,800 miles. If Azra buys a treadmill made by this manufacturer, what is the probability that the treadmill will last between 8,000 and 13,000 miles?

18. How does increasing the size of the intervals into which data are grouped affect the apparent distribution of the data in a frequency graph?

19. In a study of a new flu vaccine, the syringes containing the vaccine and those containing a placebo were prepared ahead of time, and neither the doctors giving the shots nor the participants receiving them knew who received the vaccine and who received the placebo. What term is used to describe this type of study, in which neither the researchers nor the participants know who has received the drug and who has received the placebo?

20. A company testing an asthma medication is concerned the medication may increase the risk of infections. Of the 100 people who used the new medication in the test, 8 reported they had some type of infection during the test period. Of the 80 people who received the placebo, 9 people reported they had some type of infection during the test period.

   a What percentage of subjects receiving the medication reported having an infection?

   b What percentage of subjects receiving the placebo reported having an infection?

   c Does the drug appear to increase the risk of infection? Justify your answer.

21. The average annual starting salary for a high school math teacher in the United States is $43,000 with a standard deviation of $4,500. Suppose Anton takes a job where he earns less than what 75% of his national colleagues earn. What is the maximum amount of money Anton could be earning annually?

22. **MP 2** A survey reports that $a\%$ of a sample of fishermen surveyed wear life jackets, plus or minus b percentage points.

   a Based on these results, write an expression that represents the smallest percentage of all fishermen who might be expected to wear life jackets, based on the survey.

   b Express the range of fishermen who wear life jackets as a function of b.

23. **MP 3, 8** The Law of Large Numbers states that as the number of trials of an experiment increases, the experimental probability of an event occurring approaches the theoretical probability of the event occurring. Jake received a "magic" coin from his uncle. He flipped it 100 times, and found that it came up heads 64% of the time. He flipped it another 500 times, and it came up heads 57% of the time. He then flipped it 1000 times, and it came up heads 58% of the time. Then, he flipped it 1500 times, and it came up heads 62% of the time. Based on the Law of Large Numbers, what do you think the theoretical probability of the magic coin coming up heads is? Explain how you could test your hypothesis.

Chapter Review continues . . .

24. A polling firm is conducting research on Internet use by calling the landline telephone of every tenth person listed in a local phone book. What bias may exist in the method they are using to do the poll?

25. What could a person collecting data for a survey do to avoid age bias in the results?

26. Derek has a jar of marbles—half are red and half are blue. The red marbles are slightly smaller than the blue marbles. Derek assumes that because the jar contains the same number of marbles of each color, if he closes his eyes and picks a marble, he will draw a red marble 50% of the time. Is Derek correct? Why or why not?

27. A statistician was asked to examine the weights of the members of the wrestling teams at two different high schools. The information he collected is shown below.

Garfield High School

Weight (pounds)	Number of Wrestlers
111–120	0
121–130	2
131–140	1
141–150	5
151–160	5
161–170	1
171–180	1
181–190	0

Cleveland High School

Weight (pounds)	Number of Wrestlers
111–120	1
121–130	3
131–140	0
141–150	3
151–160	4
161–170	0
171–180	1
181–190	3

a Make a bar graph to display the data from Garfield High School.

b Make a bar graph to display the data from Cleveland High School.

c Based on the two graphs, which school would you expect to have a greater standard deviation from the mean, and why?

28. **MP 2** Peter calculated that the theoretical probability of obtaining exactly two heads when flipping six coins is 23.4%. What number of heads also has a 23.4% theoretical probability of coming up when 6 coins are flipped?

29. It is estimated that about 44% of American households have consumer debt. A researcher conducts a survey of 50 randomly selected American households and finds that 20 of them have consumer debt. The researcher then devised a simulation where the computer repeatedly took samples of size 50 from a population where the true proportion of American household with consumer debt is 0.44. The researcher will compare the results of the simulation to the results of their survey.

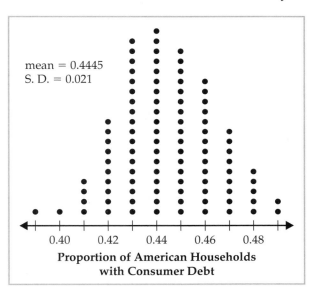

mean = 0.4445
S. D. = 0.021

Proportion of American Households with Consumer Debt

If we want to be 95% confident of our estimate, does the sample proportion obtained, 20 out of 50, fall within the margin of error developed from the simulation? Why or why not?

Cumulative Review

1. Which of the following is true about the graph of $y = 3\sin(x - 4) + 2$ compared to the graph of $y = 3\sin x$?

   A. It is shifted up by 2.
   B. It is shifted down by 2.
   C. It is shifted up by 4.
   D. It is shifted down by 4.

2. You have two dice. One die has m sides and the other die has n sides, and all of the sides are different. If you roll one die and then the other, how many possible outcomes are in the sample space?

   A. $m + n$
   B. mn
   C. $n + mn$
   D. mm

3. Which of the following cannot be used to examine the spread of a set of data?

   A. Mean of the data
   B. Bar graph of the data
   C. Box-and-whisker plot of the data
   D. Standard deviation of the data

4. To avoid making a rash decision, a drug company tests its new drug again with 70 patients. Forty received the drug, and 25 had their rashes disappear. Of the 30 who received a placebo, 20 had their rashes disappear. In this trial, does the drug seem to be working?

   A. No
   B. Yes
   C. Not enough information to tell

5. Solve: $(x + 4)^2 = 5x + 20$

6. Simplify the expression: $\dfrac{x^2 - 4}{x + 2}$

Exercises 7–8: Simplify. Assume the radicand is positive.

7. $\sqrt{(x + 3)(x - 3)(x + 3)(x - 3)}$

8. $\sqrt{3x^2 + 10x - 14 - (2x^2 + 4x - 23)}$

9. Consider the radical expression $\sqrt{abxy}$ where $ab = 2$ and xy is a perfect square less than or equal to 100. For which value(s) of xy is the radical a rational number?

Exercises 10–14: Decide if each equation represents exponential growth or decay. Explain your answer.

10. `MP 5, 7` $y = \dfrac{2^x}{3^x}$

11. $y = (3^x)^2$

12. $y = (3)^{-2x}$

13. $\dfrac{y}{2^x} = \dfrac{3}{2}$

14. $y = \dfrac{3^x}{2^x}$

15. Express $\log_8 \dfrac{\sqrt[7]{n}}{3t^4}$ in terms of $\log_8 n$, $\log_8 t$, and $\log_8 3$.

16. Express as a single logarithm with an integer argument: $\log_3 10 + \log_3 8 - \log_3 4$

17. State as a difference of logarithms: $\log_3 \dfrac{x}{5}$

18. `MP 2, 4` A bank pays 8% interest compounded annually. You deposit $1,000,000. In how many years will you have $10,000,000 in your account? State your answer to the nearest hundredth of a year.

19. Match the sequence to the function that best models the graph of the sequence.

   a. 6, 12, 24, 48, ...   A. $y = 3x - 2$
   b. −2, 1, 4, 7, ...   B. $y = 3 \cdot 2^x$
   c. −12, 36, −108, 324, ...   C. $y = 4 \cdot (-3)^x$

20. Consider the sequence 5, 13, 21, 29, ... Give a linear function that would best model the line formed by the graph of the sequence.

21. The sum of the 1st and 7th terms of an arithmetic sequence is 2, and the sum of the 2nd and 10th terms is 14. What is the 5th term?

22. **MP 2, 3** Assume $a_1, a_2, a_3, \ldots$ is a geometric sequence and m is a constant not equal to 0. Prove that $ma_1, ma_2, ma_3, \ldots$ is also a geometric sequence.

23. **MP 7, 8** The second square is created by connecting the midpoints of the 20-centimeter square, and this pattern is continued. If this pattern is continued forever, what is the sum of the areas of all of the squares?

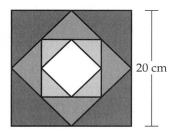

20 cm

24. Use the difference of squares and the trigonometric identity $(\sin x)^2 + (\cos x)^2 = 1$ to show that $(\cos x)^4 - (\sin x)^4 = (\cos x)^2 - (\sin x)^2$.

25. **MP 3, 7** Use the Pythagorean theorem and the diagram below to prove $(\sin \theta)^2 + (\cos \theta)^2 = 1$.

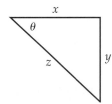

26. What is the equation of the graph shown? State your answer using the sine function.

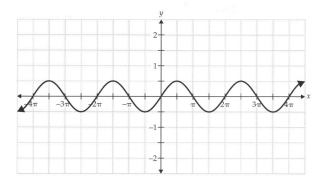

27. The value of the sine of $\frac{\pi}{3}$ is $\frac{\sqrt{3}}{2}$. What is the exact value of the sine of $\left(\pi + \frac{\pi}{3} \right)$?

28. A spinner is divided into 3 equal sections: red, green, and blue.

   a What is the theoretical probability of spinning red two times in a row, expressed as a percentage to the nearest whole percent?

   b A simulator runs 300 trials of two spins in a row. During the simulation, the number of times red is spun twice in a row is 42. What percentage of the trials produced a result of (RED, RED)?

   c If the simulator runs through 3000 trials, should you expect the absolute value of the margin of error to be greater or smaller?

29. Calculate the theoretical probabilities of obtaining 0, 1, 2, 3, 4, 5, and 6 heads when tossing 6 coins. Express your solutions as percentages rounded to the nearest tenth, and present them in a table.

Glossary

addition rule (p. 481) In probability: $P(A \text{ or } B) = P(A) + P(B) - P(A \text{ and } B)$.

adjacent leg (p. 394) In a right triangle, the leg next to the angle under consideration.

amplitude (p. 425) In the graph of a periodic function, the amplitude is the distance from the midline to the highest or lowest point, or the distance to a peak or a trough.

angle of rotation (p. 406) In a rotational transformation, the angle through which a figure is rotated about a fixed point.

argument (p. 295) In a logarithmic expression, $\log_b x = y$, x is the argument of the logarithm. It is the value of base b raised to the power y and must be greater than 0.

arithmetic sequence (p. 334) A numerical sequence in which each term equals the sum of the previous term and a constant, called the *common difference*.

arithmetic series (p. 342) The expression of the sum of the terms in an arithmetic sequence.

asymptote (p. 48) A line that a graph approaches but never reaches.

axis of symmetry (p. 41) A line across which a figure is "flipped" to create a reflected image. Each point in the figure has a matching point in the image an equal distance from the axis of symmetry.

base (exponents) (p. 223) In an exponential expression, the base is the number or variable raised to a power. In the expression, 7^5, 7 is the base.

base (logarithms) (p. 295) In a logarithmic expression, $\log_b x = y$, b is the base of the logarithm. It is the value raised to the power y so that it equals x. The base must be greater than 0 and cannot equal 1.

bias (p. 509) A flaw in the method of collecting or analyzing data in a statistical survey that results in an inaccurate representation of the population. Bias prevents a survey from being random.

binomial (p. 39) A polynomial with two terms.

binomial coefficients (p. 374) The coefficients of the terms in the power expansion of a binomial, $(a + b)^n$.

binomial distribution (p. 516) In probability theory, the distribution that results from a collection of data with two possible outcomes, each equally likely.

binomial expansion (p. 370) The polynomial expression of a binomial raised to a power, $(a + b)^n$.

binomial theorem (p. 377) The formula for calculating any term in a binomial expansion. To find the term with b^k in $(a + b)^n$, evaluate the formula $\binom{n}{k} a^{n-k} b^k$.

boundary line (p. 32) In the graph of an inequality on a grid, a line that defines the solution set of the inequality.

central angle (p. 414) An angle with its vertex at the center of a circle.

change-of-base formula (p. 313) The formula that rewrites a logarithm with one base as a logarithmic expression with a different base: $\log_a x = \dfrac{\log_b x}{\log_b a}$.

closed system (p. 185) A set of numbers is closed under a mathematical operation if, when that operation is performed on any two or more numbers in that set, the result is also a number in the set. For example, the set of whole numbers is closed under addition because adding any two whole numbers will always yield a whole number.

coefficient of determination (p. 57) When creating a mathematical model to fit data, the coefficient of determination, r^2, provides a measure of how well the model fits the data. The value of r^2 varies from 0 to 1; the closer it is to 1, the better the model fits the data.

coefficient of variation (p. 496) The ratio of the standard deviation to the mean.

combined function (p. 278) The result of adding, subtracting, multiplying, and/or dividing two or more functions.

common difference (p. 334) The number added to each term of an arithmetic sequence to get the next term.

common logarithm (p. 297) A logarithm with base 10. A logarithm written without a base number is assumed to be a common logarithm, e.g., log 5 is equivalent to $\log_{10} 5$.

common ratio (p. 350) The number by which each term of a geometric series is multiplied to get the next term.

complement (p. 483) The complement of event A is the event that A does not occur. It is denoted "not A." For a coin toss, heads is the complement of tails.

complete the square (p. 94) A technique for solving quadratic equations; to complete the square means to add a constant to a binomial to create a perfect square.

complex conjugates (p. 106) Complex numbers with the same real parts, and imaginary parts that are opposites: $a + bi$ and $a - bi$. Their product is a real number equal to $a^2 + b^2$.

complex numbers (p. 103) Numbers written in the form $a + bi$ where a and b are real numbers and i is imaginary, $i = \sqrt{-1}$.

complex rational expression (p. 189) An algebraic expression written as a fraction where the numerator and/or denominator contains a rational expression.

composite function (p. 286) A function made up of two functions in which the output of one function is used as the input of the other function.

compound event (p. 476) A combination of two or more simple events, such as drawing a club and then drawing a three when playing cards.

conditional probability (p. 487) The probability that event A occurs, given that event B occurs.

confidence interval (p. 515) In probability, the range of values that a parameter might have at a given confidence level.

confidence level (p. 515) In probability, a percent representing the degree of certainty assigned to a margin of error of a measured parameter.

constant function (p. 279) A function with the same output for all input values.

converge (p. 364) In an infinite geometric series, when the partial sums get closer and closer to a number, the series is said to converge to that number, or is convergent.

cosecant (p. 441) The reciprocal function of the sine, or the ratio of the length of the hypotenuse to the length of the leg opposite to the angle.

cosine (p. 394) In a right triangle, the cosine of an angle is the ratio of the length of the leg adjacent to the angle to the length of the hypotenuse.

cotangent (p. 441) The reciprocal function of the tangent, or the ratio of the length of the leg adjacent to the angle to the length of the leg opposite the angle.

coterminal (p. 407) Two angles with the same terminal ray.

cubic equation (p. 152) A polynomial equation of the third degree; that is, the variable appears to the third power and no higher.

dependent events (p. 473) Two events are dependent if the outcome of the first affects the outcome of the second so that the probability is changed.

Descartes' rule of signs (p. 165) A technique for finding the number of positive and negative roots to a polynomial equation with real coefficients.

difference of cubes (p. 85) The description of a polynomial in which one perfect cube is subtracted from another. For example, $x^3 - 27$.

difference of squares (p. 81) The description of a polynomial in which one perfect square is subtracted from another. For example, $x^2 - 9$.

directrix (p. 119) A line not through the focus of a parabola used to establish the locus of points of the parabola such that the distance to the focus equals the distance to the directrix.

discriminant (p. 106) In the quadratic formula, the expression $b^2 - 4ac$ is the discriminant. The discriminant determines how many real solutions there are to the quadratic equation. If it is positive, the equation has two real solutions; if it is zero, the equation has one real solution; and if it is negative, the quadratic equation has no real solutions.

domain (p. 22) The set of all possible inputs in a relation.

e (p. 305) An irrational constant whose first digits are 2.718281828459… . It is used as the base number for natural logarithms and can be evaluated as the convergence of the function $f(n) = \left(1 + \dfrac{1}{n}\right)^n$.

end behavior (p. 49) The tendency of the value of a function to become increasingly positive or negative, or approach a certain value, as the independent variable approaches positive or negative infinity.

even function (p. 52) Functions whose graphs are symmetric with respect to the y-axis. For an even function, $f(-x) = f(x)$.

event (p. 463) A set of outcomes that are of interest in probability.

experimental probability (p. 463) Determining a probability based on observation.

experimental study (p. 508) A study where the researcher intentionally imposes a treatment, procedure, or program on the participants and then measures outcome(s).

explicit formula (p. 335) A formula that produces the nth term in a sequence, defined in terms of n, as opposed to defined by other terms in the sequence relative to the nth term.

exponential decay (p. 263) The graph of an exponential function with a base greater than 0 but less than 1.

exponential function (p. 261) A function with a constant raised to a variable power. For example, $y = 2^x$.

exponential growth (p. 262) The graph of an exponential function with a base greater than 1.

exponent notation for roots (p. 239) The use of fractions as the exponent in expressions, as opposed to radical signs. For example, a denominator of n in the exponent represents taking the nth root.

extraneous solution (p. 201) A solution acquired during the solving of an equation (usually a rational equation) for which the equation does not hold true.

factorial notation (p. 374) An efficient way to write the products of integers. It is denoted by $n!$, representing the product of n and the number reduced by one ($n - 1$), and the number reduced by one more ($n - 2$) down to 1. For example, (5-factorial) $5! = 5 \cdot 4 \cdot 3 \cdot 2 \cdot 1 = 120$.

factoring by grouping (p. 84) Grouping factorable terms of a polynomial so that those groups then have a common factor.

factor theorem (p. 148) A polynomial $P(x)$ has $x - r$ as a factor if and only if $P(r) = 0$.

feasible region (p. 65) The graph of possible solutions, or choices, in a linear programming problem.

finite sequence (p. 333) A sequence that comes to an end.

focus of the parabola (p. 119) A parabola is the set of all points in a plane that are the same distance from a point, called the *focus*, and a line, called the *directrix*.

frequency (p. 424) The number of cycles contained in one unit interval of the independent variable in a periodic function. The frequency is the reciprocal of the period.

function (p. 22) A correspondence between one quantity (the input) and another quantity (the output), in which each input pairs with exactly one output.

fundamental theorem of algebra (p. 160) Every single-variable polynomial function of degree $n \geq 1$ has at least one zero in the set of complex numbers.

general term (p. 333) In a sequence, the general term is denoted a_n, or the nth term.

geometric sequence (p. 350) A sequence in which each term equals the product of the previous term and a number called the *common ratio*.

geometric series (p. 361) The expression of the sum of the terms in a geometric sequence.

horizontal scaling (p. 427) The compression or stretching of a function's values horizontally (increasing or decreasing the x-values). Horizontal scaling of a periodic function changes its frequency and period.

hypotenuse (p. 387) The side opposite the right angle in a right triangle.

imaginary numbers (p. 103) An imaginary number is denoted by the product of a real number and i, which represents the square root of -1.

independent event (p. 473) Two events are said to be independent when one event has no effect on the other. The probability of two independent events occurring is equal to the product of the probabilities of the two events.

independently combined probability model (p. 473) See *independent event*.

index (p. 223) In $\sqrt[n]{b}$, n is the index.

infinite sequence (p. 333) A sequence that does not terminate.

intercept (p. 14) The point at which a graph crosses either the x- or y-axis.

inverse function (p. 281) A function that reverses the effect of another function. It is denoted with a raised "-1." For example, $\sin^{-1} x$ is the inverse function of $\sin x$.

least common denominator (p. 195) The least common multiple of the denominators of a set of fractions.

least common multiple (p. 195) The smallest integer or simplest algebraic expression that is divisible by two or more given numbers or expressions.

like radicals (p. 232) Radical expressions with the same radical index.

limits (p. 49) Constraints on the domain and range of functions.

linear factorization theorem (p. 160) A polynomial of degree $n \geq 1$ has n complex zeros. A zero that occurs k times counts as k zeros.

linear programming (p. 65) A way to solve some real-life problems, linear programming involves maximizing or minimizing some function (such as profit or cost), where the variables defining the function are subject to some linear inequalities.

line of best fit (p. 58) The best possible trend line for a set of data.

logarithmic function (p. 295) The inverse of an exponential function. If $b^y = x$, then $y = \log_b x$.

lurking variable (p. 509) A variable that causes two other variables to have what appears to be a relationship even though there is not one.

margin of error (p. 515) A value typically added to and subtracted from a statistic from a survey. It provides a range of values for the parameter at a given confidence level.

medical trial (p. 508) A test of a new drug or treatment on humans.

midline (p. 424) A horizontal line about which a periodic function oscillates.

model (p. 54) An attempt to describe the behavior of a system and to determine a relationship between an independent variable and a dependent variable, usually with mathematical equations.

monomial (p. 39) A real number, a variable, or a product of real numbers and variables, which might be raised to various powers.

multiplication rule (p. 473) In probability, a rule that states that the probability of two independent events occurring equals the product of their individual probabilities. With two independent events A and B, $P(A \text{ and } B) = P(A) \cdot P(B)$.

multivariable polynomial (p. 133) A polynomial with more than one variable.

mutually exclusive (p. 482) Two events that cannot occur at the same time.

natural base exponential function (p. 306) A function of the form $f(x) = ae^{rx}$, where e is the base.

natural logarithm (p. 305) A logarithm with base e. A natural logarithm is written as "ln," e.g., ln 7.

normal curve (p. 494) A graph with a symmetrical, bell-shaped curve; indicates a normal distribution.

normal distribution (p. 494) A pattern of data that represents many random variables. Its graph has a symmetrical, bell-shaped curve.

objective function (p. 65) In linear programming, the function to optimize—that is, to maximize or minimize.

observation (p. 463) In probability, the noting of an event.

observational study (p. 508) A type of research in which individuals are observed or certain outcomes are measured, e.g., a medical trial.

odd function (p. 53) Functions whose graphs are symmetric about the origin. For an odd function, $f(-x) = -f(x)$.

opposite leg (p. 394) In a right triangle, the leg opposite the angle under consideration.

order of operations (p. 5) The order in which mathematical operations must be performed in an algebraic expression.

outcome (p. 463) In probability, a possible result of an observation, such as "heads" or "tails" for a coin toss.

parabola (p. 41) A conic section most simply described by an equation of the form $y = ax^2$. It can also be described as the set of points equidistant from its focus and directrix.

parent function (p. 49) The most basic function in a family of functions.

partial sum of a geometric series (p. 361) The sum of a limited number of terms of an infinite geometric sequence.

partial sum of an arithmetic series (p. 344) The sum of a limited number of terms of an infinite arithmetic sequence.

percent rate of change (p. 265) The increase or reduction over an interval expressed as a percent of the initial value.

perfect square trinomial (p. 81) The product of two identical binomials.

period (p. 424) The interval of a periodic function that contains the smallest repeating pattern of the function's graph. It is the reciprocal of the frequency.

periodic function (p. 424) A function with a pattern that repeats exactly throughout its domain.

phase identity (p. 435) A relation between a periodic function and another periodic function that is translated horizontally with respect to the first.

phase shift (p. 431) The amount by which a periodic function is translated horizontally.

placebo (p. 508) A fake drug that physically resembles a drug being tested, but that actually has no medicinal qualities; used as a control in a medical trial.

polynomial (p. 39) An expression made up of the sums and differences of two or more monomials.

power of a power rule (p. 36) When raising a power to a power, multiply the exponents together and keep the base the same: $(a^m)^n = a^{mn}$.

power of a product rule (p. 37) When raising a product to a power, raise each factor to the power and then multiply the factors' powers: $(ab)^n = a^n b^n$.

power of a quotient rule (p. 37) When raising a quotient to a power, raise the numerator and denominator to the power and then divide: $\left(\dfrac{a}{b}\right)^n = \dfrac{a^n}{b^n}$.

power principle (p. 248) If $a = b$, then $a^n = b^n$. In other words, if $a = b$, then you can raise them to any same power, and the equality still holds.

power rule for logarithms (p. 313) The logarithm of a power of M can be calculated as the product of the exponent and the logarithm of M: $\log_b M^p = p \cdot \log_b M$.

principal root (p. 224) The positive root of a number.

probability (p. 463) The study of how likely it is that an event will occur. The probability of an event is expressed by a number between 0 and 1, inclusive.

product rule (p. 36) When multiplying two powers with the same base, add the exponents and keep the base the same: $a^m a^n = a^{(m + n)}$.

product rule for logarithms (p. 311) The logarithm of a product of numbers equals the sum of the logarithms of the factors: $\log_b MN = \log_b M + \log_b N$.

product rule for radicals (p. 227) The radical of the product of two numbers is equal to the product of the radicals of the same two numbers: $\sqrt[n]{ab} = \sqrt[n]{a} \cdot \sqrt[n]{b}$.

proportion (p. 514) the fraction of the total collected data that possesses the characteristic in which we are interested.

Pythagorean identity (p. 420) A trigonometric identity that is derived using the Pythagorean theorem. It states that for any angle θ, $\sin^2 \theta + \cos^2 \theta = 1$.

Pythagorean theorem (p. 387) In a right triangle, the square of the length of the hypotenuse is equal to the sum of the squares of the lengths of the legs: $a^2 + b^2 = c^2$.

Pythagorean triple (p. 93) A set of three integers that satisfy the Pythagorean theorem.

quadratic equation (p. 89) An equation that can be written with a quadratic polynomial on one side and zero on the other side. The standard form is $ax^2 + bx + c = 0$, where $a \neq 0$.

quadratic formula (p. 97) A formula for solving quadratic equations: $x = \dfrac{-b \pm \sqrt{b^2 - 4ac}}{2a}$.

quadratic trinomial (p. 79) A polynomial in one variable with three terms: a second-degree (squared) term, a first-degree term, and a constant.

quartic equation (p. 153) A polynomial equation where the highest degree (power) to which a variable is raised is 4 (x^4).

quotient rule (p. 36) When dividing powers of the same base, subtract the exponent of the divisor from the exponent of the dividend and keep the base the same: $\dfrac{a^m}{a^n} = a^{(m - n)}$.

quotient rule for logarithms (p. 312) The logarithm of the quotient of two numbers equals the difference of the logarithms of those numbers: $\log_b \dfrac{M}{N} = \log_b M - \log_b N$.

quotient rule for radicals (p. 228) The radical of the quotient of two numbers is equal to the radical of the numerator divided by the radical of the denominator: $\sqrt[n]{\dfrac{a}{b}} = \dfrac{\sqrt[n]{a}}{\sqrt[n]{b}}$.

radian (p. 414) A unit of measure for angles. One radian is defined as the angle created when the arc length equals the radius. One radian is equal to $\dfrac{180}{\pi}$ degrees.

radian measure (p. 414) In a circle, the ratio of the length of the arc intercepted by an angle to the radius of the circle.

radical equation (p. 245) An equation with a variable under a radical sign, e.g., $\sqrt{x} + 3 = 8$.

radical expression (p. 224) An expression that contains one or more radical signs, e.g., $\sqrt{6}$, $\sqrt{x + 5}$.

radicand (p. 223) The number under a radical sign. In $\sqrt{b}$ or $\sqrt[n]{b}$, b is the radicand.

randomization (p. 508) Process by which data of a survey or study is randomly selected with no selection bias.

range (p. 22) The set of all possible outputs of a function.

rate of change (p. 18) A relationship between two quantities that describes how much one quantity changes with respect to the other.

rational expression (p. 185) An expression that can be written as a quotient of two polynomials. For example, $\dfrac{x^2 + 4}{x - 3}$.

rationalizing the denominator (p. 235) Restating a radical expression without a radical in the denominator.

real numbers (p. 103) All numbers represented by points on the number line.

reciprocal function (p. 205) The function $f(x) = \dfrac{1}{x}$.

recursive formula (p. 334) A formula that shows how to calculate a particular term of a sequence (a_n) based on the value of the previous term (a_{n-1}) or terms.

reference angle (p. 408) An angle between the terminal side of an angle and the x-axis. Reference angles range from $0°$ to $90°$.

regression (p. 57) The process of finding a function that matches a data set.

remainder theorem (p. 147) For a polynomial $P(x)$, the value of $P(c)$ equals the remainder when $P(x)$ is divided by $x - c$.

residual (p. 57) The difference between an observed y-value and the predicted y-value in a regression.

roots (p. 89) Values that make a polynomial function equal to zero; also called *zeros*.

sample space (p. 464) In theoretical probability, the set of all possible outcomes.

scatter plot (p. 54) A graphical representation of data in which data points are plotted in order to determine if there is a correlation between variables.

secant (p. 441) The reciprocal function of the cosine, or the ratio of the length of the hypotenuse to the length of the leg adjacent to the angle.

sequence (p. 333) An ordered list of objects, such as numbers.

series (p. 342) The sum of the terms in a sequence.

side effect (p. 508) A result of a medical treatment or drug that is outside its intended purpose.

sigma notation (p. 343) A way to write a series using the summation sign and the summand, e.g., $\displaystyle\sum_{n=1}^{6} 3n$.

sine (p. 394) In a right triangle, the sine of an angle is the ratio of the length of the leg opposite the angle to the length of the hypotenuse.

slope (p. 14) The measure of the steepness of a line. Slope is a number calculated by dividing the rise—vertical change between any two points on the line—by the run, or horizontal change between the same two points, with respect to a coordinate system.

slope-intercept form (p. 14) The form of a linear equation written $y = mx + b$, where m is the slope and b is the y-intercept.

square root principle (p. 88) Principle that states that the solutions to $x^2 = k$ are the positive and negative square roots of the constant k. In other words, if $x^2 = k$, then $x = \sqrt{k}$ or $x = -\sqrt{k}$.

squaring principle (p. 245) The key to solving radical equations, the squaring principle states that if $a = b$, then $a^2 = b^2$.

standard deviation (p. 494) When analyzing data, standard deviation supplies a measure of the extent to which values are spread out from or clustered around the mean.

standard form of a polynomial (p. 39) A polynomial written in descending order of degrees and with no like terms.

standard form of the equation for a parabola centered at the origin (p. 120) Vertical parabola (opening up or down): $y = \frac{1}{4p}x^2$; horizontal parabola (opening left or right): $x = \frac{1}{4p}y^2$.

structure of an equation (p. 71) The properties that enable recognition of a known, workable form of an equation.

subtraction rule (p. 483) In probability: $P(\text{not } A) = 1 - P(A)$.

summand (p. 343) The algebraic expression for the nth term of an algebraic series.

summation sign (p. 343) Σ (the Greek letter "sigma"); means to add the series of terms that follow.

sum of cubes (p. 85) A term used to describe a polynomial in which two perfect cubes are added.

survey (p. 507) Collecting information about a population by gathering data on some of its members.

synthetic division (p. 142) An algorithm that provides an efficient way to divide polynomials when the divisor is of the form $(x - c)$.

system of equations (p. 25) Two or more equations with the same set of variables that you seek to solve together.

system of inequalities (p. 33) Two or more inequalities with the same set of variables that you seek to solve together.

tangent (p. 394) In a right triangle, the tangent of an angle is the ratio of the length of its opposite leg to the length of its adjacent leg.

term (p. 333) A number in a sequence.

theoretical probability (p. 464) Probability determined using reasoning and analysis.

transformation (p. 49) A change in the location, orientation, or size of a figure or curve on a graph.

translation (p. 49) A change that shifts a figure or curve on a graph without changing its orientation or shape.

trend line (p. 56) A line that passes close to the points on a scatter plot; used to predict points not shown on the plot.

trigonometric identity (p. 419) An equality involving trigonometric functions of an angle θ that is true for any value of θ.

trigonometric ratio (p. 394) A ratio of the lengths of two sides of a right triangle. Examples are sine, cosine, and tangent.

trigonometry (p. 394) The study of the relationships of the sides and angles of triangles.

two-way table (p. 472) A table with categories for both its columns and its rows to show counts or probabilities.

unit circle (p. 417) A circle with a radius of 1, used to calculate trigonometric ratios.

vertex (p. 41) The point at which the graph of a parabola changes direction. The vertex is the highest or lowest point on the graph of a parabola opening downward or upward.

vertex form for a parabola (p. 42) The equation for a parabola in the form, $y = a(x - h)^2 + k$, where the point (h, k) is the vertex.

vertical scaling (p. 427) The compression or stretching of a function's values vertically (increasing or decreasing the y-values). Vertical scaling of a periodic function changes its amplitude.

zero-product property (p. 89) If the product of factors is 0, at least one factor must equal zero.

zeros (p. 89) The zeros of a polynomial function, also called *roots*, are the values that make the function equal to zero.

Digital Activities
and Real-World Model Problems

This Algebra 2 text includes Digital Activities, which are indicated by the open computer icon on the page numbers listed below. For access to these activities, please visit **www.amscomath.com**.

This text also includes Real-World Model Problems, indicated by the globe icon on the page numbers listed below. These problems are examples of situations that students might find in the real world.

Activities

Real-World Model Problems

Index

Circles
  circumference of, 414
  unit circle, 417–419, 421–422, 426
Circumference, 414
Closed system, 185
Coefficient of determination, 57–58
Coefficients
  binomial, 374–376
  binomial expansion, 371–372
Combined functions, 278–280
  domain of, 278–279
  evaluating, 280
  real-world model of, 279
Common denominators
  least common denominator, 195–196, 200–201
  with rational expressions, 192–194
Common difference, 334, 338
Common logarithms, 297
Common ratio, 350–351
Commutative properties, 9
Complementary angles, 397–401
Complements, 483
Complete the square, 94–96
Complex conjugates, 106
Complex numbers, 103–104, 160
  addition of, 104
  conjugates of, 106
  factoring, 107
  multiplication of, 105
  as solutions to quadratic equations, 110–111
  subtraction of, 104
Complex rational expressions, 189
Composite functions, 286–288
  domain restrictions of, 287–288
Compound events, 474–475
Compound interest, 99, 270–271, 277, 318–319
  formula for, 99, 271, 306–307
Computer algebra systems, 146
Conditional probability, 487–491
  defined, 487
  frequency tables and, 489–490
  independent events and, 487–488
Confidence interval, 515
Confidence level, 515
Constant function, 279
Constraint inequalities, 65–67
Continuous functions, 47
Continuously compound interest, 306–307
Converge, 364
Conversions
  degrees to radians, 414
  radians to degrees, 414
Cosecant, 420, 441–445
Cosine, 394–403
  angles of rotation and, 408–411
  complementary angles and, 397–401

graphing, 426. *See also* Trigonometric function graphs
  identities, 435–436
  for special triangles, 401–403
  trigonometric identities and, 419–421
  unit circle and, 417–419, 421–422, 426
Cotangent, 420, 441–445
Coterminal angles, 407
Cube root functions, graphing, 253
Cubes
  difference of, 85
  sum of, 85
Cubic equations, 152–153
Cubic regression, 170–172

D
Data
  analysis, 54–56
  modeling, with trend lines, 56–58
  normal distribution of, 494–504
  real-world model of, 56
  standard deviation, 494
Decibels (dB), 317
Decimals, rational numbers as, 367
Denominators
  addition and subtraction or rational expression with different, 194
  addition and subtraction or rational expression with same, 192–193
  least common, 195–196, 200–201
  rationalizing, 235–236
Dependent variables, 54
Descartes' rule of signs, 165–166
Difference
  common, 334, 338
  of cubes, 85
  of squares, 81, 82
Directrix, 119
Discontinuous functions, 47–48
Discriminant, 106, 109
Distributive property
  of division, 9
  of multiplication, 9, 234
Division
  distributive property of, 9
  of fractional powers, 242
  of polynomials, 138–140, 141–146
  of radical expressions, 242–243
  of rational expressions, 189–191
  synthetic, 142–145
  using computer algebra system, 146
Division property, 9
Domain, 22, 23, 48–49
  of combined functions, 278–279
  of composite functions, 287–288
  limits on, 49

solving exponential equations using, 316
Long division
of polynomials, 138–140
of polynomials with remainder, 141
Lurking variable, 508

M

Margin of error, 515
computation of, 516–519
Mathematical expressions, 22
Mean, 514
Medical trials, 508
Midline, 424
Modeling
data, 56–58
exponential functions, 268–274, 448
functions, 64–65, 448–451
geometric sequences, 353–354
infinite geometric series, 366–367
logarithms, 317–322
parabolas, 123
polynomial functions, 170–172, 448, 451
probability, 469, 477, 481, 486
quadratic formula, 99
quadratic functions, 114–115
rational equations, 198, 202–203, 212
rational expressions, 191
right triangles, 392, 396, 399–400
solving equations, 10, 93
trigonometric ratios, 396, 399–400
Models
defined, 54
linear, 56, 58–59, 448
polynomial, 448, 451
real-world, 55, 56, 64–65
regression, 57–58
scatter plots, 54–56
trend lines, 56–58
working with, 64–65
Monomials, multiplying, 39
Multiplication
of complex numbers, 105
distributive property of, 9, 234
of fractional powers, 242
of monomials, 39
of multivariable polynomials, 137
of polynomials, 39–40
properties of, 9
of radical expressions, 227–228, 231–232, 234, 242–243
of rational expressions, 187–188
Multiplication property, 9
Multiplication rule, 473
Multivariable polynomials, 133
combining like terms in, 134

evaluating, 135
operations with, 136–137
Mutually exclusive events, 482

N

Natural base exponential function, 306
Natural logarithms, 305–307
Negative exponents, 38
Negative numbers, 6
square roots of, 103–104
Negative radicands, 231–232
Negative roots, 224
Non-symmetrical functions, 47
Normal curves, 494
approximating area under, 499
Normal distribution, 494–504
activity, 498–499
defined, 494
graphing calculator problems, 502–504
margin of error and, 516
spreadsheets and, 502–504
standard deviation and, 494–496
Numbers
complex, 103–104, 160
imaginary, 103–104
irrational, 103
negative, 6
real, 103

O

Objective function, 65–68
Observation, 463
Observational studies, 508
Obtuse triangles, 389
Odd functions, 53
One-to-one functions, 284
Operations, order of, 5, 6
Opposite leg, 394
"Or," 477
Ordered pairs, 25
graphing, 23
Order of operations, 5, 6
Origin, parabolas at, 118–124
Oscillation, 424
Outcome, 463

P

Parabolas, 41–42
activity, 120
axis of symmetry, 41–42
directrix, 119
equation for, 119, 120
focus of, 119
geometric definition of, 118–120